Antenna Theory

The Harper & Row Series in Electrical Engineering

ANTENNA THEORY
Analysis and Design

CONSTANTINE A. BALANIS
West Virginia University

1817

HARPER & ROW, PUBLISHERS, New York
Cambridge, Philadelphia, San Francisco,
London, Mexico City, São Paulo, Sydney

Sponsoring Editor: Carl McNair
Project Editor: Pamela Landau
Designer: Michel Craig
Production Manager: Marion Palen
Compositor: Science Typographers, Inc.
Printer and Binder: The Murray Printing Company
Art Studio: Vantage Art Inc.

ANTENNA THEORY   **Analysis and Design**

Copyright © 1982 by Harper & Row, Publishers, Inc.

All rights reserved. Printed in the United States of America. No part of
this book may be used or reproduced in any manner whatsoever without written
permission, except in the case of brief quotations embodied in critical articles
and reviews. For information address Harper & Row, Publishers, Inc., 10 East 53d Street, New
York, NY 10022.

Library of Congress Cataloging in Publication Data

Balanis, Constantine A., 1938 –
    Antenna theory.

    (The Harper & Row series in electrical engineering)
    Includes bibliographical references and index.
    1. Antennas (Electronics)   I. Title.   II. Series.
TK7871.6.B353   621.38′028′3   81-20248
ISBN 0-06-040458-2   AACR2

To my mother, to the memory of my father,
and to my uncle and aunt

Contents

Preface

Antenna Theory is designed to meet the needs of electrical engineering and physics students at the senior undergraduate and beginning graduate levels, and those of practicing engineers as well. The text presumes that the students have a knowledge of basic undergraduate electromagnetic theory, including Maxwell's equations and the wave equation, introductory physics, and differential and integral calculus. Mathematical techniques required for understanding some advanced topics in the later chapters are incorporated in the individual chapters or are included as appendixes.

The book's main objective is to introduce, in a unifed manner, the fundamental principles of antenna theory and to apply them to the analysis, design, and measurements of antennas. Because there are so many methods of analysis and design and a plethora of antenna structures, applications are made to some of the most basic and practical configurations, such as linear dipoles; loops; arrays; broadband dipoles; traveling wave, broadband, and frequency independent antennas; aperture and microstrip antennas; horns, reflectors, and lens antennas.

Introductory material on analytical methods, such as the Moment Method (MM) and the Geometrical Theory of Diffraction (GTD), is also included. These techniques, together with the fundamental principles of antenna theory, can be applied to the analysis and design of almost any antenna configuration. A chapter on antenna measurements introduces state-of-the-art methods used in the measurements of the most basic antenna characteristics (pattern, gain, directivity, radiation efficiency, impedance, current and polarization) and updates progress made in antenna instrumentation, antenna range design, and scale modeling.

A sufficient number of topics have been covered, some for the first time in an undergraduate text, so that the book will serve not only as a text, but also as a reference for the practicing and design engineer and even the amateur radio buff. These include design procedures for horns, and Yagi-Uda and log-periodic arrays; synthesis techniques using the

Schelkunoff, Fourier transform, Woodward, Tschebyscheff, and Taylor methods; radiation characteristics of corrugated horns and microstrip antennas; and matching techniques such as the binomial, Tschebyscheff, T-, gamma, and omega matches.

The text contains sufficient mathematical detail to enable the average undergraduate electrical engineering and physics students to follow, without too much difficulty, the flow of analysis and design. A certain amount of analytical detail, rigor, and thoroughness allows many of the topics to be traced to their origin. My experiences as a student, engineer, and teacher have shown that a text for this course must not be a book of unrelated formulas, and it must not resemble a "cookbook." This book begins with the most elementary material, develops underlying concepts needed for sequential topics, and progresses to more advanced methods and systems configurations. Each chapter is subdivided into sections or subsections whose individual headings clearly identify the antenna characteristic(s) discussed, examined, or illustrated.

A distinguishing feature of this book is its three-dimensional graphical illustrations. In the past, antenna texts have displayed the three-dimensional radiated energy by a number of separate two-dimensional patterns. With the advent and revolutionary advances in digital computations and graphical displays, an additional dimension has been introduced for the first time in an undergraduate antenna text by displaying the radiated energy of a given radiator by a single, three-dimensional graphical illustration. Such an image, formed by the graphical capabilities of the computer and available at most computational facilities, gives a clear view of the energy radiated in all space surrounding the antenna. It is hoped that this will lead to a better understanding of the underlying principles of radiation, and it will provide a clearer visualization of the pattern formation in all space.

In addition, there is an abundance of general graphical illustrations, design data, references, and additional problems. Many of the principles are illuminated with examples, graphical illustrations, and physical arguments. Although students are often convinced that they understand the principles, difficulties arise when they attempt to use them. An example, especially a graphical illustration, can often better illuminate those principles. As they say, "a picture is worth a thousand words."

Numerical techniques and computer solutions are illustrated and encouraged. A number of FORTRAN computer programs and subroutines are included at the end of Chapters 2, 4, 5, 7, and 11. These can be used to perform routine calculations of complex functions and/or formulations, to carry out numerical integrations that cannot be performed in closed form, and to display solutions in graphical form. The problems at the end of each chapter can be used to apply the underlying principles of antenna theory to the analysis and design of many practical radiators.

For course use, the text is intended primarily for a two-semester (or two- or three-quarter) sequence in antenna theory. The first course should be given at the senior undergraduate level, and it should cover most of the material in Chapters 1 through 10 and Chapter 15. Some of the more advanced topics in Chapters 6 through 10 can be omitted without loss of continuity. The material in Chapters 11 through 14 and selected sections from the other chapters should be covered in a beginning graduate-level course. To cover all the material of the text in the proposed time frame would be, in some cases, a very ambitious task. Sufficient topics have been included, however, to make the text complete and to give the teacher the flexibility to emphasize, de-emphasize, or omit sections or chapters.

In the entire book an $e^{j\omega t}$ time variation is assumed, and it is suppressed. The International System of Units, which is an expanded form of the rationalized MKS system, is used in the text. In some cases, the units of length are given in meters (or centimeters) and in feet (or inches). Numbers in parentheses ( ) refer to equations, whereas those in brackets [ ] refer to references. For emphasis, the most important equations, once they are derived, are boxed. A Solutions Manual for all end of chapter problems is available for the instructor.

I would like to acknowledge the invaluable suggestions and constructive criticisms of Dr. Carlton H. Walter of the Ohio State University and Dr. Thomas E. Tice of the Arizona State University. The book, especially the graphical illustrations and the solutions to the problems, would not have been possible without the contributions from many of my former and current graduate students. It is a pleasure to acknowledge those of John L. Jeffrey, Yuk-Bun Cheng, Yang K. Yoon, and Roger D. Radcliff. I am deeply indebted to Mrs. Sheila Hively, Mrs. Julie A. Wainstock, and Mrs. Billie D. Pack for the expert typing of the manuscript. To the companies that provided the illustrations, I am most appreciative. I am also grateful to the staff of Harper & Row, Publishers, Inc. for their professional help in the production and publication of this book. Finally, I must express my gratitude to Helen, Renie, and Stephanie for their encouragement, patience, sacrifice, and understanding for the many hours of neglect during the completion of this endeavor.

Constantine A. Balanis

Antenna Theory

Chapter 1
Antennas

1.1 INTRODUCTION

An antenna is defined by Webster's Dictionary as "a usually metallic device (as a rod or wire) for radiating or receiving radio waves." The *IEEE Standard Definitions of Terms for Antennas* (IEEE Std 145-1973)* defines the antenna or aerial as "a means for radiating or receiving radio waves." In other words the antenna is the transitional structure between free-space and a guiding device, as shown in Figure 1.1. The guiding device or transmission line may take the form of a coaxial line or a hollow pipe (waveguide), and it is used to transport electromagnetic energy from the transmitting source to the antenna, or from the antenna to the receiver. In the former case we have a transmitting antenna and in the latter a receiving antenna.

In addition to receiving or transmitting energy, an antenna is usually required to *optimize* or *accentuate* the radiation energy in some directions and suppress it in others. *Thus the antenna must act as a directional device in addition to a probing device.* It must then take various forms to meet the particular need at hand, and it may be a piece of conducting wire, an aperture, an assembly of elements (array), a reflector, a lens, and so forth.

1.2 TYPES OF ANTENNAS

We will now introduce and briefly discuss some forms of the various antenna types in order to get a glance as to what will be encountered in the remainder of the book.

1.2.1 Wire Antennas

Wire antennas are familiar to the layman because they are seen virtually everywhere—on automobiles, buildings, ships, aircraft, spacecraft, and so on. There are various shapes of wire antennas such as a straight wire

---

IEEE Transactions on Antennas and Propagation, vols. AP-17, No. 3, May 1969 and AP-22, No. 1, January 1974.

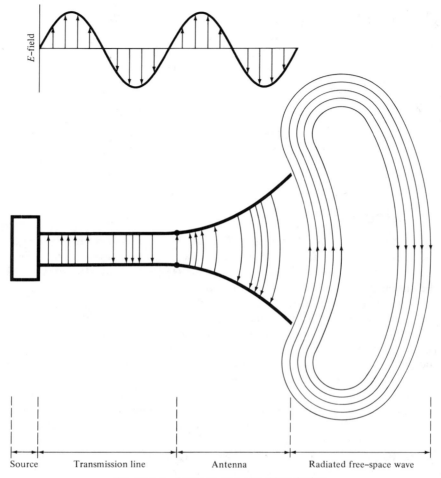

Figure 1.1   Antenna as a transition device.

(dipole), loop, and helix which are shown in Figure 1.2. Loop antennas need not only be circular. They may take the form of a rectangle, square, ellipse, or any other configuration. The circular loop is the most common because of its simplicity in construction.

1.2.2   Aperture Antennas

Aperture antennas may be more familiar to the layman today than in the past because of the increasing demand for more sophisticated forms of antennas and the utilization of higher frequencies. Some forms of aperture antennas are shown in Figure 1.3. Antennas of this type are very useful for aircraft or spacecraft applications, because they can be very conveniently

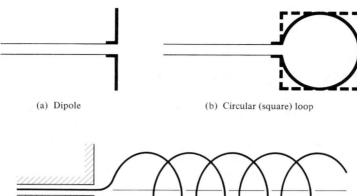

(a) Dipole

(b) Circular (square) loop

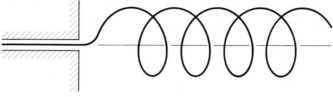

(c) Helix

Figure 1.2   Wire antenna configurations.

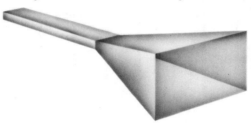

(a) Pyramidal horn

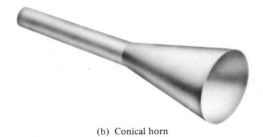

(b) Conical horn

(c) Rectangular waveguide

Figure 1.3   Aperture antenna configurations.

flush-mounted on the skin of the aircraft or spacecraft. In addition, they can be covered with a dielectric material to protect them from hazardous conditions of the environment.

1.2.3 Array Antennas

Many applications require radiation characteristics that may not be achievable by a single element. It may, however, be possible that an aggregate of radiating elements in an electrical and geometrical arrangement (an array) will result in the desired radiation characteristics. The arrangement of the array may be such that the radiation from the elements adds up to give a radiation maximum in a particular direction or directions, minimum in others, or otherwise as desired. Typical examples of arrays are shown in

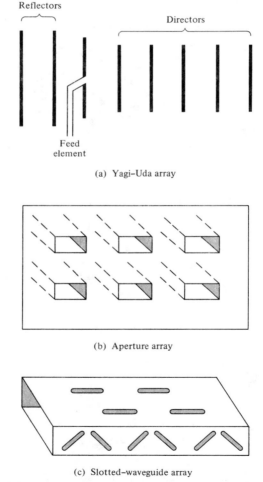

(a) Yagi–Uda array

(b) Aperture array

(c) Slotted–waveguide array

Figure 1.4 Typical wire and aperture array configurations.

Figure 1.4. Usually the term *array* is reserved for an arrangement in which the individual radiators are separate as shown in Figures 1.4(a) and (b). However the same term is also used to describe an assembly of radiators mounted on a continuous structure, shown in Figure 1.4(c).

1.2.4 Reflector Antennas

The success in the exploration of outer space has resulted in the advancement of antenna theory. Because of the need to communicate over great distances, sophisticated forms of antennas had to be used in order to transmit and receive signals that had to travel millions of miles. A very common antenna form for such an application is a parabolic reflector shown in Figures 1.5(a) and (b). Antennas of this type have been built with diameters as large as 305 m. Such large dimensions are needed to achieve the high gain required to transmit or receive signals after millions of miles of

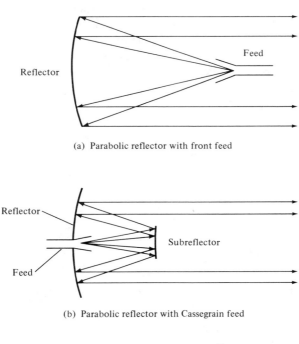

(a) Parabolic reflector with front feed

(b) Parabolic reflector with Cassegrain feed

(c) Corner reflector

Figure 1.5 Typical reflector configurations.

travel. Another form of a reflector, although not as common as the parabolic, is the corner reflector, shown in Figure 1.5(c).

1.2.5 Lens Antennas

Lenses are primarily used to collimate incident divergent energy to prevent it from spreading in undesired directions. By properly shaping the geometrical configuration and choosing the appropriate material of the lenses, they can transform various forms of divergent energy into plane waves. They can be used in most of the same applications as are the parabolic reflectors, especially at higher frequencies. Their dimensions and weight become exceedingly large at lower frequencies. Lens antennas are classified according to the material from which they are constructed, or according to their geometrical shape. Some forms are shown in Figure 1.6.

In summary, an ideal antenna is one that will radiate all the power delivered to it from the transmitter in a desired direction or directions. In practice, however, such ideal performances cannot be achieved but may be closely approached. Various types of antennas are available and each type can take different forms in order to achieve the desired radiation characteristics for the particular application.

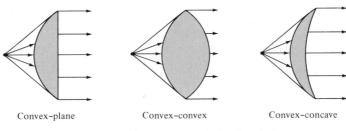

Convex–plane   Convex–convex   Convex–concave

(a) Lens antennas with index of refraction $n > 1$

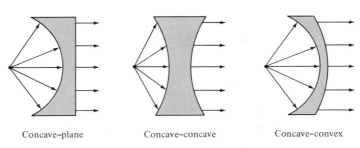

Concave–plane   Concave–concave   Concave–convex

(b) Lens antennas with index of refraction $n < 1$

Figure 1.6 Typical lens antenna configurations. (SOURCE: L. V. Blake, *Antennas*, Wiley, New York, 1966).

1.3 RADIATION MECHANISM

One of the first questions that may be asked concerning antennas would be "how is radiation accomplished?" In other words, how are the electromagnetic fields generated by the source, contained and guided within the transmission line and antenna, and finally "detached" from the antenna to form a free-space wave? The best explanation may be given by an illustration.

Let us consider a voltage source connected to a two-conductor transmission line which is connected to an antenna. This is shown in Figure 1.7(a). Applying a voltage across the two-conductor transmission line creates an electric field between the conductors. The electric field has associated with it electric lines of force which are tangent to the electric field at each point and their strength is proportional to the electric field intensity. The electric lines of force have a tendency to act on the free electrons (easily detachable from the atoms) associated with each conductor and force them to be displaced. The movement of the charges creates a current that in turn creates a magnetic field intensity. Associated with the magnetic field intensity are magnetic lines of force which are tangent to the magnetic field.

We have accepted that electric field lines start on positive charges and end on negative charges. They also can start on a positive charge and end at infinity, start at infinity and end on a negative charge, or form closed loops neither starting or ending on any charge. Magnetic field lines always form closed loops encircling current-carrying conductors because there are no magnetic charges. In some mathematical formulations, it is often convenient to introduce magnetic charges and magnetic currents to draw a parallel between solutions involving electric and magnetic sources.

The electric field lines drawn between the two conductors help to exhibit the distribution of charge. If we assume that the voltage source is sinusoidal, we expect the electric field between the conductors to also be sinusoidal with a period equal to that of the applied source. The relative magnitude of the electric field intensity will be indicated by the density (bunching) of the lines of force with the arrows showing the relative direction (positive or negative). The creation of time-varying electric and magnetic fields between the conductors forms electromagnetic waves which travel along the transmission line, as shown in Figure 1.7(a). The electromagnetic waves enter the antenna and have associated with them electric charges and corresponding currents. If we remove part of the antenna structure, as shown in Figure 1.7(b), free-space waves can be formed by "connecting" the open ends of the electric lines (shown dashed). The free-space waves are also periodic but a constant phase point P_0 moves outwardly with the speed of light and travels a distance of $\lambda/2$ (to P_1) in the time of one-half of a period. It has been shown [2] that close to the antenna the constant phase point P_0 moves faster than the speed of light but approaches the speed of light at points far away from the antenna (analogous to phase velocity inside a rectangular waveguide). Figure 1.8 displays

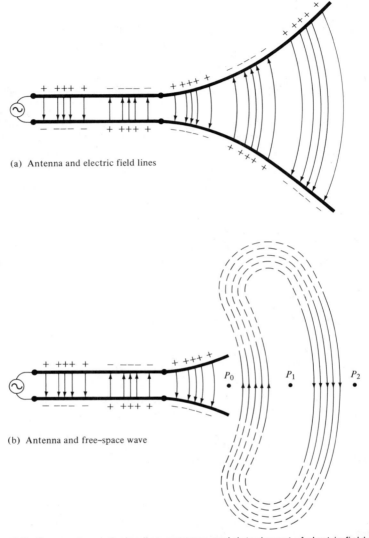

(a) Antenna and electric field lines

(b) Antenna and free–space wave

Figure 1.7   Source, transmission line, antenna, and detachment of electric field lines.

the creation and travel of free-space waves by a prolate spheroid with $\lambda/2$ interfocal distance where λ is the wavelength. The free-space waves of a center-fed $\lambda/2$ dipole, except in the immediate vicinity of the antenna, should essentially be the same as those of the prolate spheroid.

The question still unanswered is how the guided waves are detached from the antenna to create the free-space waves that are indicated as closed loops in Figures 1.7 and 1.8. Before we attempt to explain that, let us draw a parallel between the guided and free-space waves, and water waves [3]

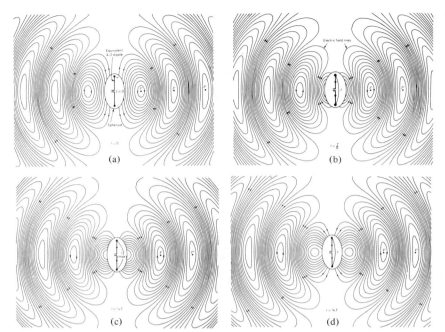

Figure 1.8   Electric field lines of free-space wave for a $\lambda/2$ antenna at $t=0$, $T/8$, $T/4$, and $3T/8$. (SOURCE: J. D. Kraus and K. R. Carver, *Electromagnetics*, 2nd ed., McGraw-Hill, New York, 1973. Reprinted with permission of J. D. Kraus and John D. Cowan, Jr.)

created by the dropping of a pebble in a calm body of water or initiated in some other manner. Once the disturbance in the water has been initiated, water waves are created which begin to travel outwardly. If the disturbance has been removed, the waves do not stop or extinguish themselves but continue their course of travel. If the disturbance persists, new waves are continuously created which lag in their travel behind the others. The same is true with the electromagnetic waves created by an electric disturbance. If the initial electric disturbance by the source is of a short duration, the created electromagnetic waves will travel inside the transmission line, then into the antenna, and finally will be radiated as free-space waves, even if the electric source has ceased to exist (as was with the water waves and their generating disturbance). If the electric disturbance is of a continuous nature, electromagnetic waves will exist continuously and follow in their travel behind the others. This is shown in Figure 1.9 for a biconical antenna. When the electromagnetic waves are within the transmission line and antenna, their existence is associated with the presence of the charges inside the conductors. However, when the waves are radiated, they form closed loops and there are no charges to sustain their existence. *This leads us to conclude that electric charges are required to excite the fields but are not*

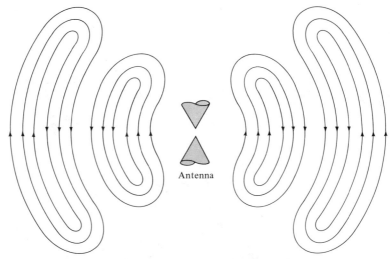

Figure 1.9 Electric field lines of free-space wave for biconical antenna.

needed to sustain them and may exist in their absence. This is in direct analogy with water waves.

Now let us attempt to explain the mechanism by which the electric lines of force are detached from the antenna to form the free-space waves. This will again be illustrated by an example of a small antenna where the time of travel is negligible. This is only necessary to give a better physical interpretation of the detachment of the lines of force. Although a somewhat simplified mechanism, it does allow one to visualize the creation of the free-space waves. Figure 1.10(a) displays the lines of force created between the arms of a small center-fed dipole in the first quarter of the period during which time the charge has reached its maximum value (assuming a sinusoidal time variation) and the lines have traveled outwardly a radial distance $\lambda/4$. For this example, let us assume that the number of lines formed are three. During the next quarter of the period, the original three lines travel an additional $\lambda/4$ (a total of $\lambda/2$ from the initial point) and the charge density on the conductors begins to diminish. This can be thought of as being accomplished by introducing opposite charges which at the end of the first half of the period have neutralized the charges on the conductors. The lines of force created by the opposite charges are three and travel a distance $\lambda/4$ during the second quarter of the first half, and they are shown dashed in Figure 1.10(b). The end result is that there are three lines of force pointed upward in the first $\lambda/4$ distance and the same number of lines directed downward in the second $\lambda/4$. Since there is no net charge on the antenna, then the lines of force must have been forced to detach themselves from the conductors and to unite together to form closed loops. This is shown in Figure 1.10(c). In the remaining second half of the period, the same

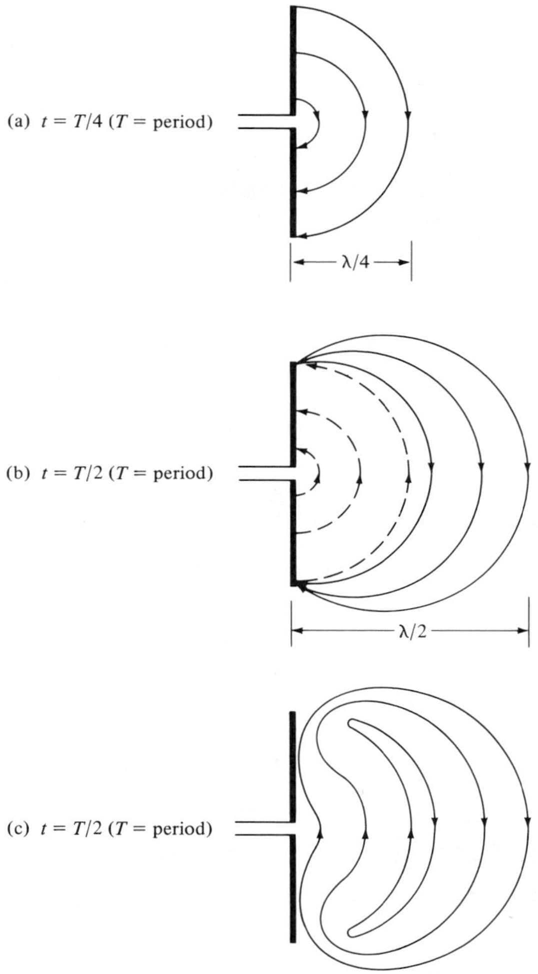

(a) $t = T/4$ (T = period)

|← λ/4 →|

(b) $t = T/2$ (T = period)

|← λ/2 →|

(c) $t = T/2$ (T = period)

Figure 1.10   Formation and detachment of electric field lines for short dipole.

procedure is followed but in the opposite direction. After that, the process is repeated and continues indefinitely.

1.4   CURRENT DISTRIBUTION ON A THIN WIRE ANTENNA

In the preceding section we discussed the movement of the free electrons on the conductors representing the transmission line and the antenna. In order to illustrate the creation of the current distribution on a linear dipole, and its subsequent radiation, let us first begin with the geometry of a lossless two-wire transmission line, as shown in Figure 1.11(a). The movement of the

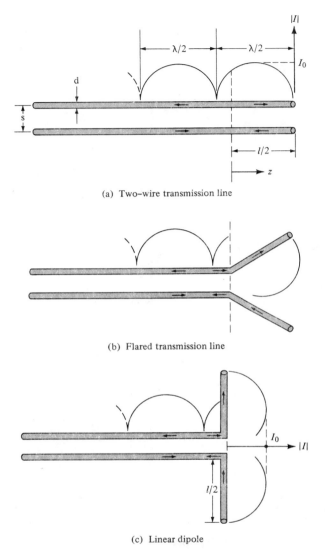

(a) Two–wire transmission line

(b) Flared transmission line

(c) Linear dipole

Figure 1.11   Current distribution on a lossless two-wire transmission line, flared transmission line, and linear dipole.

charges creates a traveling wave current, of magnitude $I_0/2$, along each of the wires. When the current arrives at the end of each of the wires, it undergoes a complete reflection (equal magnitude and 180° phase reversal). The reflected traveling wave, when combined with the incident traveling wave, forms in each wire a pure standing wave pattern of sinusoidal form as shown in Figure 1.11(a). The current in each wire undergoes a 180° phase reversal between adjoining half cycles. This is indicated in Figure 1.11(a) by the reversal of the arrow direction.

For the two-wire balanced (symmetrical) transmission line, the current in a half-cycle of one wire is of the same magnitude but 180° out-of-phase from that in the corresponding half-cycle of the other wire. If in addition the spacing between the two wires is very small ($s \ll \lambda$), the fields radiated by the current of each wire are essentially cancelled by those of the other. The net result is an almost ideal (and desired) nonradiating transmission line.

As the section of the transmission line between $0 \leq z \leq l/2$ begins to flare, as shown in Figure 1.11(b), it can be assumed that the current distribution is essentially unaltered in form in each of the wires. However, because the two wires of the flared section are not necessarily close to each other, the fields radiated by one do not necessarily cancel those of the other. Therefore there is a net radiation by the system.

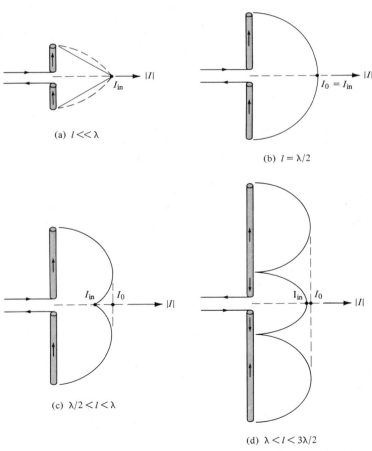

(a) $l \ll \lambda$

(b) $l = \lambda/2$

(c) $\lambda/2 < l < \lambda$

(d) $\lambda < l < 3\lambda/2$

Figure 1.12 Current distribution on linear dipoles.

Ultimately the flared section of the transmission line can take the form shown in Figure 1.11(c). This is the geometry of the widely used dipole antenna. Because of the standing wave current pattern, it is also classified as a standing wave antenna (as contrasted to the traveling wave antennas which will be discussed in detail in Chapter 9). If $l < \lambda$, the phase of the current standing wave pattern in each arm is the same throughout its length. In addition, spatially it is oriented in the same direction as that of the other arm as shown in Figure 1.11(c). Thus the fields radiated by the two arms of the dipole (vertical parts of a flared transmission line) will primarily reinforce each other toward most directions of observation (the phase due to the relative position of each small part of each arm must also be included for a complete description of the radiation pattern formation).

If the diameter of each wire is very small ($d \ll \lambda$), the ideal standing wave pattern of the current along the arms of the dipole is sinusoidal with a null at the end. However, its overall form depends on the length of each arm. For center-fed dipoles with $l \ll \lambda$, $l = \lambda/2$, $\lambda/2 < l < \lambda$ and $\lambda < l < 3\lambda/2$, the current patterns are illustrated in Figures 1.12(a)–(d). The current pattern of a very small dipole (usually $\lambda/50 < l \leq \lambda/10$) can be approximated by a triangular distribution since $\sin(kl/2) \simeq kl/2$ when $kl/2$ is very small. This is illustrated in Figure 1.12(a).

Because of its cyclical spatial variations, the current standing wave pattern of a dipole longer than $\lambda(l > \lambda)$ undergoes 180° phase reversals between adjoining half-cycles. Therefore the current in all parts of the dipole does not have the same phase. This is demonstrated graphically in Figure 1.12(d) for $\lambda < l < 3\lambda/2$. In turn, the fields radiated by some parts of the dipole will not reinforce those of the others. As a result, significant

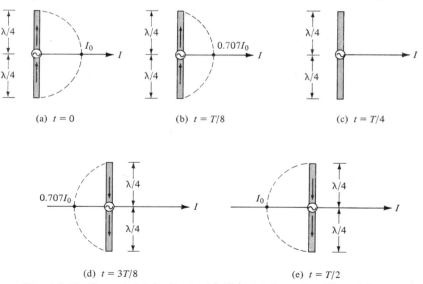

(a) $t = 0$ (b) $t = T/8$ (c) $t = T/4$

(d) $t = 3T/8$ (e) $t = T/2$

Figure 1.13   Current distribution on a $\lambda/2$ wire antenna for different times.

interference and cancelling effects will be noted in the formation of the total radiation pattern.

For a time-harmonic varying system of radian frequency $\omega = 2\pi f$, the current standing wave patterns of Figure 1.12 represent the maximum current excitation for any time. The current variations, as a function of time, on a $\lambda/2$ center-fed dipole are shown in Figure 1.13 for $0 \le t \le T/2$ where T is the period. These variations can be obtained by multiplying the current standing wave pattern of Figure 1.12(b) by $\cos(\omega t)$.

1.5 HISTORICAL ADVANCEMENT

The history of radio antennas began as early as 1887 with the first design taking the form of a loop. It was not until 1901 that Marconi used an array of 50 copper wires to perform the first transatlantic transmission. The greatest advancement of antenna theory and design was accomplished during World War II with the introduction of microwave antennas taking the form of reflectors, apertures, and arrays. Most of this work was later included in a classic book [4] edited by S. Silver. Considerable refinement in the theory of linear wire antennas was accomplished by R. W. P. King [5] and his associates at the Gordon McKay Laboratory of Harvard University. J. D. Kraus of Ohio State University introduced the helical antenna and much of his work is included in his classic book [6]. S. K. Schelkunoff of Bell Laboratories was able to provide mathematical formulations representing the radiation mechanisms of many antennas. His accomplishments bridged the gap between theory and experiment and provided better understanding of antennas [3].

With the introduction and advancement of computer techniques, antenna theory was again revived. Many mathematically intractable problems were now solved using numerical techniques. Advancements resulted from the introduction and application of the Geometrical Theory of Diffraction [7] and the Moment Method [8]. It is believed that the Geometrical Theory of Diffraction (which is most suitable for electrically large bodies), and the Moment Method (which is most suitable for electrically small bodies), today provide the two most promising analytical methods in antenna theory and design. The revival of the Geometrical Theory of Diffraction was primarily instrumented by the work of J. B. Keller and his associates at New York University in the 1950s. The introduction of the Moment Method to antenna theory resulted primarily from the work of R. F. Harrington at Syracuse University in the 1960s.

References

1. L. V. Blake, *Antennas*, Wiley, New York, 1966, p. 289.
2. J. D. Kraus and K. R. Carver, *Electromagnetics*, McGraw-Hill, New York, 1973, pp. 648–650.

3. S. K. Schelkunoff and H. T. Friis, *Antennas: Theory and Practice*, Wiley, New York, 1952.
4. S. Silver (ed.), *Microwave Antenna Theory and Design*, M. I. T. Radiation Laboratory Series, vol. 12, McGraw-Hill, New York, 1949.
5. R. W. P. King, *Theory of Linear Antennas*, Harvard University Press, Cambridge, Mass., 1956.
6. J. D. Kraus, *Antennas*, McGraw-Hill, New York, 1950.
7. J. B. Keller, "Geometrical Theory of Diffraction," *Journal of the Optical Society of America*, vol. 52, February 1962, pp. 116–130.
8. R. F. Harrington, *Field Computation by Moment Methods*, Macmillan, New York, 1968.

Chapter 2
Fundamental Parameters
of Antennas

2.1 INTRODUCTION

To describe the performance of an antenna, definitions of various parameters are necessary. Some of the parameters are interrelated and not all of them need be specified for complete description of the antenna performance. Parameter definitions will be given in this chapter. Those in quotation marks will be from the *IEEE Standard Definitions of Terms for Antennas* (IEEE Std 145-1973).*

2.2 RADIATION PATTERN

An antenna *radiation pattern* is defined as "a graphical representation of the radiation properties of the antenna as a function of space coordinates. In most cases, the radiation pattern is determined in the far-field region and is represented as a function of the directional coordinates. Radiation properties include radiation intensity, field strength, phase or polarization." The radiation property of most concern is the three-dimensional spatial distribution of radiated energy as a function of the observer's position along a constant radius. A convenient set of coordinates is shown in Figure 2.1. A trace of the received power at a constant radius is called the *power pattern*. On the other hand, a graph of the spatial variation of the electric (or magnetic) field along a constant radius is called a *field pattern*. In practice, the three-dimensional pattern is measured and recorded in a series of two-dimensional patterns. However, for most practical applications, a few

IEEE Transactions on Antennas and Propagation, vols. AP-17, No. 3, May 1969 and AP-22, No. 1, January 1974.

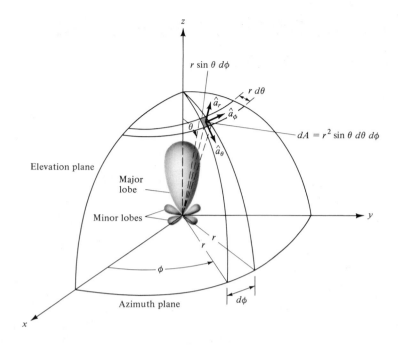

Figure 2.1   Coordinate system for antenna analysis.

plots of the pattern as a function of θ for some particular values of ϕ, plus a few plots as a function of ϕ for some particular values of θ, give most of the useful and needed information.

2.2.1   Isotropic, Directional, and Omnidirectional Patterns

An *isotropic* radiator is defined as "a hypothetical antenna having equal radiation in all directions." A point source would be an example of such a radiator. Although it is ideal and not physically realizable, it is often taken as a reference for expressing the directive properties of practical antennas. A *directional* antenna is one "having the property of radiating or receiving electromagnetic waves more effectively in some directions than in others." An example of an antenna with a directional radiation pattern is shown in Figure 2.2. It is seen that this pattern is nondirectional in the azimuth plane $[f(\phi), \theta = \text{constant}]$ and directional in the elevation plane $[g(\theta), \phi = \text{constant}]$. This type of a pattern is designated as *omnidirectional*, and it is defined as one "having an essentially nondirectional pattern in azimuth and a directional pattern in elevation." An *omnidirectional* pattern is then a special type of a *directional* pattern.

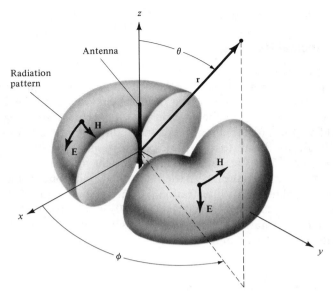

Figure 2.2　Directional (omnidirectional) antenna pattern.

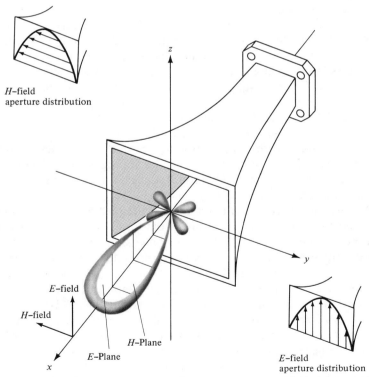

Figure 2.3　Principal *E*- and *H*-plane patterns for a pyramidal horn antenna.

2.2.2 Principal Patterns

Antenna performance is often described in terms of its principal E- and H-plane patterns. For a linearly polarized antenna, the *E-plane* pattern is defined as "the plane containing the electric-field vector and the direction of maximum radiation," and the *H-plane* as "the plane containing the magnetic-field vector and the direction of maximum radiation." Although it is very difficult to illustrate the principal patterns without considering a specific example, it is the usual practice to orient most antennas so that at least one of the principal plane patterns coincide with one of the 'geometrical principal planes. An illustration is shown in Figure 2.3. For this example, the x-z plane (elevation plane; $\phi = 0$) is the principal E-plane and the x-y plane (azimuthal plane; $\theta = \pi/2$) is the principal H-plane. Other coordinate orientations can be selected.

2.2.3 Radiation Pattern Lobes

Various parts of a radiation pattern are referred to as *lobes*, which may be subclassified into *major, minor, side,* and *back* lobes.

A *radiation lobe* is a "portion of the radiation pattern bounded by regions of relatively weak radiation intensity." Figure 2.4(a) demonstrates a symmetrical three-dimensional polar pattern with a number of radiation lobes. Some are of greater radiation intensity than others, but all are classified as lobes. Figure 2.4(b) illustrates a linear two-dimensional pattern [one plane of Figure 2.4(a)] where the same pattern characteristics are indicated.

FORTRAN computer programs which can be used to plot two-dimensional polar and linear graphs, each on a single page of computer paper, are included at the end of this chapter; the subroutines are referred to as FPOLAR and FLINE, respectively. Each program is well commented to assist the user in its implementation, and each function can be plotted in a linear scale or a logarithmic (dB) scale.

A *major lobe* (also called main beam) is defined as "the radiation lobe containing the direction of maximum radiation." In Figure 2.4 the major lobe is pointing in the $\theta = 0$ direction. In some antennas, such as split-beam antennas, there may exist more than one major lobe. A *minor lobe* is any lobe except a major lobe. In Figures 2.4(a) and (b) all the lobes with the exception of the major can be classified as minor lobes. A *side lobe* is "a radiation lobe in any direction other than the intended lobe." (Usually a side lobe is adjacent to the main lobe and occupies the hemisphere in the direction of the main beam.) A *back lobe* usually refers to a minor lobe that occupies the hemisphere in a direction opposite to that of the major (main) lobe.

Minor lobes usually represent radiation in undesired directions, and they should be minimized. Side lobes are normally the largest of the minor

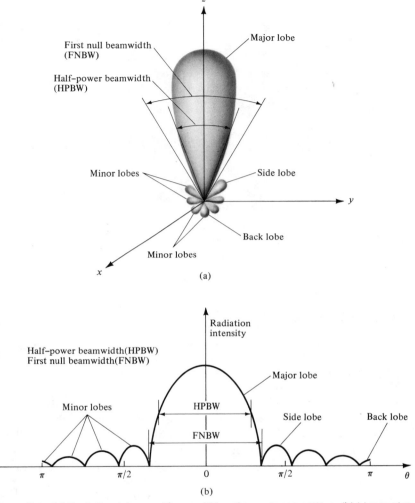

Figure 2.4   (a) Radiation lobes and beamwidths of an antenna pattern. (b) Linear plot of power pattern and its associated lobes and beamwidths.

lobes. The level of minor lobes is usually expressed as a ratio of the power density in the lobe in question to that of the major lobe. This ratio is often termed the side lobe ratio or side lobe level. Side lobe levels of −20 dB or smaller are usually not very harmful in most applications. Attainment of a side lobe level smaller than −30 dB usually requires very careful design and construction. In most radar systems, low side lobe ratios are very important to minimize false target indications through the side lobes.

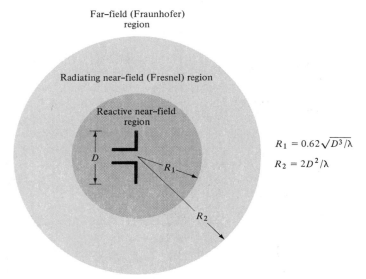

Figure 2.5   Field regions of an antenna.

2.2.4   Field Regions

The space surrounding an antenna is usually subdivided into three regions: (a) reactive near-field, (b) radiating near-field (Fresnel) and (c) far-field (Fraunhofer) regions as shown in Figure 2.5. These regions are so designated to identify the field structure in each. Although no abrupt changes in the field configurations are noted as the boundaries are crossed, there are distinct differences among them. The boundaries separating these regions are not unique, although various criteria have been established and are commonly used to identify the regions.

Reactive near-field region is defined as "that region of the field immediately surrounding the antenna wherein the reactive field predominates." For most antennas, the outer boundary of this region is commonly taken to exist at a distance $R < 0.62\sqrt{D^3/\lambda}$ from the antenna surface, where λ is the wavelength and D is the largest dimension of the antenna.

Radiating near-field (Fresnel) region is defined as "that region of the field of an antenna between the reactive near-field region and the far-field region wherein radiation fields predominate and wherein the angular field distribution is dependent upon the distance from the antenna. For an antenna focused at infinity, the radiating near-field region is sometimes referred to as the Fresnel region on the basis of analogy to optical terminology. If the antenna has a maximum overall dimension which is very small compared to the wavelength, this field region may not exist." The inner boundary is taken to be the distance $R \geq 0.62\sqrt{D^3/\lambda}$ and the outer

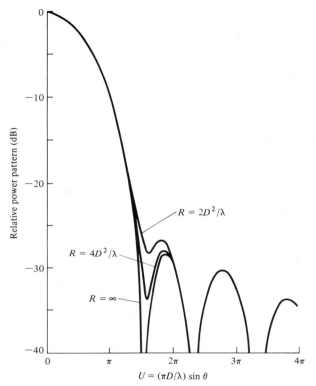

Figure 2.6   Calculated radiation patterns of a paraboloid antenna for different distances from the antenna. (SOURCE: J. S. Hollis, T. J. Lyon, and L. Clayton, Jr. (eds.), *Microwave Antenna Measurements*, Scientific-Atlanta, Inc., July 1970)

boundary the distance $R < 2D^2/\lambda$ where D is the largest* dimension of the antenna. This criterion is based on a maximum phase error of $\pi/8$. In this region the field pattern is, in general, a function of the radial distance and the radial field component may be appreciable.

Far-field (Fraunhofer) region is defined as "that region of the field of an antenna where the angular field distribution is essentially independent of the distance from the antenna. If the antenna has a maximum* overall dimension D, the far-field region is commonly taken to exist at distances greater than $2D^2/\lambda$ from the antenna, λ being the wavelength. For an antenna focused at infinity, the far-field region is sometimes referred to as the Fraunhofer region on the basis of analogy to optical terminology." In this region, the field components are essentially transverse and the angular distribution is independent of the radial distance where the measurements are made. The inner boundary is taken to be the radial distance $R = 2D^2/\lambda$ and the outer one at infinity.

*To be valid, D must also be large compared to the wavelength ($D > \lambda$).

To illustrate the pattern variation as a function of radial distance, in Figure 2.6 we have included three patterns of a parabolic reflector calculated at distances of $R = 2D^2/\lambda$, $4D^2/\lambda$, and infinity. It is observed that the patterns are almost identical, except for some differences in the pattern structure around the first null and at a level below 25 dB. Because infinite distances are not realizable in practice, the most commonly used criterion for minimum distance of far-field observations is $2D^2/\lambda$.

2.2.5   Radian and Steradian

The measure of a plane angle is a radian. One *radian* is defined as the plane angle with its vertex at the center of a circle of radius r that is subtended by an arc whose length is r. A graphical illustration is shown in Figure 2.7(a). Since the circumference of a circle of radius r is $C = 2\pi r$, there are 2π rad $(2\pi r/r)$ in a full circle.

The measure of a solid angle is a steradian. One *steradian* is defined as the solid angle with its vertex at the center of a sphere of radius r that is

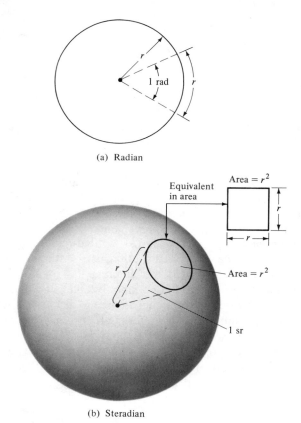

(a) Radian

(b) Steradian

Figure 2.7   Geometrical arrangements for defining a radian and a steradian.

subtended by a spherical surface area equal to that of a square with each side of length r. A graphical illustration is shown in Figure 2.7(b). Since the area of a sphere of radius r is $A = 4\pi r^2$, there are 4π sr $(4\pi r^2/r^2)$ in a closed sphere.

The infinitesimal area dA on the surface of a sphere of radius r, shown in Figure 2.1, is given by

$$dA = r^2 \sin\theta \, d\theta \, d\phi \quad (\text{m}^2) \tag{2-1}$$

Therefore, the element of solid angle $d\Omega$ of a sphere can be written as

$$d\Omega = \frac{dA}{r^2} = \sin\theta \, d\theta \, d\phi \quad (\text{sr}) \tag{2-2}$$

2.3 RADIATION POWER DENSITY

Electromagnetic waves are used to transport information through a wireless medium or a guiding structure, from one point to the other. It is then natural to assume that power and energy are associated with electromagnetic fields. The quantity used to describe the power associated with an electromagnetic wave is the instantaneous Poynting vector defined as

$$\mathcal{W} = \mathcal{E} \times \mathcal{H} \tag{2-3}$$

$\mathcal{W}$ = instantaneous Poynting vector (W/m^2)

$\mathcal{E}$ = instantaneous electric field intensity (V/m)

$\mathcal{H}$ = instantaneous magnetic field intensity (A/m)

Since the Poynting vector is a power density, the total power crossing a closed surface can be obtained by integrating the normal component of the Poynting vector over the entire surface. In equation form

$$\mathcal{P} = \oiint_S \mathcal{W} \cdot d\mathbf{s} = \oiint_S \mathcal{W} \cdot \hat{n} \, da \tag{2-4}$$

$\mathcal{P}$ = instantaneous total power (W)

da = infinitesimal area of the closed surface (m^2)

For applications of time varying fields, it is often more desirable to find the average power density which is obtained by integrating the instantaneous Poynting vector over one period and dividing by the period. For time harmonic variations of the form $e^{j\omega t}$, we define the complex fields $\mathbf{E}$ and $\mathbf{H}$ which are related to their instantaneous counterparts $\mathcal{E}$ and $\mathcal{H}$ by

$$\mathcal{E}(x, y, z; t) = \text{Re}\left[\mathbf{E}(x, y, z)e^{j\omega t}\right] \tag{2-5}$$

$$\mathcal{H}(x, y, z; t) = \text{Re}\left[\mathbf{H}(x, y, z)e^{j\omega t}\right] \tag{2-6}$$

Using the definitions of (2-5) and (2-6) and the identity $\text{Re}[\mathbf{E}e^{j\omega t}] = \frac{1}{2}[\mathbf{E}e^{j\omega t}$

$+\mathbf{E}^*e^{-j\omega t}$], (2-3) can be written as

$$\mathcal{W} = \mathcal{E} \times \mathcal{H} = \tfrac{1}{2}\,\mathrm{Re}[\mathbf{E}\times\mathbf{H}^*] + \tfrac{1}{2}\,\mathrm{Re}[\mathbf{E}\times\mathbf{H}e^{j2\omega t}] \qquad (2\text{-}7)$$

The first term of (2-7) is not a function of time, and the time variations of the second are twice the given frequency. The time average Poynting vector (average power density) can be written as

$$\boxed{\mathbf{W}_{av}(x,y,z)=\left[\mathcal{W}(x,y,z;t)\right]_{av}=\tfrac{1}{2}\,\mathrm{Re}[\mathbf{E}\times\mathbf{H}^*]} \qquad (\mathrm{W/m^2}) \quad (2\text{-}8)$$

The $\tfrac{1}{2}$ factor appears in (2-7) and (2-8) because the $\mathbf{E}$ and $\mathbf{H}$ fields represent peak values, and it should be omitted for RMS values.

A close observation of (2-8) may raise a question. If the real part of $(\mathbf{E}\times\mathbf{H}^*)/2$ represents the average (real) power density, what does the imaginary part of the same quantity represent? At this point it will be very natural to assume that the imaginary part must represent the reactive (stored) power density associated with the electromagnetic fields. In later chapters, it will be shown that the power density associated with the electromagnetic fields of an antenna in its far-field region is predominately real and will be referred to as *radiation density*.

Based upon the definition of (2-8), the average power radiated by an antenna (radiated power) can be written as

$$
\begin{aligned}
P_{rad}=P_{av}&=\oiint_S \mathbf{W}_{rad}\cdot d\mathbf{s}=\oiint_S \mathbf{W}_{av}\cdot d\mathbf{s}\\
&=\frac{1}{2}\oiint_S \mathrm{Re}(\mathbf{E}\times\mathbf{H}^*)\cdot d\mathbf{s}
\end{aligned}
\qquad (2\text{-}9)
$$

The power pattern of the antenna, whose definition was discussed in Section 2.2, is just a measure, as a function of direction, of the average power density radiated by the antenna. The observations are usually made on a large sphere of constant radius extending into the far-field. In practice, absolute power patterns are usually not desired. However, the performance of the antenna is measured in terms of the gain (to be discussed in a subsequent section) and in terms of relative power patterns. Three-dimensional patterns cannot be measured, but they can be constructed with a number of two-dimensional cuts.

Example 2.1

The radial component of the radiated power density of an antenna is given by

$$\mathbf{W}_{rad}=\hat{a}_r W_r=\hat{a}_r A_0\sin\theta/r^2 \qquad (\mathrm{W/m^2})$$

where A_0 is the peak value of the power density, θ is the usual spherical coordinate, and $\hat{a}_r$ is the radial unit vector. Determine the total radiated power.

SOLUTION
For a closed surface, a sphere of radius r is chosen. To find the total radiated power, the radial component of the power density is integrated over its surface. Thus

$$P_{\text{rad}} = \oiint_{S} \mathbf{W}_{\text{rad}} \cdot \hat{n} \, da$$

$$= \int_0^{2\pi} \int_0^{\pi} \left(\hat{a}_r A_0 \frac{\sin\theta}{r^2} \right) \cdot \left(\hat{a}_r r^2 \sin\theta \, d\theta \, d\phi \right) = \pi^2 A_0 \qquad (\text{W})$$

A three-dimensional normalized plot of the average power density at a distance of $r = 1$ m is shown in Figure 2.2.

A point source is an antenna with ideal isotropic radiating properties (radiates equally in all directions). Although it does not exist in practice, it provides a convenient isotropic reference with which to compare other antennas. Because of its symmetric radiation, its Poynting vector will not be a function of the spherical coordinate angles θ and ϕ. In addition, it will have only a radial component. Thus the total power radiated by it is given by

$$P_{\text{rad}} = \oiint_{S} \mathbf{W}_{r0} \cdot d\mathbf{s} = \int_0^{2\pi} \int_0^{\pi} \left[\hat{a}_r W_{r0}(r) \right] \cdot \left[\hat{a}_r r^2 \sin\theta \, d\theta \, d\phi \right] = 4\pi r^2 W_{r0}$$

$$(2\text{-}10)$$

and the power density by

$$\mathbf{W}_{r0} = \hat{a}_r W_{r0} = \hat{a}_r \left(\frac{P_{\text{rad}}}{4\pi r^2} \right) \qquad (\text{W}/\text{m}^2) \qquad (2\text{-}11)$$

which is uniformly distributed over the surface of a sphere of radius r.

2.4 RADIATION INTENSITY

Radiation intensity in a given direction is defined as "the power radiated from an antenna per unit solid angle." The radiation intensity is a far-field parameter, and it can be obtained by simply multiplying the radiation density by the square of the distance. In mathematical form it is expressed as

$$\boxed{U = r^2 W_{\text{rad}}} \qquad (2\text{-}12)$$

where

$U = $ radiation intensity   (W/unit solid angle)

$W_{\text{rad}} = $ radiation density   (W/m^2)

The radiation intensity is also related to the far-zone electric field of an antenna by

$$U(\theta,\phi) = \frac{r^2}{2\eta}|\mathbf{E}(r,\theta,\phi)|^2 \simeq \frac{r^2}{2\eta}\left[|E_\theta(r,\theta,\phi)|^2 + |E_\phi(r,\theta,\phi)|^2\right]$$

$$\simeq \frac{1}{2\eta}\left[|E_\theta(\theta,\phi)|^2 + |E_\phi(\theta,\phi)|^2\right]$$

(2-12a)

where

$\mathbf{E}$ = far-zone electric field intensity of the antenna

E_θ, E_ϕ = far-zone electric field components of the antenna

η = intrinsic impedance of the medium

Thus the power pattern is also a measure of the radiation intensity.

The total power is obtained by integrating the radiation intensity, as given by (2-12), over the entire solid angle of 4π. Thus

$$P_{\text{rad}} = \oiint_\Omega U\,d\Omega = \int_0^{2\pi}\int_0^\pi U\sin\theta\,d\theta\,d\phi$$

(2-13)

where $d\Omega$ = element of solid angle = $\sin\theta\,d\theta\,d\phi$.

Example 2.2

For the problem of Example 2.1, find the total radiated power using (2-13).

SOLUTION
Using (2-12)

$$U = r^2 W_{\text{rad}} = A_0\sin\theta$$

and by (2-13)

$$P_{\text{rad}} = \int_0^{2\pi}\int_0^\pi U\sin\theta\,d\theta\,d\phi = A_0\int_0^{2\pi}\int_0^\pi \sin^2\theta\,d\theta\,d\phi = \pi^2 A_0$$

which is the same as that obtained in Example 2.1. A three-dimensional plot of the relative radiation intensity is also represented by Figure 2.2.

For a point source, U will be independent of the angles θ and ϕ, as was the case for W_{rad}. Thus (2-13) can be written as

$$P_{\text{rad}} = \oiint_\Omega U_0\,d\Omega = U_0\oiint_\Omega d\Omega = 4\pi U_0$$

(2-14)

or the radiation intensity of an isotropic source as

$$U_0 = \frac{P_{\text{rad}}}{4\pi}$$

(2-15)

2.5 DIRECTIVITY

Before we define the directivity, let us first introduce the directive gain. *Directive gain* in a given direction is defined as "the ratio of the radiation intensity in that direction to the radiation intensity of a reference antenna." The reference antenna is taken to be an isotropic source. *Directivity* is "the value of the directive gain in the direction of its maximum value." Stated more simply, the directivity of a nonisotropic source is equal to the ratio of its maximum radiation intensity over that of an isotropic source. In mathematical form, using (2-15), they can be written as

$$D_g = \frac{U}{U_0} = \frac{4\pi U}{P_{\text{rad}}} \tag{2-16}$$

$$D_0 = \frac{U\big|_{\max}}{U_0} = \frac{U_{\max}}{U_0} = \frac{4\pi U_{\max}}{P_{\text{rad}}} \tag{2-17}$$

D_g = directive gain   (dimensionless)

D_0 = directivity   (dimensionless)

U = radiation intensity   (W/unit solid angle)

$U_{\max}$ = maximum radiation intensity   (W/unit solid angle)

U_0 = radiation intensity of isotropic source   (W/unit solid angle)

P_{rad} = total radiated power   (W)

For an isotropic source, it is very obvious from (2-16) and (2-17) that the directive gain and directivity will be unity since U, $U_{\max}$, and U_0 are all equal to each other.

Example 2.3

As an illustration, find the directivity of the antenna whose radiation intensity is that of Example 2.1.

SOLUTION
The radiation intensity is given by

$$U = r^2 W_{\text{rad}} = A_0 \sin\theta$$

The maximum radiation is directed along $\theta = \pi/2$. Thus

$$U_{\max} = A_0$$

In Example 2.1 it was found that

$$P_{\text{rad}} = \pi^2 A_0$$

Using (2-17), we find that the directivity is equal to

$$D_0 = \frac{4\pi U_{\max}}{P_{\mathrm{rad}}} = \frac{4}{\pi} = 1.27$$

Before proceeding with a more general discussion of directivity, it may be proper at this time to consider another example, compute its directivity, compare it with that of the previous example, and comment on what it actually represents. This may give the reader a better understanding and appreciation of the directivity.

Example 2.4

The radial component of the radiated power density of an infinitesimal linear dipole of length $l \ll \lambda$ is given by

$$\mathbf{W}_{\mathrm{av}} = \hat{a}_r W_r = \hat{a}_r A_0 \sin^2 \theta / r^2 \quad (\mathrm{W/m^2})$$

where A_0 is the peak value of the power density, θ is the usual spherical coordinate, and $\hat{a}_r$ is the radial unit vector. Determine the directivity of the antenna.

SOLUTION
The radiation intensity is given by

$$U = r^2 W_r = A_0 \sin^2 \theta$$

The maximum radiation is directed along $\theta = \pi/2$. Thus

$$U_{\max} = A_0$$

The total radiated power is given by

$$P_{\mathrm{rad}} = \oiint_{\Omega} U \, d\Omega = A_0 \int_0^{2\pi} \int_0^{\pi} \sin^2 \theta \sin \theta \, d\theta \, d\phi = A_0 \left(\frac{8\pi}{3} \right)$$

Using (2-17), we find that the directivity is equal to

$$D_0 = \frac{4\pi U_{\max}}{P_{\mathrm{rad}}} = \frac{4\pi A_0}{\frac{8\pi}{3}(A_0)} = \frac{3}{2}$$

which is greater than 1.27 found in Example 2.3.

At this time it will be proper to comment on the results of Examples 2.3 and 2.4. To better understand the discussion, we have plotted in Figure 2.8 the relative radiation intensities of Example 2.3 ($U = A_0 \sin \theta$) and Example 2.4 ($U = A_0 \sin^2 \theta$) where A_0 was set equal to unity. We see that both patterns are omnidirectional but that of Example 2.4 has more directional characteristics (is narrower) in the elevation plane. Since the directive gain and directivity are "figures-of-merit" describing how well the radiator directs energy in a certain direction, it should be convincing from Figure 2.8 that the directive gain and directivity of Example 2.4 should be higher than those of Example 2.3.

The directivity of an isotropic source is unity since its power is radiated equally well in all directions. *For all other sources, the directivity will always be greater than unity, and it is a relative "figure-of-merit" which gives an indication of the directional properties of the antenna as compared with those of an isotropic source.* In equation form, this is indicated in (2-17). The directive gain can be smaller than unity; in fact it can be equal to zero. For Examples 2.3 and 2.4, the directive gain is equal to zero in the $\theta = 0$ direction. *The values of directive gain will be equal to or greater than zero and equal to or less than the directivity $(0 \le D_g \le D_0)$.*

A more general expression for the directive gain and directivity can be developed to include sources with radiation patterns that may be functions of both spherical coordinate angles θ and ϕ. In the previous examples we considered intensities that were represented by only one coordinate angle θ, in order not to obscure the fundamental concepts by the mathematical details. So it may now be proper, since the basic definitions have been illustrated by simple examples, to formulate the more general expressions.

Let the radiation intensity of an antenna be of the form

$$U = B_0 F(\theta, \phi) \simeq \frac{1}{2\eta} \left[|E_\theta(\theta, \phi)|^2 + |E_\phi(\theta, \phi)|^2 \right] \tag{2-18}$$

where B_0 is a constant, and E_θ and E_ϕ are the antenna's far-zone electric

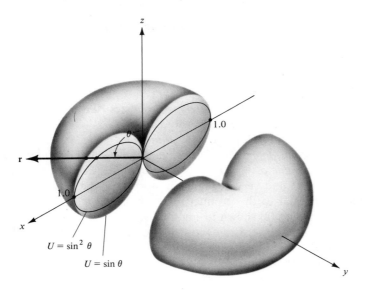

Figure 2.8 Three-dimensional radiation intensity patterns. (SOURCE: P. Lorrain and D. R. Corson, *Electromagnetic Fields and Waves*, 2nd ed., W. H. Freeman and Co. Copyright © 1970)

field components. The maximum value of (2-18) is given by

$$U_{\max} = B_0 F(\theta, \phi)|_{\max} = B_0 F_{\max}(\theta, \phi) \tag{2-19}$$

The total radiated power is found using

$$P_{\text{rad}} = \oiint_{\Omega} U(\theta, \phi)\, d\Omega = B_0 \int_0^{2\pi} \int_0^{\pi} F(\theta, \phi) \sin\theta\, d\theta\, d\phi \tag{2-20}$$

We now write the general expression for the directive gain and directivity using (2-16) and (2-17), respectively, as

$$D_g(\theta, \phi) = 4\pi \frac{F(\theta, \phi)}{\displaystyle\int_0^{2\pi}\int_0^{\pi} F(\theta, \phi) \sin\theta\, d\theta\, d\phi} \tag{2-21}$$

$$D_0 = 4\pi \frac{F(\theta, \phi)|_{\max}}{\displaystyle\int_0^{2\pi}\int_0^{\pi} F(\theta, \phi) \sin\theta\, d\theta\, d\phi} \tag{2-22}$$

Equation (2-22) can also be written as

$$D_0 = \frac{4\pi}{\left[\displaystyle\int_0^{2\pi}\int_0^{\pi} F(\theta, \phi) \sin\theta\, d\theta\, d\phi\right] \Big/ F(\theta, \phi)|_{\max}} = \frac{4\pi}{\Omega_A} \tag{2-23}$$

where Ω_A is the beam solid angle, and it is given by

$$\Omega_A = \frac{1}{F(\theta, \phi)|_{\max}} \int_0^{2\pi}\int_0^{\pi} F(\theta, \phi) \sin\theta\, d\theta\, d\phi = \int_0^{2\pi}\int_0^{\pi} F_n(\theta, \phi) \sin\theta\, d\theta\, d\phi \tag{2-24}$$

$$F_n(\theta, \phi) = \frac{F(\theta, \phi)}{F(\theta, \phi)|_{\max}} \tag{2-25}$$

Dividing by $F(\theta, \phi)|_{\max}$ merely normalizes the radiation intensity $F(\theta, \phi)$, and it makes its maximum value unity.

The beam solid angle Ω_A is defined as the solid angle through which all the power of the antenna would flow if its radiation intensity is constant (and equal to the maximum value of U) for all angles within Ω_A. For antennas with one narrow major lobe and very negligible minor lobes, the beam solid angle is approximately equal to the product of the half-power beamwidths in two perpendicular planes [2] shown in Figure 2.9(a). For a rotationally symmetric pattern, the half-power beamwidths in any two perpendicular planes are the same, as illustrated in Figure 2.9(b).

With this approximation, (2-23) can be written as

$$D_0 = \frac{4\pi}{\Omega_A} \simeq \frac{4\pi}{\Theta_{1r}\Theta_{2r}} \tag{2-26}$$

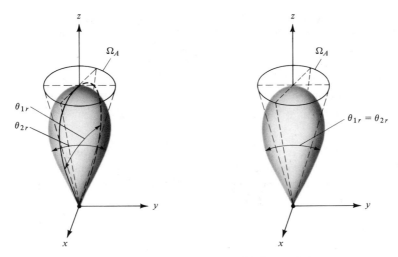

(a) Nonsymmetrical pattern   (b) Symmetrical pattern

Figure 2.9   Beam solid angles for nonsymmetrical and symmetrical radiation patterns.

The beam solid angle Ω_A has been approximated by

$$\Omega_A \simeq \Theta_{1r}\Theta_{2r} \tag{2-27}$$

where

$\Theta_{1r} =$ half-power beamwidth in one plane   (rad)

$\Theta_{2r} =$ half-power beamwidth in a plane at a right angle to the other   (rad)

If the beamwidths are known in degrees, (2-26) can be written as

$$D_0 \simeq \frac{4\pi(180/\pi)^2}{\Theta_{1d}\Theta_{2d}} = \frac{41,253}{\Theta_{1d}\Theta_{2d}} \tag{2-28}$$

where

$\Theta_{1d} =$ half-power beamwidth in one plane   (degrees)

$\Theta_{2d} =$ half-power beamwidth in a plane at a right angle to the other   (degrees)

For planar arrays, a better approximation to (2-28) is [3]

$$\boxed{D_0 \simeq \frac{32,400}{\Omega_A(\text{degrees})^2} = \frac{32,400}{\Theta_{1d}\Theta_{2d}}} \tag{2-28a}$$

The validity of (2-26) and (2-28) is based on a pattern that has only one major lobe and any minor lobes, if present, should be of very low intensity. For a pattern with two identical major lobes, the value of the directivity using (2-26) or (2-28) will be twice its actual value. For patterns with significant minor lobes, the values of directivity obtained using (2-26) or (2-28), which neglect any minor lobes, will usually be too high.

___

Example 2.5

The radiation intensity of the major lobe of many antennas can be adequately represented by

$$U = B_0 \cos \theta$$

where B_0 is the maximum radiation intensity. The radiation intensity exists only in the upper hemisphere ($0 \le \theta \le \pi/2, 0 \le \phi \le 2\pi$), and it is shown in Figure 2.10. Find the directivity using (2-26) or (2-28) and compare it with its exact value.

SOLUTION
The half-power point of the pattern occurs at $\theta = 60°$. Thus the beamwidth in the θ direction is 120° or

$$\Theta_{1r} = \frac{2\pi}{3}$$

Since the pattern is independent of the ϕ coordinate, the beamwidth in the other plane is also equal to

$$\Theta_{2r} = \frac{2\pi}{3}$$

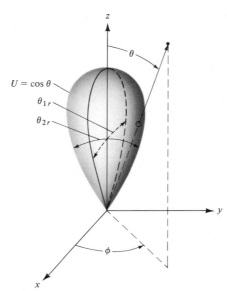

Figure 2.10   Radiation intensity pattern of the form $U = \cos \theta$ in the upper hemisphere.

The directivity, using (2-26), is then equal to

$$D_0 \simeq \frac{4\pi}{(2\pi/3)^2} = \frac{9}{\pi} = 2.87$$

Now let us find the exact value of the directivity and compare the results.

$$U = B_0 \cos\theta$$

$$U_{max} = B_0 \cos\theta|_{max} = B_0$$

$$P_{rad} = \int_0^{2\pi} \int_0^{\pi/2} B_0 \cos\theta \sin\theta \, d\theta \, d\phi = 2\pi B_0 \int_0^{\pi/2} \cos\theta \sin\theta \, d\theta$$

$$P_{rad} = \pi B_0 \int_0^{\pi/2} \sin(2\theta) \, d\theta = \pi B_0$$

$$D_0 = \frac{4\pi U_{max}}{P_{rad}} = \frac{4\pi B_0}{\pi B_0} = 4 \qquad \text{(dimensionless)}$$

The exact directivity is 4 and its approximate value, using (2-26), is 2.87. Better approximations can be obtained if the patterns have much narrower beamwidths, which will be demonstrated later in this section.

Many times it is desirable to express the directive gain and directivity in decibels (dB) instead of dimensionless quantities. The expressions for converting the dimensionless quantities of directive gain and directivity to decibels (dB) are

$$D_g(\text{dB}) = 10\log_{10}\left[D_g(\text{dimensionless})\right] \qquad (2\text{-}29)$$

$$D_0(\text{dB}) = 10\log_{10}\left[D_0(\text{dimensionless})\right] \qquad (2\text{-}30)$$

It has also been proposed [4] that the directivity of an antenna can also be obtained approximately by using the formula

$$\frac{1}{D_0} = \frac{1}{2}\left(\frac{1}{D_1} + \frac{1}{D_2}\right) \qquad (2\text{-}31)$$

where

$$D_1 \simeq \frac{1}{\left[\dfrac{1}{2\ln 2}\displaystyle\int_0^{\Theta_{1r}/2} \sin\theta \, d\theta\right]} \simeq \frac{16\ln 2}{\Theta_{1r}^2} \qquad (2\text{-}31a)$$

$$D_2 \simeq \frac{1}{\left[\dfrac{1}{2\ln 2}\displaystyle\int_0^{\Theta_{2r}/2} \sin\theta \, d\theta\right]} \simeq \frac{16\ln 2}{\Theta_{2r}^2} \qquad (2\text{-}31b)$$

Θ_{1r} and Θ_{2r} are the half-power beamwidths (in radians) of the E- and H-planes, respectively. The formula of (2-31) will be referred to as the arithmetic mean of the directivity. Using (2-31a) and (2-31b) we can write

(2-31) as

$$\frac{1}{D_0} \simeq \frac{1}{2\ln 2}\left(\frac{\Theta_{1r}^2}{16} + \frac{\Theta_{2r}^2}{16}\right) = \frac{\Theta_{1r}^2 + \Theta_{2r}^2}{32\ln 2} \tag{2-32}$$

or

$$\boxed{D_0 \simeq \frac{32\ln 2}{\Theta_{1r}^2 + \Theta_{2r}^2} = \frac{22.181}{\Theta_{1r}^2 + \Theta_{2r}^2}} \tag{2-32a}$$

$$D_0 \simeq \frac{22.181(180/\pi)^2}{\Theta_{1d}^2 + \Theta_{2d}^2} = \frac{72{,}815}{\Theta_{1d}^2 + \Theta_{2d}^2} \tag{2-32b}$$

where Θ_{1d} and Θ_{2d} are the half-power beamwidths in degrees. Equation (2-32a) is to be contrasted with (2-26) while (2-32b) should be compared with (2-28).

In order to make an evaluation and comparison of the accuracies of (2-26) and (2-32a), examples whose radiation intensities (power patterns) can be represented by

$$U(\theta,\phi) = \begin{cases} B_0\cos^n(\theta) & 0\le\theta\le\pi/2, \quad 0\le\phi\le 2\pi \\ 0 & \text{elsewhere} \end{cases} \tag{2-33}$$

where $n = 1-10$, 15, and 20 are considered. The directivities were computed using (2-26) and (2-32a) and compared with the exact values as obtained using (2-22). The results are shown in Table 2.1. From the comparison, it is evident that Kraus' formula gives better results for beam patterns with $n \le 10$. The results are shown plotted in Figure 2.11.

Table 2.1 COMPARISON OF EXACT AND APPROXIMATE VALUES OF DIRECTIVITY FOR $U = \cos^n\theta$ POWER PATTERNS

n	EXACT EQUATION (2-22)	KRAUS EQUATION (2-26)	KRAUS % ERROR	TAI AND PEREIRA EQUATION (2-32a)	TAI AND PEREIRA % ERROR
1	4	2.86	28.50	2.53	36.75
2	6	5.09	15.27	4.49	25.17
3	8	7.35	8.12	6.48	19.00
4	10	9.61	3.90	8.48	15.20
5	12	11.87	1.08	10.47	12.75
6	14	14.13	0.93	12.46	11.00
7	16	16.39	2.48	14.47	9.56
8	18	18.66	3.68	16.47	8.50
9	20	20.93	4.64	18.47	7.65
10	22	23.19	5.41	20.47	6.96
15	32	34.52	7.88	30.46	4.81
20	42	45.89	9.26	40.46	3.67

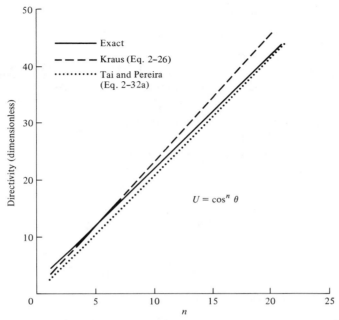

Figure 2.11 Comparison of exact and approximate values of directivity for $\cos^n\theta$ power patterns.

2.6 NUMERICAL TECHNIQUES

For most practical antennas, their radiation patterns are so complex that closed form mathematical expressions are not available. Even in those cases where expressions are available, their form is so complex that integration to find the radiated power, required to compute the directivity, cannot be performed. Instead of using the approximate expressions of Kraus, and Tai and Pereira, alternate and more accurate techniques may be desirable. With the high-speed computer systems now available, the answer may be to apply numerical methods.

Let us assume that the radiation intensity of a given antenna is separable, and it is given by

$$U = B_0 f(\theta) g(\phi) \tag{2-34}$$

where B_0 is a contrast. The directivity for such a system is given by

$$D_0 = \frac{4\pi U_{max}}{P_{rad}} \tag{2-35}$$

where

$$P_{rad} = B_0 \int_0^{2\pi} \left\{ \int_0^{\pi} f(\theta) g(\phi) \sin\theta \, d\theta \right\} d\phi \tag{2-36}$$

which can also be written as

$$P_{rad} = B_0 \int_0^{2\pi} g(\phi) \left\{ \int_0^{\pi} f(\theta) \sin\theta \, d\theta \right\} d\phi \qquad (2\text{-}37)$$

If the integrations in (2-37) cannot be performed analytically, then from integral calculus we can write a series approximation

$$\int_0^{\pi} f(\theta) \sin\theta \, d\theta = \sum_{i=1}^{N} \left[f(\theta_i) \sin\theta_i \right] \Delta\theta_i \qquad (2\text{-}38)$$

For N uniform divisions over the π interval,

$$\Delta\theta_i = \frac{\pi}{N} \qquad (2\text{-}38a)$$

Referring to Figure 2.12, θ_i can take many different forms. Two schemes are shown in Figure 2.12 such that

$$\theta_i = i \left(\frac{\pi}{N} \right), \qquad i = 1, 2, 3, \ldots, N \qquad (2\text{-}38b)$$

or

$$\theta_i = \frac{\pi}{2N} + (i-1) \frac{\pi}{N}, \qquad i = 1, 2, 3, \ldots, N \qquad (2\text{-}38c)$$

In the former case, θ_i is taken at the trailing edge of each division; in the latter case, θ_i is selected at the middle of each division. The scheme that is

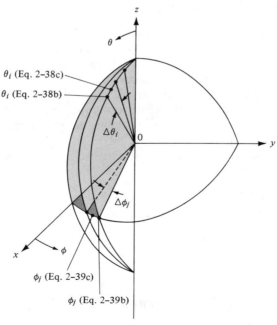

Figure 2.12 Digitization in spherical coordinates.

more desirable will depend upon the problem under investigation. Many other schemes are available.

In a similar manner, we can write for the ϕ variations that

$$\int_0^{2\pi} g(\phi)\, d\phi = \sum_{j=1}^{M} g(\phi_j)\, \Delta\phi_j \tag{2-39}$$

where for M uniform divisions

$$\Delta\phi_j = \frac{2\pi}{M} \tag{2-39a}$$

Again referring to Figure 2.12

$$\phi_j = j\left(\frac{2\pi}{M}\right), \qquad j=1,2,3,\ldots,M \tag{3-39b}$$

or

$$\phi_j = \frac{2\pi}{2M} + (j-1)\frac{2\pi}{M}, \qquad j=1,2,3,\ldots,M \tag{2-39c}$$

Combining (2-38), (2-38a), (2-39), and (2-39a) we can write (2-37) as

$$P_{\text{rad}} = B_0\left(\frac{\pi}{N}\right)\left(\frac{2\pi}{M}\right) \sum_{j=1}^{M} \left\{ g(\phi_j)\left[\sum_{i=1}^{N} f(\theta_i)\sin\theta_i \right] \right\} \tag{2-40}$$

The double summation of (2-40) is performed by adding for each value of j ($j=1,2,3,\ldots,M$) all values of i ($i=1,2,3,\ldots,N$). In a computer program flowchart, this can be performed by a loop within a loop. Physically, (2-40) can be interpreted by referring to Figure 2.12. It simply states that for each value of $g(\phi)$ at the azimuthal angle $\phi=\phi_j$, the values of $f(\theta)\sin\theta$ are added for all values of $\theta=\theta_i$ ($i=1,2,3,\ldots,N$). The values of θ_i and ϕ_j can be determined by using either of the forms as given by (2-38b) or (2-38c) and (2-39b) or (2-39c).

Since the θ and ϕ variations are separable, (2-40) can also be written as

$$P_{\text{rad}} = B_0\left(\frac{\pi}{N}\right)\left(\frac{2\pi}{M}\right) \left[\sum_{j=1}^{M} g(\phi_j) \right]\left[\sum_{i=1}^{N} f(\theta_i)\sin\theta_i \right] \tag{2-41}$$

in which case each summation can be performed separately.

If the θ and ϕ variations are not separable, and the radiation intensity is given by

$$U = B_0 F(\theta,\phi) \tag{2-42}$$

the digital form of the radiated power can be written as

$$\boxed{P_{\text{rad}} = B_0\left(\frac{\pi}{N}\right)\left(\frac{2\pi}{M}\right) \sum_{j=1}^{M}\left[\sum_{i=1}^{N} F(\theta_i,\phi_j)\sin\theta_i \right]} \tag{2-43}$$

θ_i and ϕ_j take different forms, two of which were introduced and are shown pictorially in Figure 2.12. The evaluation and physical interpretation of (2-43) is similar to that of (2-40).

To examine the accuracy of the technique, two examples will be considered.

Example 2.6(a)

The radiation intensity of an antenna is given by

$$U(\theta, \phi) = \begin{cases} B_0 \sin\theta \sin^2\phi, & 0 \le \theta \le \pi, \quad 0 \le \phi \le \pi \\ 0 & \text{elsewhere} \end{cases}$$

Determine the directivity numerically by using (2-41) with θ_i and ϕ_j of (2-38b) and (2-39b), respectively. Compare it with the exact value.

SOLUTION

Let us divide the θ and ϕ intervals each into 18 equal segments ($N = M = 18$). Since $0 \le \phi \le \pi$, then $\Delta\phi_j = \pi/M$ and (2-41) reduces to

$$P_{\text{rad}} = B_0 \left(\frac{\pi}{18}\right)^2 \left[\sum_{j=1}^{18} \sin^2\phi_j\right]\left[\sum_{i=1}^{18} \sin^2\theta_i\right]$$

with

$$\theta_i = i\left(\frac{\pi}{18}\right) = i(10°), \qquad i = 1,2,3,\ldots,18$$

$$\phi_j = j\left(\frac{\pi}{18}\right) = j(10°), \qquad j = 1,2,3,\ldots,18$$

Thus

$$P_{\text{rad}} = B_0 \left(\frac{\pi}{18}\right)^2 \left[\sin^2(10°) + \sin^2(20°) + \cdots + \sin^2(180°)\right]^2$$

$$P_{\text{rad}} = B_0 \left(\frac{\pi}{18}\right)^2 (9)^2 = B_0 \left(\frac{\pi^2}{4}\right)$$

and

$$D_0 = \frac{4\pi U_{\text{max}}}{P_{\text{rad}}} = \frac{4\pi}{\pi^2/4} = \frac{16}{\pi} = 5.0929$$

The exact value is given by

$$P_{\text{rad}} = B_0 \int_0^\pi \sin^2\phi \, d\phi \int_0^\pi \sin^2\theta \, d\theta = \frac{\pi}{2}\left(\frac{\pi}{2}\right) B_0 = \frac{\pi^2}{4} B_0$$

and

$$D_0 = \frac{4\pi U_{\text{max}}}{P_{\text{rad}}} = \frac{4\pi}{\pi^2/4} = \frac{16}{\pi} = 5.0929$$

which is the same as the value obtained numerically!

Example 2.6(b)

Given the same radiation intensity as that in Example 2.6(a), determine the directivity using (2-41) with θ_i and ϕ_j of (2-38c) and (2-39c).

SOLUTION

Again using 18 divisions in each interval, we can write (2-41) as

$$P_{rad} = B_0 \left(\frac{\pi}{18} \right)^2 \left[\sum_{j=1}^{18} \sin^2 \phi_j \right] \left[\sum_{i=1}^{18} \sin^2 \theta_i \right]$$

with

$$\theta_i = \frac{\pi}{36} + (i-1)\frac{\pi}{18} = 5° + (i-1)10°, \qquad i=1,2,3,\ldots,18$$

$$\phi_j = \frac{\pi}{36} + (j-1)\frac{\pi}{18} = 5° + (j-1)10°, \qquad j=1,2,3,\ldots,18$$

Because of the symmetry of the divisions about the $\theta = \pi/2$ and $\phi = \pi/2$ angles, we can write

$$P_{rad} = B_0 \left(\frac{\pi}{18} \right)^2 \left[2 \sum_{j=1}^{9} \sin^2 \phi_j \right] \left[2 \sum_{i=1}^{9} \sin^2 \theta_i \right]$$

$$P_{rad} = B_0 \left(\frac{\pi}{18} \right)^2 4 \left[\sin^2(5°) + \sin^2(15°) + \cdots + \sin^2(85°) \right]^2$$

$$P_{rad} = B_0 \left(\frac{\pi}{18} \right)^2 4(4.5)^2 = B_0 \left(\frac{\pi}{18} \right)^2 (81) = B_0 \left(\frac{\pi^2}{4} \right)$$

which is identical to that of the previous example. Thus

$$D_0 = \frac{4\pi U_{max}}{P_{rad}} = \frac{4\pi}{\pi^2/4} = \frac{16}{\pi} = 5.0929$$

which again is equal to the exact value!

It is interesting to note that decreasing the number of divisions (M and/or N) to 9, 6, 4, and even 2 leads to the same answer, which also happens to be the exact value! To demonstrate as to why the number of divisions does not affect the answer for this pattern, let us refer to Figure 2.13 where we have plotted the $\sin^2 \phi$ function and divided the $0° \leq \phi \leq 180°$ interval into six divisions. The exact value of the directivity uses the area under the solid curve. Doing the problem numerically, we find the area under the rectangles, which is shown shaded. Because of the symmetrical nature of the function, it can be shown that the shaded area in section #1 (included in the numerical evaluation) is equal to the blank area in section #1′ (left out by the numerical method). The same is true for the areas in sections #2 and #2′, and #3 and #3′. Thus, there is a one-to-one compensation. Similar justification is applicable for the other number of divisions.

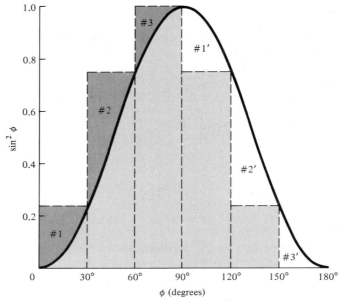

Figure 2.13 Digitized form of $\sin^2 \phi$ function.

It should be emphasized that all functions, even though they may contain some symmetry, do not give the same answers independent of the number of divisions. As a matter of fact, in most cases the answer only approaches the exact value as the number of divisions is increased to a large number.

A FORTRAN computer program called DIRECTIVITY has been developed to compute the directivity of any antenna whose radiation intensity is $U = F(\theta, \phi)$ based on the formulation of (2-43). The intensity function F does not have to be a function of both θ and ϕ. The numerical evaluations are made at the trailing edge, as defined by (2-38b) and (2-39b). The program is included at the end of this chapter. It contains a SUBROUTINE for which the intensity factor $U = F(\theta, \phi)$ for the required application must be specified by the user. As an illustration, the antenna intensity $U = \sin \theta \sin^2 \phi$ has been inserted in the subroutine. In addition, the upper and lower limits of θ and ϕ must be specified by inserting, for each application of the same pattern, a DATA card in the end of the program. The lower and upper limits must be read with the FORMAT specified by the READ statement of the main program.

2.7 GAIN

Another useful measure describing the performance of an antenna is the *gain*. Although the gain of the antenna is closely related to the directivity, it is a measure that takes into account the efficiency of the antenna as well as its directional capabilities. Remember that directivity is a measure that describes only the directional properties of the antenna, and it is therefore controlled only by the pattern.

Power gain of an antenna in a given direction is defined as "4π times the ratio of the radiation intensity in that direction to the net power accepted by the antenna from a connected transmitter." *When the direction is not stated, the power gain is usually taken in the direction of maximum radiation.* Thus, in general

$$\text{gain} = 4\pi \frac{\text{radiation intensity}}{\text{total input power}} = 4\pi \frac{U(\theta,\phi)}{P_{\text{in}}} \qquad \text{(dimensionless)} \qquad (2\text{-}44)$$

In most cases we deal with *relative gain*, which is defined as "the ratio of the power gain in a given direction to the power gain of a reference antenna in its referenced direction." The power input must be the same for both antennas. The reference antenna is usually a dipole, horn, or any other antenna whose gain can be calculated or it is known. In most cases, however, the reference antenna is a *lossless isotropic source.* Thus

$$G_g = \frac{4\pi U(\theta,\phi)}{P_{\text{in}} \text{ (lossless isotropic source)}} \qquad \text{(dimensionless)} \qquad (2\text{-}45)$$

Referring to Figure 2.14(a), we can write that the total radiated power (P_{rad}) is related to the total input power (P_{in}) by

$$P_{\text{rad}} = e_t P_{\text{in}} \qquad (2\text{-}46)$$

where e_t is the total antenna efficiency (dimensionless). Using (2-46) reduces (2-45) to

$$G_g(\theta,\phi) = e_t \left[4\pi \frac{U(\theta,\phi)}{P_{\text{rad}}} \right] \qquad (2\text{-}47)$$

which is related to the directive gain of (2-21) by

$$\boxed{G_g(\theta,\phi) = e_t D_g(\theta,\phi)} \qquad (2\text{-}48)$$

In a similar manner, the maximum value of the gain is related to the directivity by

$$\boxed{G_0 = G_g(\theta,\phi)|_{\text{max}} = e_t D_g(\theta,\phi)|_{\text{max}} = e_t D_0} \qquad (2\text{-}49)$$

For many practical antennas an approximate formula for the gain, corresponding to (2-28) or (2-28b) for the directivity, is

$$\boxed{G_0 \simeq \frac{30{,}000}{\Theta_{1d}\Theta_{2d}}} \qquad (2\text{-}49b)$$

In practice, whenever the term "gain" is used, it usually refers to the *maximum power gain* as defined by (2-49).

Usually the gain is given in terms of decibels instead of the dimensionless quantity of (2-49). The conversion formula is given by

$$G_0(dB) = 10 \log_{10}[e_t D_0 \quad \text{(dimensionless)}]$$ (2-50)

2.8 ANTENNA EFFICIENCY

The total antenna efficiency e_t is used to take into account losses at the input terminals and within the structure of the antenna. Such losses may be due, referring to Figure 2.14(b), to

1. reflections because of the mismatch between the transmission line and the antenna
2. I^2R losses (conduction and dielectric)

In general, the overall efficiency can be written as

$$\boxed{e_t = e_r e_c e_d}$$ (2-51)

where

e_t = total overall efficiency   (dimensionless)

e_r = reflection (mismatch) efficiency = $(1 - |\Gamma|^2)$ (dimensionless)

e_c = conduction efficiency   (dimensionless)

e_d = dielectric efficiency   (dimensionless)

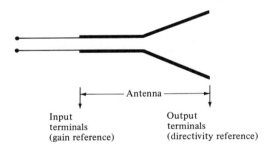

Input
terminals
(gain reference)

Output
terminals
(directivity reference)

— Antenna —

(a) Antenna reference terminals

(b) Reflection, conduction, and dielectric losses

Figure 2.14   Reference terminals and losses of an antenna.

Γ = voltage reflection coefficient at the input terminals of the antenna [$\Gamma = (Z_{in} - Z_0)/(Z_{in} + Z_0)$ where Z_{in} = antenna input impedance, Z_0 = characteristic impedance of the transmission line]

Usually e_c and e_d are very difficult to compute, but they can be determined experimentally. Even by measurements they cannot be separated, and it is usually more convenient to write (2-51) as

$$e_t = e_r e_{cd} = e_{cd}(1 - |\Gamma|^2) \qquad (2-52)$$

where $e_{cd} = e_c e_d$ = antenna radiation efficiency.

Example 2.7

A lossless resonant half-wavelength dipole antenna, with input impedance of 73 ohms, is to be connected to a transmission line whose characteristic impedance is 50 ohms. Assuming that the pattern of the antenna is given approximately by

$$U = B_0 \sin^3 \theta$$

find the overall gain of this antenna.

SOLUTION
Let us first compute the directivity of the antenna. For this

$$U|_{max} = U_{max} = B_0$$

$$P_{rad} = \int_0^{2\pi} \int_0^\pi U(\theta, \phi) \sin \theta \, d\theta \, d\phi = 2\pi B_0 \int_0^\pi \sin^4 \theta \, d\theta = B_0 \left(\frac{3\pi^2}{4} \right)$$

$$D_0 = 4\pi \frac{U_{max}}{P_{rad}} = \frac{16}{3\pi} = 1.697$$

The next step will be to find the efficiencies. Thus

$$e_r = (1 - |\Gamma|^2) = \left(1 - \left| \frac{73 - 50}{73 + 50} \right|^2 \right) = 0.965$$

$e_{cd} = 1$ because lossless antenna

$$e_t = e_r e_{cd} = 0.965$$

$$G_0 = e_t D_0 = 0.965(1.697) = 1.64$$

$$G_0 \, (\text{dB}) = 10 \log_{10}(1.64) = 2.14$$

The gain in dB can also be obtained by converting the directivity and efficiencies in dB and then adding them. Thus

$$e_r(dB) = 10\log_{10}(0.965) = -0.155$$

$$e_{cd}(dB) = 10\log_{10}(1.0) = 0$$

$$D_0(dB) = 10\log_{10}(1.697) = 2.297$$

$$G_0(dB) = e_r(dB) + e_{cd}(dB) + D_0(dB) = -0.155 + 2.297 \simeq 2.14$$

which is the same as obtained previously.

2.9 HALF-POWER BEAMWIDTH

The *half-power beamwidth* is defined as: "In a plane containing the direction of the maximum of a beam, the angle between the two directions in which the radiation intensity is one-half the maximum value of the beam." Often the term beamwidth is used to describe the angle between any two points on the pattern, such as the angle between the 10-dB points. In this case the specific points on the pattern must be described to avoid confusion. However the term *beamwidth* by itself is usually reserved to describe the 3-dB beamwidth.

2.10 BEAM EFFICIENCY

Another parameter that is frequently used to judge the quality of transmitting and receiving antennas is the *beam efficiency*. For an antenna with its major lobe directed along the z-axis ($\theta = 0$), as shown in Figure 2.4(a), the beam efficiency (BE) is defined by

$$BE = \frac{\text{power transmitted (received) within cone angle } \theta_1}{\text{power transmitted (received) by the antenna}} \quad (2\text{-}53)$$

$$(\text{dimensionless})$$

where θ_1 is the half-angle of the cone within which the percentage of the total power is to be found. Equation (2-53) can be written as

$$BE = \frac{\displaystyle\int_0^{2\pi}\int_0^{\theta_1} U(\theta,\phi)\sin\theta\,d\theta\,d\phi}{\displaystyle\int_0^{2\pi}\int_0^{\pi} U(\theta,\phi)\sin\theta\,d\theta\,d\phi} \quad (2\text{-}54)$$

If θ_1 is chosen as the angle where the first null or minimum occurs (see Figure 2.4), then the beam efficiency will indicate the amount of power in the major lobe compared to the total power. A very high beam efficiency (between the nulls or minimums), usually in the high 90's, is necessary for antennas used in radiometry, astronomy, radar, and other applications where received signals through the minor lobes must be minimized. The beam efficiencies of some typical circular and rectangular aperture antennas will be discussed in Chapter 11.

2.11 BANDWIDTH

The *bandwidth* of an antenna is defined as "the range of frequencies within which the performance of the antenna, with respect to some characteristic, conforms to a specified standard." The bandwidth can be considered to be the range of frequencies, on either side of a center frequency (usually the resonance frequency for a dipole), where the antenna characteristics (such as input impedance, pattern, beamwidth, polarization, side lobe level, gain, beam direction, radiation efficiency) are within an acceptable value of those at the center frequency. For broadband antennas, the bandwidth is usually expressed as the ratio of the upper-to-lower frequencies of acceptable operation. For example, a 10 : 1 bandwidth indicates that the upper frequency is 10 times greater than the lower. For narrowband antennas, the bandwidth is expressed as a percentage of the frequency difference (upper minus lower) over the center frequency of the bandwidth. For example, a 5% bandwidth indicates that the frequency difference of acceptable operation is 5% of the center frequency of the bandwidth.

Because the characteristics (input impedance, pattern, gain, polarization, etc.) of an antenna do not necessarily vary in the same manner or are even critically affected by the frequency, there is no unique characterization of the bandwidth. The specifications are set in each case to meet the needs of the particular application. Usually there is a distinction made between pattern and input impedance variations. Accordingly *pattern bandwidth* and *impedance bandwidth* are used to emphasize this distinction. Associated with pattern bandwidth are gain, side lobe level, beamwidth, polarization, and beam direction while input impedance and radiation efficiency are related to impedance bandwidth. For example, the pattern of a linear dipole with overall length less than a half-wavelength ($l < \lambda/2$) is insensitive to frequency. The limiting factor for this antenna is its impedance, and its bandwidth can be formulated in terms of the Q. The Q of antennas or arrays with dimensions large compared to the wavelength, excluding superdirective designs, is near unity. Therefore the bandwidth is usually formulated in terms of beamwidth, side lobe level, and pattern characteristics. For intermediate length antennas, the bandwidth may be limited by either pattern or impedance variations, depending upon the particular application. For these antennas, a 2 : 1 bandwidth indicates a good design. For others, large bandwidths are needed. Antennas with very large bandwidths (like 40 : 1 or greater) have been designed in recent years. These are known as frequency independent antennas, and they are discussed in Chapter 10.

The above discussion presumes that the coupling networks (transformers, baluns, etc.) and/or the dimensions of the antenna are not altered in any manner as the frequency is changed. It is possible to increase the acceptable frequency range of a narrowband antenna if proper adjustments can be made on the critical dimensions of the antenna and/or on the coupling networks as the frequency is changed. Although not an easy or possible task in general, there are applications where this can be accomplished. The most common examples are the antenna of a car radio and the "rabbit ears" of a television. Both usually have adjustable lengths which can be used to tune the antenna for better reception.

2.12 POLARIZATION

Polarization of an antenna in a given direction is defined as "the polarization of the radiated wave, when the antenna is excited. Alternatively, the polarization of an incident wave from the given direction which results in maximum available power at the antenna terminals. *Note*: When the direction is not stated, the polarization is taken to be the polarization in the direction of maximum gain." In practice, polarization of the radiated energy varies with the direction from the center of the antenna, so that different parts of the pattern may have different polarizations.

Polarization of a radiated wave is defined as "that property of a radiated electromagnetic wave describing the time varying direction and relative magnitude of the electric-field vector; specifically, the figure traced as a function of time by the extremity of the vector at a fixed location in space, and the sense in which it is traced, *as observed along the direction of propagation*." Polarization then is the curve traced by the end point of the arrow representing the instantaneous electric field. The field must be observed along the direction of propagation. A typical trace as a function of time is shown in Figures 2.15(a) and (b).

Polarization may be classified as linear, circular, or elliptical. If the vector that describes the electric field at a point in space as a function of time is always directed along a line, the field is said to be *linearly* polarized. In general, however, the figure that the electric field traces is an ellipse, and the field is said to be elliptically polarized. Linear and circular polarizations are special cases of elliptical, and they can be obtained when the ellipse becomes a straight line or a circle, respectively. The figure of the electric field is traced in a *clockwise* (CW) or *counterclockwise* (CCW) sense. *Clockwise* rotation of the electric field vector is designated as *right-hand polarization* and *counterclockwise* as *left-hand polarization*.

2.12.1 Linear, Circular, and Elliptical Polarizations

The instantaneous field of a plane wave, traveling in the negative z direction, can be written as

$$\mathcal{E}(z;t) = \hat{a}_x \mathcal{E}_x(z;t) + \hat{a}_y \mathcal{E}_y(z;t) \tag{2-55}$$

According to (2-5), the instantaneous components are related to their

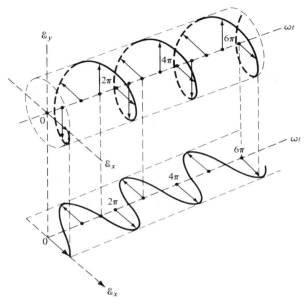

(a) Rotation of wave

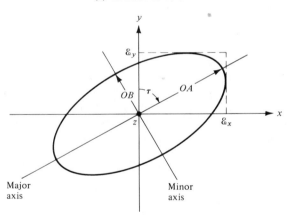

(b) Polarization ellipse

Figure 2.15 Rotation of a plane electromagnetic wave and its polarization ellipse at $z=0$ as a function of time.

complex counterparts by

$$\mathscr{E}_x(z;t) = \mathrm{Re}\left[E_x^{\,-} e^{j(\omega t + kz)}\right] = \mathrm{Re}\left[E_x e^{j(\omega t + kz + \phi_x)}\right]$$
$$= E_x \cos(\omega t + kz + \phi_x) \tag{2-56}$$

$$\mathscr{E}_y(z;t) = \mathrm{Re}\left[E_y^{\,-} e^{j(\omega t + kz)}\right] = \mathrm{Re}\left[E_y e^{j(\omega t + kz + \phi_y)}\right]$$
$$= E_y \cos(\omega t + kz + \phi_y) \tag{2-57}$$

where E_x and E_y are, respectively, the maximum magnitudes of the x and y components.

A. LINEAR POLARIZATION

For the wave to have linear polarization, the time-phase difference between the two components must be

$$\Delta\phi = \phi_y - \phi_x = n\pi, \qquad n = 0, 1, 2, 3, \ldots \tag{2-58}$$

B. CIRCULAR POLARIZATION

Circular polarization can be achieved *only* when the magnitudes of the two components are the same *and* the time-phase difference between them is odd multiples of $\pi/2$. That is,

$$|\mathscr{E}_x| = |\mathscr{E}_y| \Rightarrow E_x = E_y \tag{2-59}$$

$$\Delta\phi = \phi_y - \phi_x = \begin{cases} +\left(\tfrac{1}{2} + 2n\right)\pi, & n = 0, 1, 2, \ldots \quad \text{for CW} & (2\text{-}60) \\ -\left(\tfrac{1}{2} + 2n\right)\pi, & n = 0, 1, 2, \ldots \quad \text{for CCW} & (2\text{-}61) \end{cases}$$

If the direction of wave propagation is reversed (i.e., $+z$ direction), the phases in (2-60) and (2-61) for CW and CCW rotation must be interchanged.

C. ELLIPTICAL POLARIZATION

Elliptical polarization can be attained *only* when the time-phase difference between the two components is odd multiples of $\pi/2$ *and* their magnitudes are not the same *or* when the time-phase difference between the two components is not equal to multiples of $\pi/2$ (irrespective of their magnitudes). That is,

$$|\mathscr{E}_x| \neq |\mathscr{E}_y| \Rightarrow E_x \neq E_y$$

$$\text{when } \Delta\phi = \phi_y - \phi_x = \begin{cases} +\left(\tfrac{1}{2} + 2n\right)\pi & \text{for CW} & (2\text{-}62\text{a}) \\ -\left(\tfrac{1}{2} + 2n\right)\pi & \text{for CCW} & (2\text{-}62\text{b}) \end{cases}$$
$$n = 0, 2, 2 \ldots$$

or

$$\Delta\phi = \phi_y - \phi_x \neq \pm \frac{n}{2}\pi = \begin{cases} >0 & \text{for CW} & (2\text{-}63) \\ <0 & \text{for CCW} & (2\text{-}64) \end{cases}$$
$$n = 0, 1, 2, 3, \ldots$$

For elliptical polarization, the curve traced at a given position as a function of time is, in general, a tilted ellipse, as shown in Figure 2.15(b). The ratio of the major axis to the minor axis is referred to as the axial ratio

(AR), and it is equal to

$$AR = \frac{\text{major axis}}{\text{minor axis}} = \frac{OA}{OB}, \qquad 1 \leq AR \leq \infty \tag{2-65}$$

where

$$OA = \left[\tfrac{1}{2} \left\{ E_x^2 + E_y^2 + \left[E_x^4 + E_y^4 + 2 E_x^2 E_y^2 \cos(2\Delta\phi) \right]^{1/2} \right\} \right]^{1/2} \tag{2-66}$$

$$OB = \left[\tfrac{1}{2} \left\{ E_x^2 + E_y^2 - \left[E_x^4 + E_y^4 + 2 E_x^2 E_y^2 \cos(2\Delta\phi) \right]^{1/2} \right\} \right]^{1/2} \tag{2-67}$$

The tilt of the ellipse, *relative to the y axis*, is represented by the angle τ given by

$$\tau = \frac{\pi}{2} - \frac{1}{2} \tan^{-1} \left[\frac{2 E_x E_y}{E_x^2 - E_y^2} \cos(\Delta\phi) \right] \tag{2-68}$$

When the ellipse is aligned with the principal axes $[\tau = n\pi/2, n = 0, 1, 2, \ldots]$, the major (minor) axis is equal to $E_x(E_y)$ or $E_y(E_x)$ and the axial ratio is equal to E_x/E_y or E_y/E_x.

2.12.2 Polarization Loss Factor

In general, the polarization of the receiving antenna will not be the same as the polarization of the incoming (incident) wave. This is commonly stated as "polarization mismatch." The amount of power extracted by the antenna from the incoming signal will not be maximum because of the polarization loss. Assuming that the electric field of the incoming wave can be written as

$$\mathbf{E}_i = \hat{\rho}_w E_i \tag{2-69}$$

where $\hat{\rho}_w$ is the unit vector of the wave, and the polarization of the electric field of the receiving antenna can be expressed as

$$\mathbf{E}_a = \hat{\rho}_a E_a \tag{2-70}$$

where $\hat{\rho}_a$ is its unit vector, the polarization loss can be taken into account by introducing a *polarization loss factor* (PLF). It is defined as

$$PLF = |\hat{\rho}_w \cdot \hat{\rho}_a^*|^2 = |\cos \psi_p|^2 \text{ (dimensionless)} \tag{2-71}$$

where ψ_p is the angle between the two unit vectors. The relative alignment of the polarization of the incoming wave and of the antenna is shown in Figure 2.16. If the antenna is polarization matched, its PLF will be unity and the antenna will extract maximum power from the incoming wave.

To illustrate the principle of polarization mismatch, an example will be considered.

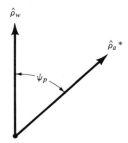

Figure 2.16   Polarization unit vectors of incident wave ($\hat{\rho}_w$) and antenna ($\hat{\rho}_a$), and polarization loss factor (PLF).

Example 2.8

The electric field of a linearly polarized electromagnetic wave given by

$$\mathbf{E}_i = \hat{a}_x E_0(x, y) e^{-jkz}$$

is incident upon a linearly polarized antenna whose electric field polarization can be expressed as

$$\mathbf{E}_a \simeq (\hat{a}_x + \hat{a}_y) E(r, \theta, \phi)$$

Find the polarization loss factor (PLF).

SOLUTION
For the incident wave

$$\hat{\rho}_w = \hat{a}_x$$

and for the antenna

$$\hat{\rho}_a = \frac{1}{\sqrt{2}} (\hat{a}_x + \hat{a}_y)$$

The PLF is then equal to

$$\text{PLF} = |\hat{\rho}_w \cdot \hat{\rho}_a{}^*|^2 = |\hat{a}_x \cdot \frac{1}{\sqrt{2}} (\hat{a}_x + \hat{a}_y)|^2 = \tfrac{1}{2}$$

which in dB is equal to

$$\text{PLF(dB)} = 10 \log_{10} \text{PLF(dimensionless)} = 10 \log_{10}(0.5) = -3$$

Even though both the incoming wave and the antenna are linearly polarized, there is a 3-dB loss in extracted power because the polarization of the incoming wave is not aligned with the polarization of the antenna. If the polarization of the incoming wave is orthogonal to the polarization of the antenna, then there will be no power extracted by the antenna from the incoming wave and the PLF will be zero or $-\infty$ dB. In Figures 2.17(a) and (b) we illustrate the polarization loss factors (PLF) of two types of antennas; wires, and apertures.

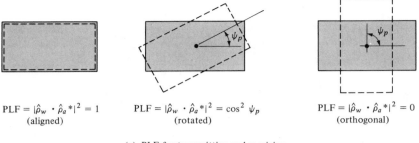

$$\text{PLF} = |\hat{\rho}_w \cdot \hat{\rho}_a{}^*|^2 = 1$$
(aligned)

$$\text{PLF} = |\hat{\rho}_w \cdot \hat{\rho}_a{}^*|^2 = \cos^2 \psi_p$$
(rotated)

$$\text{PLF} = |\hat{\rho}_w \cdot \hat{\rho}_a{}^*|^2 = 0$$
(orthogonal)

(a) PLF for transmitting and receiving
aperture antennas

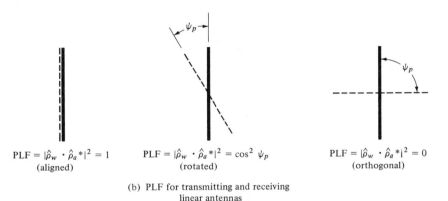

$$\text{PLF} = |\hat{\rho}_w \cdot \hat{\rho}_a{}^*|^2 = 1$$
(aligned)

$$\text{PLF} = |\hat{\rho}_w \cdot \hat{\rho}_a{}^*|^2 = \cos^2 \psi_p$$
(rotated)

$$\text{PLF} = |\hat{\rho}_w \cdot \hat{\rho}_a{}^*|^2 = 0$$
(orthogonal)

(b) PLF for transmitting and receiving
linear antennas

Figure 2.17   Polarization loss factors (PLF) for aperture and wire antennas.

The polarization loss must always be taken into account in the link calculations design of a communication system because in some cases it may be a very critical factor. Link calculations of communication systems for outer space explorations are very stringent because of limitations in spacecraft weight. In such cases, power is a limiting consideration. The design must properly take into account all loss factors to ensure a successful operation of the system.

2.13   INPUT IMPEDANCE

Input impedance is defined as "the impedance presented by an antenna at its terminals or the ratio of the voltage to current at a pair of terminals or the ratio of the appropriate components of the electric to magnetic fields at a point." In this section we are primarily interested in the input impedance at a pair of terminals which are the input terminals of the antenna. In Figure 2.18(a) these terminals are designated as $a-b$. The ratio of the voltage to current at these terminals, with no load attached, defines the impedance of

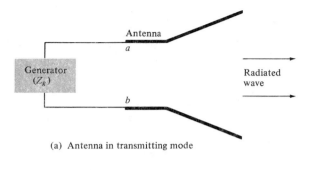

(a) Antenna in transmitting mode

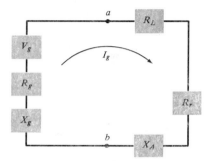

(b) Thévenin equivalent

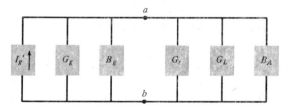

(c) Norton equivalent

Figure 2.18 Transmitting antenna and its equivalent circuits.

the antenna as

$$Z_A = R_A + jX_A$$
(2-72)

where

Z_A = antenna impedance at terminals a–b (ohms)

R_A = antenna resistance at terminals a–b (ohms)

X_A = antenna reactance at terminals a–b (ohms)

In general the resistive part of (2-72) consists of two components; that is

$$R_A = R_r + R_L$$
(2-73)

where

R_r = radiation resistance of the antenna

R_L = loss resistance of the antenna

The radiation resistance will be considered in more detail in later chapters, and it will be illustrated with examples.

If we assume that the antenna is attached to a generator with internal impedance

$$Z_g = R_g + jX_g \qquad (2\text{-}74)$$

where

R_g = resistance of generator impedance   (ohms)

X_g = reactance of generator impedance   (ohms)

and the antenna is used in the transmitting mode, we can represent the antenna and generator by an equivalent circuit* shown in Figure 2.18(b). To find the amount of power delivered to R_r for radiation and the amount dissipated in R_L as heat ($I^2R_L/2$), we first find the current developed within the loop which is given by

$$I_g = \frac{V_g}{Z_t} = \frac{V_g}{Z_A + Z_g} = \frac{V_g}{(R_r + R_L + R_g) + j(X_A + X_g)} \qquad (A) \qquad (2\text{-}75)$$

and its magnitude by

$$|I_g| = \frac{|V_g|}{\left[(R_r + R_L + R_g)^2 + (X_A + X_g)^2\right]^{1/2}} \qquad (2\text{-}75a)$$

where V_g is the peak generator voltage. The power delivered to the antenna for radiation is given by

$$P_r = \frac{1}{2}|I_g|^2 R_r = \frac{|V_g|^2}{2}\left[\frac{R_r}{(R_r + R_L + R_g)^2 + (X_A + X_g)^2}\right] \qquad (W) \quad (2\text{-}76)$$

and that dissipated as heat by

$$P_L = \frac{1}{2}|I_g|^2 R_L = \frac{|V_g|^2}{2}\left[\frac{R_L}{(R_r + R_L + R_g)^2 + (X_A + X_g)^2}\right] \qquad (W) \quad (2\text{-}77)$$

The remaining power is dissipated as heat on the internal resistance R_g of the generator, and it is given by

$$P_g = \frac{|V_g|^2}{2}\left[\frac{R_g}{(R_r + R_L + R_g)^2 + (X_A + X_g)^2}\right] \qquad (W) \qquad (2\text{-}78)$$

---

*This circuit can be used to represent small and simple antennas. It cannot be used for antennas with lossy dielectric or antennas over lossy ground because their loss resistance cannot be represented in series with the radiation resistance.

The maximum power delivered to the antenna occurs when we have conjugate matching; that is when

$$R_r + R_L = R_g \tag{2-79}$$

$$X_A = -X_g \tag{2-80}$$

For this case

$$P_r = \frac{|V_g|^2}{2}\left[\frac{R_r}{4(R_r+R_L)^2}\right] = \frac{|V_g|^2}{8}\left[\frac{R_r}{(R_r+R_L)^2}\right] \tag{2-81}$$

$$P_L = \frac{|V_g|^2}{8}\left[\frac{R_L}{(R_r+R_L)^2}\right] \tag{2-82}$$

$$P_g = \frac{|V_g|^2}{8}\left[\frac{R_g}{(R_r+R_L)^2}\right] = \frac{|V_g|^2}{8}\left[\frac{1}{R_r+R_L}\right] = \frac{|V_g|^2}{8R_g} \tag{2-83}$$

From (2-81)–(2-83), it is clear that

$$P_g = P_r + P_L = \frac{|V_g|^2}{8}\left[\frac{R_g}{(R_r+R_L)^2}\right] = \frac{|V_g|^2}{8}\left[\frac{R_r+R_L}{(R_r+R_L)^2}\right] \tag{2-84}$$

The power supplied by the generator during conjugate matching is

$$P_s = \frac{1}{2}V_g I_g^* = \frac{1}{2}V_g\left[\frac{V_g^*}{2(R_r+R_L)}\right] = \frac{|V_g|^2}{4}\left[\frac{1}{R_r+R_L}\right] \quad (W) \tag{2-85}$$

Of the power that is provided by the generator, half is dissipated as heat in the internal resistance (R_g) of the generator and the other half is delivered to the antenna. This only happens when we have conjugate matching. Of the power that is delivered to the antenna, part is radiated through the mechanism provided by the radiation resistance and the other is dissipated as heat which influences part of the overall efficiency of the antenna. If the antenna is lossless ($e_{cd} = 1$), then half of the total power supplied by the generator is radiated by the antenna during conjugate matching. In this section we have assumed a perfect match between the antenna and the interconnecting transmission line ($e_r = 1$). Any mismatch losses will reduce the overall efficiency. Figure 2.18(c) illustrates the Norton equivalent of the antenna and its source in the transmitting mode.

The use of the antenna in the receiving mode is shown in Figure 2.19(a). The incident wave impinges upon the antenna, and it induces a voltage V_T which is analogous to V_g of the transmitting mode. The Thévenin equivalent circuit of the antenna and its load is shown in Figure 2.19(b) and the Norton equivalent in Figure 2.19(c). The discussion for the antenna and its load in the receiving mode parallels that for the transmitting mode.

The input impedance of an antenna is generally a function of frequency. Thus the antenna will be matched to the interconnecting transmission line

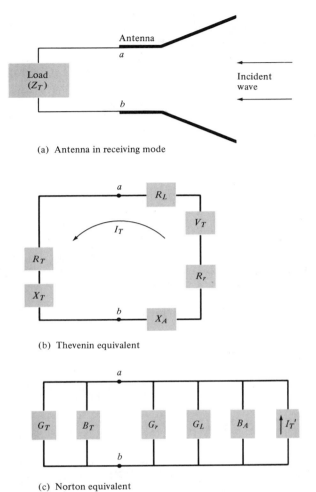

(a) Antenna in receiving mode

(b) Thevenin equivalent

(c) Norton equivalent

Figure 2.19 Antenna and its equivalent circuits in the receiving mode.

and other associated equipment only within a bandwidth. In addition, the input impedance of the antenna depends on many factors including its geometry, its method of excitation, and its proximity to surrounding objects. Because of their complex geometries, only a limited number of practical antennas have been investigated analytically. For many others, the input impedance has been determined experimentally.

2.14 ANTENNA RADIATION EFFICIENCY

The antenna efficiency that takes into account the reflection, conduction, and dielectric losses was discussed in Section 2.8. The conduction and dielectric losses of an antenna are very difficult to compute and in most cases they are measured. Even with measurements, they are difficult to separate and they are usually lumped together to form the e_{cd} efficiency. The resistance R_L is used to represent the conduction-dielectric losses.

The *conduction-dielectric efficiency e_{cd}* is defined as *the ratio of the power delivered to the radiation resistance R_r to the power delivered to R_r and R_L.* Using (2-76) and (2-77), the radiation efficiency can be written as

$$e_{cd} = \left[\frac{R_r}{R_L + R_r} \right] \qquad \text{(dimensionless)} \qquad (2\text{-}86)$$

For a metal rod of length l and uniform cross-sectional area A, the dc resistance is given by

$$R_{dc} = \frac{1}{\sigma} \frac{l}{A} \qquad \text{(ohms)} \qquad (2\text{-}86a)$$

If the skin depth $\delta [\delta = \sqrt{2/(\omega\mu_0\sigma)}]$ of the metal is very small compared to the smallest diagonal of the cross section of the rod, the current is confined to a thin layer near the conductor surface. Therefore the high-frequency resistance can be written as

$$R_{hf} = \frac{l}{P} R_s = \frac{l}{P} \sqrt{\frac{\omega\mu_0}{2\sigma}} \qquad \text{(ohms)} \qquad (2\text{-}86b)$$

where P is the perimeter of the cross section of the rod ($P = C = 2\pi b$ for a circular wire of radius b), R_s is the conductor surface resistance, ω is the angular frequency, μ_0 is the permeability of free-space, and σ is the conductivity of the metal.

Example 2.9

A resonant half-wavelength dipole is made out of copper ($\sigma = 5.7 \times 10^7$ S/m) wire. Determine the conduction-dielectric (radiation) efficiency of the dipole antenna at $f = 100$ MHz if the radius of the wire b is $3 \times 10^{-4}\lambda$, and the radiation resistance of the $\lambda/2$ dipole is 73 ohms.

SOLUTION
At $f = 10^8$ Hz

$$\lambda = \frac{v}{f} = \frac{3 \times 10^8}{10^8} = 3 \text{ m}$$

$$l = \frac{\lambda}{2} = \frac{3}{2} \text{ m}$$

$$C = 2\pi b = 2\pi(3 \times 10^{-4})\lambda = 6\pi \times 10^{-4}\lambda$$

For a wire antenna, $R_L = R_{hf}$. According to (2-86b)

$$R_L = R_{hf} = \frac{0.5}{6\pi \times 10^{-4}} \sqrt{\frac{\pi(10^8)(4\pi \times 10^{-7})}{5.7 \times 10^7}} = 0.698 \text{ ohms}$$

Thus

$$e_{cd} \text{(dimensionless)} = \frac{73}{73 + 0.698} = 0.9905 = 99.05\%$$

$$e_{cd}\text{(dB)} = 10\log_{10}(0.9905) = -0.04$$

2.15 ANTENNA AS AN APERTURE: EFFECTIVE APERTURE

An antenna in the receiving mode, whether it is in the form of a wire, aperture, array, dielectric rod, etc., is used to capture (receive) electromagnetic waves and to extract power from them, as shown in Figures 2.20(a) and (b). For each antenna, an equivalent aperture can then be formed. It is usually referred to as *effective aperture* (or effective area), and it is defined as *the ratio of the power delivered to the load to the incident power density*. In

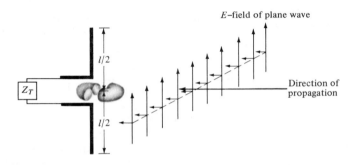

(a) Dipole antenna in receiving mode

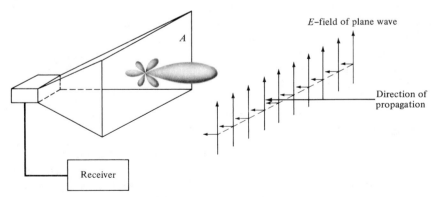

(b) Aperture antenna in receiving mode

Figure 2.20   Uniform plane wave incident upon dipole and aperture antennas.

equation form, it is written as

$$A_e = \frac{P_T}{W_i} = \frac{|I_T|^2 R_T/2}{W_i} \qquad (2\text{-}87)$$

where

A_e = effective aperture (effective area) (m^2)

P_T = power delivered to the load (W)

W_i = power density of incident wave (W/m^2)

The effective aperture is the area which when multiplied by the incident power density gives the power delivered to the load. Using the equivalent of Figure 2.19, we can write (2-87) as

$$A_e = \frac{|V_T|^2}{2W_i} \left[\frac{R_T}{(R_r + R_L + R_T)^2 + (X_A + X_T)^2} \right] \qquad (2\text{-}88)$$

Under conditions of maximum power transfer (conjugate matching), $R_r + R_L = R_T$ and $X_A = -X_T$, the effective aperture of (2-88) reduces to the maximum effective aperture given by

$$A_{em} = \frac{|V_T|^2}{8W_i} \left[\frac{R_T}{(R_L + R_r)^2} \right] = \frac{|V_T|^2}{8W_i} \left[\frac{1}{R_r + R_L} \right] \qquad (2\text{-}89)$$

The effective aperture of an antenna is not necessarily the same as the physical aperture. It will be shown in later chapters that aperture antennas with constant amplitude and phase field distributions have maximum effective apertures equal to the physical areas; they are smaller for nonconstant field distributions. In addition, the maximum effective aperture of wire antennas is greater than the physical area (if taken as the area of a cross section of the wire when split lengthwise along its diameter). Thus the wire antenna can capture much more power than is intercepted by its physical size! This should not come as a surprise. If the wire antenna would only capture the power incident on its physical size, it would be almost useless. So electrically, the wire antenna looks much bigger than its physical stature.

To illustrate the concept of effective aperture, especially as applied to a wire antenna, let us consider an example. In later chapters, we will consider examples of aperture antennas.

Example 2.10

A uniform plane wave is incident upon a very short lossless dipole ($l \ll \lambda$), as shown in Figure 2.20(a). Find the maximum effective aperture assuming that the radiation resistance of the dipole is $R_r = 80(\pi l/\lambda)^2$, and the incident field is linearly polarized along the axis of the dipole.

SOLUTION

For $R_L = 0$, the maximum effective aperture of (2-89) reduces to

$$A_{em} = \frac{|V_T|^2}{8W_i} \left[\frac{1}{R_r} \right]$$

Since the dipole is very short, the induced current can be assumed to be constant and of uniform phase. The induced voltage is

$$V_T = El$$

where

V_T = induced voltage on the dipole

E = electric field of incident wave

l = length of dipole

For a uniform plane wave, the incident power density can be written as

$$W_i = \frac{E^2}{2\eta}$$

where η is the intrinsic impedance of the medium ($\simeq 120\pi$ ohms for a free-space medium). Thus

$$A_{em} = \frac{(El)^2}{8(E^2/2\eta)(80\pi^2 l^2/\lambda^2)} = \frac{3\lambda^2}{8\pi} = 0.119\lambda^2$$

The above value is only valid for a lossless antenna (the losses of a short dipole are usually significant). If the loss resistance is equal to the radiation resistance $(R_L = R_r)$ and the sum of the two is equal to the load (receiver) resistance $(R_T = R_r + R_L = 2R_r)$, then the effective aperture is only one-half of the maximum effective aperture given above.

Let us now examine the significance of the effective aperture. From Example 2.10, the maximum effective aperture of a short dipole with $l \ll \lambda$ was equal to $A_{em} = 0.119\lambda^2$. Typical antennas that fall under this category are dipoles whose lengths are $l \le \lambda/50$. For the purpose of demonstration, let us assume that $l = \lambda/50$. Because $A_{em} = 0.119\lambda^2 = lw_e = (\lambda/50)w_e$, the maximum effective electrical width of this dipole is $w_e = 5.95\lambda$. Typical physical diameters (widths) of wires used for dipoles may be about $w_p = \lambda/300$. Thus the maximum effective width w_e is about 1785 times larger than its physical width.

2.16 DIRECTIVITY AND MAXIMUM EFFECTIVE APERTURE

To derive the relationship between directivity and maximum effective aperture, the geometrical arrangement of Figure 2.21 is chosen. Antenna 1 is used as a transmitter and 2 as a receiver. The effective apertures and

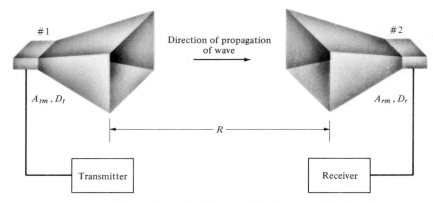

Figure 2.21   Two antennas separated by a distance R.

directive gains of each are designated as A_t, A_r and D_{gt}, D_{gr}. If antenna 1 were isotropic, its radiated power density at a distance R would be

$$W_0 = \frac{P_t}{4\pi R^2} \qquad (2\text{-}90)$$

where P_t is the total radiated power. Because of the directive properties of the antenna, its actual density is

$$W_t = W_0 D_{gt} = \frac{P_t D_{gt}}{4\pi R^2} \qquad (2\text{-}91)$$

The power collected (received) by the antenna and transferred to the load would be

$$P_r = W_t A_r = \frac{P_t D_{gt} A_r}{4\pi R^2} \qquad (2\text{-}92)$$

or

$$D_{gt} A_r = \frac{P_r}{P_t} (4\pi R^2) \qquad (2\text{-}92a)$$

If antenna 2 is used as a transmitter, 1 as a receiver, and the intervening medium is linear, passive, and isotropic, we can write that

$$D_{gr} A_t = \frac{P_r}{P_t} (4\pi R^2) \qquad (2\text{-}93)$$

Equating (2-92a) and (2-93) reduces to

$$\frac{D_{gt}}{A_t} = \frac{D_{gr}}{A_r} \qquad (2\text{-}94)$$

Increasing the directive gains of an antenna increases its effective aperture in direct proportion. Thus (2-94) can be written as

$$\frac{D_t}{A_{tm}} = \frac{D_r}{A_{rm}} \qquad (2\text{-}95)$$

where A_{tm} and A_{rm} (D_t and D_r) are the *maximum* effective apertures (directivities) of antennas 1 and 2, respectively.

If antenna 1 is isotropic, then $D_t = 1$ and its maximum effective aperture can be expressed as

$$A_{tm} = \frac{A_{rm}}{D_r} \tag{2-96}$$

Equation (2-96) states that the maximum effective aperture of an isotropic source is equal to the ratio of the maximum effective aperture to the directivity of any other source. For example, let the other antenna be a very short ($l \ll \lambda$) dipole whose effective aperture ($0.119\lambda^2$ from Example 2.10) and directivity (1.5) are known. The maximum effective aperture of the isotropic source is then equal to

$$A_{tm} = \frac{A_{rm}}{D_r} = \frac{0.119\lambda^2}{1.5} = \frac{\lambda^2}{4\pi} \tag{2-97}$$

Using (2-97), we can write (2-96) as

$$A_{rm} = D_r A_{tm} = D_r \left(\frac{\lambda^2}{4\pi} \right) \tag{2-98}$$

In general then, the *maximum effective aperture* (A_{em}) *of any antenna is related to its directivity* (D_0) *by*

$$\boxed{A_{em} = \frac{\lambda^2}{4\pi} D_0} \tag{2-99}$$

If there are losses (including polarization mismatches) associated with an antenna, its maximum effective aperture of (2-99) must be modified to account for conduction-dielectric losses, and impedance and polarization mismatches. Thus

$$\boxed{\begin{aligned} A_{em} &= e_t \left(\frac{\lambda^2}{4\pi} \right) D_0 |\hat{\rho}_w \cdot \hat{\rho}_a{}^*|^2 \\ &= e_{cd}(1 - |\Gamma|^2) \left(\frac{\lambda^2}{4\pi} \right) D_0 |\hat{\rho}_w \cdot \hat{\rho}_a{}^*|^2 \end{aligned}} \tag{2-100}$$

2.17 FRIIS TRANSMISSION EQUATION AND RADAR RANGE EQUATION

The analysis and design of radar and communications systems often require the use of the *Friis Transmission Equation* and the *Radar Range Equation*. Because of the importance [5] of the two equations, a few pages will be devoted for their derivation.

2.17.1 Friis Transmission Equation

The Friis Transmission Equation relates the power received to the power transmitted between two antennas separated by a distance $R > 2D^2/\lambda$, where D is the largest dimension of either antenna. Referring to Figure 2.22, let us assume that the transmitting antenna is initially isotropic. If the input power at the terminals of the transmitting antenna is P_t, then its power density W_0 at distance R from the antenna is

$$W_0 = e_{tt} \frac{P_t}{4\pi R^2} \tag{2-101}$$

where e_{tt} is the total efficiency of the transmitting antenna. For a nonisotropic transmitting antenna, the power of (2-101) in the direction θ_t, ϕ_t can be written as

$$W_t = \frac{P_t G_{0t}(\theta_t, \phi_t)}{4\pi R^2} = e_{tt} \frac{P_t D_{gt}(\theta_t, \phi_t)}{4\pi R^2} \tag{2-102}$$

where $G_{0t}(\theta_t, \phi_t)$ is the gain and $D_{gt}(\theta_t, \phi_t)$ is the directive gain of the antenna in the direction θ_t, ϕ_t. Since the effective aperture A_r of the antenna is related to its efficiency e_{tr} and directive gain D_{gr} by

$$A_r = e_{tr} D_{gr}(\theta_r, \phi_r) \left(\frac{\lambda^2}{4\pi}\right) \tag{2-103}$$

the amount of power P_r collected by the receiving antenna can be written, using (2-102), (2-103), and the polarization loss factor as

$$P_r = e_{tr} D_{gr}(\theta_r, \phi_r) \frac{\lambda^2}{4\pi} W_t = e_{tt} e_{tr} \frac{\lambda^2 D_{gt}(\theta_t, \phi_t) D_{gr}(\theta_r, \phi_r) P_t}{(4\pi R)^2} |\hat{\rho}_t \cdot \hat{\rho}_r{}^*|^2 \tag{2-104}$$

or

$$\boxed{\frac{P_r}{P_t} = e_{cdt} e_{cdr} \left(1 - |\Gamma_t|^2\right)\left(1 - |\Gamma_r|^2\right)\left(\frac{\lambda}{4\pi R}\right)^2 D_{gt}(\theta_t, \phi_t) D_{gr}(\theta_r, \phi_r)|\hat{\rho}_t \cdot \hat{\rho}_r{}^*|^2} \tag{2-105}$$

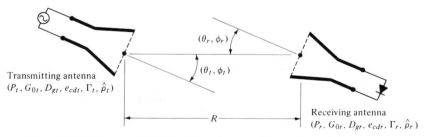

Figure 2.22 Geometrical orientation of transmitting and receiving antennas.

For polarization matched antennas aligned for maximum directional radiation and reception, (2-105) reduces to

$$\boxed{\frac{P_r}{P_t} = \left(\frac{\lambda}{4\pi R}\right)^2 G_{0t}G_{0r}}$$

(2-106)

Equation (2-105) or (2-106) is known as the *Friis Transmission Equation*, and it relates the power P_r (delivered to the receiver load) to the input power of the transmitting antenna P_t. The term $(\lambda/4\pi R)^2$ is called the *free-space loss factor*, and it takes into account the losses due to the spherical spreading of the energy by the antenna.

2.17.2 Radar Range Equation

Now let us assume that the transmitted power is incident upon a target, as shown in Figure 2.23. We now introduce a quantity known as the *radar cross section* or *echo area* (σ) of a target which is defined as *the area intercepting that amount of power which, when scattered isotropically, produces at the receiver a density which is equal to that scattered by the actual target.* In equation form

$$\lim_{R \to \infty}\left[\frac{\sigma W_i}{4\pi R^2}\right] = W_s$$

(2-107)

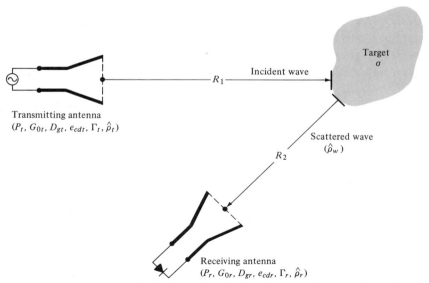

Figure 2.23 Geometrical arrangement of transmitter, target, and receiver for radar range equation.

or

$$\sigma = \lim_{R \to \infty} \left[4\pi R^2 \frac{W_s}{W_i} \right]$$

(2-107a)

where

σ = radar cross section or echo area (m^2)

R = observation distance from target (m)

W_i = incident power density (W/m^2)

W_s = scattered power density (W/m^2)

Using the definition of radar cross section, we can consider that the transmitted power incident upon the target is initially captured and then it is reradiated isotropically, insofar as the receiver is concerned. The amount of captured power P_c is obtained by multiplying the incident power density of (2-102) by the radar cross section σ, or

$$P_c = \sigma W_t = \sigma \frac{P_t G_{0t}(\theta_t, \phi_t)}{4\pi R_1^{\,2}} = e_{tt} \sigma \frac{P_t D_{gt}(\theta_t, \phi_t)}{4\pi R_1^{\,2}}$$

(2-108)

The power captured by the target is reradiated isotropically, and the scattered power density can be written as

$$W_s = \frac{P_c}{4\pi R_2^{\,2}} = e_{tt} \sigma \frac{P_t D_{gt}(\theta_t, \phi_t)}{(4\pi R_1 R_2)^2}$$

(2-109)

The amount of power delivered to the receiver load is given by

$$P_r = A_r W_s |\hat{\rho}_w \cdot \hat{\rho}_r{}^*|^2$$
$$= e_{tt} e_{tr} \sigma \frac{P_t D_{gt}(\theta_t, \phi_t) D_{gr}(\theta_r, \phi_r)}{4\pi} \left(\frac{\lambda}{4\pi R_1 R_2} \right)^2 |\hat{\rho}_w \cdot \hat{\rho}_r{}^*|^2$$

(2-110)

where A_r is the effective aperture of the receiving antenna as defined by (2-103).

Equation (2-110) can also be written as

$$\frac{P_r}{P_t} = e_{cdt} e_{cdr} \left(1 - |\Gamma_t|^2 \right) \left(1 - |\Gamma_r|^2 \right) \sigma \frac{D_{gt}(\theta_t, \phi_t) D_{gr}(\theta_r, \phi_r)}{4\pi}$$
$$\times \left(\frac{\lambda}{4\pi R_1 R_2} \right)^2 |\hat{\rho}_w \cdot \hat{\rho}_r{}^*|^2$$

(2-111)

where

$\hat{\rho}_w$ = polarization unit vector of the scattered waves

$\hat{\rho}_r$ = polarization unit vector of the receiving antenna

For polarization matched antennas aligned for maximum directional radiation and reception, (2-111) reduces to

$$\boxed{\frac{P_r}{P_t} = \sigma \frac{G_{0t}G_{0r}}{4\pi} \left[\frac{\lambda}{4\pi R_1 R_2} \right]^2}$$
(2-111a)

Equation (2-111) or (2-111a) is known as the *Radar Range Equation*. It relates the power P_r (delivered to the receiver load) to the input power P_t transmitted by an antenna, after it has been scattered by a target with a radar cross section (echo area) of σ.

Example 2.11

Two *lossless* X-band (8.2–12.4 GHz) horn antennas are separated by a distance of 100λ. The reflection coefficients at the terminals of the transmitting and receiving antennas are 0.1 and 0.2, respectively. The directivities of the transmitting and receiving antennas (over isotropic) are 16 dB and 20 dB, respectively. Assuming that the power at the input terminals of the transmitting antenna is 2 W, and the antennas are aligned for maximum radiation between them and are polarization matched, find the power delivered to the load of the receiver.

SOLUTION
For this problem

$e_{cdt} = e_{cdr} = 1$ because antennas are lossless.

$|\hat{\rho}_t \cdot \hat{\rho}_r^*|^2 = 1$ because antennas are polarization matched

$\left. \begin{array}{l} D_{gt} = D_{0t} \\ D_{gr} = D_{0r} \end{array} \right\}$ because antennas are aligned for
maximum radiation between them

$D_{0t} = 16$ dB $\Rightarrow 39.81$ (dimensionless)

$D_{0r} = 20$ dB $\Rightarrow 100$ (dimensionless)

Using (2-111), we can write

$$P_r = \left[1 - (0.1)^2 \right]\left[1 - (0.2)^2 \right]\left[\lambda / 4\pi (100\lambda) \right]^2 (39.81)(100)(2)$$
$$= 4.777 \text{ mW}$$

2.18   ANTENNA TEMPERATURE

Every object with a physical temperature above absolute zero ($0°\text{K} = -273°\text{C}$) radiates energy [6]. The amount of energy radiated is usually represented by an equivalent temperature T_B, better known as brightness temperature, and it is defined as

$$T_B(\theta, \phi) = \varepsilon(\theta, \phi)T_m = \left(1 - |\Gamma|^2 \right)T_m$$
(2-112)

where

T_B = brightness temperature   (equivalent temperature; °K)

ε = emissivity   (dimensionless)

T_m = molecular (physical) temperature   (°K)

$\Gamma(\theta, \phi)$ = reflection coefficient of the surface for the polarization of the wave

Since the values of emissivity are $0 \leq \varepsilon \leq 1$, the maximum value the brightness temperature can achieve is equal to the molecular temperature. Usually the emissivity is a function of the frequency of operation, polarization of the emitted energy, and molecular structure of the object. Some of the better natural emitters of energy at microwave frequencies are (a) the ground with equivalent temperature of about 300°K and (b) the sky with equivalent temperature of about 5°K when looking toward zenith and about 100–150°K toward the horizon.

The brightness temperature emitted by the different sources is intercepted by antennas, and it appears at their terminals as an antenna temperature. The temperature appearing at the terminals of an antenna is that given by (2-112), after it is weighted by the gain pattern of the antenna. In equation form, this can be written as

$$T_A = \frac{\int_0^{2\pi} \int_0^{\pi} T_B(\theta, \phi) G(\theta, \phi) \sin\theta \, d\theta \, d\phi}{\int_0^{2\pi} \int_0^{\pi} G(\theta, \phi) \sin\theta \, d\theta \, d\phi} \qquad (2\text{-}113)$$

where

T_A = antenna temperature (effective noise temperature of the antenna radiation resistance; °K)

$G(\theta, \phi)$ = gain (power) pattern of the antenna

Assuming no mismatch losses and a lossless transmission line between the antenna and the receiver, the noise power transferred to the receiver is given by

$$P_r = k T_A \Delta f \qquad (2\text{-}114)$$

where

P_r = antenna noise power   (W)

k = Boltzmann's constant $(1.38 \times 10^{-23} \text{ J}/°K)$

T_A = antenna temperature   (°K)

Δf = bandwidth   (Hz)

If the transmission line between the antenna and receiver is lossy, the antenna temperature T_A as seen by the receiver through (2-114) must be modified to include the line losses. If a transmission line of length l, constant physical temperature T_0 throughout its length, and uniform attenuation of α (Np/unit length) is used to connect an antenna to a receiver, as shown in Figure 2.24, the effective antenna temperature at the receiver terminals is given by

$$T_a = T_A e^{-2\alpha l} + T_0(1 - e^{-2\alpha l}) \tag{2-115}$$

where

$\quad T_a$ = antenna temperature at the receiver terminals $\quad$ (°K)

$\quad T_A$ = antenna temperature at the antenna terminals (2-113) $\quad$ (°K)

$\quad \alpha$ = attenuation coefficient of transmission line $\quad$ (Np/m)

$\quad l$ = length of transmission line $\quad$ (m)

$\quad T_0$ = physical temperature of the transmission line $\quad$ (°K)

The antenna noise power of (2-114) must also be modified and written as

$$P_r = kT_a \Delta f \tag{2-116}$$

where T_a is the antenna temperature at the receiver input as given by (2-115).

If the receiver itself has a certain noise temperature T_r (due to thermal noise in the receiver components), the *system noise power at the receiver terminals* is given by

$$P_s = k(T_a + T_r)\Delta f = kT_s \Delta f \tag{2-117}$$

where

$\quad P_s$ = system noise power (at receiver terminals)

$\quad T_a$ = antenna noise temperature (at receiver terminals)

$\quad T_r$ = receiver noise temperature (at receiver terminals)

$\quad T_s = T_a + T_r$ = effective system noise temperature (at receiver terminals)

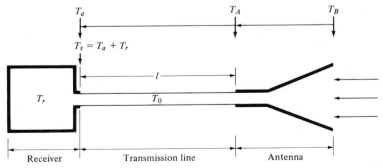

Figure 2.24 Antenna, transmission line, and receiver arrangement for system noise power calculation.

A graphical relation of all the parameters is shown in Figure 2.24. The effective system noise temperature T_s of radio astronomy antennas and receivers varies from very few degrees (typically $\simeq 10°$K) to thousands of degrees Kelvin depending upon the type of antenna, receiver, and frequency of operation. Antenna temperature changes at the antenna terminals, due to variations in the target emissions, may be as small as a fraction of one degree. To detect such changes, the receiver must be very sensitive and be able to differentiate changes of a fraction of a degree.

Example 2.12

The effective antenna temperature of a target at the input terminals of the antenna is 150°K. Assuming that the antenna is connected to a receiver through an X-band (8.2–12.4 GHz) rectangular waveguide of 10 m (loss of waveguide = 0.13 dB/m) and at a temperature of 300°K, find the effective antenna temperature at the receiver terminals.

SOLUTION
We first convert the attenuation coefficient from dB to Np by $\alpha(\mathrm{dB/m}) = 20(\log_{10} e)\alpha(\mathrm{Np/m}) = 20(0.434)\alpha(\mathrm{Np/m}) = 8.68\alpha(\mathrm{Np/m})$. Thus $\alpha(\mathrm{Np/m}) = \alpha(\mathrm{dB/m})/8.68 = 0.13/8.68 = 0.0149$. The effective antenna temperature at the receiver terminals can be written, using (2-115), as

$$T_a = 150 e^{-0.149(2)} + 300[1 - e^{-0.149(2)}] = 111.345 + 77.31 = 188.655°\mathrm{K}$$

The results of the above example illustrate that the antenna temperature at the input terminals of the antenna and at the terminals of the receiver can differ by quite a few degrees. For a smaller transmission line or a transmission line with much smaller losses, the difference can be reduced appreciably and can be as small as a fraction of a degree.

References

1. J. S. Hollis, T. J. Lyon, and L. Clayton, Jr. (eds.), *Microwave Antenna Measurements*, Scientific-Atlanta, Inc., July 1970.
2. J. D. Kraus, *Antennas*, McGraw-Hill, New York, 1950, p. 25.
3. R. S. Elliott, "Beamwidth and Directivity of Large Scanning Arrays," Last of Two Parts, *The Microwave Journal*, January 1964, pp. 74–82.
4. C.-T. Tai and C. S. Pereira, "An Approximate Formula for Calculating the Directivity of an Antenna," *IEEE Transactions on Antennas and Propagation*, vol. AP-24, March 1976, pp. 235–236.
5. M. I. Skolnik, *Radar Systems*, McGraw-Hill, New York, 1962, Chapter 2.
6. J. D. Kraus, *Radio Astronomy*, McGraw-Hill, New York, 1966.
7. P. Lorrain and D. R. Corson, *Electromagnetic Fields and Waves*, Second Edition, W. H. Freeman and Co., San Francisco, 1970.

PROBLEMS

2.1. Derive (2-7) given the definitions of (2-5) and (2-6).

2.2. The maximum radiation intensity of a 90% efficiency antenna is 200 mW/unit solid angle. Find the directivity and gain (dimensionless and in dB) when the
   (a) input power is 40π mW
   (b) radiated power is 40π mW

2.3. A beam antenna has half-power beamwidths of 30° and 35° in perpendicular planes intersecting at the maximum of the main beam. Find its approximate maximum effective aperture using (a) Kraus' and (b) Tai and Pereira's formulas. The minor lobes are very small and can be neglected.

2.4. The normalized radiation intensity of a given antenna is given by
   (a) $U = \sin\theta \sin\phi$ (b) $U = \sin\theta \sin^2\phi$
   (c) $U = \sin\theta \sin^3\phi$ (d) $U = \sin^2\theta \sin\phi$
   (e) $U = \sin^2\theta \sin^2\phi$ (f) $U = \sin^2\theta \sin^3\phi$
   The intensity exists only in the $0 \le \theta \le \pi, 0 \le \phi \le \pi$ region, and it is zero elsewhere. Find the
   (a) exact directivity (dimensionless and in dB).
   (b) azimuthal and elevation plane half-power beamwidths (in degrees).

2.5. Find the directivity (dimensionless and in dB) for the antenna of Problem 2.4 using
   (a) Kraus' approximate formula (2-26)
   (b) Tai and Pereira's approximate formula (2-32a)

2.6. Find the directivity (dimensionless and in dB) for the antenna of Problem 2.4 using numerical techniques with 10° uniform divisions and with the field evaluated at the
   (a) midpoint
   (b) trailing edge of each division

2.7. Compute the directivity values of Problem 2.4 using the computer program at the end of this chapter.

2.8. The far-zone electric field intensity (array factor) of an end-fire two-element array antenna, placed along the z-axis and radiating into free-space, is given by

$$E = \cos\left[\frac{\pi}{4}(\cos\theta - 1)\right]\frac{e^{-jkr}}{r}, \qquad 0 \le \theta \le \pi$$

Find the directivity using
   (a) Kraus' approximate formula
   (b) the computer program at the end of this chapter

2.9. The radiation intensity of an aperture antenna, mounted on an infinite ground plane with z perpendicular to the aperture, is rotationally symmetric (not a function of ϕ), and it is given by

$$U = \left[\frac{\sin(\pi\sin\theta)}{\pi\sin\theta}\right]^2$$

Find the approximate directivity (dimensionless and in dB) using
   (a) numerical integration. Use the computer program at the end of this chapter.
   (b) Kraus' formula
   (c) Tai and Pereira's formula

2.10. The normalized far-zone field pattern of an antenna is given by

$$E = \begin{cases} \left(\sin\theta \cos^2\phi \right)^{1/2} & 0 \le \theta \le \pi \quad \text{and} \quad 0 \le \phi \le \pi/2, \\ & 3\pi/2 \le \phi \le 2\pi \\ 0 & \text{elsewhere} \end{cases}$$

Find the directivity using
(a) the exact expression
(b) Kraus' approximate formula
(c) Tai and Pereira's approximate formula
(d) the computer program at the end of this chapter

2.11. The normalized field pattern of the main beam of a conical horn antenna, mounted on an infinite ground plane with z perpendicular to the aperture, is given by

$$\frac{J_1(ka\sin\theta)}{\sin\theta}$$

where a is its radius at the aperture. Assuming that $a = \lambda$, find the
(a) half-power beamwidth.
(b) directivity using Kraus' approximate formula.

2.12. A uniform plane wave, of a form similar to (2-55), is traveling in the positive z-axis. Find the polarization (linear, circular, or elliptical), sense of rotation (CW or CCW), axial ratio (AR), and tilt angle τ (in degrees) when
(a) $E_x = E_y$, $\Delta\phi = \phi_y - \phi_x = 0$ (b) $E_x \ne E_y$, $\Delta\phi = \phi_y - \phi_x = 0$
(c) $E_x = E_y$, $\Delta\phi = \phi_y - \phi_x = \pi/2$ (d) $E_x = E_y$, $\Delta\phi = \phi_y - \phi_x = -\pi/2$
(e) $E_x = E_y$, $\Delta\phi = \phi_y - \phi_x = \pi/4$ (f) $E_x = E_y$, $\Delta\phi = \phi_y - \phi_x = -\pi/4$
(g) $E_x = 0.5E_y$, $\Delta\phi = \phi_y - \phi_x = \pi/2$ (h) $E_x = 0.5E_y$, $\Delta\phi = \phi_y - \phi_x = -\pi/2$
In all cases, justify the answer.

2.13. Derive (2-66), (2-67), and (2-68).

2.14. Write a general expression for the polarization loss factor (PLF) of two linearly polarized antennas if
(a) both lie in the same plane
(b) both do not lie in the same plane

2.15. A linearly polarized wave traveling in the z-direction is incident upon a circularly polarized antenna. Find the polarization loss factor PLF (dimensionless and in dB) when the antenna is (based upon its transmission mode operation)
(a) right-handed (CW)
(b) left-handed (CCW)

2.16. A circularly polarized wave, traveling in the positive z-direction, is incident upon a circularly polarized antenna. Find the polarization loss factor PLF (dimensionless and in dB) for right-hand (CW) and left-hand (CCW) wave and antenna.

2.17. The electric field radiated by a rectangular aperture, mounted on an infinite ground plane with z perpendicular to the aperture, is given by

$$\mathbf{E} = \left[\hat{a}_\theta \cos\phi - \hat{a}_\phi \sin\phi \cos\theta \right] f(r,\theta,\phi)$$

where $f(r,\theta,\phi)$ is a scalar function which describes the field variation of the antenna. Assuming that the receiving antenna is linearly polarized along the x-axis, find the polarization loss factor (PLF).

2.18. A circularly polarized wave, traveling in the $+z$-direction, is received by an elliptically polarized antenna whose reception characteristics near the main lobe are given approximately by

$$\mathbf{E}_a \simeq \left[2\hat{a}_x + j\hat{a}_y\right] f(r, \theta, \phi)$$

Find the polarization loss factor (dimensionless and in dB) when the incident wave is
(a) right-hand (CW)
(b) left-hand (CCW)
circularly polarized. Repeat the problem when

$$\mathbf{E}_{\hat{a}} \simeq \left[2\hat{a}_x - j\hat{a}_y\right] f(r, \theta, \phi)$$

In each case, what is the polarization of the antenna? How does it match with that of the wave?

2.19. A $\lambda/2$ dipole, with a total loss resistance of 1 ohm, is connected to a generator whose internal impedance is $50 + j25$. Assuming that the peak voltage of the generator is 2 V and the impedance of the dipole is $73 + j42.5$, find the power
(a) supplied by the source (real)
(b) radiated by the antenna
(c) dissipated by the antenna

2.20. The antenna and generator of Problem 2.19 are connected via a 50-ohm $\lambda/2$-long lossless transmission line. Find the power
(a) supplied by the source (real)
(b) radiated by the antenna
(c) dissipated by the antenna

2.21. For the receiving antenna of Figure 2.19, show that for conjugate matching

$$P_T = \text{power delivered to load } R_T = \frac{V_T^2}{8}\left(\frac{1}{R_T}\right)$$

$$P_r = \text{reradiated power} = \frac{V_T^2}{8}\left[\frac{R_r}{(R_r + R_L)^2}\right]$$

$$P_L = \text{power dissipated as heat by } R_L = \frac{V_T^2}{8}\left[\frac{R_L}{(R_r + R_L)^2}\right]$$

2.22. Show that the effective height of a linear antenna can be written as

$$h_e = \sqrt{\frac{A_e|Z_t|^2}{\eta R_T}}$$

which for a lossless antenna and maximum power transfer reduces to

$$h_e = 2\sqrt{\frac{A_{em}R_r}{\eta}}$$

A_e and A_{em} represent, respectively, the effective and maximum effective apertures of the antenna.

2.23. For an X-band (8.2–12.4 GHz) rectangular horn, with aperture dimensions of 5.5 and 7.4 cm, find its maximum effective aperture (in cm^2) when its gain

(over isotropic) is
   (a) 14.8 dB at 8.2 GHz
   (b) 16.5 dB at 10.3 GHz
   (c) 18.0 dB at 12.4 GHz

2.24. Two X-band (8.2–12.4 GHz) rectangular horns, with aperture dimensions of 5.5 and 7.4 cm and each with a gain of 16.3 dB (over isotropic) at 10 GHz, are used as transmitting and receiving antennas. Assuming that the input power is 200 mW, the VSWR of each is 1.1, the conduction-dielectric efficiency is 100%, and the antennas are polarization matched, find the maximum received power when the horns are separated in air by
   (a) 5 m
   (b) 50 m
   (c) 500 m

2.25. Transmitting and receiving antennas operating at 1 GHz with gains (over isotropic) of 20 and 15 dB, respectively, are separated by a distance of 1 km. Find the maximum power delivered to the load when the input power is 150 W. Assume that the
   (a) antennas are polarization matched
   (b) transmitting antenna is circularly polarized (either right- or left-hand) and the receiving antenna is linearly polarized.

2.26. A rectangular X-band horn, with aperture dimensions of 5.5 and 7.4 cm and a gain of 16.3 dB (over isotropic) at 10 GHz, is used to transmit and receive energy scattered from a perfectly conducting sphere of radius $a=5\lambda$. Find the maximum scattered power delivered to the load when the distance between the horn and the sphere is
   (a) 200λ
   (b) 500λ
   Assume that the input power is 200 mW, and the radar cross section is equal to the geometrical cross section.

2.27. The effective antenna temperature of an antenna looking toward zenith is approximately 5°K. Assuming that the temperature of the transmission line (waveguide) is 72°F, find the effective temperature at the receiver terminals when the attenuation of the transmission line is 4 dB/100 ft and its length is
   (a) 2 ft
   (b) 100 ft
   Compare it to a receiver noise temperature of about 54°K.

2.28. Derive (2-115). Begin with an expression that assumes that the physical temperature and the attenuation of the transmission line are not constant.

COMPUTER PROGRAM—POLAR PLOT

```
C     ************************************************************
C
C SUBROUTINE FPOLAR
C     SUBROUTINE TO PRODUCE A POLAR GRAPH OF A FUNCTION OF AN
C         ANGLE THETA.
C
C             R=F(THETA)     SINGLE FUNCTION - SINGLE GRAPH
C
C       CALLING SEQUENCE:   CALL FPOLAR(R,THETA,NMEM,ICHAR,MODE,
C                           TITLE,NCHAR)
C                   R IS A REAL ARRAY SUCH THAT R IS A FUNCTION OF
C                       THETA.
C                   THETA IS A REAL ARRAY IN DEGREES.
C                   NMEM- IS ARRAY SIZE OF BOTH R AND THETA (NO
C                           GREATER THAN 500)
C                   ICHAR - A LOGICAL*1 (ONE BYTE)  PRINTING
C                           CHARACTER OR ICHAR MAY BE A SINGLE
C                           CHARACTER PASSED IN QUOTES ('A')
C                   MODE - VALUES OF 0,1,2
C                           0 - A REGULAR POLAR PLOT OF R VS THETA
C                           1 - A PLOT OF 20*LOG(R) VS THETA
C                               (LOGARITHMIC PLOT)
C                           2 - A REGULAR POLAR PLOT FOLLOWED BY A
C                               LOGARITHMIC PLOT
C                   TITLE - A QUOTED STRING CONTAINING THE PLOT'S
C                           TITLE
C                   NCHAR - NUMBER OF CHARACTERS IN TITLE (NOT TO
C                           EXCEED 120)
C
C       EXAMPLE:   R=SIN(THETA)
C           DIMENSION R(360),THETA(360)
C           CALL FPOLAR (R,THETA,360,'*',0,'SIN FUNCTION',12)
C       THIS WILL GENERATE A REGULAR POLAR PLOT WITH TITLE
C       AND INDICATE POINTS WITH CHARACTER '*'.
C
C
C     ************************************************************
      SUBROUTINE FPOLAR (RARRY,THETA,N,ICHAR,MODE,TITLE,NCH
     1AR)
      REAL*4 RARRY(N),THETA(N),RRAY(500)
      INTEGER*4 IXARRY(500),IYARRY(500)
      LOGICAL*1 PRARRY(73,93),TWO,SEVEN,ZERO,ULINE,NINE
     *,BLANK,ONE,EIGHT,ICAR,ICHAR,PERIOD,FIVE,TITLE(120)
     *,BUFFER(120)
      DATA TWO/'2'/,SEVEN/'7'/,ZERO/'0'/,ULINE/'-'/,NINE
     /'9'/,BLANK/' '/ ,ONE/'1'/,EIGHT/'8'/,ICAR/'I'/,PERIOD/
     *'.'/,FIVE/'5'/
      AMAX=1.0
      PI=3.1415926
      DO 10 I=1,N
      RRAY(I)=RARRY(I)
10    IF (ABS(RARRY(I)).GT.AMAX)AMAX=ABS(RARRY(I))
C NORMALIZE THE ARRAY
      DO 20 I=1,N
20    RRAY(I)=ABS(RARRY(I))/AMAX
25    IF (MODE.EQ.1)GOTO 500
      DO 30 I=1,N
      AX=RRAY(I)*COS(THETA(I)*PI/180.)
      AY=RRAY(I)*SIN(THETA(I)*PI/180.)
      IF(AX.GE.0.0)IXARRY(I)=AX*44+.5
        IF (AX.LT.0.0)IXARRY(I)=AX*44-.5
      IF (AY.GE.0.0)IYARRY(I)=AY*35+.5
        IF (AY.LT.0.0)IYARRY(I)=AY*35-.5
30    CONTINUE
C    CLEAR AND FILL OUTPUT ARRAY   PARRY
35    DO 40 I=1,73
      DO 40 J=1,93
```

```
             PRARRY(I,J)=BLANK
             IF((((FLOAT(J-48))/44)**2+((FLOAT(I-37))/35.)**2.GE.
            *.98.AND.((FLOAT
            *(J-48))/44.)**2+((FLOAT(I-37))/35.)**2.LE.1.02)PRARRY
            *(I,J)=PERIOD
             IF((J-48)/4*4.EQ.J-48.AND.(I-37)/3*3.EQ.I-37.AND.J.GE
            *.16.AND.J.LE.
            *80.AND.IABS((J-48)/4).EQ.IABS((I-37)/3))PRARRY(I,J)=
            *PERIOD
      40     CONTINUE
             DO 45 J=2,72
      45     PRARRY(J,48)=ICAR
             DO 50 I=4,92
      50     PRARRY(37,I)=ULINE
      C   AXIS HAVE BEEN INCLUDED, NOW ADD EXTERIOR LABELS
             DO 300 K=1,N
      300    PRARRY(37-IYARRY(K),IXARRY(K)+48)=ICHAR
             PRARRY(37,1)=ONE
             PRARRY(37,2)=EIGHT
             PRARRY(37,3)=ZERO
             PRARRY(37,93)=ZERO
             PRARRY(1,47)=NINE
             PRARRY(1,48)=ZERO
             PRARRY(73,47)=TWO
             PRARRY(73,48)=SEVEN
             PRARRY(73,49)=ZERO
             IF (MODE-1)350,370,350
      350    PRARRY(2,49)=ONE
             PRARRY(38,4)=ONE
             PRARRY(38,92)=ONE
             PRARRY(72,49)=ONE
             PRARRY(19,49)=PERIOD
             PRARRY(55,49)=PERIOD
             PRARRY(38,25)=PERIOD
             PRARRY(38,70)=PERIOD
             PRARRY(19,50)=FIVE
             PRARRY(55,50)=FIVE
             PRARRY(38,26)=FIVE
             PRARRY(38,71)=FIVE
             GOTO 390
      370    PRARRY(2,49)=ZERO
             PRARRY(38,4)=ZERO
             PRARRY(38,92)=ZERO
             PRARRY(72,49)=ZERO
             PRARRY(19,49)=TWO
             PRARRY(55,49)=TWO
             PRARRY(38,25)=TWO
             PRARRY(38,70)=TWO
             PRARRY(19,50)=ZERO
             PRARRY(55,50)=ZERO
             PRARRY(38,26)=ZERO
             PRARRY(38,71)=ZERO
      C   WRITE STATEMENTS .......
      C
      390    DO 391 I=1,120
      391    BUFFER(I)=BLANK
             IOFF=(120-NCHAR)/2
             DO 392 I=1,NCHAR
             BUFFER(I+IOFF)=TITLE(I)
      392    CONTINUE
             WRITE (6,393)(BUFFER(I),I=1,120)
      393    FORMAT(8X,120A1)
             DO 400 J=1,73
      400    WRITE(6,450)(PRARRY(J,I),I=1,93)
      450    FORMAT(20X,93A1)
             IF (MODE.NE.2)GOTO 1000
             DO 490 I=1,N
```

```
490    RRAY(I)=ABS(RARRY(I))/AMAX
       DO 495 I=1,N
       IF(RRAY(I).LT.0)GOTO 494
       GOTO 495
494    RRAY(I)=-1.0*RRAY(I)
       THETA(I)=THETA(I)+180.
495    CONTINUE
500    DO 510 I=1,N
       IF (RRAY(I).EQ.0)GOTO 505
       RRAY(I)=20.0*ALOG10(RRAY(I))
       IF (RRAY(I).LE.-40.0)RRAY(I)=-40.0
       GOTO 510
505    RRAY(I)=-40.0
510    CONTINUE
520    DO 530 I=1,N
       IXARRY(I)=(40.0+RRAY(I))*COS(THETA(I)*(PI/180.))*
      *44.0/40.0
       IYARRY(I)=(40.0+RRAY(I))*SIN(THETA(I)*PI/180.)*
      *35.0/40.0
530    CONTINUE
       IF (MODE.EQ.2)WRITE (6,600)
600    FORMAT('1')
       MODE=1
       GOTO 35
1000   RETURN
       END
```

COMPUTER PROGRAM—LINEAR PLOT

```
C ***********************************************************
C     FLINE
C        A LINEAR LINE PRINTER PLOTTING ROUTINE. CREATES MULT-
C        IPLE LINEAR PLOTS OF FUNCTIONS IE. Y=F(X).
C     CALLING SEQUENCE
C        CALL FLINE (X,Y,NPT,PCHAR,NG,MAXPT,MODE)
C        Y IS A FUNCTION OF X
C        X - IS A REAL ARRAY OF VALUES OF X. (X(I), I=1,2,..N)
C        Y - IS A REAL ARRAY OF VALUES OF Y. (Y(I), I=1,2,..N)
C        NPT - IS AN ARRAY CONTAINING NUMBER OF VALUES OF X
C              AND Y FOR EACH GRAPH.
C        PCHAR - IS A CHARACTER STRING TO BE PLOTTED FOR
C                POINTS.
C        NG - IS THE NUMBER OF DIFFERENT GRAPHS TO PLOT.
C        MAXPT - IS THE LARGEST NUMBER OF POINTS TO BE
C                PLOTTED IN ANY OF THE GRAPHS.
C        MODE - VALUES OF 0 OR 1
C                 0 - A REGULAR PLOT OF Y VS. X
C                 1 - A PLOT OF 20*LOG(Y) VS. X (LOGARITHMIC
C                     PLOT)
C        NOTE:  IF NG GREATER THAN ONE X AND Y NEED TO BE TWO
C               DIMENSIONAL ARRAYS AND MUST BE SUBSCRIPTED AS
C               X(MAXPT.NG) ALSO IF NG IS GREATER THAN ONE NPT
C               IS AN ARRAY FOR THE SITUATION OF PLOTTING ONLY
C               ONE GRAPH X AND Y ARE ONE DIMENSIONAL ARRAYS
C               AND NPT IS A SINGLE NUMBER.
C        EXAMPLE FOR TWO CURVES, ONE WITH 50 POINTS AND ONE
C           WITH 25.
C        INTEGER*4 NPT(2)/50,25/,PCHAR(2),/'****'/,/'$$$$'/
C        REAL*4 X(50,2),Y(50,2)
C        CALL FLINE(X,Y,NPT,PCHAR,2,50,0)
C
C        THE CHARACTER 'X' SHOULD NOT BE USED FOR PLOTTING AS
C        IT IS THE COINCIDENCE CHARACTER. (POINTS COMMON TO
C        MORE THAN ONE GRAPH).
C ***********************************************************
      SUBROUTINE FLINE(X,Y,NPT,PCHAR,NG,MAXPT,MODE)
      INTEGER*4 BLANK/'    '/,XXX/'XXXX'/,APLOT(1326),CHAR
      INTEGER*4 MO(4)/ZFF000000,ZFF0000,ZFF00,ZFF/
      INTEGER*4 MI(4)/ZFFFFFF,ZFF00FFFF,ZFFFF00FF,ZFFFFFF00/
      INTEGER*4 BLANX(4)/Z40000000,Z400000,Z4000,Z40/
      INTEGER*4 AND,OR,PLOT(51,26),PCHAR(NG),NPT(NG)
      REAL*4 X(MAXPT,NG),Y(MAXPT,NG),XX(6),YY(6),YP(200,5)
      EQUIVALENCE (XMIN,XX(1)),(XMAX,XX(6)),(YMAX,YY(1)),
     A(YMIN,YY(6)),(XDIF,DELX,APLOT(1),PLOT(1,1)),(YDIF,
     BDELY,APLOT(2)),(IK,IX),(IY,JY)
      IF(MODE-1)1000,2000,1000
 2000 IF(NG.GT.5.OR.MAXPT.GT.200)GOTO 2001
      DO 2010 I=1,NG
      DO 2010 J=1,MAXPT
 2010 YP(J,I)=Y(J,I)
      DO 2030 I=1,NG
      RMAX=0.0
      L=NPT(I)
      DO 2020 J=1,L
 2020 IF (ABS(Y(J,I)).GT.RMAX)RMAX=ABS(Y(J,I))
      DO 2025 J=1,L
      Y(J,I)=20*ALOG10(ABS(Y(J,I))/RMAX)
 2025 IF (Y(J,I).LT.-40.0)Y(J,I)=-40.0
 2030 CONTINUE
      GOTO 1000
```

```
2040    DO 2050 I=1,NG
        DO 2050 J=1,MAXPT
2050    Y(J,I)=YP(J,I)
        GOTO 3000
2001    WRITE(6,2002)
2002    FORMAT('0','ERROR IN FLINE TOO LARGE ARRAYS')
        GOTO 3000
1000    XMIN=X(1,1)
        XMAX=XMIN
        YMIN=Y(1,1)
        YMAX=YMIN
        N=NG
        DO 10 I=1,N
        M=NPT(I)
        DO 10 J=1,M
        XMIN=AMIN1(XMIN,X(J,I))
        XMAX=AMAX1(XMAX,X(J,I))
        YMIN=AMIN1(YMIN,Y(J,I))
        YMAX=AMAX1(YMAX,Y(J,I))
10      CONTINUE
        XDIF=XMAX-XMIN
        YDIF=YMAX-YMIN
        SX=100./XDIF
        SY=50./YDIF
        DELX=XDIF/5.
        DELY=YDIF/5.
        DO 20 I=2,5
20      XX(I)=XX(I-1)+DELX
        DO 30 I=2,5
30      YY(I)=YY(I-1)-DELY
        DO 40 I=1,1326
40      APLOT(I)=BLANK
        DO 50 J=1,N
        M=NPT(J)
        DO 50 I=1,M
        IX=SX*(X(I,J)-XMIN)+0.5
        IY=SY*(Y(I,J)-YMIN)+0.5
        JY=51-IY
        JX=IX/4+1
        CHAR=XXX
        KX=MOD(IX,4)+1
        IF(AND(PLOT(JY,YX),MO(KX)).EQ.BLANX(KX))CHAR=PCHAR(J)
50      PLOT(JY,JX)=OR(AND(PLOT(JY,JX),MI(KX)),AND(CHAR,
       *MO(KX)))
        WRITE(6,300) XX
300     FORMAT(9X,6(G12.4,8X)/14X,'.',
       *5('I.................'),'I.')
        J=1
        DO 70 K=1,51
        IF(MOD(K,10).EQ.1)GOTO 60
        WRITE(6,310) (PLOT(K,I),I=1,26)
310     FORMAT(14X,'.',25A4,A1,'.')
        GOTO 70
60      WRITE(6,320) YY(J),(PLOT(K,I),I=1,26),YY(J)
320     FORMAT(' ',G12.4,' -',25A4,A1,'-',G12.4)
        J=J+1
70      CONTINUE
        WRITE (6,330) XX
330     FORMAT(14X,'.',5('I.................'),'I.'/9X,
       *6(G12.4,8X))
        IF(MODE-1)3000,2040,3000
3000    RETURN
        END
```

COMPUTER PROGRAM—DIRECTIVITY

```
C  **************************************************************
C  DESCRIPTION:
C    THIS PROGRAM COMPUTES THE RADIATED POWER AND DIRECT-
C  IVITY OF ANY ANTENNA PROVIDED ITS RADIATION INTENSITY
C  U=F(THETA,PHI) IS INSERTED INTO THE SUBROUTINE U.THE
C  DIRECTIVITY IS CALCULATED USING THE TRAILING EDGE METH-
C  OD IN INCREMENTS OF 1 DEGREE IN THETA AND PHI.
C    THE INPUT DATA CARD SHOULD CONTAIN THE LOWER AND UPPER
C  BOUNDS ON THETA AND PHI,WITH THE FORMAT GIVEN IN STATEMENT
C  1.FOR EXAMPLE,IF THE ANTENNA IS RADIATING ONLY IN THE
C  UPPER HEMISPHERE,THE BOUNDS ON THETA WOULD BE 0 AND 90
C  AND THE BOUNDS ON PHI WOULD BE 0 AND 360 DEGREES.
C  MORE THAN ONE DATA CARD MAY BE READ IN FOR EACH RADIA-
C  TION INTENSITY FUNCTION.
C  **************************************************************
       INTEGER PL,PLL,PU,TL,TLL,TU
       PI=3.14159
       WRITE(6,6)
     6 FORMAT(1H1)
     4 PRAD=0.0
       UMAX=0.0
C
C  READ LOWER AND UPPER BOUNDS ON THETA AND PHI
C
       READ(5,1,END=200) TL,TU,PL,PU
     1 FORMAT(4I5)
C
C  DEFINE THE INCREMENTS
C
       THETA=PI/180.0
       PHI=PI/180.0
C
C  SINCE U (IN GENERAL) VARIES IN THETA AND PHI,A NESTED
C  DO LOOP IS REQUIRED
C
       PLL=PL+1
       DO 2 J=PLL,PU
C
C  CONVERT TO RADIANS
C
       XJ=FLOAT(J)*PI/180.0
       TLL=TL+1
       DO 2 I=TLL,TU
       XI=FLOAT(I)*PI/180.0
C
C  SUBROUTION IS CALLED TO OBTAIN F(THETA,PHI) FOR THE
C  PARTICULAR THETA AND PHI
C
       CALL U(XI,XJ,F)
C
C  MAXIMUM RADIATION INTENSITY IS FOUND
C
       IF(F.GT.UMAX) UMAX=F
       UA=THETA*PHI*F*SIN(XI)
       PRAD=PRAD+UA
     2 CONTINUE
C
C  CALCULATE DIRECTIVITY AND PRINT RESULTS
C
       DR=4.0*PI*UMAX/PRAD
       WRITE(6,3) TL,TU,PL,PU,PRAD,DR
     3 FORMAT(////,10X,'LIMITS ON THETA (DEGREES):',/,
      115X,I3,5X,I3,//,10X
      2,'LIMITS ON PHI:',//,15X,I3,5X,I3,/,10X,'THE RAD
```

```
       3IATED POWER IS',F10.4,'WATTS',//,10X,'THE DIRE
       4CTIVITY IS',F10.5)
       GO TO 4
 200   STOP
       END

       SUBROUTINE U(THETA,PHI,F)
C
C INSERT EXPRESSION FOR RADIATION INTENSITY HERE
C      EXAMPLE:
       F=SIN(THETA)*(SIN(PHI))**2
       RETURN
       END
```

Chapter 3
Radiation Integrals and Auxiliary Potential Functions

3.1 INTRODUCTION

In the analysis of radiation problems, the usual procedure is to specify the sources and then require the fields radiated by the sources. This is in contrast to the synthesis problem where the radiated fields are specified, and we are required to find the sources.

It is a very common practice in the analysis procedure to introduce auxiliary functions, known as vector potentials, which will aid in the solution of the problems. The most common vector potential functions are the $\mathbf{A}$ (magnetic vector potential) and $\mathbf{F}$ (electric vector potential). Another pair is the Hertz potentials $\mathbf{\Pi}_e$ and $\mathbf{\Pi}_h$. *Although the electric and magnetic field intensities ($\mathbf{E}$ and $\mathbf{H}$) represent physically measurable quantities, among most engineers the potentials are strictly mathematical tools.* The introduction of the potentials often simplifies the solution even though it may require determination of additional functions. While it is possible to calculate the $\mathbf{E}$ and $\mathbf{H}$ fields directly from the source-current densities $\mathbf{J}$ and $\mathbf{M}$, as shown in Figure 3.1, it is often much simpler to calculate the auxiliary potential functions first and then determine the $\mathbf{E}$ and $\mathbf{H}$. This two-step procedure is also shown in Figure 3.1.

The one-step procedure, through path 1, relates the $\mathbf{E}$ and $\mathbf{H}$ fields to $\mathbf{J}$ and $\mathbf{M}$ by integral relations. The two-step procedure, through path 2, relates the $\mathbf{A}$ and $\mathbf{F}$ (or $\mathbf{\Pi}_e$ and $\mathbf{\Pi}_h$) potentials to $\mathbf{J}$ and $\mathbf{M}$ by integral relations. The $\mathbf{E}$ and $\mathbf{H}$ are then determined simply by differentiating $\mathbf{A}$ and $\mathbf{F}$ (or $\mathbf{\Pi}_e$ and $\mathbf{\Pi}_h$). Although the two-step procedure requires both integration and differentiation, where path 1 requires only integration, the integrands in the two-step procedure are much simpler.

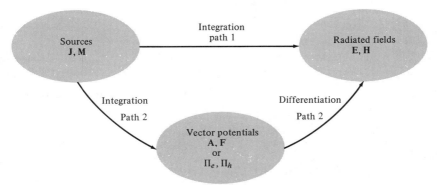

Figure 3.1 Block diagram for computing radiated fields from electric and magnetic sources.

The most difficult operation in the two-step procedure is the integration to determine **A** and **F** (or $\mathbf{\Pi}_e$ and $\mathbf{\Pi}_h$). Once the vector potentials are known, then **E** and **H** can always be determined because any well behaved function, no matter how complex, can always be differentiated.

The integration required to determine the potential functions is restricted over the bounds of the sources **J** and **M**. This will result in the **A** and **F** (or $\mathbf{\Pi}_e$ and $\mathbf{\Pi}_h$) to be functions of the observation point coordinates; the differentiation to determine **E** and **H** must be done in terms of the observation point coordinates. The integration in the one-step procedure also requires that its limits be determined by the bounds of the sources.

The vector Hertz potential $\mathbf{\Pi}_e$ is analogous to **A** and $\mathbf{\Pi}_h$ is analogous to **F**. The functional relation between them is a proportionality constant which is a function of the frequency and the constitutive parameters of the medium. In the solution of a problem, only one set, **A** and **F** or $\mathbf{\Pi}_e$ and $\mathbf{\Pi}_h$, is required. The author prefers the use of **A** and **F**, which will be used throughout the book. The derivation of the functional relations between **A** and $\mathbf{\Pi}_e$, and **F** and $\mathbf{\Pi}_h$ are assigned at the end of the chapter as problems. (Problems 3.1 and 3.2).

3.2 THE VECTOR POTENTIAL A FOR AN ELECTRIC CURRENT SOURCE J

The vector potential **A** is useful in solving for the EM field generated by a given harmonic electric current **J**. The magnetic flux **B** is always solenoidal; that is, $\nabla \cdot \mathbf{B} = 0$. Therefore, it can be represented as the curl of another vector because it obeys the vector identity

$$\nabla \cdot \nabla \times \mathbf{A} = 0 \tag{3-1}$$

where **A** is an arbitrary vector. Thus we define

$$\mathbf{B}_A = \mu \mathbf{H}_A = \nabla \times \mathbf{A} \tag{3-2}$$

or

$$\boxed{\mathbf{H}_A = \frac{1}{\mu} \nabla \times \mathbf{A}}$$

(3-2a)

where subscript A indicates the field due to the $\mathbf{A}$ potential. Substituting (3-2a) into Maxwell's curl equation

$$\nabla \times \mathbf{E}_A = -j\omega\mu\mathbf{H}_A$$

(3-3)

reduces it to

$$\nabla \times \mathbf{E}_A = -j\omega\mu\mathbf{H}_A = -j\omega\nabla \times \mathbf{A}$$

(3-4)

which can also be written as

$$\nabla \times [\mathbf{E}_A + j\omega\mathbf{A}] = 0$$

(3-5)

From the vector identity

$$\nabla \times (-\nabla\phi_e) = 0$$

(3-6)

and (3-5), it follows that

$$\mathbf{E}_A + j\omega\mathbf{A} = -\nabla\phi_e$$

(3-7)

or

$$\boxed{\mathbf{E}_A = -\nabla\phi_e - j\omega\mathbf{A}}$$

(3-7a)

ϕ_e represents an arbitrary electric scalar potential which is a function of position.

Taking the curl of both sides of (3-2) and using the vector identity

$$\nabla \times \nabla \times \mathbf{A} = \nabla(\nabla \cdot \mathbf{A}) - \nabla^2\mathbf{A}$$

(3-8)

reduces it to

$$\nabla \times (\mu\mathbf{H}_A) = \nabla(\nabla \cdot \mathbf{A}) - \nabla^2\mathbf{A}$$

(3-8a)

For a homogeneous medium, (3-8a) reduces to

$$\mu\nabla \times \mathbf{H}_A = \nabla(\nabla \cdot \mathbf{A}) - \nabla^2\mathbf{A}$$

(3-9)

Equating Maxwell's equation

$$\boxed{\nabla \times \mathbf{H}_A = \mathbf{J} + j\omega\varepsilon\mathbf{E}_A}$$

(3-10)

to (3-9) leads to

$$\mu\mathbf{J} + j\omega\mu\varepsilon\mathbf{E}_A = \nabla(\nabla \cdot \mathbf{A}) - \nabla^2\mathbf{A}$$

(3-11)

Substituting (3-7a) into (3-11) reduces it to

$$\nabla^2\mathbf{A} + k^2\mathbf{A} = -\mu\mathbf{J} + \nabla(\nabla \cdot \mathbf{A}) + \nabla(j\omega\mu\varepsilon\phi_e)$$
$$= -\mu\mathbf{J} + \nabla(\nabla \cdot \mathbf{A} + j\omega\mu\varepsilon\phi_e)$$

(3-12)

where $k^2 = \omega^2\mu\varepsilon$.

In (3-2), the curl of **A** was defined. Now we are at liberty to define the divergence of **A**, which is independent of its curl. In order to simplify (3-12), let

$$\nabla \cdot \mathbf{A} = -j\omega\varepsilon\mu\phi_e \Rightarrow \phi_e = -\frac{1}{j\omega\mu\varepsilon}\nabla \cdot \mathbf{A} \qquad (3\text{-}13)$$

which is known as the *Lorentz condition*. Substituting (3-13) into (3-12) leads to

$$\nabla^2\mathbf{A} + k^2\mathbf{A} = -\mu\mathbf{J} \qquad (3\text{-}14)$$

In addition, (3-7a) reduces to

$$\mathbf{E}_A = -\nabla\phi_e - j\omega\mathbf{A} = -j\omega\mathbf{A} - j\frac{1}{\omega\mu\varepsilon}\nabla(\nabla \cdot \mathbf{A}) \qquad (3\text{-}15)$$

Once **A** is known, $\mathbf{H}_A$ can be found from (3-2a) and $\mathbf{E}_A$ from (3-15). $\mathbf{E}_A$ can just as easily be found from Maxwell's equation (3-10) with $\mathbf{J} = 0$. It will be shown later how to find **A** in terms of the current density **J**. It will be a solution to the inhomogeneous Helmholtz equation of (3-14).

3.3 THE VECTOR POTENTIAL F FOR A MAGNETIC CURRENT SOURCE M

Although magnetic currents appear to be physically unrealizable, equivalent magnetic currents arise when we use the volume or the surface equivalence theorems. The field generated by a harmonic magnetic current in a homogeneous region, with $\mathbf{J} = 0$ but $\mathbf{M} \neq 0$, must satisfy $\nabla \cdot \mathbf{D} = 0$. Therefore, $\mathbf{E}_F$ can be expressed as the curl of the vector potential **F** by

$$\mathbf{E}_F = -\frac{1}{\varepsilon}\nabla \times \mathbf{F} \qquad (3\text{-}16)$$

Substituting (3-16) into Maxwell's curl equation

$$\nabla \times \mathbf{H}_F = j\omega\varepsilon\mathbf{E}_F \qquad (3\text{-}17)$$

reduces it to

$$\nabla \times (\mathbf{H}_F + j\omega\mathbf{F}) = 0 \qquad (3\text{-}18)$$

From the vector identity of (3-6), it follows that

$$\mathbf{H}_F = -\nabla\phi_m - j\omega\mathbf{F} \qquad (3\text{-}19)$$

where ϕ_m represents an arbitrary magnetic scalar potential which is a function of position. Taking the curl of (3-16)

$$\nabla \times \mathbf{E}_F = -\frac{1}{\varepsilon} \nabla \times \nabla \times \mathbf{F} = -\frac{1}{\varepsilon} [\nabla \nabla \cdot \mathbf{F} - \nabla^2 \mathbf{F}] \tag{3-20}$$

and equating it to Maxwell's equation

$$\boxed{\nabla \times \mathbf{E}_F = -\mathbf{M} - j\omega\mu\mathbf{H}_F} \tag{3-21}$$

leads to

$$\nabla^2 \mathbf{F} + j\omega\mu\varepsilon\mathbf{H}_F = \nabla \nabla \cdot \mathbf{F} - \varepsilon\mathbf{M} \tag{3-22}$$

Substituting (3-19) into (3-22) reduces it to

$$\nabla^2 \mathbf{F} + k^2 \mathbf{F} = -\varepsilon\mathbf{M} + \nabla(\nabla \cdot \mathbf{F}) + \nabla(j\omega\mu\varepsilon\phi_m) \tag{3-23}$$

By letting

$$\boxed{\nabla \cdot \mathbf{F} = -j\omega\mu\varepsilon\phi_m \Rightarrow \phi_m = -\frac{1}{j\omega\mu\varepsilon} \nabla \cdot \mathbf{F}} \tag{3-24}$$

reduces (3-23) to

$$\boxed{\nabla^2 \mathbf{F} + k^2 \mathbf{F} = -\varepsilon\mathbf{M}} \tag{3-25}$$

and (3-19) to

$$\boxed{\mathbf{H}_F = -j\omega\mathbf{F} - \frac{j}{\omega\mu\varepsilon} \nabla(\nabla \cdot \mathbf{F})} \tag{3-26}$$

Once $\mathbf{F}$ is known, $\mathbf{E}_F$ can be found from (3-16) and $\mathbf{H}_F$ from (3-26) or (3-21) with $\mathbf{M} = 0$. It will be shown later how to find $\mathbf{F}$ once $\mathbf{M}$ is known. It will be a solution to the inhomogeneous Helmholtz equation of (3-25).

3.4 ELECTRIC AND MAGNETIC FIELDS FOR ELECTRIC (J) AND MAGNETIC (M) CURRENT SOURCES

In the previous two sections we have developed equations that can be used to find the electric and magnetic fields generated by an electric current source $\mathbf{J}$ and a magnetic current source $\mathbf{M}$. The procedure requires that the auxiliary potential functions $\mathbf{A}$ and $\mathbf{F}$ generated, respectively, by $\mathbf{J}$ and $\mathbf{M}$ are found first. In turn, the corresponding electric and magnetic fields are then determined ($\mathbf{E}_A, \mathbf{H}_A$ due to $\mathbf{A}$ and $\mathbf{E}_F, \mathbf{H}_F$ due to $\mathbf{F}$). The total fields are then obtained by the superposition of the individual fields due to $\mathbf{A}$ and $\mathbf{F}$ ($\mathbf{J}$ and $\mathbf{M}$).

In summary form, the procedure that can be used to find the fields is as follows:

Summary

1. Specify **J** and **M** (electric and magnetic current density sources).
2. a. Find **A** (due to **J**) using

$$A = \frac{\mu}{4\pi} \iiint\limits_V \mathbf{J} \frac{e^{-jkR}}{R} dv' \tag{3-27}$$

which is a solution to the inhomogeneous vector wave equation of (3-14).

   b. Find **F** (due to **M**) using

$$F = \frac{\varepsilon}{4\pi} \iiint\limits_V \mathbf{M} \frac{e^{-jkR}}{R} dv' \tag{3-28}$$

which is a solution to the inhomogeneous vector wave equation of (3-25). In (3-27) and (3-28), $k^2 = \omega^2\mu\varepsilon$ and R is the distance from any point in the source to the observation point. In a latter section, we will demonstrate that (3-27) is a solution to (3-14) as (3-28) is to (3-25).

3. a. Find $\mathbf{H}_A$ using (3-2a) and $\mathbf{E}_A$ using (3-15). $\mathbf{E}_A$ can also be found using Maxwell's equation of (3-10) with $\mathbf{J}=0$.

   b. Find $\mathbf{E}_F$ using (3-16) and $\mathbf{H}_F$ using (3-26). $\mathbf{H}_F$ can also be found using Maxwell's equation of (3-21) with $\mathbf{M}=0$.

4. The total fields are then given by

$$\mathbf{E} = \mathbf{E}_A + \mathbf{E}_F = -j\omega\mathbf{A} - j\frac{1}{\omega\mu\varepsilon}\nabla(\nabla\cdot\mathbf{A}) - \frac{1}{\varepsilon}\nabla\times\mathbf{F} \tag{3-29}$$

or

$$\mathbf{E} = \mathbf{E}_A + \mathbf{E}_F = \frac{1}{j\omega\varepsilon}\nabla\times\mathbf{H}_A - \frac{1}{\varepsilon}\nabla\times\mathbf{F} \tag{3-29a}$$

and

$$\mathbf{H} = \mathbf{H}_A + \mathbf{H}_F = \frac{1}{\mu}\nabla\times\mathbf{A} - j\omega\mathbf{F} - j\frac{1}{\omega\mu\varepsilon}\nabla(\nabla\cdot\mathbf{F}) \tag{3-30}$$

or

$$\mathbf{H} = \mathbf{H}_A + \mathbf{H}_F = \frac{1}{\mu}\nabla\times\mathbf{A} - \frac{1}{j\omega\mu}\nabla\times\mathbf{E}_F \tag{3-30a}$$

Whether (3-15) or (3-10) is used to find $\mathbf{E}_A$ and (3-26) or (3-21) to find $\mathbf{H}_F$ depends largely upon the problem. In many instances one may be more complex than the other or vice versa. In computing fields in the far-zone, it will be easier to use (3-15) for $\mathbf{E}_A$ and (3-26) for $\mathbf{H}_F$ because, as it will be shown, the second term in each expression becomes negligible in that region.

3.5 SOLUTION OF THE INHOMOGENEOUS VECTOR POTENTIAL WAVE EQUATION

In the previous section we indicated that the solution to the inhomogeneous vector wave equation of (3-14) is (3-27).

To derive it, let us assume that a source with current density J_z, which in the limit is an infinitesimal point source, is placed at the origin of a x, y, z coordinate system, as shown in Figure 3.2(a). Since the current density is directed along the z-axis (J_z), only an A_z component will exist. Thus we can write (3-14) as

$$\nabla^2 A_z + k^2 A_z = -\mu J_z \tag{3-31}$$

At points removed from the source ($J_z = 0$), the wave equation reduces to

$$\nabla^2 A_z + k^2 A_z = 0 \tag{3-32}$$

Since in the limit the source is a point, it requires that A_z is not a function of direction (θ and ϕ); in a spherical coordinate system, $A_z = A_z(r)$ where r is the radial distance. Thus (3-32) can be written as

$$\nabla^2 A_z(r) + k^2 A_z(r) = \frac{1}{r^2} \frac{\partial}{\partial r} \left[r^2 \frac{\partial A_z(r)}{\partial r} \right] + k^2 A_z(r) = 0 \tag{3-33}$$

which when expanded reduces to

$$\frac{d^2 A_z(r)}{dr^2} + \frac{2}{r} \frac{dA_z(r)}{dr} + k^2 A_z(r) = 0 \tag{3-34}$$

The partial derivative has been replaced by the ordinary derivative since A_z is only a function of the radial coordinate.

The differential equation of (3-34) has two independent solutions

$$A_{z1} = C_1 \frac{e^{-jkr}}{r} \tag{3-35}$$

$$A_{z2} = C_2 \frac{e^{+jkr}}{r} \tag{3-36}$$

Equation (3-35) represents an outwardly (in the radial direction) traveling wave and (3-36) describes an inwardly traveling wave (assuming an $e^{j\omega t}$ time variation). For this problem, the source is placed at the origin with the radiated fields traveling in the outward radial direction. Therefore, we

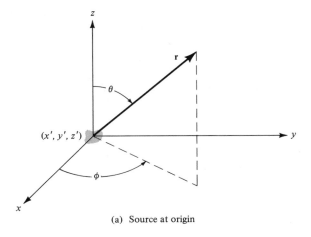

(a) Source at origin

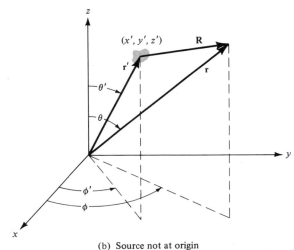

(b) Source not at origin

Figure 3.2   Coordinate systems for computing radiation fields.

choose the solution of (3-35), or

$$A_z = A_{z1} = C_1 \frac{e^{-jkr}}{r} \tag{3-37}$$

In the static case ($\omega = 0$, $k = 0$), (3-37) simplifies to

$$A_z = \frac{C_1}{r} \tag{3-38}$$

which is a solution to the wave equation of (3-32), (3-33), or (3-34) when $k = 0$. Thus at points removed from the source, the time-varying and the static solutions of (3-37) and (3-38) differ only by the e^{-jkr} factor; or the time-varying solution of (3-37) can be obtained by multiplying the static solution of (3-38) by e^{-jkr}.

In the presence of the source ($J_z \neq 0$) and $k=0$ the wave equation of (3-31) reduces to

$$\nabla^2 A_z = -\mu J_z \qquad (3\text{-}39)$$

This equation is recognized to be Poisson's equation whose solution is widely documented. The most familiar equation with Poisson's form is that relating the scalar electric potential ϕ to the electric charge density ρ. This is given by

$$\nabla^2 \phi = -\frac{\rho}{\varepsilon} \qquad (3\text{-}40)$$

whose solution is

$$\phi = \frac{1}{4\pi\varepsilon} \iiint_V \frac{\rho}{r} \, dv' \qquad (3\text{-}41)$$

where r is the distance from any point on the charge density to the observation point. Since (3-39) is similar in form to (3-40), its solution is similar to (3-41), or

$$A_z = \frac{\mu}{4\pi} \iiint_V \frac{J_z}{r} \, dv' \qquad (3\text{-}42)$$

Equation (3-42) represents the solution to (3-31) when $k=0$ (static case). Using the comparative analogy between (3-37) and (3-38), the time-varying solution of (3-31) can be obtained by multiplying the static solution of (3-42) by e^{-jkr}. Thus

$$\boxed{A_z = \frac{\mu}{4\pi} \iiint_V J_z \frac{e^{-jkr}}{r} \, dv'} \qquad (3\text{-}43)$$

which is a solution to (3-31).

If the current densities were in the x- and y-directions (J_x and J_y), the wave equation for each would reduce to

$$\nabla^2 A_x + k^2 A_x = -\mu J_x \qquad (3\text{-}44)$$

$$\nabla^2 A_y + k^2 A_y = -\mu J_y \qquad (3\text{-}45)$$

with corresponding solutions similar in form to (3-43), or

$$\boxed{A_x = \frac{\mu}{4\pi} \iiint_V J_x \frac{e^{-jkr}}{r} \, dv'} \qquad (3\text{-}46)$$

$$\boxed{A_y = \frac{\mu}{4\pi} \iiint_V J_y \frac{e^{-jkr}}{r} \, dv'} \qquad (3\text{-}47)$$

The solutions of (3-43), (3-46), and (3-47) allow us to write the solution to the vector wave equation of (3-14) as

$$\mathbf{A} = \frac{\mu}{4\pi} \iiint_V \mathbf{J} \frac{e^{-jkr}}{r} dv' \qquad (3\text{-}48)$$

If the source is removed from the origin and placed at a position represented by the primed coordinates (x', y', z'), as shown in Figure 3.2(b), (3-48) can be written as

$$\mathbf{A}(x, y, z) = \frac{\mu}{4\pi} \iiint_V \mathbf{J}(x', y', z') \frac{e^{-jkR}}{R} dv' \qquad (3\text{-}49)$$

where the primed coordinates represent the source, the unprimed the observation point, and R the distance from any point in the source to the observation point. In a similar fashion we can show that the solution of (3-25) is given by

$$\mathbf{F}(x, y, z) = \frac{\varepsilon}{4\pi} \iiint_V \mathbf{M}(x', y', z') \frac{e^{-jkR}}{R} dv' \qquad (3\text{-}50)$$

If $\mathbf{J}$ and $\mathbf{M}$ represent linear densities (m^{-1}), (3-49) and (3-50) reduce to surface integrals, or

$$\mathbf{A} = \frac{\mu}{4\pi} \iint_S \mathbf{J}_s(x', y', z') \frac{e^{-jkR}}{R} ds' \qquad (3\text{-}51)$$

$$\mathbf{F} = \frac{\varepsilon}{4\pi} \iint_S \mathbf{M}_s(x', y', z') \frac{e^{-jkR}}{R} ds' \qquad (3\text{-}52)$$

For electric and magnetic currents $\mathbf{I}_e$ and $\mathbf{I}_m$, they in turn reduce to line integrals of the form

$$\mathbf{A} = \frac{\mu}{4\pi} \int_C \mathbf{I}_e(x', y', z') \frac{e^{-jkR}}{R} dl' \qquad (3\text{-}53)$$

$$\mathbf{F} = \frac{\varepsilon}{4\pi} \int_C \mathbf{I}_m(x', y', z') \frac{e^{-jkR}}{R} dl' \qquad (3\text{-}54)$$

3.6 FAR-FIELD RADIATION

The fields radiated by antennas of finite dimensions are spherical waves. For these radiators, a general solution to the vector wave equation of (3-14) in spherical components, each as a function of r, θ, ϕ, takes the general form of

$$\mathbf{A} = \hat{a}_r A_r(r, \theta, \phi) + \hat{a}_\theta A_\theta(r, \theta, \phi) + \hat{a}_\phi A_\phi(r, \theta, \phi) \tag{3-55}$$

The amplitude variations of r in each component of (3-55) are of the form $1/r^n, n = 1, 2, \ldots$ [1]. Neglecting higher order terms of $1/r^n$ ($1/r^n = 0, n = 2, 3, \ldots$) reduces (3-55) to

$$\mathbf{A} \simeq \left[\hat{a}_r A_r'(\theta, \phi) + \hat{a}_\theta A_\theta'(\theta, \phi) + \hat{a}_\phi A_\phi'(\theta, \phi) \right] \frac{e^{-jkr}}{r}, \qquad r \to \infty \tag{3-56}$$

The r variations are separable from those of θ and ϕ. This will be demonstrated in the chapters that follow by many examples.

Substituting (3-56) into (3-15) reduces it to

$$\mathbf{E} = \frac{1}{r} \left\{ -j\omega e^{-jkr} \left[\hat{a}_r(0) + \hat{a}_\theta A_\theta'(\theta, \phi) + \hat{a}_\phi A_\phi'(\theta, \phi) \right] \right\}$$
$$+ \frac{1}{r^2} [\cdots] + \cdots \tag{3-57}$$

The radial $\mathbf{E}$-field component has no $1/r$ terms, because its contributions from the first and second terms of (3-15) cancel each other.

Similarly, by using (3-56), we can write (3-2a) as

$$\mathbf{H} = \frac{1}{r} \left\{ j\frac{\omega}{\eta} e^{-jkr} \left[\hat{a}_r(0) + \hat{a}_\theta A_\phi'(\theta, \phi) - \hat{a}_\phi A_\theta'(\theta, \phi) \right] \right\}$$
$$+ \frac{1}{r^2} \{\cdots\} + \cdots \tag{3-57a}$$

where $\eta = \sqrt{\mu/\varepsilon}$ is the intrinsic impedance of the medium.

Neglecting higher order terms of $1/r^n$, the radiated $\mathbf{E}$- and $\mathbf{H}$-fields have only θ and ϕ components. They can be expressed as

Far-Field Region

$$\left.\begin{array}{l} E_r \simeq 0 \\ E_\theta \simeq -j\omega A_\theta \\ E_\phi \simeq -j\omega A_\phi \end{array}\right\} \Rightarrow \boxed{\mathbf{E}_A \simeq -j\omega \mathbf{A}}$$
(for the θ and ϕ components only since $E_r \simeq 0$) $\qquad$ (3-58a)

$$\left.\begin{array}{l} H_r \simeq 0 \\ H_\theta \simeq +j\frac{\omega}{\eta} A_\phi = -\frac{E_\phi}{\eta} \\ H_\phi \simeq -j\frac{\omega}{\eta} A_\theta = +\frac{E_\theta}{\eta} \end{array}\right\} \Rightarrow \boxed{\mathbf{H}_A \simeq \frac{\hat{a}_r}{\eta} \times \mathbf{E}_A = -j\frac{\omega}{\eta} \hat{a}_r \times \mathbf{A}}$$
(for the θ and ϕ components only since $H_r \simeq 0$) $\qquad$ (3-58b)

Radial field components exist only for higher order terms of $1/r^n$.

In a similar manner, the far-zone fields due to a magnetic source **M** (potential **F**) can be written as

Far-Field Region

$$\left. \begin{array}{l} H_r \simeq 0 \\ H_\theta \simeq - j\omega F_\theta \\ H_\phi \simeq - j\omega F_\phi \end{array} \right\} \Rightarrow \quad \boxed{\mathbf{H}_F \simeq - j\omega \mathbf{F}}$$
$$\text{(for the } \theta \text{ and } \phi \text{ components only} \quad \text{(3-59a)}$$
$$\text{since } H_r \simeq 0)$$

$$\left. \begin{array}{l} E_r \simeq 0 \\ E_\theta \simeq - j\omega\eta F_\phi = \eta H_\phi \\ E_\phi \simeq + j\omega\eta F_\theta = - \eta H_\theta \end{array} \right\} \Rightarrow \quad \boxed{\mathbf{E}_F = - \eta \hat{a}_r \times \mathbf{H}_F = j\omega\eta \hat{a}_r \times \mathbf{F}}$$
$$\text{(for the } \theta \text{ and } \phi \text{ components} \quad \text{(3-59b)}$$
$$\text{only since } E_r \simeq 0)$$

Simply stated, *the corresponding far-zone* **E**- *and* **H**-*field components are orthogonal to each other and form TEM (to r) mode fields.* This is a very useful relation, and it will be adopted in the chapters that follow for the solution of the far-zone radiated fields. The far-zone (far-field) region for a radiator is defined in Figure 2.5. Its smallest radial distance is $2D^2/\lambda$ where D is the largest dimension of the radiator.

3.7 DUALITY THEOREM

When two equations that describe the behavior of two different variables are of the same mathematical form, their solutions will also be identical. The variables in the two equations that occupy identical positions are known as *dual* quantities and a solution of one can be formed by a systematic interchange of symbols to the other. This concept is known as the *duality theorem*.

Comparing Equations (3-2a), (3-3), (3-10), (3-14), and (3-15) to (3-16), (3-17), (3-21), (3-25), and (3-26), respectively, it is evident that they are to each other dual equations and their variables dual quantities. Thus knowing the solutions to one set (i.e., $\mathbf{J} \neq 0, \mathbf{M} = 0$), the solutions to the other set ($\mathbf{J} = 0, \mathbf{M} \neq 0$) can be formed by a proper interchange of quantities. The dual equations and their dual quantities are listed in Tables 3.1 and 3.2 for electric and magnetic sources, respectively. Duality only serves as a guide to form mathematical solutions. It can be used in an abstract manner to explain the motion of magnetic charges giving rise to magnetic currents, when compared to their dual quantities of moving electric charges creating electric currents. It must, however, be emphasized that this is purely mathematical in nature since it is known as of today, that there are no magnetic charges or currents in nature.

Table 3.1 DUAL EQUATIONS FOR ELECTRIC (**J**) AND MAGNETIC (**M**) CURRENT SOURCES

ELECTRIC SOURCES ($\mathbf{J}\neq 0, \mathbf{M}=0$)	MAGNETIC SOURCES ($\mathbf{J}=0, \mathbf{M}\neq 0$)
$\nabla\times\mathbf{E}_A=-j\omega\mu\mathbf{H}_A$	$\nabla\times\mathbf{H}_F=j\omega\varepsilon\mathbf{E}_F$
$\nabla\times\mathbf{H}_A=\mathbf{J}+j\omega\varepsilon\mathbf{E}_A$	$-\nabla\times\mathbf{E}_F=\mathbf{M}+j\omega\mu\mathbf{H}_F$
$\nabla^2\mathbf{A}+k^2\mathbf{A}=-\mu\mathbf{J}$	$\nabla^2\mathbf{F}+k^2\mathbf{F}=-\varepsilon\mathbf{M}$
$\mathbf{A}=\dfrac{\mu}{4\pi}\iiint\limits_V \mathbf{J}\dfrac{e^{-jkR}}{R}\,dv'$	$\mathbf{F}=\dfrac{\varepsilon}{4\pi}\iiint\limits_V \mathbf{M}\dfrac{e^{-jkR}}{R}\,dv'$
$\mathbf{H}_A=\dfrac{1}{\mu}\nabla\times\mathbf{A}$	$\mathbf{E}_F=-\dfrac{1}{\varepsilon}\nabla\times\mathbf{F}$
$\mathbf{E}_A=-j\omega\mathbf{A}-j\dfrac{1}{\omega\mu\varepsilon}\nabla(\nabla\cdot\mathbf{A})$	$\mathbf{H}_F=-j\omega\mathbf{F}-j\dfrac{1}{\omega\mu\varepsilon}\nabla(\nabla\cdot\mathbf{F})$

Table 3.2 DUAL QUANTITIES FOR ELECTRIC (**J**) AND MAGNETIC (**M**) CURRENT SOURCES

ELECTRIC SOURCES ($\mathbf{J}\neq 0, \mathbf{M}=0$)	MAGNETIC SOURCES ($\mathbf{J}=0, \mathbf{M}\neq 0$)
$\mathbf{E}_A$	$\mathbf{H}_F$
$\mathbf{H}_A$	$-\mathbf{E}_F$
$\mathbf{J}$	$\mathbf{M}$
$\mathbf{A}$	$\mathbf{F}$
ε	μ
μ	ε
k	k
η	$1/\eta$
$1/\eta$	η

3.8 RECIPROCITY AND REACTION THEOREMS

We are all well familiar with the reciprocity theorem, as applied to circuits, which states that *in any physical linear network, the positions of an ideal voltage source (zero internal impedance) and an ideal current source (infinite internal impedance) can be interchanged without affecting their readings.* We want now to discuss the reciprocity theorem as it applies to electromagnetic theory. This is done best by the use of Maxwell's equations.

Let us assume that within a linear and isotropic medium, but not necessarily homogeneous, there exist two sets of sources $\mathbf{J}_1, \mathbf{M}_1$, and $\mathbf{J}_2, \mathbf{M}_2$ which are allowed to radiate simultaneously or individually inside the same medium at the frequency and produces fields $\mathbf{E}_1, \mathbf{H}_1$ and $\mathbf{E}_2, \mathbf{H}_2$, respectively. It can be shown [1] that the sources and fields satisfy

$$-\nabla\cdot(\mathbf{E}_1\times\mathbf{H}_2-\mathbf{E}_2\times\mathbf{H}_1)=\mathbf{E}_1\cdot\mathbf{J}_2+\mathbf{H}_2\cdot\mathbf{M}_1-\mathbf{E}_2\cdot\mathbf{J}_1-\mathbf{H}_1\cdot\mathbf{M}_2 \quad (3\text{-}60)$$

which is called the *Lorentz Reciprocity Theorem* in differential form.

Taking a volume integral of both sides of (3-60) and using the divergence theorem on the left side, we can write it as

$$-\oint_S (\mathbf{E}_1 \times \mathbf{H}_2 - \mathbf{E}_2 \times \mathbf{H}_1) \cdot d\mathbf{s}$$

$$= \iiint_V (\mathbf{E}_1 \cdot \mathbf{J}_2 + \mathbf{H}_2 \cdot \mathbf{M}_1 - \mathbf{E}_2 \cdot \mathbf{J}_1 - \mathbf{H}_1 \cdot \mathbf{M}_2) \, dv \qquad (3\text{-}61)$$

which is designated as the *Lorentz Reciprocity Theorem* in integral form.

For a source-free ($\mathbf{J}_1 = \mathbf{J}_2 = \mathbf{M}_1 = \mathbf{M}_2 = 0$) region, (3-60) and (3-61) reduce, respectively, to

$$\nabla \cdot (\mathbf{E}_1 \times \mathbf{H}_2 - \mathbf{E}_2 \times \mathbf{H}_1) = 0 \qquad (3\text{-}62)$$

and

$$\oint_S (\mathbf{E}_1 \times \mathbf{H}_2 - \mathbf{E}_2 \times \mathbf{H}_1) \cdot d\mathbf{s} = 0 \qquad (3\text{-}63)$$

Equations (3-62) and (3-63) are special cases of the Lorentz Reciprocity Theorem and must be satisfied in source-free regions. Substituting (3-63) into (3-61) reduces it to

$$\iiint_V (\mathbf{E}_1 \cdot \mathbf{J}_2 - \mathbf{H}_1 \cdot \mathbf{M}_2) \, dv = \iiint_V (\mathbf{E}_2 \cdot \mathbf{J}_1 - \mathbf{H}_2 \cdot \mathbf{M}_1) \, dv \qquad (3\text{-}64)$$

The reciprocity theorem, as expressed by (3-64), is the most useful form. It is applicable when the relation between the $\mathbf{E}$- and $\mathbf{H}$- field components are those of (3-58b) and (3-59b), which are satisfied when observations are made at large distances (ideally infinity) while the sources are contained within a finite region.

A close observation of (3-61) will reveal that it does not, in general, represent relations of power because no conjugates appear. The same is true for the special cases represented by (3-63) and (3-64). Each of the integrals in (3-64) have been defined as *Reaction* [2] denoted by

$$\langle 1,2 \rangle = \iiint_V (\mathbf{E}_1 \cdot \mathbf{J}_2 - \mathbf{H}_1 \cdot \mathbf{M}_2) \, dv \qquad (3\text{-}65)$$

$$\langle 2,1 \rangle = \iiint_V (\mathbf{E}_2 \cdot \mathbf{J}_1 - \mathbf{H}_2 \cdot \mathbf{M}_1) \, dv \qquad (3\text{-}66)$$

The relation $\langle 1,2 \rangle$ of (3-65) relates the reaction of fields $(\mathbf{E}_1, \mathbf{H}_1)$ to sources $(\mathbf{J}_2, \mathbf{M}_2)$, where $\langle 2,1 \rangle$ relates the reaction of fields $(\mathbf{E}_2, \mathbf{H}_2)$ to sources $(\mathbf{J}_1, \mathbf{M}_1)$. For reciprocity to hold, it will require that the reactions of the sources with their corresponding fields must be equal. In equation form, it is written as

$$\langle 1,2 \rangle = \langle 2,1 \rangle \qquad (3\text{-}67)$$

There are many applications to the reciprocity theorem. To demonstrate its potential, an antenna example will be considered. Two antennas, whose input impedances are Z_1 and Z_2, are separated by a linear and isotropic (but not necessarily homogeneous) medium, as shown in Figure 3.3. One antenna (#1) is used as a transmitter and the other (#2) as a receiver. The equivalent network of each antenna is given in Figure 3.4. The internal impedance of the generator Z_g is assumed to be the conjugate of the impedance of antenna #1 ($Z_g = Z_1^* = R_1 - jX_1$) while the load impedance Z_L is equal to the conjugate of the impedance of antenna #2 ($Z_L = Z_2^* = R_2 - jX_2$). These assumptions are made only for convenience.

The power delivered by the generator to antenna #1 is given by

$$P_1 = \frac{1}{2} \operatorname{Re}[V_1 I_1^*] = \frac{1}{2} \operatorname{Re}\left[\left(\frac{V_g Z_1}{Z_1 + Z_g}\right) \frac{V_g^*}{(Z_1 + Z_g)^*}\right] = \frac{|V_g|^2}{8R_1} \tag{3-68}$$

If the transfer admittance of the combined network consisting of the generator impedance, antennas, and load impedance is Y_{21}, the current through the load is $V_g Y_{21}$ and the power delivered to the load is

$$P_2 = \frac{1}{2} \operatorname{Re}\left[Z_2(V_g Y_{21})(V_g Y_{21})^*\right] = \frac{1}{2} R_2 |V_g|^2 |Y_{21}|^2 \tag{3-69}$$

The ratio of (3-69) to (3-68) is

$$\frac{P_2}{P_1} = 4R_1 R_2 |Y_{21}|^2 \tag{3-70}$$

In a similar manner, we can show that when antenna #2 is transmitting and #1 is receiving, the power ratio of P_1/P_2 is given by

$$\frac{P_1}{P_2} = 4R_2 R_1 |Y_{12}|^2 \tag{3-71}$$

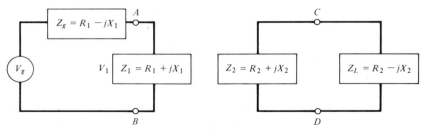

Figure 3.3 Transmitting and receiving antenna systems.

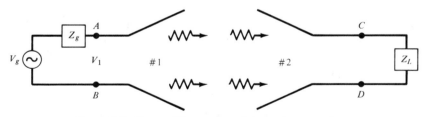

Figure 3.4 Two antenna systems with conjugate loads.

Under conditions of reciprocity ($Y_{12} = Y_{21}$), the power delivered in either direction is the same.

3.8.1 Reciprocity for Radiation Patterns

The radiation pattern is a very important antenna characteristic. Although it is most convenient and practical to measure the pattern in the receiving mode, it is identical to that of the transmitting mode because of reciprocity.

To detail the procedure and foundation of pattern measurements and reciprocity, let us refer to Figures 3.5(a) and (b). The antenna under test is #1 while the probe antenna (#2) is oriented to transmit or receive maximum radiation. The voltages and currents V_1, I_1 at terminals 1–1 of antenna #1 and V_2, I_2 at the terminals 2–2 of antenna #2 are related by

$$V_1 = Z_{11}I_1 + Z_{12}I_2$$
$$V_2 = Z_{21}I_1 + Z_{22}I_2 \tag{3-72}$$

where

$$Z_{11} = \text{self-impedance of antenna \#1}$$
$$Z_{22} = \text{self-impedance of antenna \#2}$$
$$Z_{12}, Z_{21} = \text{mutual impedances between antennas \#1 and \#2}$$

If a current I_1 is applied at the terminals 1–1 and voltage V_2 (designated as V_{2oc}) is measured at the *open* ($I_2 = 0$) terminals of antenna #2, then an equal voltage V_{1oc} will be measured at the *open* ($I_1 = 0$) terminals of antenna #1 provided the current I_2 of antenna #2 is equal to I_1. In

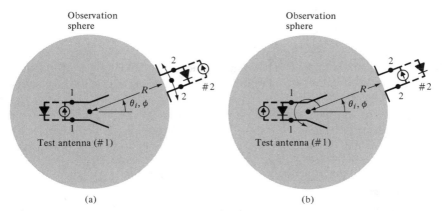

(a)　　　　　　　　　　　　　(b)

Figure 3.5　Antenna arrangement for pattern measurements and reciprocity theorem.

equation form, we can write

$$Z_{21} = \frac{V_{2oc}}{I_1} \bigg|_{I_2 = 0} \tag{3-73a}$$

$$Z_{12} = \frac{V_{1oc}}{I_2} \bigg|_{I_1 = 0} \tag{3-73b}$$

If the medium between the two antennas is linear, passive, isotropic, and the waves monochromatic, then because of reciprocity

$$Z_{21} = \frac{V_{2oc}}{I_1} \bigg|_{I_2 = 0} = \frac{V_{1oc}}{I_2} \bigg|_{I_1 = 0} = Z_{12} \tag{3-74}$$

If in addition $I_1 = I_2$, then

$$V_{2oc} = V_{1oc} \tag{3-75}$$

The above are valid for any position and any mode of operation between the two antennas.

Reciprocity will now be reviewed for two modes of operation. In one mode, antenna #1 is held stationary while #2 is allowed to move on the surface of a constant radius sphere, as shown in Figure 3.5(a). In the other mode, antenna #2 is maintained stationary while #1 pivots about a point, as shown in Figure 3.5(b).

In the mode of Figure 3.5(a), antenna #1 can be used either as a transmitter or receiver. In the transmitting mode, while antenna #2 is moving on the constant radius sphere surface, the open terminal voltage V_{2oc} is measured. In the receiving mode, the open terminal voltage V_{1oc} is recorded. The three-dimensional plots of V_{2oc} and V_{1oc}, as a function of θ and ϕ, have been defined in Section 2.2 as *field patterns*. Since the three-dimensional graph of V_{2oc} is identical to that of V_{1oc} (due to reciprocity), the *transmitting* (V_{2oc}) *and receiving* (V_{1oc}) field patterns are also equal. The same conclusion can be arrived at if antenna #2 is allowed to remain stationary while #1 rotates, as shown in Figure 3.5(b).

The conditions of reciprocity hold whether antenna #1 is used as a transmitter and #2 as a receiver *or* antenna #2 as a transmitter and #1 as a receiver. In practice, the most convenient mode of operation is that of Figure 3.5(b). Antenna #2 is usually placed in the far-field of the test antenna (#1) in order that its radiated fields are plane waves in the vicinity of #1.

The mode of operation of Figure 3.5(b) is most widely used to measure antenna patterns, because the transmitting equipment is in most cases bulky and heavy while the receiver is small and lightweight. In some cases, the receiver is nothing more than a simple diode detector. The transmitting equipment usually consists of sources and amplifiers. To make precise measurements, especially at microwave frequencies, it is necessary to have frequency and power stabilities. Therefore, the equipment must be placed on vibration-free platforms. This can best be accomplished by allowing the transmitting equipment to be held stationary and the receiving equipment to rotate.

An excellent manuscript on test procedures for antenna measurements of amplitude, phase, impedance, polarization, gain, directivity, efficiency, and others has been published by IEEE [3]. A condensed summary of it is found in [4], and a review is presented in Chapter 15 of this text.

References

1. R. F. Harrington, *Time-Harmonic Electromagnetic Fields*, McGraw-Hill, New York, 1961.
2. V. H. Rumsey, "The Reaction Concept in Electromagnetic Theory," *Physical Review*, Series 2, vol. 94, No. 6, pp. 1483–1491, June 15, 1954.
3. *IEEE Standard Test Procedures for Antennas*, IEEE Std 149-1979, IEEE, Inc., New York, 1979.
4. W. H. Kummer and E. S. Gillespie, "Antenna Measurements—1978," *Proc. IEEE*, vol. 66, No. 4, April 1978, pp. 483–507.

PROBLEMS

3.1. If $\mathbf{H}_e = j\omega\varepsilon\nabla\times\mathbf{\Pi}_e$, where $\mathbf{\Pi}_e$ is the electric Hertzian potential, show that

  (a) $\nabla^2\mathbf{\Pi}_e + k^2\mathbf{\Pi}_e = j\dfrac{1}{\omega\varepsilon}\mathbf{J}$

  (b) $\mathbf{E}_e = k^2\mathbf{\Pi}_e + \nabla(\nabla\cdot\mathbf{\Pi}_e)$

  (c) $\mathbf{\Pi}_e = -j\dfrac{1}{\omega\mu\varepsilon}\mathbf{A}$

3.2. If $\mathbf{E}_m = -j\omega\mu\nabla\times\mathbf{\Pi}_m$, where $\mathbf{\Pi}_m$ is the magnetic Hertzian potential, show that

  (a) $\nabla^2\mathbf{\Pi}_m + k^2\mathbf{\Pi}_m = j\dfrac{1}{\omega\mu}\mathbf{M}$

  (b) $\mathbf{H}_m = k^2\mathbf{\Pi}_m + \nabla(\nabla\cdot\mathbf{\Pi}_m)$

  (c) $\mathbf{\Pi}_m = -j\dfrac{1}{\omega\mu\varepsilon}\mathbf{F}$

3.3. Verify that (3-35) and (3-36) are solutions to (3-34).

3.4. Show that (3-42) is a solution to (3-39) and (3-43) is a solution to (3-31).

3.5. Verify (3-57) and (3-57a).

3.6. Derive (3-60) and (3-61).

Chapter 4
Linear Wire Antennas

4.1 INTRODUCTION

Wire antennas, linear or curved, are some of the oldest, simplest, cheapest, and in many cases the most versatile for many applications. It should not then come as a surprise to the reader that we begin our analysis of antennas by considering some of the oldest and simplest types. Initially we will try to minimize the complexity of the antenna structure and geometry to keep the mathematical details to a minimum.

4.2 INFINITESIMAL DIPOLE

An infinitesimal linear wire ($l \ll \lambda$) is positioned symmetrically at the origin of the coordinate system and oriented along the z axis, as shown in Figure 4.1(a). Although infinitesimal dipoles are not very practical, they are used to represent capacitor-plate (also referred to as top-hat-loaded) antennas. In addition, they are utilized as building blocks of more complex geometries. The wire, in addition to being very small ($l \ll \lambda$), is very thin. The current is assumed to be constant and given by

$$\mathbf{I}(z') = \hat{a}_z I_0 \tag{4-1}$$

where $I_0 = $ constant.

4.2.1 Radiated Fields

To find the fields radiated by the current element, the two-step procedure of Figure 3.1 will be used. It will be required to determine first $\mathbf{A}$ and $\mathbf{F}$ and then find the $\mathbf{E}$ and $\mathbf{H}$. The functional relation between $\mathbf{A}$ and the source $\mathbf{J}$ is given by (3-49), (3-51), or (3-53). Similar relations are available for $\mathbf{F}$ and $\mathbf{M}$, as given by (3-50), (3-52), and (3-54).

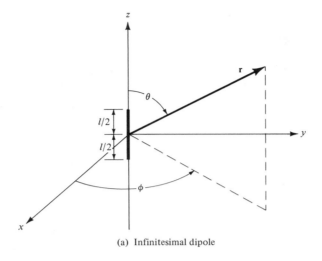

(a) Infinitesimal dipole

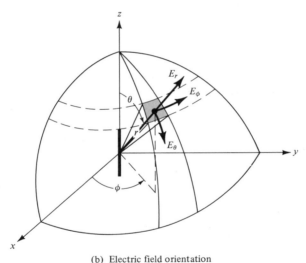

(b) Electric field orientation

Figure 4.1 Geometrical arrangement of an infinitesimal dipole and its associated electric field components on a spherical surface.

Since the source only carries an electric current $\mathbf{I}_e$, $\mathbf{I}_m$ and the potential function $\mathbf{F}$ are zero. To find $\mathbf{A}$ we write

$$\mathbf{A}(x, y, z) = \frac{\mu}{4\pi} \int_C \mathbf{I}_e(x', y', z') \frac{e^{-jkR}}{R} dl' \tag{4-2}$$

where (x, y, z) represent the observation point coordinates, (x', y', z') represent the coordinates of the source, R is the distance from any point on the source to the observation point, and path C is along the length of the source. For the problem of Figure 4.1

$$\mathbf{I}_e(x', y', z') = \hat{a}_z I_0 \tag{4-3a}$$

$$x' = y' = z' = 0 \quad \text{(infinitesimal dipole)} \tag{4-3b}$$

$$R = \sqrt{(x-x')^2 + (y-y')^2 + (z-z')^2} = \sqrt{x^2 + y^2 + z^2}$$

$$= r = \text{constant} \tag{4-3c}$$

$$dl' = dz' \tag{4-3d}$$

so we can write (4-2) as

$$\boxed{\mathbf{A}(x, y, z) = \hat{a}_z \frac{\mu I_0}{4\pi r} e^{-jkr} \int_{-l/2}^{+l/2} dz' = \hat{a}_z \frac{\mu I_0 l}{4\pi r} e^{-jkr}} \tag{4-4}$$

The next step of the procedure will be to find $\mathbf{H}_A$ using (3-2a) and then $\mathbf{E}_A$ using (3-15) or (3-10) with $\mathbf{J} = 0$. To do this, it is often much simpler to transform (4-4) from rectangular to spherical components and then use (3-2a) and (3-15) or (3-10) in spherical coordinates to find $\mathbf{H}$ and $\mathbf{E}$.

The transformation between rectangular and spherical components is given, in matrix form, by (see Appendix VII)

$$\begin{bmatrix} A_r \\ A_\theta \\ A_\phi \end{bmatrix} = \begin{bmatrix} \sin\theta\cos\phi & \sin\theta\sin\phi & \cos\theta \\ \cos\theta\cos\phi & \cos\theta\sin\phi & -\sin\theta \\ -\sin\phi & \cos\phi & 0 \end{bmatrix} \begin{bmatrix} A_x \\ A_y \\ A_z \end{bmatrix} \tag{4-5}$$

For this problem $A_x = A_y = 0$, so (4-5) using (4-4) reduces to

$$A_r = A_z \cos\theta = \frac{\mu I_0 l e^{-jkr}}{4\pi r} \cos\theta \tag{4-6a}$$

$$A_\theta = -A_z \sin\theta = -\frac{\mu I_0 l e^{-jkr}}{4\pi r} \sin\theta \tag{4-6b}$$

$$A_\phi = 0 \tag{4-6c}$$

Using the symmetry of the problem (no variations in ϕ), (3-2a) can be expanded in spherical coordinates and written in simplified form as

$$\mathbf{H} = \hat{a}_\phi \frac{1}{\mu r} \left[\frac{\partial}{\partial r}(rA_\theta) - \frac{\partial A_r}{\partial\theta} \right] \tag{4-7}$$

Substituting (4-6a)–(4-6c) into (4-7) reduces it to

$$\boxed{\begin{array}{l} H_r = H_\theta = 0 \\ \\ H_\phi = j\dfrac{kI_0 l \sin\theta}{4\pi r}\left[1 + \dfrac{1}{jkr}\right]e^{-jkr} \end{array}} \qquad \begin{array}{l} (4\text{-}8a) \\ \\ (4\text{-}8b) \end{array}$$

The electric field **E** can now be found using (3-15) or (3-10) with **J**=0. That is,

$$\mathbf{E}=\mathbf{E}_A= - j\omega\mathbf{A} - j\frac{1}{\omega\mu\varepsilon}\nabla(\nabla\cdot\mathbf{A})=\frac{1}{j\omega\varepsilon}\nabla\times\mathbf{H} \tag{4-9}$$

Substituting (4-6a)–(4-6c) or (4-8a)–(4-8b) into (4-9) reduces it to

$$E_r=\eta\frac{I_0l\cos\theta}{2\pi r^2}\left[1+\frac{1}{jkr}\right]e^{-jkr} \tag{4-10a}$$

$$E_\theta=j\eta\frac{kI_0l\sin\theta}{4\pi r}\left[1+\frac{1}{jkr}-\frac{1}{(kr)^2}\right]e^{-jkr} \tag{4-10b}$$

$$E_\phi=0 \tag{4-10c}$$

The **E**- and **H**-field components are valid everywhere, except on the source itself, and they are sketched in Figure 4.1(b) on the surface of a sphere of radius r. It is a simple exercise to verify Equations (4-10a)–(4-10c), and this is left as an exercise to the reader (Prob. 4.3).

4.2.2 Power Density and Radiation Resistance

The input impedance of an antenna, which consists of real and imaginary parts, was discussed in Section 2.13. For a lossless antenna, the real part of the input impedance was designated as radiation resistance. It is through the mechanism of the radiation resistance that power is transferred from the guided wave to the free-space wave. To find the input resistance for a lossless antenna, the Poynting vector is formed in terms of the **E**- and **H**-fields radiated by the antenna. By integrating the Poynting vector over a closed surface (usually a sphere of constant radius), the total power radiated by the source is found. The real part of it is related to the input resistance.

For the infinitesimal dipole, the complex Poynting vector can be written using (4-8a)–(4-8b) and (4-10a)–(4-10c) as

$$\mathbf{W}=\tfrac{1}{2}(\mathbf{E}\times\mathbf{H}^*)=\tfrac{1}{2}(\hat{a}_r E_r+\hat{a}_\theta E_\theta)\times(\hat{a}_\phi H_\phi^*)$$

$$=\tfrac{1}{2}(\hat{a}_r E_\theta H_\phi^* - \hat{a}_\theta E_r H_\phi^*) \tag{4-11}$$

whose radial W_r and transverse W_θ components are given, respectively, by

$$W_r=\frac{\eta}{8}\left|\frac{I_0l}{\lambda}\right|^2\frac{\sin^2\theta}{r^2}\left[1-j\frac{1}{(kr)^3}\right] \tag{4-12a}$$

$$W_\theta=j\eta\frac{k|I_0l|^2\cos\theta\sin\theta}{16\pi^2 r^3}\left[1+\frac{1}{(kr)^2}\right] \tag{4-12b}$$

The complex power moving in the radial direction is obtained by integrating

(4-11)–(4-12b) over a closed sphere of radius r. Thus it can be written as

$$P = \oiint_S \mathbf{W} \cdot d\mathbf{s} = \int_0^{2\pi} \int_0^{\pi} (\hat{a}_r W_r + \hat{a}_\theta W_\theta) \cdot \hat{a}_r r^2 \sin\theta \, d\theta \, d\phi \qquad (4\text{-}13)$$

which reduces to

$$P = \int_0^{2\pi} \int_0^{\pi} W_r r^2 \sin\theta \, d\theta \, d\phi = \eta \frac{\pi}{3} \left| \frac{I_0 l}{\lambda} \right|^2 \left[1 - j \frac{1}{(kr)^3} \right] \qquad (4\text{-}14)$$

The transverse component W_θ of the power density does not contribute to the integral. Thus (4-14) does not represent the total complex power radiated by the antenna. Since W_θ, as given by (4-12b), is purely imaginary, it will not contribute to any real radiated power. However, it does contribute to the imaginary (reactive) power which along with the second term of (4-14) can be used to determine the total reactive power of the antenna. The reactive power density, which is most dominant for small values of kr, has both radial and transverse components. It merely changes between outward and inward directions to form a standing wave at a rate of twice per cycle. It also moves in the transverse direction as suggested by (4-12b).

Equation (4-13), which gives the real and imaginary power that is moving outwardly, can also be written as

$$P = \frac{1}{2} \iint_S \mathbf{E} \times \mathbf{H}^* \cdot d\mathbf{s} = \eta \left(\frac{\pi}{3} \right) \left| \frac{I_0 l}{\lambda} \right|^2 \left[1 - j \frac{1}{(kr)^3} \right]$$

$$= P_{\text{rad}} + j2\omega (\tilde{W}_m - \tilde{W}_e) \qquad (4\text{-}15)$$

where

$$P = \text{power (in radial direction)}$$

$$P_{\text{rad}} = \text{time-average power radiated}$$

$$\tilde{W}_m = \text{time-average magnetic energy (in radial direction)}$$

$$\tilde{W}_e = \text{time-average electric energy (in radial direction)}$$

$$2\omega(\tilde{W}_m - \tilde{W}_e) = \text{time-average imaginary (reactive) power} \\ \text{(in radial direction)}$$

From (4-14)

$$P_{\text{rad}} = \eta \left(\frac{\pi}{3} \right) \left| \frac{I_0 l}{\lambda} \right|^2 \qquad (4\text{-}16)$$

and

$$2\omega(\tilde{W}_m - \tilde{W}_e) = -\eta \left(\frac{\pi}{3} \right) \left| \frac{I_0 l}{\lambda} \right|^2 \frac{1}{(kr)^3} \qquad (4\text{-}17)$$

It is clear from (4-17) that the radial electric energy must be larger than the radial magnetic energy. For large values of kr ($kr \gg 1$ or $r \gg \lambda$), the reactive power diminishes and vanishes when $kr = \infty$.

Since the antenna radiates its real power through the radiation resistance, for the infinitesimal dipole it is found by equating (4-16) to

$$\boxed{P_{\mathrm{rad}} = \eta \left(\frac{\pi}{3} \right) \left| \frac{I_0 l}{\lambda} \right|^2 = \frac{1}{2} |I_0|^2 R_r} \tag{4-18}$$

where R_r is the radiation resistance. Equation (4-18) reduces to

$$\boxed{R_r = \eta \left(\frac{2\pi}{3} \right) \left(\frac{l}{\lambda} \right)^2 = 80\pi^2 \left(\frac{l}{\lambda} \right)^2} \tag{4-19}$$

for a free-space medium ($\eta \simeq 120\pi$). It should be pointed out that the radiation resistance of (4-19) represents the total radiation resistance since (4-12b) does not contribute to it.

For a wire antenna to be classified as an infinitesimal dipole, its overall length must be very small (usually $l \leq \lambda/50$).

Example 4.1

Find the radiation resistance of an infinitesimal dipole whose overall length is $l = \lambda/50$.

SOLUTION
Using (4-19)

$$R_r = 80\pi^2 \left(\frac{l}{\lambda} \right)^2 = 80\pi^2 \left(\frac{1}{50} \right)^2 = 0.316 \text{ ohms}$$

Since the radiation resistance of an infinitesimal dipole is about 0.3 ohms, it will present a very large mismatch when connected to practical transmission lines, many of which have characteristic impedances of 50 or 75 ohms. The reflection efficiency (e_r) and hence the overall efficiency (e_t) will be very small.

The reactance of an infinitesimal dipole is capacitive. This can be illustrated by considering the dipole as a flared open-circuited transmission line, as discussed in Section 1.4. Since the input impedance of an open-circuited transmission line a distance $l/2$ from its open end is given by $Z_{\mathrm{in}} = -jZ_0 \cot(\beta l/2)$, where Z_0 is its characteristic impedance, it will always be negative (capacitive) for $l \ll \lambda$.

4.2.3 Near-Field ($kr \ll 1$) Region

The **E**- and **H**-fields for the infinitesimal dipole, as represented by (4-8a)–(4-8b) and (4-10a)–(4-10c), are valid everywhere (except on the source itself). An inspection of these equations will reveal that if $kr \ll 1$ or $r \ll \lambda$ they can be reduced to much simpler forms. For example, the second term within the brackets in (4-8b) and (4-10a) will be larger than the first (unity), so it can be neglected. In (4-10b) the third term within the brackets is more dominant than the second and the second is more dominant than the first. It is clear then that for $kr \ll 1$ the fields can be approximated by

$$E_r \simeq -j\eta \frac{I_0 le^{-jkr}}{2\pi kr^3} \cos\theta \quad \left.\right\} \tag{4-20a}$$

$$E_\theta \simeq -j\eta \frac{I_0 le^{-jkr}}{4\pi kr^3} \sin\theta \quad \left| \quad kr \ll 1 \right. \tag{4-20b}$$

$$E_\phi = H_r = H_\theta = 0 \tag{4-20c}$$

$$H_\phi \simeq \frac{I_0 le^{-jkr}}{4\pi r^2} \sin\theta \tag{4-20d}$$

The E-field components, E_r and E_θ, are in time phase but they are in time phase quadrature with the H-field component H_ϕ. The fields form a standing wave, instead of a traveling wave, and there is no time average power flow associated with them. This is demonstrated by forming the time-average power density as

$$\mathbf{W}_{av} = \tfrac{1}{2}\text{Re}[\mathbf{E} \times \mathbf{H}^*] = \tfrac{1}{2}\text{Re}\left[\hat{a}_r E_\theta H_\phi^* - \hat{a}_\theta E_r H_\phi^*\right] \tag{4-21}$$

which by using (4-20a)–(4-20d) reduces to

$$\mathbf{W}_{av} = \frac{1}{2}\text{Re}\left[-\hat{a}_r j\frac{\eta}{k}\left|\frac{I_0 l}{4\pi}\right|^2 \frac{\sin^2\theta}{r^5} + \hat{a}_\theta j\frac{\eta}{k}\frac{|I_0 l|^2}{8\pi^2}\frac{\sin\theta\cos\theta}{r^5}\right] = 0 \tag{4-22}$$

The condition of $kr \ll 1$ can be satisfied at moderate distances away from the antenna provided that the frequency of operation is very low. Equations (4-20a) and (4-20b) are similar to those of a static electric dipole and (4-20d) to that of a static current element. Thus we usually refer to (4-20a)–(4-20d) as the *quasistationary fields*.

4.2.4 Intermediate-Field ($kr > 1$) Region

As the values of kr begin to increase and become greater than unity, the terms that were dominant for $kr \ll 1$ become smaller and eventually vanish. For moderate values of kr the E-field components lose their in-phase condition and approach time-phase quadrature. Since their magnitude is not the same, in general, they form a rotating vector whose extremity traces an ellipse. This is analogous to the polarization problem except that the vector rotates in a plane parallel to the direction of propagation and is usually referred to as the *cross field*. At these intermediate values of kr, the E_θ and H_ϕ components approach time-phase, which is an indication of the formation of time-average power flow in the outward (radial) direction (radiation phenomenon).

As the values of kr become moderate ($kr > 1$), the field expressions can be approximated again but in a different form. In contrast to the region where $kr \ll 1$, the first term within the brackets in (4-8b) and (4-10a) becomes more dominant and the second term can be neglected. The same is true for (4-10b) where the second and third terms become less dominant than the first. Thus we can write for $kr > 1$

$$E_r \simeq \eta \frac{I_0 l e^{-jkr}}{2\pi r^2} \cos\theta \quad \left.\vphantom{\begin{matrix}\\\\\\\\\end{matrix}}\right\} \tag{4-23a}$$

$$E_\theta \simeq j\eta \frac{kI_0 l e^{-jkr}}{4\pi r} \sin\theta \quad\left.\vphantom{\begin{matrix}\\\\\end{matrix}}\right\} kr>1 \tag{4-23b}$$

$$E_\phi = H_r = H_\theta = 0 \tag{4-23c}$$

$$H_\phi \simeq j \frac{kI_0 l e^{-jkr}}{4\pi r} \sin\theta \tag{4-23d}$$

The total electric field is given by

$$\mathbf{E} = \hat{a}_r E_r + \hat{a}_\theta E_\theta \tag{4-24}$$

whose magnitude can be written as

$$|\mathbf{E}| + \sqrt{|E_r|^2 + |E_\theta|^2} \tag{4-25}$$

4.2.5 Far-Field ($kr \gg 1$) Region

Since (4-23a)–(4-23d) are valid only for values of $kr > 1$ ($r > \lambda$), then E_r will be smaller than E_θ because E_r is inversely proportional to r^2 where E_θ is inversely proportional to r. In a region where $kr \gg 1$, (4-23a)–(4-23d) can be simplified and approximated by

$$E_\theta \simeq j\eta \frac{kI_0 l e^{-jkr}}{4\pi r} \sin\theta \quad\left.\vphantom{\begin{matrix}\\\\\\\end{matrix}}\right\} \tag{4-26a}$$

$$E_r \simeq E_\phi = H_r = H_\theta = 0 \quad\left.\vphantom{\begin{matrix}\\\\\end{matrix}}\right\} kr\gg1 \tag{4-26b}$$

$$H_\phi \simeq j \frac{kI_0 l e^{-jkr}}{4\pi r} \sin\theta \tag{4-26c}$$

The ratio of E_θ to H_ϕ is equal to

$$Z_w = \frac{E_\theta}{H_\phi} \simeq \eta \tag{4-27}$$

where

Z_w = wave impedance

η = intrinsic impedance ($377 \simeq 120\pi$ ohms for free-space)

The **E**- and **H**-field components are perpendicular to each other, transverse to the radial direction of propagation, and the r variations are separable from those of θ and ϕ. The shape of the pattern is not a function of the radial distance r, and the fields form a *T*ransverse *E*lectro*M*agnetic (TEM) wave whose wave impedance is equal to the intrinsic impedance of the medium. As it will become even more evident in later chapters, this relationship is applicable in the far-field region of all antennas of finite dimensions. Equations (4-26a)–(4-26c) can also be derived using the procedure outlined and relationships developed in Section 3.6. This is left as an exercise to the reader (Prob. 4.5).

4.2.6 Directivity

The real power P_{rad} radiated by the dipole was found in Section 4.2.2, as given by (4-16). The same expression can be obtained by first forming the average power density, using (4-26a)–(4-26c). That is,

$$\mathbf{W}_{av} = \frac{1}{2} \operatorname{Re}(\mathbf{E} \times \mathbf{H}^*) = \hat{a}_r \frac{1}{2\eta} |E_\theta|^2 = \hat{a}_r \frac{\eta}{2} \left| \frac{kI_0 l}{4\pi} \right|^2 \frac{\sin^2 \theta}{r^2} \tag{4-28}$$

Integrating (4-28) over a closed sphere of radius r reduces it to (4-16). This is left as an exercise to the reader (Prob. 4.4).

Associated with the average power density of (4-28) is a radiation intensity U which is given by

$$U = r^2 W_{av} = \frac{\eta}{2} \left(\frac{kI_0 l}{4\pi} \right)^2 \sin^2 \theta = \frac{r^2}{2\eta} |E_\theta(r, \theta, \phi)|^2 \tag{4-29}$$

and it conforms with (2-12a). The normalized pattern of (4-29) is shown in Figure 4.2. The maximum value occurs at $\theta = \pi/2$ and it is equal to

$$U_{max} = \frac{\eta}{2} \left(\frac{kI_0 l}{4\pi} \right)^2 \tag{4-30}$$

Using (4-16) and (4-30), the directivity reduces to

$$D_0 = 4\pi \frac{U_{max}}{P_{rad}} = \frac{3}{2} \tag{4-31}$$

and the maximum effective aperture to

$$A_{em} = \left(\frac{\lambda^2}{4\pi} \right) D_0 = \frac{3\lambda^2}{8\pi} \tag{4-32}$$

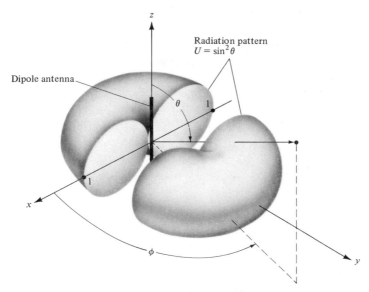

Figure 4.2 Three-dimensional radiation pattern of infinitesimal dipole.

The radiation resistance of the dipole can be obtained by the definition of (4-18). Since the radiated power obtained by integrating (4-28) over a closed sphere is the same as that of (4-16), the radiation resistance using it will also be the same as obtained previously and given by (4-19).

Integrating the complex Poynting vector over a closed sphere, as was done in (4-13), results in the power (real and imaginary) directed in the radial direction. Any transverse components of power density, as given by (4-12b), will not contribute even though they are part of the overall power. Because of this limitation, this method cannot be used to derive the input reactance of the antenna.

4.3 SMALL DIPOLE

The creation of the current distribution on a thin wire was discussed in Section 1.4, and it was illustrated with some examples in Figure 1.12. The radiation properties of an infinitesimal dipole, which is usually taken to have a length $l \leq \lambda/50$, were discussed in the previous section. Its current distribution was assumed to be constant. Although a constant current distribution is not realizable, it is a mathematical quantity that is used to represent actual current distributions of antennas that have been incremented into many small lengths.

A better approximation of the current distribution of wire antennas, whose lengths are usually $\lambda/50 \leq l \leq \lambda/10$, is the triangular variation of Figure 1.12(a). The sinusoidal variations of Figures 1.12(b)–(c) are more accurate representations of the current distribution of any length wire antenna.

The most convenient geometrical arrangement for the analysis of a dipole is usually to have it positioned symmetrically about the origin with its length directed along the z-axis, as shown in Figure 4.3(a). This is not necessary, but it is usually the simplest. The current distribution of a small dipole ($\lambda/50 < l \leq \lambda/10$) is shown in Figure 4.3(b), and it is given by

$$
\mathbf{I}_e(x', y', z') = \begin{cases} \hat{a}_z I_0\left(1 - \frac{2}{l}z'\right), & 0 \leq z' \leq l/2 \\ \hat{a}_z I_0\left(1 + \frac{2}{l}z'\right), & -l/2 \leq z' \leq 0 \end{cases} \tag{4-33}
$$

where $I_0 = $ constant.

Following the procedure established in the previous section, the vector potential of (4-2) can be written using (4-33) as

$$
\mathbf{A}(x, y, z) = \frac{\mu}{4\pi}\left[\hat{a}_z \int_{-l/2}^0 I_0\left(1 + \frac{2}{l}z'\right)\frac{e^{-jkR}}{R}dz' \right.
$$
$$
\left. + \hat{a}_z \int_0^{l/2} I_0\left(1 - \frac{2}{l}z'\right)\frac{e^{-jkR}}{R}dz'\right] \tag{4-34}
$$

Because the overall length of the dipole is very small (usually $l \leq \lambda/10$), the values of R for different values of z' along the length of the wire ($-l/2 \leq z' \leq l/2$) are not much different from r. Thus R can be approximated by $R \simeq r$ throughout the integration path. The maximum phase error in (4-34) by allowing $R = r$ for $\lambda/50 < l \leq \lambda/10$, will be $kl/2 = \pi/10$ rad $= 18°$ for $l = \lambda/10$. Smaller values will occur for the other lengths. As it will be shown in the next section, this amount of phase error is usually considered negligible and has very little effect on the overall radiation characteristics. Performing the integration, (4-34) reduces to

$$
\mathbf{A} = \hat{a}_z A_z = \hat{a}_z \frac{1}{2}\left[\frac{\mu I_0 l e^{-jkr}}{4\pi r}\right] \tag{4-35}
$$

which is one-half of that obtained in the previous section for the infinitesimal dipole and given by (4-4).

The potential function given by (4-35) becomes a more accurate approximation as $kr \to \infty$. This is also the region of most practical concern, and it has been designated as the far-field region. Since the potential function for the triangular distribution is one-half of the corresponding one for the constant (uniform) current distribution, the corresponding fields of the former are one-half of the latter. Thus we can write the **E**- and **H**-fields

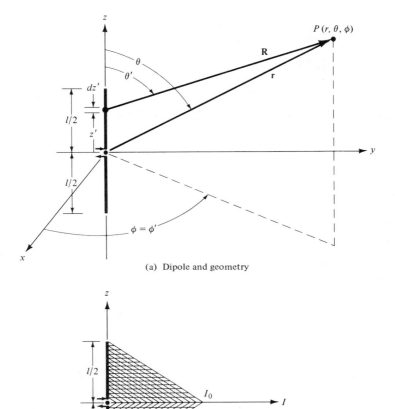

(a) Dipole and geometry

(b) Current distribution

Figure 4.3 Geometrical arrangement of dipole and current distribution.

radiated by a small dipole as

$$E_\theta \simeq j\eta \frac{kI_0le^{-jkr}}{8\pi r}\sin\theta$$ (4-36a)

$$E_r \simeq E_\phi = H_r = H_\theta = 0 \left.\right\} kr \gg 1$$ (4-36b)

$$H_\phi \simeq j\frac{kI_0le^{-jkr}}{8\pi r}\sin\theta$$ (4-36c)

with the wave impedance equal, as before, to (4-27).

Since the directivity of an antenna is controlled by the relative shape of the field or power pattern, the directivity and maximum effective area of this antenna are the same as the ones with the constant current distribution given by (4-31) and (4-32), respectively.

The radiation resistance of the antenna is strongly dependent upon the current distribution. Using the procedure established for the infinitesimal dipole, it can be shown that for the small dipole its radiated power is one-fourth $(\frac{1}{4})$ of (4-18). Thus the radiation resistance reduces to

$$R_r = \frac{2P_{\text{rad}}}{|I_0|^2} = 20\pi^2\left(\frac{l}{\lambda}\right)^2 \tag{4-37}$$

which is also one-fourth $(\frac{1}{4})$ of that obtained for the infinitesimal dipole as given by (4-19). Their relative patterns (shapes) are the same and are shown in Figure 4.2.

4.4 REGION SEPARATION

Before we attempt to solve for the fields radiated by a finite dipole of any length, it would be very desirable to discuss the separation of the space surrounding an antenna into three regions; namely, the *reactive near-field*, *radiating near-field* (*Fresnel*) and the *far-field* (*Fraunhofer*) which were introduced briefly in Section 2.2. This is necessary because for a dipole antenna of any length and any current distribution, it will become increasingly difficult to solve for the fields everywhere. Approximations can be made, especially for the far-field (Fraunhofer) region which is usually the one of most practical concern, to simplify the formulation to yield closed form solutions. The same approximations used to simplify the formulation of the fields radiated by a finite dipole are also used to formulate the fields radiated by most practical antennas. So it will be very important to introduce them properly and understand their implications upon the solution.

The difficulties in obtaining closed form solutions that are valid everywhere for any practical antenna stem from the inability to perform the integration of

$$\mathbf{A}(x, y, z) = \frac{\mu}{4\pi} \int_C \mathbf{I}_e(x', y', z') \frac{e^{-jkR}}{R} dl' \tag{4-38}$$

where

$$R = \sqrt{(x-x')^2 + (y-y')^2 + (z-z')^2} \tag{4-38a}$$

For a finite dipole with sinusoidal current distribution, the integral of (4-38) can be reduced to a closed form that is valid everywhere! This will be shown in Chapter 7. The length R is defined as the distance from any point on the source to the observation point. The integral of (4-38) was used to solve for the fields of infinitesimal and small dipoles in Sections 4.1 and 4.2. However in the first case (infinitesimal dipole) $R=r$ and in the second case (small dipole) R was approximated by r ($R\simeq r$) because the length of the dipole was restricted to be $l\leq\lambda/10$. The major simplification of (4-38) will be in the approximation of R.

A very thin dipole of finite length l is symmetrically positioned about the origin with its length directed along the z-axis, as shown in Figure 4.4(a). Because the wire is assumed to be very thin ($x'=y'=0$), we can write (4-38)

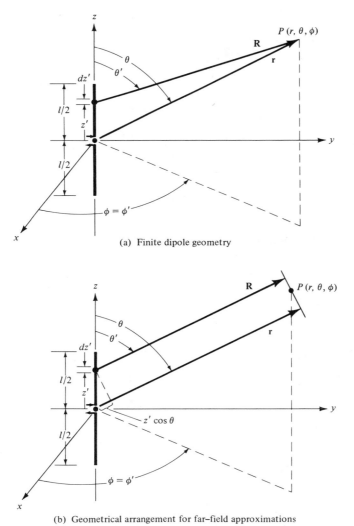

(a) Finite dipole geometry

(b) Geometrical arrangement for far–field approximations

Figure 4.4 Finite dipole geometry and far-field approximations.

as

$$R=\sqrt{(x-x')^2+(y-y')^2+(z-z')^2}=\sqrt{x^2+y^2+(z-z')^2} \qquad (4\text{-}39)$$

which when expanded can be written as

$$R=\sqrt{(x^2+y^2+z^2)+(-2zz'+z'^2)}=\sqrt{r^2+(-2rz'\cos\theta+z'^2)} \quad (4\text{-}40)$$

where

$$r^2=x^2+y^2+z^2 \qquad (4\text{-}40a)$$

$$z=r\cos\theta \qquad (4\text{-}40b)$$

Using the binomial expansion, we can write (4-40) in a series

$$R=r-z'\cos\theta+\frac{1}{r}\left(\frac{z'^2}{2}\sin^2\theta\right)+\frac{1}{r^2}\left(\frac{z'^3}{2}\cos\theta\sin^2\theta\right)+\cdots \qquad (4\text{-}41)$$

whose higher order terms become less significant provided $r\gg z'$.

4.4.1 Far-Field (Fraunhofer) Region

The most convenient simplification of (4-41), other than $R\simeq r$, will be to approximate it by its first two terms, or

$$R\simeq r-z'\cos\theta \qquad (4\text{-}42)$$

The most significant neglected term of (4-41) is the third whose maximum value is

$$\frac{1}{r}\left(\frac{z'^2}{2}\sin^2\theta\right)_{max}=\frac{z'^2}{2r} \qquad \text{when } \theta=\pi/2 \qquad (4\text{-}43)$$

When (4-43) attains its maximum value, the fourth term of (4-41) vanishes because $\theta=\pi/2$. It can be shown that the higher order terms not shown in (4-41) also vanish. Therefore approximating (4-41) by (4-42) introduces a *maximum* error given by (4-43).

It has been shown by many investigators through numerous examples that for most practical antennas, *with overall lengths greater than a wavelength* ($l>\lambda$), a maximum total phase error of $\pi/8$ rad (22.5°) is not very detrimental in their analytical formulation. Using that as a criterion we can write, using (4-43), that the maximum phase error should always be

$$\frac{k(z')^2}{2r}\le\frac{\pi}{8} \qquad (4\text{-}44)$$

which for $-l/2\le z'\le l/2$ reduces to

$$r\ge 2\left(\frac{l^2}{\lambda}\right) \qquad (4\text{-}45)$$

Equation (4-45) simply states that to maintain the maximum phase error of an antenna equal to or less than $\pi/8$ rad (22.5°), the observation

distance r must equal or be greater than $2l^2/\lambda$ where l is the largest*
dimension of the antenna structure. The usual simplification for the far-field
region is to approximate the R in the exponential (e^{-jkR}) of (4-38) by (4-42)
and the R in the denominator of (4-38) by $R \simeq r$. These simplifications are
designated as the far-field approximations and are usually denoted in the
literature as

Far-field Approximations

$$R \simeq r - z' \cos\theta \qquad \text{for phase terms}$$

$$R \simeq r \qquad \text{for amplitude terms} \tag{4-46}$$

provided r satisfies (4-45).

It may be advisable to illustrate the approximation (4-46) geometri-
cally. For $R \simeq r - z' \cos\theta$, where θ is the angle measured from the z-axis, the
radial vectors **R** and **r** must be parallel to each other, as shown in Figure
4.4(b). For any other antenna whose maximum dimension is D, the approximation of (4-46) is valid provided the observations are made at a
distance

$$r \geq 2D^2/\lambda \tag{4-47}$$

For an aperture antenna the maximum dimension is taken to be its
diagonal.

For most practical antennas, whose overall length is large compared to
the wavelength, these are adequate approximations which have been shown
by many investigators through numerous examples to give valid results in
pattern predictions. Some discrepancies are evident in regions of low
intensity (usually below -25 dB). This is illustrated in Figure 2.6 where the
patterns of a paraboloidal antenna for $R = \infty$ and $R = 2D^2/\lambda$ differ at levels
below -25 dB. Allowing R to have a value of $R = 4D^2/\lambda$ gives better
results.

It would seem that the approximation of R in (4-46) for the amplitude
is more severe than that for the phase. However a close observation will
reveal this is not the case. Since the observations are made at a distance
where r is very large, any small error in the approximation of the denominator (amplitude) will not make much difference in the answer. However,
because of the periodic nature of the phase (repeats every 2π rad), it can be
a major fraction of a period. The best way to illustrate it will be to consider
an example.

Example 4.2

For an antenna with an overall length $l = 5\lambda$, the observations are made at
$r = 60\lambda$. Find the errors in phase and amplitude using (4-46).

*Provided the overall length (l) of the antenna is large compared to the wavelength [see IEEE
Standard Definitions of Terms for Antennas, IEEE Std (45-1973)].

SOLUTION
For $\theta=90°$, $z'=2.5\lambda$, and $r=10\lambda$, (4-40) reduces to

$$R_1=\lambda\sqrt{(60)^2+(2.5)^2}=60.052\lambda$$

and (4-46) to

$$R_2=r=60\lambda$$

Therefore the phase difference is

$$\Delta\phi=k\,\Delta R=\frac{2\pi}{\lambda}(R_1-R_2)=2\pi(0.052)=0.327\text{ rad}=18.74°$$

which in an appreciable fraction ($\simeq\frac{1}{20}$) of a full period (360°).
The difference of the inverse values of R is

$$\frac{1}{R_2}-\frac{1}{R_1}=\frac{1}{\lambda}\left(\frac{1}{60}-\frac{1}{60.052}\right)=\frac{1.44\times10^{-5}}{\lambda}$$

which should always be a very small value.

4.4.2 Radiating Near-Field (Fresnel) Region

If the observation point is chosen to be smaller than $r=2l^2/\lambda$, the maximum phase error by the approximation of (4-46) is greater than $\pi/8$ rad (22.5°) which may be undesirable in many applications. If it is necessary to choose observation distances smaller than (4-45), another term (the third) in the series solution of (4-41) must be retained to maintain a maximum phase error of $\pi/8$ rad (22.5°). Doing this, the infinite series of (4-41) can be approximated by

$$R\simeq r-z'\cos\theta+\frac{1}{r}\left(\frac{z'^2}{2}\sin^2\theta\right) \tag{4-48}$$

The most significant term that we are neglecting from the infinite series of (4-41) is the fourth. To find the maximum phase error introduced by the omission of the next most significant term, the angle θ at which this occurs must be found. To do this, the neglected term is differentiated with respect to θ and the result is set equal to zero. Thus

$$\frac{\partial}{\partial\theta}\left[\frac{1}{r^2}\left(\frac{z'^3}{2}\cos\theta\sin^2\theta\right)\right]=\frac{z'^3}{2r^2}\sin\theta[-\sin^2\theta+2\cos^2\theta]=0 \tag{4-49}$$

The angle $\theta=0$ is not chosen as a solution because for that value the fourth term is equal to zero. In other words, $\theta=0$ gives the minimum error. The maximum error occurs when the second term of (4-49) vanishes; that is when

$$[-\sin^2\theta+2\cos^2\theta]_{\theta=\theta_1}=0 \tag{4-50}$$

or

$$\theta_1=\tan^{-1}(\pm\sqrt{2}) \tag{4-50a}$$

If the maximum phase error is allowed to be equal or less than $\pi/8$ rad, the distance r at which this occurs can be found from

$$\frac{kz'^3}{2r^2}\cos\theta\sin^2\theta\bigg|_{\substack{z'=l/2\\\theta=\tan^{-1}\sqrt{2}}}=\frac{\pi}{\lambda}\frac{l^3}{8r^2}\left(\frac{1}{\sqrt{3}}\right)\left(\frac{2}{3}\right)=\frac{\pi}{12\sqrt{3}}\left(\frac{l^3}{\lambda r^2}\right)\leq\frac{\pi}{8}$$

(4-51)

which reduces to

$$r^2\geq\frac{2}{3\sqrt{3}}\left(\frac{l^3}{\lambda}\right)=0.385\left(\frac{l^3}{\lambda}\right)$$

(4-52)

or

$$r\geq0.62\sqrt{l^3/\lambda}$$

(4-52a)

A value of r greater than that of (4-52a) will lead to an error less than $\pi/8$ rad (22.5°). Thus the region where the first three terms of (4-41) are significant, and the omission of the fourth introduces a maximum phase error of $\pi/8$ rad (22.5°), is defined by

$$2l^2/\lambda>r\geq0.62\sqrt{l^3/\lambda}$$

(4-53)

where l is the length of the antenna. This region is designated as *radiating near-field* because the radiating power density is greater than the reactive power density and the field pattern (its shape) is a function of the radial distance r. This region is also called the *Fresnel region* because the field expressions in this region reduce to Fresnel integrals.

The discussion has centered around the finite length antenna of length l with the observation considered to be a point source. If the antenna is not a line source, l in (4-53) must represent the largest dimension of the antenna (which for an aperture is the diagonal). Also if the transmitting antenna has maximum length l_t, and the receiving antenna has maximum length l_r, then the *sum of* l_t *and* l_r must be used in place of l in (4-53).

The boundaries for separating the far-field (Fraunhofer), the radiating near-field (Fresnel), and the reactive near-field regions are not very rigid. Other criteria have also been established [1] but the ones introduced here are the most "popular." Also the fields, as the boundaries from one region to the other are crossed, do not change abruptly but undergo a very gradual transition.

4.4.3 Reactive Near-Field Region

If the distance of observation is smaller than the inner boundary of the Fresnel region, this region is usually designated as *reactive near-field* with inner and outer boundaries defined by

$$0.62\sqrt{l^3/\lambda}>r>0$$

(4-54)

where l is the length of the antenna. In this region the reactive power density predominates, as was demonstrated in Section 4.1 for the infinitesimal dipole.

In summary, the space surrounding an antenna is divided into three regions whose boundaries are determined by

$$\text{reactive near-field } \left[0.62\sqrt{D^3/\lambda} > r > 0\right] \tag{4-55a}$$

$$\text{radiating near-field (Fresnel) } \left[2D^2/\lambda > r \geq 0.62\sqrt{D^3/\lambda}\,\right] \tag{4-55b}$$

$$\text{far-field (Fraunhofer) } \left[\infty \geq r \geq 2D^2/\lambda\right] \tag{4-55c}$$

where D is the largest dimension of the antenna ($D=l$ for a wire antenna).

4.5 FINITE LENGTH DIPOLE

The techniques that were developed previously can also be used to analyze the radiation characteristics of a linear dipole of any length. To reduce the mathematical complexities, it will be assumed in this chapter that the dipole has a negligible diameter (ideally zero). This is a good approximation provided the diameter is considerably smaller than the operating wavelength. Finite radii dipoles will be analyzed in Chapters 7 and 8.

4.5.1 Current Distribution

For a very thin dipole (ideally zero diameter), the current distribution can be written, to a good approximation, as

$$\mathbf{I}_e(x', y', z') = \begin{cases} \hat{a}_z I_0 \sin\left[k\left(\dfrac{l}{2} - z'\right)\right], & 0 \leq z' \leq l/2 \\[2mm] \hat{a}_z I_0 \sin\left[k\left(\dfrac{l}{2} + z'\right)\right], & -l/2 \leq z' \leq 0 \end{cases} \tag{4-56}$$

This distribution assumes that the antenna is *center-fed and the current vanishes at the end points* ($z' = \pm l/2$). Experimentally it has been verified that the current in a center-fed wire antenna has sinusoidal form with nulls at the end points. For $l = \lambda/2$ and $\lambda/2 < l < \lambda$ the current distribution of (4-56) is shown plotted in Figures 1.12(b) and 1.12(c), respectively. The geometry of the antenna is that shown in Figure 4.4.

4.5.2 Radiated Fields: Element Factor, Space Factor, and Pattern Multiplication

For the current distribution of (4-56) it will be shown in Chapter 7 that closed form expressions for the **E**- and **H**-fields can be obtained which are valid in all regions (any observation point except on the source itself). In general, however, this is not the case. Usually we are limited to the far-field region, because of the mathematical complications provided in the integration of the vector potential **A** of (4-2). Since closed form solutions, which are valid everywhere, cannot be obtained for many antennas, the observations will be restricted to the far-field region. This will be done first in order to illustrate the procedure. In some cases, even in that region it may become impossible to obtain closed form solutions.

The finite dipole antenna of Figure 4.4 is subdivided into a number of infinitesimal dipoles of length $\Delta z'$. As the number of subdivisions is increased, each infinitesimal dipole approaches a length dz'. For an infinitesimal dipole of length dz' positioned along the z-axis at z', the electric and magnetic field components in the far-field are given, using (4-26a)–(4-26c), as

$$dE_\theta \simeq j\eta \frac{kI_e(x', y', z')e^{-jkR}}{4\pi R} \sin\theta \, dz' \tag{4-57a}$$

$$dE_r \simeq dE_\phi = dH_r = dH_\theta = 0 \tag{4-57b}$$

$$dH_\phi \simeq j\frac{kI_e(x', y', z')e^{-jkR}}{4\pi R} \sin\theta \, dz' \tag{4-57c}$$

where R is given by (4-39) or (4-40).

Using the far-field approximations given by (4-46), (4-57a) can be written as

$$dE_\theta \simeq j\eta \frac{kI_e(x', y', z')e^{-jkr}}{4\pi r} \sin\theta e^{+jkz'\cos\theta} \, dz' \tag{4-58}$$

Summing the contributions from all the infinitesimal elements, the summation reduces, in the limit, to an integration. Thus

$$E_\theta = \int_{-l/2}^{+l/2} dE_\theta = j\eta \frac{ke^{-jkr}}{4\pi r} \sin\theta \left[\int_{-l/2}^{+l/2} I_e(x', y', z')e^{jkz'\cos\theta} \, dz' \right]$$

$$\tag{4-58a}$$

The factor outside the brackets is designated as the *element factor* and that within the brackets as the *space factor*. For this antenna, the element factor is equal to the field of a unit length infinitesimal dipole located at a reference point (the origin). In general, the element factor depends on the type of current and its direction of flow while the space factor is a function of the current distribution along the source.

The total field of the antenna is equal to the product of the element and space factors. This is referred to as *pattern multiplication* for continuously distributed sources, and it can be written as

$$\boxed{\text{total field} = (\text{element factor}) \times (\text{space factor})} \tag{4-59}$$

The pattern multiplication for continuous sources is analogous to the pattern multiplication of (6-5) for discrete-element antennas (arrays).

For the current distribution of (4-56), (4-58a) can be written as

$$
E_\theta \simeq j\eta \frac{kI_0 e^{-jkr}}{4\pi r} \sin\theta \left[\int_{-l/2}^{0} \sin\left[k\left(\frac{l}{2}+z'\right)\right] e^{+jkz'\cos\theta}\, dz' \right.
$$

$$
\left. + \int_{0}^{+l/2} \sin\left[k\left(\frac{l}{2}-z'\right)\right] e^{+jkz'\cos\theta}\, dz' \right] \tag{4-60}
$$

Each one of the integrals in (4-60) can be integrated using

$$
\int e^{\alpha x} \sin(\beta x + \gamma)\, dx = \frac{e^{\alpha x}}{\alpha^2 + \beta^2} \left[\alpha \sin(\beta x + \gamma) - \beta \cos(\beta x + \gamma) \right] \tag{4-61}
$$

where

$$
\alpha = jk\cos\theta \tag{4-61a}
$$

$$
\beta = \pm k \tag{4-61b}
$$

$$
\gamma = kl/2 \tag{4-61c}
$$

After some mathematical manipulations, (4-60) takes the form of

$$
E_\theta \simeq j\eta \frac{I_0 e^{-jkr}}{2\pi r} \left[\frac{\cos\left(\frac{kl}{2}\cos\theta\right) - \cos\left(\frac{kl}{2}\right)}{\sin\theta} \right] \tag{4-62a}
$$

In a similar manner, or by using the established relationship between the E_θ and H_ϕ in the far-field as given by (3-58b) or (4-27), the total H_ϕ component can be written as

$$
H_\phi \simeq \frac{E_\theta}{\eta} \simeq j \frac{I_0 e^{-jkr}}{2\pi r} \left[\frac{\cos\left(\frac{kl}{2}\cos\theta\right) - \cos\left(\frac{kl}{2}\right)}{\sin\theta} \right] \tag{4-62b}
$$

4.5.3 Power Density, Radiation Intensity, and Radiation Resistance

For the dipole, the average Poynting vector can be written as

$$
\mathbf{W}_{av} = \frac{1}{2}\,\mathrm{Re}[\mathbf{E}\times\mathbf{H}^*] = \frac{1}{2}\,\mathrm{Re}\left[\hat{a}_\theta E_\theta \times \hat{a}_\phi H_\phi^*\right] = \frac{1}{2}\,\mathrm{Re}\left[\hat{a}_\theta E_\theta \times \hat{a}_\phi \frac{E_\theta^*}{\eta}\right]
$$

$$
\mathbf{W}_{av} = \hat{a}_r W_{av} = \hat{a}_r \frac{1}{2\eta}|E_\theta|^2 = \eta \frac{|I_0|^2}{8\pi^2 r^2} \left[\frac{\cos\left(\frac{kl}{2}\cos\theta\right) - \cos\left(\frac{kl}{2}\right)}{\sin\theta} \right]^2 \tag{4-63}
$$

and the radiation intensity as

$$
U = r^2 W_{av} = \eta \frac{|I_0|^2}{8\pi^2} \left[\frac{\cos\left(\frac{kl}{2}\cos\theta\right) - \cos\left(\frac{kl}{2}\right)}{\sin\theta} \right]^2 \tag{4-64}
$$

The normalized (to 0 dB) elevation power patterns, as given by (4-64), for $l = \lambda/4$, $\lambda/2$, $3\lambda/4$, and λ are shown plotted in Figure 4.5. The current distribution of each is given by (4-56). The power patterns for an infinitesimal dipole $l \ll \lambda$ ($U \sim \sin^2 \theta$) is also included for comparison. As the length of the antenna increases, the beam becomes narrower. Because of that, the directivity should also increase with length. It is found that the 3-dB

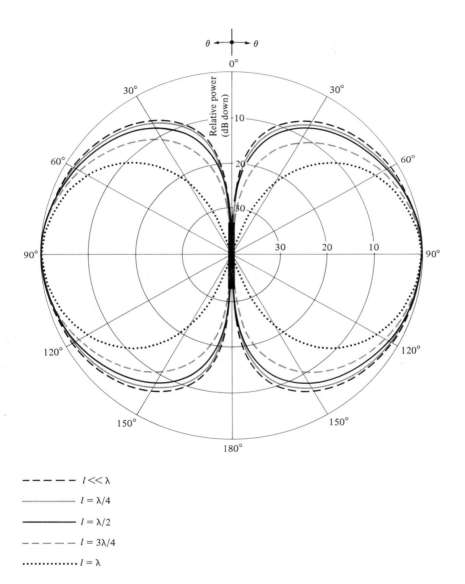

Figure 4.5 Elevation plane amplitude patterns for a thin dipole with sinusoidal current distribution ($l = \lambda/4, \lambda/2, 3\lambda/4, \lambda$).

beamwidth of each is equal to

$l \ll \lambda$ 3-dB beamwidth $= 90°$

$l = \lambda/4$ 3-dB beamwidth $= 87°$

$l = \lambda/2$ 3-dB beamwidth $= 78°$ (4-65)

$l = 3\lambda/4$ 3-dB beamwidth $= 64°$

$l = \lambda$ 3-dB beamwidth $= 47.8°$

As the length of the dipole increases beyond one wavelength ($l > \lambda$), the number of lobes begin to increase. The normalized power pattern for a dipole with $l = 1.25\lambda$ is shown in Figure 4.6. The current distribution for the dipoles with $l = \lambda/4, \lambda/2, \lambda, 3\lambda/2$, and 2λ, as given by (4-56), is shown in Figure 4.7.

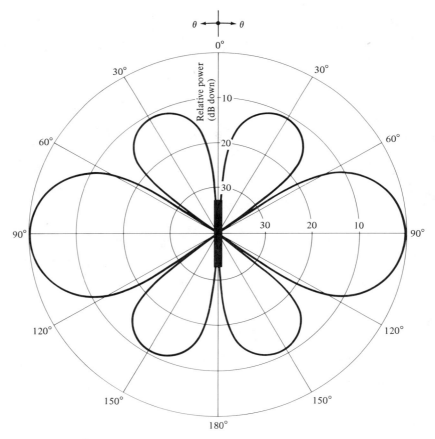

Figure 4.6 Elevation plane amplitude pattern for a thin dipole of $l = 1.25\lambda$ and sinusoidal current distribution.

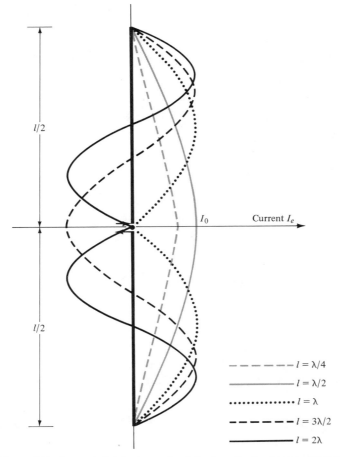

Figure 4.7 Current distributions along the length of a linear wire antenna.

To find the total power radiated, the average Poynting vector of (4-63) is integrated over a sphere of radius r. Thus

$$P_{rad} = \oiint_S \mathbf{W}_{av} \cdot d\mathbf{s} = \int_0^{2\pi} \int_0^\pi \hat{a}_r W_{av} \cdot \hat{a}_r r^2 \sin\theta \, d\theta \, d\phi$$

$$= \int_0^{2\pi} \int_0^\pi W_{av} r^2 \sin\theta \, d\theta \, d\phi \qquad (4\text{-}66)$$

Using (4-63), we can write (4-66) as

$$P_{rad} = \int_0^{2\pi} \int_0^\pi W_{av} r^2 \sin\theta \, d\theta \, d\phi$$

$$= \eta \frac{|I_0|^2}{4\pi} \int_0^\pi \frac{\left[\cos\left(\dfrac{kl}{2} \cos\theta \right) - \cos\left(\dfrac{kl}{2} \right) \right]^2}{\sin\theta} \, d\theta \qquad (4\text{-}67)$$

After some extensive mathematical manipulations, it can be shown that (4-67) reduces to

$$P_{rad} = \eta \frac{|I_0|^2}{4\pi} \{ C + \ln(kl) - C_i(kl) + \tfrac{1}{2}\sin(kl)[S_i(2kl) - 2S_i(kl)]$$
$$+ \tfrac{1}{2}\cos(kl)[C + \ln(kl/2) + C_i(2kl) - 2C_i(kl)] \} \qquad (4\text{-}68)$$

where $C = 0.5772$ (Euler's constant) and $C_i(x)$ and $S_i(x)$ are the cosine and sine integrals (see Appendix III) given by

$$C_i(x) = -\int_x^\infty \frac{\cos y}{y} dy = \int_\infty^x \frac{\cos y}{y} dy \qquad (4\text{-}68a)$$

$$S_i(x) = \int_0^x \frac{\sin y}{y} dy \qquad (4\text{-}68b)$$

The derivation of (4-68) from (4-67) is assigned as a problem at the end of the chapter (Prob. 4.10). $C_i(x)$ is related to $C_{in}(x)$ by

$$C_{in}(x) = \ln(\gamma x) - C_i(x) = \ln(\gamma) + \ln(x) - C_i(x)$$
$$= 0.5772 + \ln(x) - C_i(x) \qquad (4\text{-}69)$$

where

$$C_{in}(x) = \int_0^x \left(\frac{1 - \cos y}{y} \right) dy \qquad (4\text{-}69a)$$

$C_i(x)$, $S_i(x)$ and $C_{in}(x)$ are tabulated in Appendix III.

The radiation resistance can be obtained using (4-18) and (4-68) and can be written as

$$R_r = \frac{2P_{rad}}{|I_0|^2} = \frac{\eta}{2\pi} \{ C + \ln(kl) - C_i(kl) + \tfrac{1}{2}\sin(kl)$$
$$\times [S_i(2kl) - 2S_i(kl)] + \tfrac{1}{2}\cos(kl)$$
$$\times [C + \ln(kl/2) + C_i(2kl) - 2C_i(kl)] \} \qquad (4\text{-}70)$$

Shown in Figure 4.8 is a plot of R_r as a function of l (in wavelengths) when the antenna is radiating into free-space ($\eta \simeq 120\pi$).

4.5.4 Directivity

As was illustrated in Figure 4.5, the radiation pattern of a dipole becomes more directional as its length increases. When the overall length is greater than about one wavelength, the number of lobes increases and the antenna

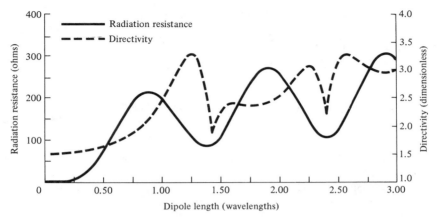

Figure 4.8 Radiation resistance and directivity of a thin dipole with sinusoidal current distribution.

loses its directional properties. The parameter that is used as a "figure-of-merit" for the directional properties of the antenna is the directivity which was defined in Section 2.5.

The directivity was defined mathematically by (2-22), or

$$D_0 = 4\pi \frac{F(\theta, \phi)|_{max}}{\int_0^{2\pi} \int_0^{\pi} F(\theta, \phi) \sin\theta \, d\theta \, d\phi} \tag{4-71}$$

where $F(\theta, \phi)$ is related to the radiation intensity U by (2-18), or

$$U = U_0 F(\theta, \phi) \tag{4-72}$$

From (4-64), the dipole antenna of length l has

$$F(\theta, \phi) = F(\theta) = \left[\frac{\cos\left(\frac{kl}{2}\cos\theta\right) - \cos\left(\frac{kl}{2}\right)}{\sin\theta} \right]^2 \tag{4-73}$$

and

$$U_0 = \eta \frac{|I_0|^2}{8\pi^2} \tag{4-73a}$$

Because the pattern is not a function of ϕ, (4-71) reduces to

$$D_0 = \frac{2F(\theta)|_{max}}{\int_0^{\pi} F(\theta) \sin\theta \, d\theta} \tag{4-74}$$

Equation (4-74) can be written, using (4-67), (4-68), and (4-73), as

$$D_0 = \frac{2F(\theta)|_{max}}{Q} \tag{4-75}$$

where

$$Q = \{ C + \ln(kl) + C_i(kl) + \tfrac{1}{2}\sin(kl)[S_i(2kl) - 2S_i(kl)] \\ + \tfrac{1}{2}\cos(kl)[C + \ln(kl/2) + C_i(2kl) - 2C_i(kl)] \} \tag{4-75a}$$

The maximum value of $F(\theta)$ varies and depends upon the length of the dipole.

Values of the directivity, as given by (4-75) and (4-75a), have been obtained for $0 \le \lambda \le 3\lambda$ and are shown plotted in Figure 4.8. The corresponding values of the maximum effective aperture are related to the directivity by

$$A_{em} = \frac{\lambda^2}{4\pi} D_0 \tag{4-76}$$

4.5.5 Input Resistance

In Section 2.13 the input impedance was defined as "the ratio of the voltage to current at a pair of terminals or the ratio of the appropriate components of the electric to magnetic fields at a point." The real part of the input impedance was defined as the input resistance which for a lossless antenna reduces to the radiation resistance. It is through the radiation resistance that the antenna radiates real power.

In Section 4.1, the radiation resistance of an infinitesimal dipole was derived using the definition of (4-18). The radiation resistance of a dipole of length l with sinusoidal current distribution, of the form given by (4-56), is expressed by (4-70). By this definition, the radiation resistance is referred to the maximum current which for some lengths ($l = \lambda/4$, $3\lambda/4$, λ, etc.) does not occur at the input terminals of the antenna (see Figure 4.7). To refer the radiation resistance to the input terminals of the antenna, the antenna itself is first assumed to be lossless ($R_L = 0$). Then the power at the input terminals is equated to the power at the current maximum.

Referring to Figure 4.9, we can write

$$\frac{|I_{in}|^2}{2} R_{in} = \frac{|I_0|^2}{2} R_r \tag{4-77}$$

or

$$R_{in} = \left[\frac{I_0}{I_{in}} \right]^2 R_r \tag{4-77a}$$

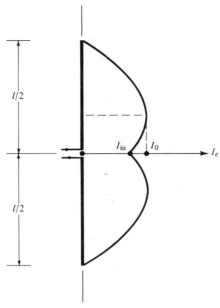

Figure 4.9 Current distribution of a linear wire antenna when current maximum does not occur at the input terminals.

where

R_{in} = radiation resistance at input (feed) terminals

R_r = radiation resistance at current maximum Eq. (4-70)

I_0 = current maximum

I_{in} = current at input terminals

For a dipole of length l, the current at the input terminals (I_{in}) is related to the current maximum (I_0), referring to Figure 4.9, by

$$I_{in} = I_0 \sin\left(\frac{kl}{2}\right) \qquad (4\text{-}78)$$

Thus the input radiation resistance of (4-77a) can be written as

$$\boxed{R_{in} = \frac{R_r}{\sin^2\left(\dfrac{kl}{2}\right)}} \qquad (4\text{-}79)$$

To compute the radiation resistance (in ohms), directivity (dimensionless and in dB), and input resistance (in ohms) for a dipole of length l, a FORTRAN computer program has been developed. The program is based on the definitions of each as given by (4-70), (4-71), and (4-79). The radiated power P_{rad} is computed by numerically integrating (over a closed sphere) the radiation intensity of (4-72)–(4-73a). The listing of the program is included at the end of this chapter. The length of the dipole (in wavelengths) must be punched in a data card, according to the FORMAT of the READ statement in the program.

When the overall length of the antenna is a multiple of λ (i.e., $l = n\lambda, n = 1, 2, 3, \ldots$), it is apparent from (4-56) and from Figure 4.7 that $I_{in} = 0$. That is,

$$I_{in} = I_0 \sin\left[k\left(\frac{l}{2} \pm z'\right)\right]\Bigg|_{\substack{z'=0 \\ l=n\lambda, n=0,1,2,\ldots}} = 0 \qquad (4\text{-}80)$$

which indicates that the radiation resistance at the input terminals, as given by (4-77a) or (4-79) is infinite. In practice this is not the case because the current distribution does not follow an exact sinusoidal distribution, especially at the feed point. It has, however, very high values. Two of the primary factors which contribute to the nonsinusoidal current distribution on an actual wire antenna are the nonzero radius of the wire and finite gap spacing at the terminals.

4.5.6 Finite Feed Gap

To analytically account for a nonzero current at the feed point for antennas with a finite gap at the terminals, Schelkunoff and Friis [2] have changed the current of (4-56) by including a quadrature term in the distribution. The additional term is inserted to take into account the effects of radiation on the antenna current distribution. In other words, once the antenna is excited by the "ideal" current distribution of (4-56), electric and magnetic fields are generated which in turn disturb the "ideal" current distribution. This reaction is included by modifying (4-56) to

$$\mathbf{I}_e(x', y', z') = \begin{cases} \hat{a}_z I_0 \sin\left[k\left(\frac{l}{2} - z'\right)\right] + jpI_0\left[\cos(kz') - \cos\left(\frac{k}{2}l\right)\right], \\ \qquad\qquad\qquad\qquad\qquad\qquad\qquad 0 \le z' \le l/2 \\ \hat{a}_z I_0 \sin\left[k\left(\frac{l}{2} + z'\right)\right] + jpI_0\left[\cos(kz') - \cos\left(\frac{k}{2}l\right)\right], \\ \qquad\qquad\qquad\qquad\qquad\qquad\qquad -l/2 \le z' \le 0 \end{cases}$$

$$(4\text{-}81)$$

where p is a coefficient that is dependent upon the overall length of the antenna and the gap spacing at the terminals. The values of p become smaller as the radius of the wire and the gap decrease.

When $l = \lambda/2$,

$$\mathbf{I}_e(x', y', z') = \hat{a}_z I_0(1 + jp)\cos(kz') \qquad 0 \le |z'| \le \lambda/4 \qquad (4\text{-}82)$$

and for $l = \lambda$

$$\mathbf{I}_e(x', y', z') = \begin{cases} \hat{a}_z I_0 \{ \sin(kz') + jp[1 + \cos(kz')] \} & 0 \leq z' \leq \lambda/2 \\ \hat{a}_z I_0 \{ -\sin(kz') + jp[1 + \cos(kz')] \} & -\lambda/2 < z' < 0 \end{cases}$$

(4-83)

Thus for $l = \lambda/2$ the shape of the current is not changed while for $l = \lambda$ it is modified by the second term which is more dominant for small values of z'.

It has been shown by Schelkunoff and Friis that for a full wavelength dipole ($l = \lambda$), the coefficient p is given by

$$p = \frac{199.1}{4Z_0}$$

(4-84)

which is more valid when the gap spacing at the terminals and the radius of the wire are small. The parameter Z_0 is the characteristic impedance of the transmission line attached to the antenna terminals. For $Z_0 = 200$ and 400 ohms, the current distributions as given by the first term in (4-83), and by the two terms of (4-83) with (4-84) are shown listed in Table 4.1 and plotted in Figure 4.10. It is evident that the largest deviations occur near the input (feed) terminals of the antenna. Using the modified current distribution which includes both terms of (4-83) leads to a noninfinite radiation resistance at the input (feed) terminals of the full wavelength antenna.

A straightforward analytical formulation that accounts for the finite gap at the feed as well as the radius of the wire, for any length l, will be presented in Chapter 7, Section 7.5. The technique is an integral formulation involving numerical computations which can be performed efficiently.

Table 4.1 TABULATED VALUES OF CURRENT DISTRIBUTIONS FOR FULL WAVELENGTH DIPOLE EXHIBITING IN-PHASE TERM, QUADRATURE TERM, AND MAGNITUDE

		$Z_0 = 200$		$Z_0 = 400$	
z'	$\sin(kz')$ IN-PHASE	$p(1 + \cos kz')$ QUADRATURE	$\lvert I_e \rvert / I_0$ MAGNITUDE	$p(1 + \cos kz')$ QUADRATURE	$\lvert I_e \rvert / I_0$ MAGNITUDE
0	0	0.498	0.498	0.249	0.249
$\pm\lambda/16$	0.383	0.479	0.613	0.239	0.451
$\pm\lambda/8$	0.707	0.425	0.825	0.212	0.738
$\pm 3\lambda/16$	0.924	0.344	0.986	0.172	0.940
$\pm\lambda/4$	1.000	0.249	1.031	0.124	1.007
$\pm 5\lambda/16$	0.924	0.154	0.936	0.077	0.927
$\pm 3\lambda/8$	0.707	0.073	0.711	0.036	0.708
$\pm 7\lambda/16$	0.383	0.019	0.383	0.009	0.383
$\pm\lambda/2$	0	0	0	0	0

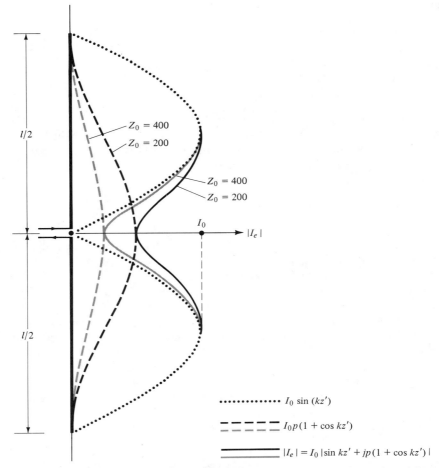

Figure 4.10 Current distribution for full wavelength dipole exhibiting in-phase term (•••••), quadrature term (– – –), and total magnitude (———).

4.6 HALF-WAVELENGTH DIPOLE

One of the most commonly used antennas is the half-wavelength ($l = \lambda/2$) dipole. Because its radiation resistance is 73 ohms, which is very near the 75-ohm characteristic impedance of some transmission lines, its matching to the line is simplified especially at resonance. Because of its wide acceptance in practice, a few pages will be devoted to probe its radiation characteristics.

The electric and magnetic field components of a half-wavelength dipole can be obtained from (4-62a) and (4-62b) by letting $l = \lambda/2$. Doing this, they reduce to

$$E_\theta \simeq j\eta \frac{I_0 e^{-jkr}}{2\pi r} \left[\frac{\cos\left(\frac{\pi}{2}\cos\theta\right)}{\sin\theta} \right]$$

(4-85)

$$H_\phi \simeq j \frac{I_0 e^{-jkr}}{2\pi r} \left[\frac{\cos\left(\frac{\pi}{2}\cos\theta\right)}{\sin\theta} \right]$$

(4-86)

In turn, the time-average power density and radiation intensity can be written, respectively, as

$$W_{av} = \eta \frac{|I_0|^2}{8\pi^2 r^2} \left[\frac{\cos^2\left(\frac{\pi}{2}\cos\theta\right)}{\sin^2\theta} \right]$$

(4-87)

and

$$U = r^2 W_{av} = \eta \frac{|I_0|^2}{8\pi^2} \left[\frac{\cos^2\left(\frac{\pi}{2}\cos\theta\right)}{\sin^2\theta} \right]$$

(4-88)

which are shown plotted in Figure 4.5.

The total power radiated can be obtained as a special case of (4-67), or

$$P_{rad} = \eta \frac{|I_0|^2}{4\pi} \int_0^\pi \frac{\cos^2\left(\frac{\pi}{2}\cos\theta\right)}{\sin\theta} d\theta$$

(4-89)

which when integrated reduces, as a special case of (4-68), to

$$P_{rad} = \eta \frac{|I_0|^2}{8\pi} \int_0^{2\pi} \left(\frac{1-\cos y}{y} \right) dy = \eta \frac{|I_0|^2}{8\pi} C_{in}(2\pi)$$

(4-90)

By the definition of $C_{in}(x)$, as given by (4-69), $C_{in}(2\pi)$ is equal to

$$C_{in}(2\pi) = 0.5772 + \ln(2\pi) - C_i(2\pi) = 0.5772 + 1.838 - (-0.02) \simeq 2.435$$

(4-91)

where $C_i(2\pi)$ is obtained from the tables in Appendix III.

Using (4-88), (4-90), and (4-91), the directivity of the half-wavelength dipole reduces to

$$D_0 = 4\pi \frac{U_{max}}{P_{rad}} = 4\pi \frac{U|_{\theta=\pi/2}}{P_{rad}} = \frac{4}{C_{in}(2\pi)} = \frac{4}{2.435} \simeq 1.643$$

(4-92)

The corresponding maximum effective area is equal to

$$A_{em} = \frac{\lambda^2}{4\pi} D_0 = \frac{\lambda^2}{4\pi}(1.643) \simeq 0.13\lambda^2 \qquad (4\text{-}93)$$

and the radiation resistance, for a free-space medium ($\eta \simeq 120\pi$) is given by

$$R_r = \frac{2P_{rad}}{|I_0|^2} = \frac{\eta}{4\pi} C_{in}(2\pi) = 30(2.435) \simeq 73 \qquad (4\text{-}94)$$

The radiation resistance of (4-94) is also the radiation resistance at the input terminals (input resistance) since the current maximum for a dipole of $l = \lambda/2$ occurs at the input terminals (see Figure 4.7). As it will be shown in Chapter 7, the imaginary part (reactance) associated with the input impedance of a dipole is a function of its length (for $l = \lambda/2$, it is equal to $j42.5$). Thus the total input impedance for $l = \lambda/2$ is equal to $Z_{in} = 73 + j42.5$. To reduce the imaginary part of the input impedance to zero, the antenna is matched or reduced in length until the reactance vanishes. The latter is most commonly used in practice for half-wavelength dipoles.

4.7 LINEAR ELEMENTS NEAR OR ON INFINITE PLANE CONDUCTORS

Thus far we have considered the radiation characteristics of antennas radiating into an unbounded medium. The presence of an obstacle, especially when it is near the radiating element, can significantly alter the overall radiation properties of the antenna system. In practice the most common obstacle that is always present, even in the absence of anything else, is the ground. Any energy from the radiating element directed toward the ground undergoes a reflection. The amount of reflected energy and its direction are controlled by the geometry and constitutive parameters of the ground.

In general, the ground is a lossy medium ($\sigma \neq 0$) whose effective conductivity increases with frequency. Therefore it should be expected to act as a very good conductor above a certain frequency, depending primarily upon its moisture content. To simplify the analysis, it will first be assumed that the ground is a perfect electric conductor, flat, and infinite in extent. The effects of finite conductivity and earth curvature will be incorporated later. The same procedure can also be used to investigate the characteristics of any radiating element near any other infinite, flat, perfect electric conductor. Although infinite structures are not realistic, the developed procedures can be used to simulate very large (electrically) obstacles. The effects that finite dimensions have on the radiation properties of a radiating element can be conveniently accounted for by the use of the Geometrical Theory of Diffraction (Chapter 11, Section 11.9) and/or the Moment Method (Chapter 7, Section 7.5).

4.7.1 Image Theory

To analyze the performance of an antenna near an infinite plane conductor, virtual sources (images) will be introduced to account for the reflections. As the name implies, these are not real sources but imaginary ones, which when combined with the real sources, form an equivalent system. For analysis purposes only, the equivalent system gives the same radiated field above the conductor as the actual system itself. Below the conductor, the equivalent system does not give the correct field. However, in this region the field is zero and there is no need for the equivalent.

To begin the discussion, let us assume that a vertical electric dipole is placed a distance h above an infinite, flat, perfect electric conductor as shown in Figure 4.11(a). The arrow indicates the polarity of the source. Energy from the actual source is radiated in all directions in a manner determined by its unbounded medium directional properties. For an observation point P_1, there is a direct wave. In addition, a wave from the actual source radiated toward point R_1 of the interface will undergo a reflection. The direction is determined by the law of reflection ($\theta_1{}^i = \theta_1{}^r$) which assures that the energy in homogeneous media travels in straight lines along the shortest paths. This wave will pass through the observation point P_1. By extending its actual path below the interface, it will seem to originate from a virtual source positioned a distance h below the boundary. For another observation point P_2 the point of reflection is R_2, but the virtual source is the same as before. The same is concluded for all other points above the interface.

The amount of reflection is generally determined by the respective constitutive parameters of the media below and above the interface. For a perfect electric conductor below the interface, the incident wave is completely reflected and the field below the boundary is zero. According to the boundary conditions, the tangential components of the electric field must vanish at all points along the interface. Thus for an incident electric field with vertical polarization shown by the arrows, the polarization of the reflected waves must be as indicated in the figure to satisfy the boundary conditions. To excite the polarization of the reflected waves, the virtual source must also be vertical and with a polarity in the same direction as that of the actual source (thus a reflection coefficient of $+1$).

Another orientation of the source will be to have the radiating element in a horizontal position, as shown in Figure 4.11(b). Following a procedure similar to that of the vertical dipole, the virtual source (image) is also placed a distance h below the interface but with a 180° polarity difference relative to the actual source (thus a reflection coefficient of -1).

In addition to electric sources, artificial equivalent "magnetic" sources and magnetic conductors have been introduced to aid in the analyses of electromagnetic boundary value problems. Figure 4.12(a) displays the sources and their images for an electric plane conductor. The single arrow indicates an electric element and the double a magnetic one. The direction of the

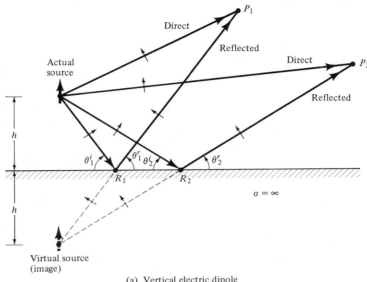

(a) Vertical electric dipole

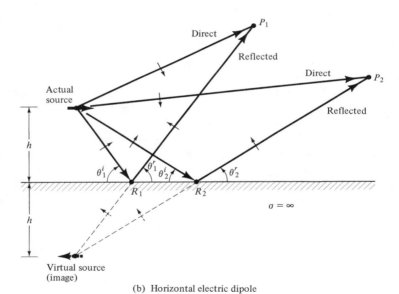

(b) Horizontal electric dipole

Figure 4.11 Vertical and horizontal electric dipoles above an infinite, flat, perfect electric conductor.

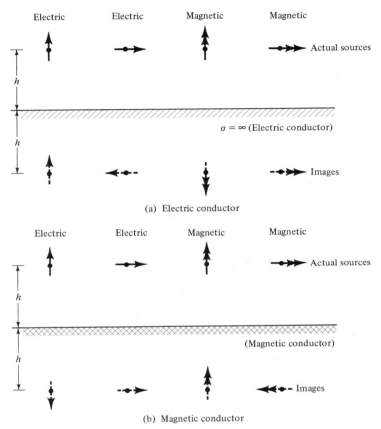

(a) Electric conductor

(b) Magnetic conductor

Figure 4.12 Electric and magnetic sources and their images near electric and magnetic conductors.

arrow identifies the polarity. Since many problems can be solved using duality, Figure 4.12(b) illustrates the sources and their images when the obstacle is an infinite, flat, perfect "magnetic" conductor.

4.7.2 Vertical Electric Dipole

The analysis procedure for vertical and horizontal electric and magnetic elements near infinite electric and magnetic plane conductors, using image theory, was illustrated graphically in the previous section. Based on the graphical model of Figure 4.11, the mathematical expressions for the fields of a vertical linear element near a perfect electric conductor will now be developed. For simplicity, only far-field observations will be considered.

Referring to the geometry of Figure 4.13(a), the far-zone direct component of the electric field of the infinitesimal dipole of length l, constant current I_0, and observation point P_1 is given according to (4-26a) by

$$E_\theta^d = j\eta \frac{kI_0 le^{-jkr_1}}{4\pi r_1} \sin\theta_1 \tag{4-95}$$

The reflected component can be accounted for by the introduction of the virtual source (image), as shown in Figure 4.13(a), and it can be written as

$$E_\theta^r = jR_v\eta \frac{kI_0 le^{-jkr_2}}{4\pi r_2} \sin\theta_2 \tag{4-96}$$

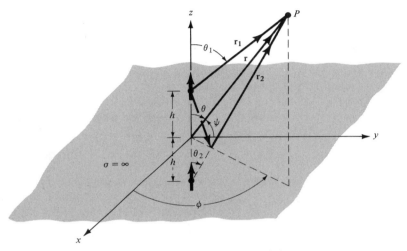

(a) Vertical electric dipole above ground plane

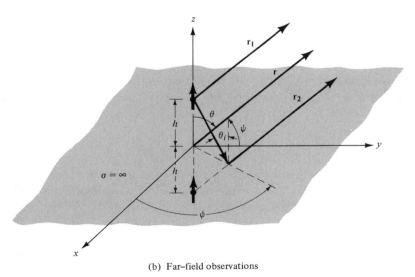

(b) Far–field observations

Figure 4.13　Vertical electric dipole above infinite electric conductor.

or

$$E_\theta^r = j\eta \frac{kI_0 le^{-jkr_2}}{4\pi r_2} \sin\theta_2 \qquad (4\text{-}96a)$$

since the reflection coefficient R_v is equal to unity.

The total field above the interface ($z \geq 0$) is equal to the sum of the direct and reflected components as given by (4-95) and (4-96a). Since a field cannot exist inside a perfect electric conductor, it is equal to zero below the interface. To simplify the expression for the total electric field, it is referred to the origin of the coordinate system ($z = 0$).

In general, we can write that

$$r_1 = [r^2 + h^2 - 2rh\cos\theta]^{1/2} \qquad (4\text{-}97a)$$

$$r_2 = [r^2 + h^2 - 2rh\cos(\pi - \theta)]^{1/2} \qquad (4\text{-}97b)$$

For far-field observations ($r \gg h$), (4-97a) and (4-97b) reduce using the binomial expansion to

$$r_1 \simeq r - h\cos\theta \qquad (4\text{-}98a)$$

$$r_2 \simeq r + h\cos\theta \qquad (4\text{-}98b)$$

As shown in Figure 4.13(b), geometrically (4-98a) and (4-98b) represent parallel lines. Since the amplitude variations are not as critical

$$r_1 \simeq r_2 \simeq r \qquad \text{for amplitude variations} \qquad (4\text{-}98c)$$

Using (4-98a)–(4-98c), the sum of (4-95) and (4-96b) can be written as

$$\left. \begin{aligned} E_\theta &\simeq j\eta \frac{kI_0 le^{-jkr}}{4\pi r} \sin\theta [2\cos(kh\cos\theta)] && z \geq 0 \\ E_\theta &= 0 && z < 0 \end{aligned} \right\} \qquad (4\text{-}99)$$

It is evident that the total electric field is equal to the product of the field of a single source positioned symmetrically about the origin and a factor [within the brackets in (4-99)] which is a function of the antenna height (h) and the observation point (θ). This is referred to as *pattern multiplication* and the factor is known as the *array factor*. This will be developed and discussed in more detail and for more complex configurations in Chapter 6.

The shape and amplitude of the field is not only controlled by the field of the single element but also by the positioning of the element relative to the ground. To examine the field variations as a function of the height h, the normalized (to 0 dB) power patterns for $h = 0, \lambda/8, \lambda/4, 3\lambda/8, \lambda/2$, and λ have been plotted in Figure 4.14. Because of symmetry, only half of each pattern is shown. For $h > \lambda/4$ more minor lobes, in addition to the major ones, are formed. As h attains values greater than λ, an even greater number of minor lobes is introduced. In general, the total number of lobes is equal

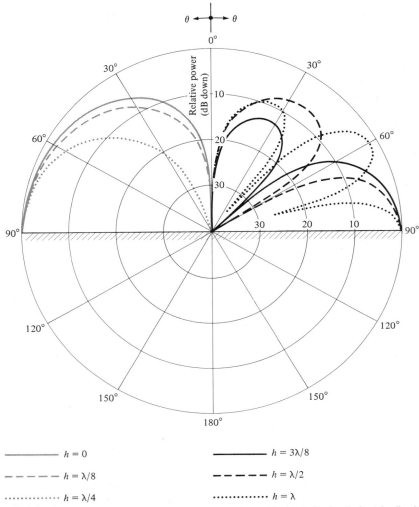

Figure 4.14 Elevation plane amplitude patterns of a vertical infinitesimal electric dipole for different heights above an infinite plane electric conductor.

to the integer that is closest to

$$\boxed{\text{number of lobes} \simeq \frac{2h}{\lambda} + 1} \tag{4-100}$$

Since the total field of the antenna system is different from that of a single element, the directivity and radiation resistance are also different. To derive expressions for them, we first find the total radiated power over the upper hemisphere of radius r using

$$P_{rad} = \oiint_S \mathbf{W}_{av} \cdot d\mathbf{s} = \frac{1}{2\eta} \int_0^{2\pi} \int_0^{\pi/2} |E_\theta|^2 r^2 \sin\theta \, d\theta \, d\phi$$

$$= \frac{\pi}{\eta} \int_0^{\pi/2} |E_\theta|^2 r^2 \sin\theta \, d\theta \qquad (4\text{-}101)$$

which simplifies, with the aid of (4-99), to

$$P_{rad} = \pi\eta \left|\frac{I_0 l}{\lambda}\right|^2 \left[\frac{1}{3} - \frac{\cos(2kh)}{(2kh)^2} + \frac{\sin(2kh)}{(2kh)^3}\right] \qquad (4\text{-}102)$$

As $kh \to \infty$ the radiated power, as given by (4-102), is equal to that of an isolated element. However for $kh \to 0$, it can be shown by expanding the sine and cosine functions into series that the power is twice that of an isolated element. Using (4-99), the radiation intensity can be written as

$$U = r^2 W_{av} = r^2 \left(\frac{1}{2\eta}|E_\theta|^2\right) = \frac{\eta}{2} \left|\frac{I_0 l}{\lambda}\right|^2 \sin^2\theta \cos^2(kh\cos\theta) \qquad (4\text{-}103)$$

The maximum value of (4-103) occurs at $\theta = \pi/2$ and is given, excluding $kh \to \infty$, by

$$U_{max} = U\big|_{\theta = \pi/2} = \frac{\eta}{2} \left|\frac{I_0 l}{\lambda}\right|^2 \qquad (4\text{-}103a)$$

which is four times greater than that of an isolated element. With (4-102) and (4-103a), the directivity can be written as

$$D_0 = \frac{4\pi U_{max}}{P_{rad}} = \frac{2}{\left[\dfrac{1}{3} - \dfrac{\cos(2kh)}{(2kh)^2} + \dfrac{\sin(2kh)}{(2kh)^3}\right]} \qquad (4\text{-}104)$$

whose value for $kh = 0$ is 3. The maximum value occurs when $kh = 2.881$ ($h = 0.4585\lambda$), and it is equal to 6.566 which is greater than four times that of an isolated element (1.5). The pattern for $h = 0.4585\lambda$ is shown plotted in Figure 4.15 while the directivity, as given by (4-104), is displayed in Figure 4.16 for $0 \le h \le 5\lambda$.

Using (4-102), the radiation resistance can be written as

$$R_r = \frac{2P_{rad}}{|I_0|^2} = 2\pi\eta \left(\frac{l}{\lambda}\right)^2 \left[\frac{1}{3} - \frac{\cos(2kh)}{(2kh)^2} + \frac{\sin(2kh)}{(2kh)^3}\right] \qquad (4\text{-}105)$$

whose value for $kh \to \infty$ is the same and for $kh = 0$ is twice that of the isolated element as given by (4-19). When $kh = 0$, the value of R_r as given by (4-105) is only one-half the value of an $l' = 2l$ isolated element according to (4-19). The radiation resistance, as given by (4-105), is plotted in Figure 4.16 for $0 \le h \le 5\lambda$ when $l = \lambda/50$ and the element is radiating into free-space

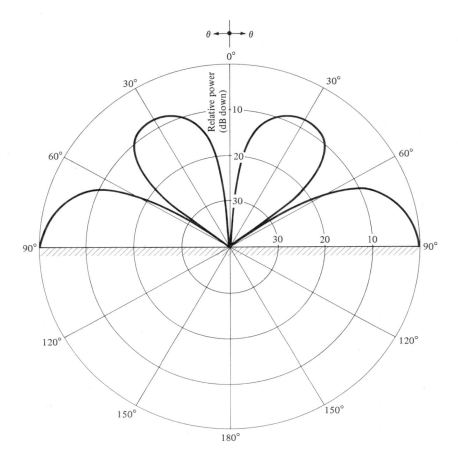

$h = 0.4585\lambda$

Figure 4.15 Elevation plane amplitude pattern of a vertical infinitesimal electric dipole at a height of 0.4585λ above an infinite plane electric conductor.

($\eta \simeq 120\pi$). It can be compared to the value of $R_r = 0.316$ ohms for the isolated element of Example 4.1.

In practice, a wide use has been made of a quarter-wavelength monopole ($l = \lambda/4$) mounted above a ground plane, as shown in Figure 4.17(a). For analysis purposes, a $\lambda/4$ image is introduced and it forms the $\lambda/2$ equivalent of Figure 4.17(b). It should be emphasized that the $\lambda/2$ equivalent of Figure 4.17(b) gives the correct field values for the actual system of Figure 4.17(a) only above the interface ($z \geq 0, 0 \leq \theta \leq \pi/2$). Thus, the far-zone electric and magnetic fields for the $\lambda/4$ monopole above the ground plane are given, respectively, by (4-85) and (4-86).

From the discussions of the resistance of an infinitesimal dipole above a ground plane for $kh = 0$, it follows that the input impedance of a $\lambda/4$

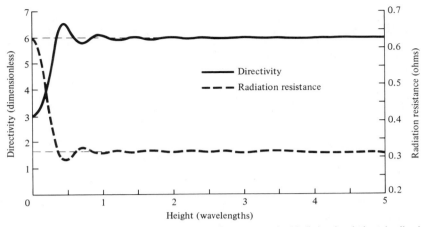

Figure 4.16 Directivity and radiation resistance of a vertical infinitesimal electric dipole as a function of its height above an infinite plane electric conductor.

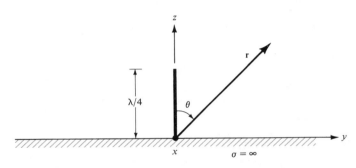

(a) λ/4 monopole on infinite electric conductor

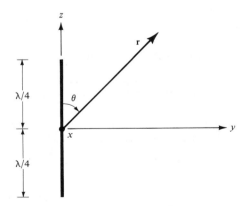

(b) Equivalent of λ/4 monopole on infinite electric conductor

Figure 4.17 Quarter-wavelength monopole on an infinite electric conductor.

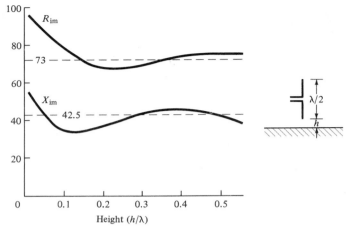

Figure 4.18 Input impedance (referred to current maximum) of a vertical $\lambda/2$ dipole above an infinite electric conductor. (SOURCE: W. L. Weeks, *Antenna Engineering*, McGraw-Hill, New York, 1968)

monopole above a ground plane is equal to one-half that of an isolated $\lambda/2$ dipole. Thus, referred to the current maximum, the input impedance Z_{im} is given by

$$Z_{im} = \tfrac{1}{2}[73 + j42.5] = 36.5 + j21.25 \qquad (4\text{-}106)$$

where $73 + j42.5$ is the input impedance (and also the impedance referred to the current maximum) of a $\lambda/2$ dipole.

The same procedure can be followed for any other length. The input impedance $Z_{im} = R_{im} + jX_{im}$ (referred to the current maximum) of a $\lambda/2$ dipole placed near an infinite perfect electric conductor, as a function of height above the ground plane, is plotted in Figure 4.18. It is observed that the values of the resistance and reactance oscillate about the corresponding ones of the isolated element (73 ohms for the resistance and 42.5 ohms for the reactance).

4.7.3 Horizontal Electric Dipole

Another configuration will be to have the linear element placed horizontally relative to the infinite electric ground plane, as shown in Figure 4.19(a). The analysis procedure of this is identical to the one of the vertical dipole. Introducing an image and assuming far-field observations, as shown in Figure 4.19(b), the direct component can be written as

$$E_\psi^d = j\eta \frac{kI_0 le^{-jkr_1}}{4\pi r_1}\sin\psi \qquad (4\text{-}107)$$

and the reflected one by

$$E_\psi^r = jR_h\eta \frac{kI_0 le^{-jkr_2}}{4\pi r_2}\sin\psi \qquad (4\text{-}108)$$

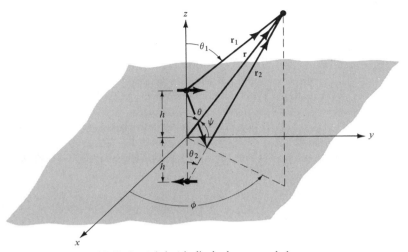

(a) Horizontal electric dipole above ground plane

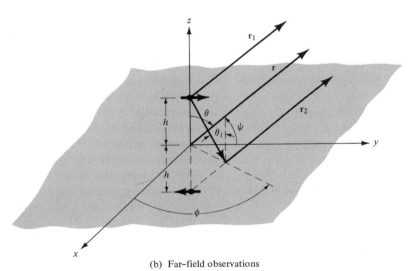

(b) Far–field observations

Figure 4.19   Horizontal electric dipole above an infinite electric conductor.

or

$$E_\psi^r = - j\eta \frac{kI_0 le^{-jkr_2}}{4\pi r_2} \sin \psi \qquad (4\text{-}108a)$$

since the reflection coefficient is equal to $R_h = -1$.

To find the angle ψ, which is measured from the y-axis toward the observation point, we first form

$$\cos \psi = \hat{a}_y \cdot \hat{a}_r = \hat{a}_y \cdot (\hat{a}_x \sin \theta \cos \phi + \hat{a}_y \sin \theta \sin \phi + \hat{a}_z \cos \theta) = \sin \theta \sin \phi \qquad (4\text{-}109)$$

from which we find

$$\sin \psi = \sqrt{1 - \cos^2 \psi} = \sqrt{1 - \sin^2 \theta \sin^2 \phi} \qquad (4\text{-}110)$$

Since for far-field observations

$$\left. \begin{array}{l} r_1 \simeq r - h\cos\theta \\ r_2 \simeq r + h\cos\theta \end{array} \right\} \qquad \text{for phase variations} \qquad (4\text{-}111\text{a})$$

$$r_1 \simeq r_2 \simeq r \qquad \text{for amplitude variations} \qquad (4\text{-}111\text{b})$$

the total field, which is valid only above the ground plane ($z \geq 0; 0 \leq \theta \leq \pi/2, 0 \leq \phi \leq 2\pi$), can be written as

$$E_\psi = E_\psi^d + E_\psi^r = j\eta \frac{kI_0 le^{-jkr}}{4\pi r} \sqrt{1 - \sin^2\theta\sin^2\phi} \left[2j\sin(kh\cos\theta)\right] \tag{4-112}$$

Equation (4-112) again consists of the product of the field of a single isolated element placed symmetrically at the origin and a factor (within the brackets) known as the array factor. This again is the pattern multiplication rule which will be discussed in more detail in Chapter 6.

To examine the variations of the total field as a function of the element height above the ground plane, the two-dimensional elevation plane patterns (normalized to 0 dB) for $\phi = 90°$ (y-z plane) when $h = 0$, $\lambda/8$, $\lambda/4$, $3\lambda/8$, $\lambda/2$, and λ are plotted in Figure 4.20. Since this antenna system is not symmetric, the azimuthal plane (x-y plane) pattern will not be isotropic.

To obtain a better visualization of the radiation intensity in all directions above the interface, the three-dimensional pattern for $h = \lambda$ is shown plotted in Figure 4.21. The radial distance on the x-y plane represents the elevation angle θ from $0°$ to $90°$, and the z-axis represents the normalized amplitude of the radiation field intensity from 0 to 1. The azimuthal angle ϕ ($0 \leq \phi \leq 2\pi$) is measured from the x- toward the y-axis on the x-y plane.

As the height increases beyond one wavelength ($h > \lambda$), a larger number of lobes is again formed. The total number of lobes is equal to the integer that most closely is equal to

$$\boxed{\text{number of lobes} \simeq 2\left(\frac{h}{\lambda}\right)} \tag{4-113}$$

with unity being the smallest number.

Following a procedure similar to the one performed for the vertical dipole, the radiated power can be written as

$$P_{\text{rad}} = \eta \frac{\pi}{2} \left| \frac{I_0 l}{\lambda} \right|^2 \left[\frac{2}{3} - \frac{\sin(2kh)}{2kh} - \frac{\cos(2kh)}{(2kh)^2} + \frac{\sin(2kh)}{(2kh)^3} \right] \tag{4-114}$$

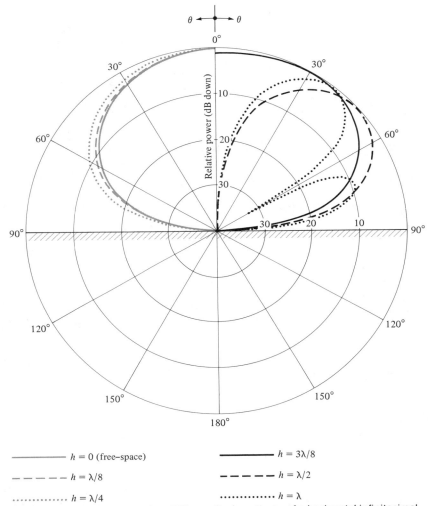

Figure 4.20   Elevation plane ($\phi=90°$) amplitude patterns of a horizontal infinitesimal electric dipole for different heights above an infinite plane electric conductor.

and the radiation resistance as

$$R_r = \eta\pi\left(\frac{l}{\lambda}\right)^2\left[\frac{2}{3} - \frac{\sin(2kh)}{2kh} - \frac{\cos(2kh)}{(2kh)^2} + \frac{\sin(2kh)}{(2kh)^3}\right] \tag{4-115}$$

By expanding the sine and cosine functions into series, it can be shown that (4-115) reduces for small values of kh to

$$R_r \overset{kh\to0}{=} \eta\pi\left(\frac{l}{\lambda}\right)^2\left[\frac{2}{3} - \frac{2}{3} + \frac{8}{15}\left(\frac{2\pi h}{\lambda}\right)^2\right] = \eta\frac{32\pi^3}{15}\left(\frac{l}{\lambda}\right)\left(\frac{h}{\lambda}\right)^2 \tag{4-116}$$

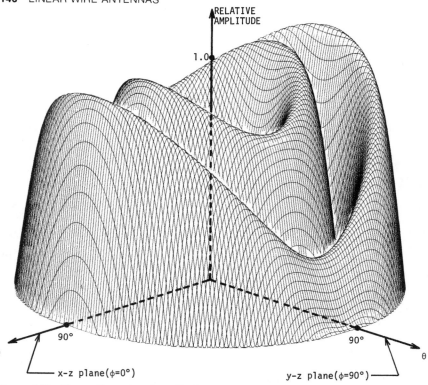

Figure 4.21 Three-dimensional amplitude pattern of an infinitesimal horizontal dipole a distance $h=\lambda$ above an infinite plane electric conductor.

For $kh \to \infty$, (4-115) reduces to that of an isolated element. The radiation resistance, as given by (4-115), is plotted in Figure 4.22 for $0 \leq h \leq 5\lambda$ when $l = \lambda/50$ and the antenna is radiating into free space ($\eta \simeq 120\pi$).

The radiation intensity is given by

$$U \simeq \frac{r^2}{2\eta}|E_\psi|^2 = \frac{\eta}{2}\left|\frac{I_0 l}{\lambda}\right|^2 \left(1 - \sin^2\theta \sin^2\phi\right)\sin^2(kh\cos\theta) \qquad (4\text{-}117)$$

whose maximum value for $\theta = 0$ and any ϕ, excluding $kh \to \infty$, is equal to

$$U_{\max} = U(\theta = 0, \phi) = \frac{\eta}{2}\left|\frac{I_0 l}{\lambda}\right|^2 \sin^2(kh) \qquad (4\text{-}118)$$

Using (4-114) and (4-118), the directive gain in the $\theta = 0°$ direction can be written as

$$D_g\big|_{\theta=0} = \frac{4\pi U_{\max}\big|_{\theta=0°}}{P_{\text{rad}}} = \frac{4\sin^2(kh)}{\left[\dfrac{2}{3} - \dfrac{\sin(2kh)}{2kh} - \dfrac{\cos(2kh)}{(2kh)^2} + \dfrac{\sin(2kh)}{(2kh)^3}\right]} \qquad (4\text{-}119)$$

For small values of kh ($kh \to 0$), (4-119) reduces to

$$D_0 \stackrel{kh \to 0}{=} \frac{4\sin^2(kh)}{\left[\dfrac{2}{3} - \dfrac{2}{3} + \dfrac{8}{15}(kh)^2\right]} = 7.5\left(\frac{\sin kh}{kh}\right)^2 \tag{4-120}$$

For $h = 0$ the element is shorted and it does not radiate. The directive gain, as given by (4-119), is plotted for $0 < h \le 5\lambda$ in Figure 4.22. It exhibits a maximum value of 7.5 for small values of h. Maximum values of 6 occur when $h \simeq (0.725 + n/2)\lambda$, $n = 0, 1, 2, 3, \dots$.

The input impedance $Z_{im} = R_{im} + jX_{im}$ (referred to the current maximum) of a $\lambda/2$ dipole above an infinite ground plane is shown plotted in

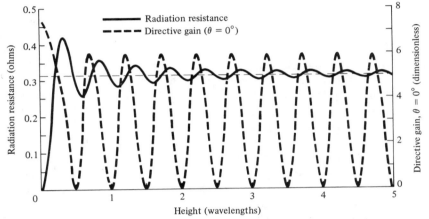

Figure 4.22   Radiation resistance and directive gain ($\theta = 0°$) of a horizontal infinitesimal electric dipole as a function of its height above an infinite plane electric conductor.

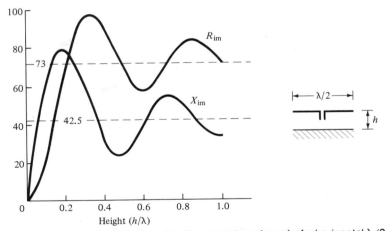

Figure 4.23   Input impedance (referred to the current maximum) of a horizontal $\lambda/2$ dipole above an infinite electric conductor. (SOURCE: W. L. Weeks, *Antenna Engineering*, McGraw-Hill, New York, 1968)

Figure 4.23 for $0 \le h \le \lambda$. The values of the resistance and reactance oscillate about the corresponding values of the isolated element (73 ohms for the resistance and 42.5 ohms for the reactance).

4.8 GROUND EFFECTS

In the previous two sections the variations of the radiation characteristics (pattern, radiation resistance, directivity) of infinitesimal vertical and horizontal linear elements were examined when they were placed above plane perfect electric conductors. Although ideal electric conductors ($\sigma = \infty$) are not realizable, their effects can be used as guidelines for good conductors ($\sigma \gg \omega\varepsilon$, where ε is the permittivity of the medium).

One obstacle that is not an ideal conductor, and it is always present in any antenna system, is the ground (earth). In addition, the earth is not a plane surface. To simplify the analysis, however, the earth will initially be assumed to be a flat surface. For pattern analysis, this is a very good engineering approximation provided the radius of the earth is large compared to the wavelength and the observation angles are greater than about $57.3/(ka)^{1/3}$ degrees from grazing (a is the earth radius) [3]. Usually these angles are greater than about $3°$.

In general, the characteristics of an antenna at low (LF) and medium (MF) frequencies are profoundly influenced by the lossy earth. This is particularly evident in the input resistance. When the antenna is located at a height that is small compared to the skin depth of the conducting earth, the input resistance may even be greater than its free-space values [3]. This leads to antennas with very low efficiencies. Improvements in the efficiency can be obtained by placing radial wires or metallic disks on the ground.

The analytical procedures that will be introduced to examine the ground effects are based on the geometrical optics models of the previous sections. The image (virtual) source is again placed a distance h below the interface to account for the reflections. However, for each polarization nonunity reflection coefficients are introduced which, in general, will be a function of the angles of incidence and the constitutive parameters of the two media. Although plane wave reflection coefficients are used, even though spherical waves are radiated by the source, the error is small for conducting media [4]. The spherical nature of the wavefront begins to dominate the reflection phenomenon at grazing angles (i.e., as the point of reflection approaches the horizon) [5]. If the height (h) of the antenna above the interface is much less than the skin depth $\delta[\delta = \sqrt{2/(\omega\mu\sigma)}]$ of the ground, the image depth h below the interface should be increased [4] by a complex distance $\delta(1-j)$.

The geometrical optics formulations are valid provided the sources are located inside the lossless medium. When the sources are placed within the ground, the formulations should include possible surface-wave contributions. Exact boundary-value solutions, based on Sommerfeld integral formulations, are available [3]. However they are too complex to be included in an introductory chapter.

4.8.1 Vertical Electric Dipole

The field radiated by an electric infinitesimal dipole when placed above the ground can be obtained by referring to the geometry of Figures 4.13(a) and (b). Assuming the earth is flat and the observations are made in the far-field, the direct component of the field is given by (4-95) and the reflected by (4-96) where the reflection coefficient R_v is given by

$$R_v = \frac{\eta_0 \cos \theta_i - \eta_1 \cos \theta_t}{\eta_0 \cos \theta_i + \eta_1 \cos \theta_t} \tag{4-121}$$

where

$$\eta_0 = \sqrt{\frac{\mu_0}{\varepsilon_0}} = \text{intrinsic impedance of free-space (air)}$$

$$\eta_1 = \sqrt{\frac{j\omega\mu_1}{\sigma_1 + j\omega\varepsilon_1}} = \text{intrinsic impedance of the ground}$$

$\theta_i = $ angle of incidence (relative to the normal)

$\theta_t = $ angle of refraction (relative to the normal)

The angles θ_i and θ_t are related by Snell's law of refraction

$$\gamma_0 \sin \theta_i = \gamma_1 \sin \theta_t \tag{4-122}$$

where

$\gamma_0 = j\beta_0 = $ propagation constant for free-space (air)

$\beta_0 = $ phase constant for free-space (air)

$\gamma_1 = (\alpha_1 + j\beta_1) = $ propagation constant for the ground

$\alpha_1 = $ attenuation constant for the ground

$\beta_1 = $ phase constant for the ground

Using the far-field approximations of (4-98a)–(4-98c), the total electric field above the ground ($z \geq 0$) can be written as

$$E_\theta = j\eta \frac{kI_0 le^{-jkr}}{4\pi r} \sin\theta \left[e^{jkh\cos\theta} + R_v e^{-jkh\cos\theta} \right] \qquad z \geq 0 \tag{4-123}$$

where R_v is given by (4-121).

The permittivity and conductivity of the earth are strong functions of the ground's geological constituents, especially its moisture. Typical values for the relative permittivity ε_r (dielectric constant) are in the range of 5–100 and for the conductivity σ in the range of 10^{-3}–10^{-1} S/m.

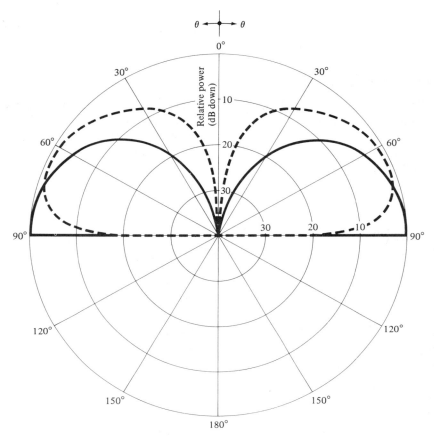

Figure 4.24 Normalized amplitude patterns of an infinitesimal vertical dipole above a perfect electric conductor ($\sigma_1 = \infty$) and a flat earth ($\sigma_1 = 0.01$ S/m, $\varepsilon_{r_1} = 5$, $f = 1$ GHz).

A normalized (to 0 dB) pattern for an infinitesimal dipole above the ground with $h = \lambda/4$, $\varepsilon_{r_1} = 5$, $f = 1$ GHz, $\sigma_1 = 10^{-2}$ S/m is shown plotted in Figure 4.24 (dashed curves) where it is compared with that (solid curve) of a perfect conductor ($\sigma_1 = \infty$). In the presence of the ground, the radiation toward the vertical direction ($60° > \theta > 0°$) is more intense than for the perfect electric conductor, but it vanishes for grazing angles ($\theta = 90°$). The null field toward the horizon ($\theta = 90°$) is formed because the reflection coefficient approaches -1 as $\theta_i \to 90°$. Thus the ground effects on the pattern of a vertically polarized antenna are significantly different from those of a perfect conductor.

Significant changes also occur in the impedance. Because the formulation for the impedance is much more complex [3], it will not be presented here. Graphical illustrations for the impedance change of a vertical dipole placed a height h above a homogeneous lossy half-space, as compared to those in free-space, are shown in Figure 4.25. They are based on numerical results obtained by Vogler and Noble [6]. The variations in impedance are expressed in terms of changes in resistance ($\Delta R/R_0$) and in reactance ($\Delta X/R_0$), where R_0 is the radiation resistance of an infinitesimal dipole radiating in an infinite free-space [as given by (4-19)]. The parameter N_1 is defined by

$$N_1 = \sqrt{\frac{\sigma_1 + j\omega\varepsilon_1}{j\omega\varepsilon_0}} = |N_1| e^{-j\left(\frac{\pi}{4} - \psi\right)} \tag{4-124}$$

where σ_1, ε_1 are the conductivity and permittivity, respectively, of the homogeneous lossy half-space, ε_0 is the free-space permittivity, and ψ is the phase angle of N_1.

The curve in Figure 4.25(a) represents the data for a perfectly conducting ($|N_1| = \infty$) half-space. As expected, the magnitude of $\Delta R/R_0$ approaches unity as $2k_0h \to 0$, which corresponds to doubling the radiation resistance, while the magnitude of ΔX approaches infinity as $2k_0h \to 0$. The curves for both ΔR and ΔX become oscillatory as $2k_0h$ exceeds approximately π or the height h exceeds $\lambda_0/4$.

For the finite conductivity half-space, the $\psi = \pi/4$ curves correspond to a perfect dielectric half-space ($\sigma_1 = 0$) while the $\psi = 0$ curves represent negligible displacement currents in the lossy half-space. The curves for $|N_1^2| = 100$ are not too different from that of a perfectly conducting half-space ($|N_1| = \infty$). Significant changes are evident as the values of $|N_1^2|$ decrease particularly in the resistive portion of the $\psi = 0$ curves.

4.8.2 Horizontal Electric Dipole

The analytical formulation of the horizontal dipole above the ground can also be obtained in a similar manner as for the vertical electric dipole. Referring to Figures 4.19(a) and (b), the direct component is given by (4-107) and the reflected by (4-108) where the reflection coefficient R_h is given by

$$R_h = \frac{\eta_1 \cos\theta_i - \eta_0 \cos\theta_t}{\eta_1 \cos\theta_i + \eta_0 \cos\theta_t} \tag{4-125}$$

The angles θ_i and θ_t are again related by Snell's law of refraction as given by (4-122).

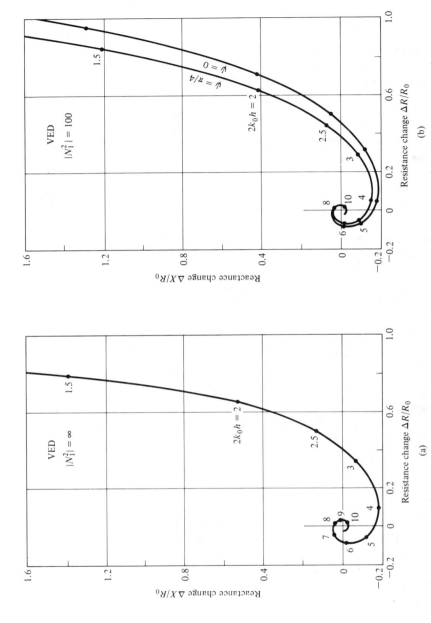

Figure 4.25 Vertical electric dipole (VED) impedance change as a function of height above a homogeneous lossy half-space. (SOURCE: R. E. Collin and F. J. Zucker (eds.), *Antenna Theory Part 2*, McGraw-Hill, New York, 1969)

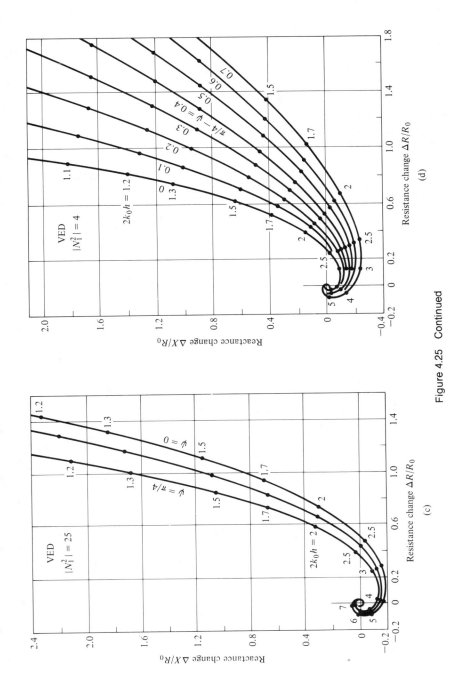

Figure 4.25 Continued

Using the far-field approximations of (4-111a) and (4-111b), the total field above the ground ($z \geq 0$) can be written as

$$E_\psi = j\eta \frac{kI_0 e^{-jkr}}{4\pi r} \sqrt{1 - \sin^2\theta \sin^2\phi} \left[e^{jkh\cos\theta} + R_h e^{-jkh\cos\theta} \right],$$

$$z \geq 0 \quad (4\text{-}126)$$

where R_h is given by (4-125).

The normalized (to 0 dB) pattern in the y-z plane ($\phi = \pi/2$) for $h = \lambda/4$ is shown plotted in Figure 4.26 (dashed curve) where it is compared with that (solid curve) of a perfect conductor ($\sigma_1 = \infty$). In the space above the interface, the pattern in the presence of the ground is not significantly different from that of a perfect conductor. This becomes more

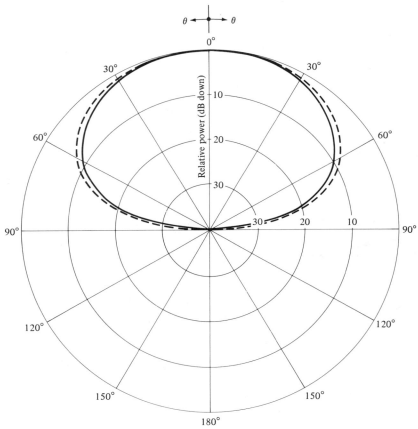

$h = \lambda/4, \phi = \pi/2$

———— $\sigma_1 = \infty$

– – – – – $\sigma_1 = 10^{-2}$ S/m, $\epsilon_{r1} = 5, f = 1$ GHz

Figure 4.26 Normalized amplitude patterns of an infinitesimal horizontal dipole above a perfect electric conductor ($\sigma_1 = \infty$) and a flat earth ($\sigma_1 = 0.01$ S/m, $\varepsilon_{r1} = 5, f = 1$ GHz).

evident by examining R_h as given by (4-125). For a ground medium, the values of R_h are not much different from -1 (the value of R_h for a perfect conductor). For grazing angles ($\theta_i \rightarrow 90°$), the value of R_h for both cases is -1. Thus the pattern of a horizontal dipole is not significantly different from that of a perfect conductor.

4.8.3 Earth Curvature

The analytical formulations of Sections 4.8.1 and 4.8.2 for the patterns of vertical and horizontal dipoles assume that the earth is flat. This is a good approximation provided the curvature of the earth is large compared to the wavelength and the angle of observation is greater than about 3° [or more accurately greater than about $57.3/(ka)^{1/3}$ degrees, where a is the radius of the earth] from grazing [7]. The curvature of the earth has a tendency to spread out (weaken, diffuse, diverge) the reflected energy more than a corresponding flat surface. The spreading of the reflected energy from a curved surface as compared to that from a flat surface is taken into account by introducing a divergence factor D [5], [8] defined as

$$D = \text{divergence factor} = \frac{\text{reflected field from curved surface}}{\text{reflected field from flat surface}} \qquad (4\text{-}127)$$

The formula for D can be derived using purely geometrical considerations. It is accomplished by comparing the ray energy density in a small cone reflected from a sphere near the principal point of reflection with the energy density the rays (within the same cone) would have if they were reflected from a plane surface. Based on the geometrical optics energy conservation law for a bundle of rays within a cone, the reflected rays within the cone will subtend a circle on a perpendicular plane for reflections from a flat surface, as shown in Figure 4.27(a). However according to the geometry of Figure 4.27(b), it will subtend an ellipse for a spherical reflecting surface. Therefore the divergence factor of (4-127) can also be defined as

$$D = \frac{E_s}{E_f} = \left[\frac{\text{area contained in circle}}{\text{area contained in ellipse}} \right]^{1/2} \qquad (4\text{-}128)$$

where

E_s = reflected field from spherical surface

E_f = reflected field from flat surface

Using the geometry of Figure 4.28 and assuming that the divergence of rays in the azimuthal plane (plane vertical to the page) is negligible, the divergence factor can be written as

$$D \simeq \left[1 + 2 \frac{ss'}{ad \tan \psi} \right]^{-1/2} \qquad (4\text{-}129)$$

where ψ is the grazing angle. Thus the divergence factor of (4-129) takes into

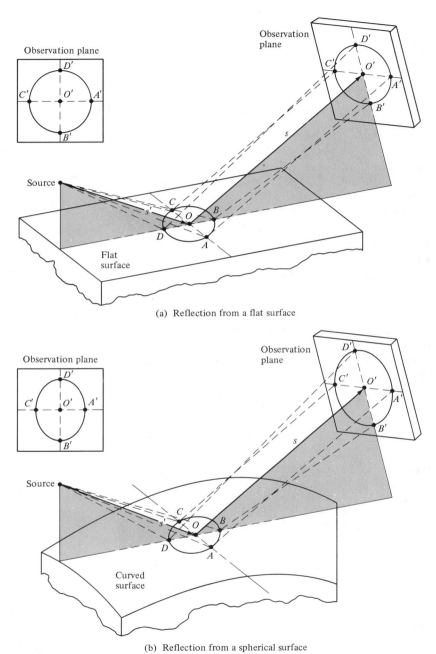

(a) Reflection from a flat surface

(b) Reflection from a spherical surface

Figure 4.27 Reflection from flat and spherical surfaces.

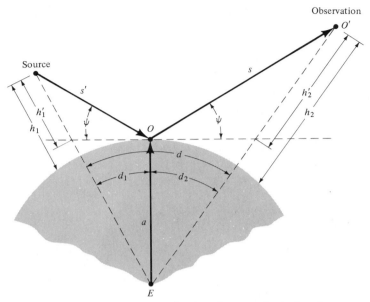

Figure 4.28 Geometry for reflections from a spherical surface.

account energy spreading primarily in the elevation plane. When $d \ll a$, then

$$s' \simeq \frac{h_1'}{\sin \psi}, \qquad \tan \psi \simeq \frac{h_1'}{d_1} \qquad\qquad (4\text{-}130a)$$

$$s \simeq \frac{h_2'}{\sin \psi}, \qquad \tan \psi \simeq \frac{h_2'}{d_2} \qquad\qquad (4\text{-}130b)$$

For low grazing angles (ψ small), $\sin \psi \simeq \tan \psi$. Using (4-130a) and (4-130b) reduces (4-129) to

$$D \simeq \left[1 + 2\frac{h_1'h_2'}{ad\tan^3 \psi} \right]^{-1/2} \simeq \left[1 + 2\frac{d_1^2 d_2}{adh_1'} \right]^{-1/2} \simeq \left[1 + 2\frac{d_1 d_2^2}{adh_2'} \right]^{-1/2}$$

$$(4\text{-}131)$$

$h_1' =$ height of the source above the earth (with respect to the tangent at the point of reflection)

$h_2' =$ height of the observation point above the earth (with respect to the tangent at the point of reflection)

$d =$ range (along the surface of the earth) between the source and the observation point

$a =$ radius of the earth (3959 mi). Usually a $\frac{4}{3}$ radius ($\simeq 5280$ mi) is used.

$\psi =$ reflection angle (with respect to the tangent at the point of reflection).

d_1 = distance (along the surface of the earth) from the source to the reflection point

d_2 = distance (along the surface of the earth) from the observation point to the reflection point

The divergence factor can be included in the formulation of the fields radiated by a vertical or a horizontal dipole, in the presence of the earth, by modifying (4-123) and (4-126) and writing them, respectively, as

$$E_\theta = j\eta \frac{kI_0 le^{-jkr}}{4\pi r} \sin\theta \left[e^{jkh\cos\theta} + DR_v e^{-jkh\cos\theta} \right] \qquad (4\text{-}132\text{a})$$

$$E_\psi = j\eta \frac{kI_0 le^{-jkr}}{4\pi r} \sqrt{1 - \sin^2\theta \sin^2\phi} \left[e^{jkh\cos\theta} + DR_h e^{-jkh\cos\theta} \right] \qquad (4\text{-}132\text{b})$$

Plots of the divergence factor as a function of the grazing angle ψ (or as a function of the observation point h_2') for different source heights are shown in Figure 4.29. It is observed that the divergence factor is somewhat different and smaller than unity for small grazing angles, and it approaches unity as the grazing angle becomes larger. The variations of D displayed in Figure 4.29 are typical but not unique. For different positions of the source and observation point, the variations will be somewhat different. More detailed information on the variation of the divergence factor and its effect on the overall field pattern is available [9]. The most difficult task usually involves the determination of the reflection point from a knowledge of the heights of the source and observation points, and the range d between them. Procedures to do this have been developed [8]–[10].

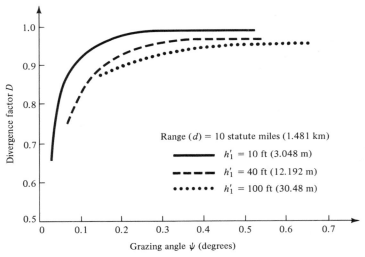

Figure 4.29 Divergence factor for a 4/3 radius earth ($a_e = 5,280$ mi $= 8,497.3$ km) as a function of grazing angle ψ.

References

1. C. H. Walter, *Traveling Wave Antennas*, McGraw-Hill, 1965, pp. 32–44.
2. S. K. Schelkunoff and H. T. Friis, *Antennas: Theory and Practice*, Wiley, New York, 1952, pp. 243–244, 351–353.
3. R. E. Collin and F. J. Zucker (eds.), *Antenna Theory Part 2*, Chapters 23 and 24 (by J. R. Wait), McGraw-Hill, New York, 1969.
4. P. R. Bannister, "Image Theory Results for the Mutual Impedance of Crossing Earth Return Circuits," *IEEE Trans. Electromagn. Compat.*, vol. 15, No. 4, 1973, pp. 158–160.
5. D. E. Kerr, *Propagation of Short Radio Waves*, MIT Radiation Laboratory Series, McGraw-Hill, New York, 1951, vol. 13, pp. 98–109, 112–122, 396–444.
6. L. E. Vogler and J. L. Noble, "Curves of Input Impedance Change due to Ground for Dipole Antennas," U.S. National Bureau of Standards, Monograph 72, Jan. 31, 1964.
7. J. R. Wait and A. M. Conda, "Pattern of an Antenna on a Curved Lossy Surface," *IRE Trans. Antennas Propag.*, vol. AP-6, No. 4, October 1958, pp. 348–359.
8. H. R. Reed and C. M. Russell, *Ultra High Frequency Propagation*, Boston Technical Publishers, Inc., Lexington, Mass., 1964, Chapter 4, pp. 102–116.
9. C. A. Balanis, "Divergence Factor and Multipath Interference," Prepared for Naval Air Station, Patuxent River, Maryland, 1982.
10. G. May, "Determining the Point of Reflection on MW Radio Links," *Microwave Journal*, vol. 20, No. 9, September 1977, pp. 74, 76.
11. W. L. Weeks, *Antenna Engineering*, McGraw-Hill, New York, 1968, pp. 194–195.

PROBLEMS

4.1. An infinitesimal magnetic dipole of constant current I_m and length l is symmetrically placed about the origin along the z-axis. Find the
   (a) spherical **E**- and **H**-field components radiated by the dipole in all space
   (b) directivity of the antenna

4.2. For the infinitesimal magnetic dipole of Problem 4.1, find the far-zone fields when the element is placed along the
   (a) x-axis
   (b) y-axis

4.3. Derive (4-10a)–(4-10c) using (4-8a)–(4-9).

4.4. Derive the radiated power of (4-16) by forming the average power density, using (4-26a)–(4-26c), and integrating it over a sphere of radius r.

4.5. Derive the far-zone fields of an infinitesimal electric dipole, of length l and constant current I_0, using (4-4) and the procedure outlined in Section 3.6. Compare the results with (4-26a)–(4-26c).

4.6. Derive the fifth term of (4-41).

4.7. For an antenna with a maximum linear dimension of D, find the inner and outer boundaries of the Fresnel region so that the maximum phase error does not exceed
   (a) $\pi/16$ rad
   (b) $\pi/4$ rad

4.8. The current distribution on a terminated and matched long linear (traveling wave) antenna of length l, positioned along the z-axis and fed at its one end, is given by

$$\mathbf{I} = \hat{a}_z I_0 e^{-jkz'}, \qquad 0 \leq z' \leq l$$

where I_0 is a constant. Derive expressions for the
(a) far-zone spherical electric and magnetic field components
(b) radiation power density

4.9. A line source of infinite length and constant current I_0 is positioned along the z-axis. Find the
(a) vector potential $\mathbf{A}$
(b) cylindrical $\mathbf{E}$- and $\mathbf{H}$-field components radiated

$$\text{Hint:} \quad \int_{-\infty}^{+\infty} \frac{e^{-j\beta\sqrt{b^2 + t^2}}}{\sqrt{b^2 + t^2}} \, dt = -j\pi H_0^{(2)}(\beta b)$$

where $H_0^{(2)}(\alpha x)$ is the Hankel function of the second kind of order zero.

4.10. Show that (4-67) reduces to (4-68) and (4-89) to (4-90).

4.11. A center-fed electric dipole of length l is attached to a balanced lossless transmission line whose characteristic impedance is 50 ohms. Assuming the dipole is resonant at the given length, find the input VSWR when
(a) $l = \lambda/4$ (b) $l = \lambda/2$
(c) $l = 3\lambda/4$ (d) $l = \lambda$

4.12. Find the radiation efficiency of resonant linear electric dipoles of length
(a) $l = \lambda/50$ (b) $l = \lambda/4$
(c) $l = \lambda/2$ (d) $l = \lambda$
Assume that each dipole is made out of copper $[\sigma = 5.7 \times 10^7$ S/m$]$, has a radius of $10^{-3}\lambda$, and is operating at $f = 10$ MHz.

4.13. Derive (4-102) using (4-99).

4.14. Determine the smallest height that an infinitesimal dipole of $l = \lambda/50$ must be placed above an electric ground plane so that its pattern has only one null (aside from the null toward the vertical), and it occurs at 30° from the vertical. For that height, find the directivity and radiation resistance.

4.15. A $\lambda/50$ linear dipole is placed vertically at a height $h = 2\lambda$ above an infinite electric ground plane. Determine the angles (in degrees) where all the nulls of its pattern occur.

4.16. A linear infinitesimal dipole of length l and constant current is placed vertically a distance h above an infinite electric ground plane. Find the first five smallest heights (in ascending order) so that a null is formed (for each height) in the far-field pattern at an angle of 60° from the vertical.

4.17. A half-wavelength dipole is placed vertically on an infinite electric ground plane. Assuming that the dipole is fed at its base, find the
(a) radiation impedance (referred to the current maximum)
(b) input impedance (referred to the input terminals)
(c) VSWR when the antenna is connected to a lossless 50-ohm transmission line

4.18. Derive (4-114) using (4-112).

4.19. An infinitesimal horizontal electric dipole of length $l = \lambda/50$ is placed a height h above an infinite electric ground plane.

    (a) Find the smallest height h (excluding $h = 0$) that the antenna must be elevated so that a null in the $\phi = 90°$ plane will be formed at an angle of $\theta = 45°$ from the vertical axis.

    (b) For the height of part (a), determine the (1) radiation resistance and (2) directive gain (for $\theta = 0°$) of the antenna system.

4.20. A horizontal $\lambda/50$ infinitesimal dipole of constant current and length l is placed a distance $h = 0.707\lambda$ above an infinite electric ground plane. Find *all* the nulls formed by the antenna system in the $\phi = 90°$ plane.

4.21. A vertical $\lambda/2$ dipole, operating at 1 GHz, is placed a distance of 5 m (with respect to the tangent at the point of reflection) above the earth. Find the total field at a point 20 km from the source ($d = 20 \times 10^3$ m), at a height of 1000 m (with respect to the tangent) above the ground. Use a $\frac{4}{3}$ radius earth and assume that the electrical parameters of the earth are $\varepsilon_r = 5$, $\sigma = 10^{-2}$ S/m.

COMPUTER PROGRAM—LINEAR DIPOLE: DIRECTIVITY, RADIATION RESISTANCE, AND INPUT RESISTANCE

```
C ************************************************************
C DESCRIPTION:
C     THIS PROGRAM COMPUTES THE DIRECTIVITY(DIMENSIONLESS &
C DB),RADIATION RESISTANCE,AND INPUT RESISTANCE FOR FINITE
C DIPLOES OF ANY LENGTH.THE DIPOLES ARE RADIATING IN FREE
C SPACE.THE FAR FIELD ELECTRIC FIELD COMPONENT ETHETA EX-
C ISTS FOR THETA BETWEEN 0 AND PI AND PHI BETWEEN 0 AND
C 2PI INCLUSIVE BEING ZERO ELESEWHERE.THE DIRECTIVITY,
C RADIATION RESISTANCE,AND INPUT RESISTANCE ARE CALCU-
C LATED USING THE TRAILING EDGE METHOD IN INCREMENTS
C OF 1 DEGREE IN THETA.THE INPUT DATA CARDS CONTAIN
C THE DIPOLE LENGTHS IN WAVELENGTHS, ONE TO A CARD.
C ************************************************************
      REAL L
C
C DEFINE CONSTANTS AND INCREMENT TAKEN.
C
      PI=3.14159
      E=120.0*PI
      THETA=PI/180.0
      WRITE(6,65)
   65 FORMAT(1H1)
C
C THE DIPOLE LENGTH(IN WAVELENGTHS)IS READ IN.
C
      DO 30 J=1,1000
   40 READ(5,50,END=1000) L
   50 FORMAT(F7.4)
C
C INITIALIZE PRAD AND UMAX TO 0.0 EACH TIME THROUGH THE
C LOOP TO CLEAR PRAD AND UMAX FOR A NEW COMPUTATION.
C
      UMAX=0.0
      PRAD=0.0
      A=L*PI
C
C A SINGLE DO LOOP IS USED TO COMPUTE PRAD(INTEGRAL OF
C THE RADIATION INTENSITY U),SINCE U VARIES ONLY IN
C THETA.
C
      DO 60 I=1,180
C
C DEGREE INCREMENTS ARE CHANGED TO RADIANS FOR COMPUT-
C ATION
C
      XI=FLOAT(I)*PI/180.0
C
C IF SIN(XI)=0.0 A DIVIDE BY ZERO ERROR WILL OCCUR.
C
      IF(XI.EQ.PI) GO TO 55
```

```
      U=((COS(A*COS(XI))-COS(A))/SIN(XI))**2*
     1(E/(8.0*PI**2))
C
C THE MAXIMUM RADIATION INTENSITY OF ALL THE U VALUES
C IS STORED FOR THE DIRECTIVITY CALCULATION.
C
      IF(U.GT.UMAX) UMAX=U
   55 CONTINUE
      UA=U*SIN(XI)*THETA*2.0*PI
      PRAD=PRAD+UA
   60 CONTINUE
C
C COMPUTE THE DIRECTIVITY (DIMENSIONLESS AND IN DB)
C AND RADIATION RESISTANCE
C
      D=(4.0*PI*UMAX)/PRAD
      DDB=10.0*ALOG10(D)
C
C NOTE: THE RADIATION RESISTANCE=2*PRAD/IO**2. THE
C        CONSTANT CURRENT IO CANCELS OUT SINCE IO**2
C        IS CONTAINED IN PRAD ALSO.
C
      RR=2.0*PRAD
C IF SIN(A)=0.0 A DIVIDE BY ZERO ERROR WILL OCCUR.
C
      IF(A.EQ.PI) GO TO 71
C
C COMPUTE THE INPUT RESISTANCE.IF THE DIPOLE LENGTH
C IS AN INTEGER MULTIPLE OF 1.0 WAVELENGTH THEN RIN
C =INFINITY
C
      RIN=RR/SIN(A)**2
   71 WRITE(6,70) L,D,DDB,RR
   70 FORMAT(/////,10X,'THE DIPOLE LENGTH IS',F9.4,
     1'WAVELENGTHS',/,10X,'THE DIMENIONLESS DIRECT
     2IVITY IS',F11.7,/,10X,'THE DIRECTIVITY IN DB
     3 IS',F10.5,'DB',/,10X,'THE RADIATION RESISTA
     4NCE IS',F10.5,'OHMS')
      IF(A.EQ.PI) GO TO 100
      WRITE(6,75) RIN
   75 FORMAT(10X,'THE INPUT RESISTANCE IS',F10.5,
     1' OHMS')
      GO TO 30
  100 WRITE(6,103)
  103 FORMAT(10X,'THE INPUT RESISTANCE IS INFINITY')
   30 CONTINUE
 1000 STOP
      END
```

Chapter 5
Loop Antennas

5.1 INTRODUCTION

Another simple, inexpensive, and very versatile antenna type is the loop antenna. Loop antennas take many different forms such as a rectangle, square, triangle, ellipse, circle, and many other configurations. Because of the simplicity in analysis and construction, the circular loop is the most popular and has received the widest attention. It will be shown that a small loop (circular or square) is equivalent to an infinitesimal magnetic dipole whose axis is perpendicular to the plane of the loop. That is, the fields radiated by an electrically small circular or square loop are of the same mathematical form as those radiated by an infinitesimal magnetic dipole.

Loop antennas with electrically small circumferences or perimeters have small radiation resistances that are usually smaller than their loss resistances. Thus they are very poor radiators, and they are seldom employed for transmission in radio communication. When they are used in any such application, it is usually in the receiving mode where antenna efficiency is not as important as the signal-to-noise ratio. The radiation efficiency of the loop can be increased, and made comparable to the characteristic impedance of practical transmission lines, by increasing (electrically) its perimeter and/or the number of turns.

Another way to increase the radiation resistance of the loop is to insert, within its circumference or perimeter, a ferrite core of very high permeability which will raise the magnetic field intensity and hence the radiation resistance. This forms the so-called ferrite loop.

5.2 SMALL CIRCULAR LOOP

The most convenient geometrical arrangement for the field analysis of a loop antenna is to position the antenna symmetrically on the x-y plane, at $z = 0$, as shown in Figure 5.1(a). The wire is assumed to be very thin and the

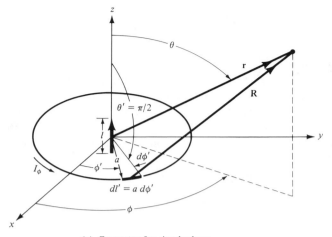

(a) Geometry for circular loop

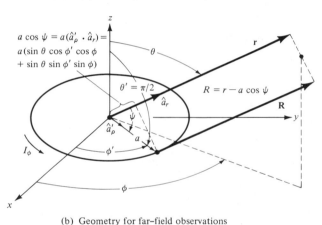

(b) Geometry for far–field observations

Figure 5.1 Geometrical arrangement for loop antenna analysis.

current distribution is given by

$$I_\phi = I_0 \tag{5-1}$$

where I_0 is a constant. Although this type of current distribution is accurate only for a loop antenna with a very small circumference, a more complex distribution makes the mathematical formulation quite cumbersome.

5.2.1 Radiated Fields

To find the fields radiated by the loop, the same procedure is followed as for the linear dipole. The potential function **A** given by (3-53) as

$$\mathbf{A}(x, y, z) = \frac{\mu}{4\pi} \int_C \mathbf{I}_e(x', y', z') \frac{e^{-jkR}}{R} dl' \tag{5-2}$$

is first evaluated. Referring to Figure 5.1(a), R is the distance from any point on the loop to the observation point and dl' is an infinitesimal section of the antenna. In general, the current distribution $\mathbf{I}_e(x', y', z')$ can be written as

$$\mathbf{I}_e(x', y', z') = \hat{a}_x I_x(x', y', z') + \hat{a}_y I_y(x', y', z') + \hat{a}_z I_z(x', y', z') \quad (5\text{-}3)$$

whose form is more convenient for linear geometries. For the circular loop antenna of Figure 5.1(a), whose current is directed along a circular path, it would be more convenient to write the rectangular current components of (5-3) in terms of the cylindrical components using the transformation (see Appendix VII)

$$\begin{bmatrix} I_x \\ I_y \\ I_z \end{bmatrix} = \begin{bmatrix} \cos\phi' & -\sin\phi' & 0 \\ \sin\phi' & \cos\phi' & 0 \\ 0 & 0 & 1 \end{bmatrix} \begin{bmatrix} I_\rho \\ I_\phi \\ I_z \end{bmatrix} \quad (5\text{-}4)$$

which when expanded can be written as

$$\left.\begin{aligned} I_x &= I_\rho \cos\phi' - I_\phi \sin\phi' \\ I_y &= I_\rho \sin\phi' + I_\phi \cos\phi' \\ I_z &= I_z \end{aligned}\right\} \quad (5\text{-}5)$$

Since the radiated fields are usually determined in spherical components, the rectangular unit vectors of (5-3) are transformed to spherical unit vectors using the transformation matrix given by (4-5). That is,

$$\left.\begin{aligned} \hat{a}_x &= \hat{a}_r \sin\theta\cos\phi + \hat{a}_\theta \cos\theta\cos\phi - \hat{a}_\phi \sin\phi \\ \hat{a}_y &= \hat{a}_r \sin\theta\sin\phi + \hat{a}_\theta \cos\theta\sin\phi + \hat{a}_\phi \cos\phi \\ \hat{a}_z &= \hat{a}_r \cos\theta \quad - \hat{a}_\theta \sin\theta \end{aligned}\right\} \quad (5\text{-}6)$$

Substituting (5-5) and (5-6) in (5-3) reduces it to

$$\begin{aligned} \mathbf{I}_e = &\, \hat{a}_r \big[I_\rho \sin\theta\cos(\phi-\phi') + I_\phi \sin\theta\sin(\phi-\phi') + I_z \cos\theta \big] \\ &+ \hat{a}_\theta \big[I_\rho \cos\theta\cos(\phi-\phi') + I_\phi \cos\theta\sin(\phi-\phi') - I_z \sin\theta \big] \\ &+ \hat{a}_\phi \big[-I_\rho \sin(\phi-\phi') + I_\phi \cos(\phi-\phi') \big] \end{aligned} \quad (5\text{-}7)$$

It should be emphasized that the source coordinates are designated as primed (ρ', ϕ', z') and the observation coordinates as unprimed (r, θ, ϕ). For the circular loop, the current is flowing in the ϕ direction (I_ϕ) so that (5-7) reduces to

$$\mathbf{I}_e = \hat{a}_r I_\phi \sin\theta\sin(\phi - \phi') + \hat{a}_\theta I_\phi \cos\theta\sin(\phi - \phi') + \hat{a}_\phi I_\phi \cos(\phi - \phi') \quad (5\text{-}8)$$

The distance R, from any point on the loop to the observation point, can be written as

$$R = \sqrt{(x - x')^2 + (y - y')^2 + (z - z')^2} \quad (5\text{-}9)$$

Since

$$x = r\sin\theta\cos\phi$$
$$y = r\sin\theta\sin\phi$$
$$z = r\cos\theta$$
$$x^2 + y^2 + z^2 = r^2$$
$$x' = a\cos\phi'$$
$$y' = a\sin\phi'$$
$$z' = 0$$
$$x'^2 + y'^2 + z'^2 = a^2 \tag{5-10}$$

(5-9) reduces to

$$R = \sqrt{r^2 + a^2 - 2ar\sin\theta\cos(\phi - \phi')}. \tag{5-11}$$

By referring to Figure 5.1(a), the differential element length is given by

$$dl' = a\,d\phi' \tag{5-12}$$

Using (5-8), (5-11), and (5-12), the ϕ-components of (5-2) can be written as

$$A_\phi = \frac{a\mu}{4\pi}\int_0^{2\pi} I_\phi\cos(\phi-\phi')\frac{e^{-jk\sqrt{r^2+a^2-2ar\sin\theta\cos(\phi-\phi')}}}{\sqrt{r^2+a^2-2ar\sin\theta\cos(\phi-\phi')}}d\phi' \tag{5-13}$$

Since the current I_ϕ as given by (5-1) is constant, the field radiated by the loop will not be a function of the observation angle ϕ. Thus any observation angle ϕ can be chosen; for simplicity $\phi = 0$. Therefore (5-13) can be written as

$$A_\phi = \frac{a\mu I_0}{4\pi}\int_0^{2\pi}\cos\phi'\frac{e^{-jk\sqrt{r^2+a^2-2ar\sin\theta\cos\phi'}}}{\sqrt{r^2+a^2-2ar\sin\theta\cos\phi'}}d\phi' \tag{5-14}$$

The integration of (5-14) cannot be carried out without any approximations. For small loops, the function

$$f = \frac{e^{-jk\sqrt{r^2+a^2-2ar\sin\theta\cos\phi'}}}{\sqrt{r^2+a^2-2ar\sin\theta\cos\phi'}} \tag{5-15}$$

which is part of the integrand of (5-14), can be expanded in a Maclaurin series about $a = 0$ using

$$f = f(o) + f'(o)a + \frac{1}{2!}f''(o)a^2 + \cdots + \frac{1}{(n-1)!}f^{(n-1)}(o)a^{n-1} + \cdots \tag{5-15a}$$

where $f'(o) = \partial f/\partial a|_{a=0}$, $f''(o) = \partial^2 f/\partial a^2|_{a=0}$, and so forth. Taking into account only the first two terms of (5-15a), or

$$f(o) = \frac{e^{-jkr}}{r} \tag{5-15b}$$

$$f'(o) = \left(\frac{jk}{r} + \frac{1}{r^2} \right) e^{-jkr} \sin\theta \cos\phi' \tag{5-15c}$$

$$f \simeq \left[\frac{1}{r} + a \left(\frac{jk}{r} + \frac{1}{r^2} \right) \sin\theta \cos\phi' \right] e^{-jkr} \tag{5-15d}$$

reduces (5-14) to

$$A_\phi \simeq \frac{a\mu I_0}{4\pi} \int_0^{2\pi} \cos\phi' \left[\frac{1}{r} + a \left(\frac{jk}{r} + \frac{1}{r^2} \right) \sin\theta \cos\phi' \right] e^{-jkr} d\phi'$$

$$A_\phi \simeq \frac{a^2\mu I_0}{4} e^{-jkr} \left(\frac{jk}{r} + \frac{1}{r^2} \right) \sin\theta \tag{5-16}$$

In a similar manner, the r- and θ-components of (5-2) can be written as

$$A_r \simeq \frac{a\mu I_0}{4\pi} \sin\theta \int_0^{2\pi} \sin\phi' \left[\frac{1}{r} + a \left(\frac{jk}{r} + \frac{1}{r^2} \right) \sin\theta \cos\phi' \right] e^{-jkr} d\phi' \tag{5-16a}$$

$$A_\theta \simeq -\frac{a\mu I_0}{4\pi} \cos\theta \int_0^{2\pi} \sin\phi' \left[\frac{1}{r} + a \left(\frac{jk}{r} + \frac{1}{r^2} \right) \sin\theta \cos\phi' \right] e^{-jkr} d\phi' \tag{5-16b}$$

which when integrated reduce to zero. Thus

$$\mathbf{A} \simeq \hat{a}_\phi A_\phi = \hat{a}_\phi \frac{a^2\mu I_0}{4} e^{-jkr} \left[\frac{jk}{r} + \frac{1}{r^2} \right] \sin\theta$$

$$= \hat{a}_\phi j \frac{k\mu a^2 I_0 \sin\theta}{4r} \left[1 + \frac{1}{jkr} \right] e^{-jkr} \tag{5-17}$$

Substituting (5-17) into (3-2a) reduces the magnetic field components to

$$H_r = j \frac{ka^2 I_0 \cos\theta}{2r^2} \left[1 + \frac{1}{jkr} \right] e^{-jkr} \tag{5-18a}$$

$$H_\theta = -\frac{(ka)^2 I_0 \sin\theta}{4r} \left[1 + \frac{1}{jkr} - \frac{1}{(kr)^2} \right] e^{-jkr} \tag{5-18b}$$

$$H_\phi = 0 \tag{5-18c}$$

Using (3-15) or (3-10) with $\mathbf{J} = 0$, the corresponding electric field components can be written as

$$E_r = E_\theta = 0 \tag{5-19a}$$

$$E_\phi = \eta \frac{(ka)^2 I_0 \sin\theta}{4r} \left[1 + \frac{1}{jkr}\right] e^{-jkr} \tag{5-19b}$$

5.2.2 Small Loop and Infinitesimal Magnetic Dipole

A comparison of (5-18a)–(5-19b) with those of the infinitesimal dipole indicates that they have similar forms. In fact, the electric and magnetic field components of an infinitesimal magnetic dipole of length l and constant "magnetic" current I_m are given by

$$E_r = E_\theta = H_\phi = 0 \tag{5-20a}$$

$$E_\phi = -j \frac{kI_m l \sin\theta}{4\pi r} \left[1 + \frac{1}{jkr}\right] e^{-jkr} \tag{5-20b}$$

$$H_r = \frac{I_m l \cos\theta}{2\pi \eta r^2} \left[1 + \frac{1}{jkr}\right] e^{-jkr} \tag{5-20c}$$

$$H_\theta = j \frac{kI_m l \sin\theta}{4\pi \eta r} \left[1 + \frac{1}{jkr} - \frac{1}{(kr)^2}\right] e^{-jkr} \tag{5-20d}$$

These can be obtained from the fields of an infinitesimal electric dipole, (4-8a)–(4-10c), by applying the principle of duality. When (5-20a)–(5-20d) are compared with (5-18a)–(5-19b), they indicate that *a magnetic dipole of magnetic moment $I_m l$ is equivalent to a small electric loop of radius a and constant electric current I_0 provided that*

$$I_m l = jS\omega\mu I_0 \tag{5-21}$$

where $S = \pi a^2$ (area of the loop). Thus for analysis purposes, the small electric loop can be replaced by a small linear magnetic dipole of constant current. The geometrical equivalence is illustrated in Figure 5.1(a) where the magnetic dipole is directed along the z-axis which is also perpendicular to the plane of the loop.

5.2.3 Power Density and Radiation Resistance

The fields radiated by a small loop, as given by (5-18a)–(5-19b), are valid everywhere except at the origin. As was discussed in Section 4.1 for the infinitesimal dipole, the power in the region very close to the antenna (near-field, $kr \ll 1$) is predominantly reactive and in the far-field ($kr \gg 1$) it is predominantly real. To illustrate this for the loop, the complex power density

$$\mathbf{W} = \tfrac{1}{2}(\mathbf{E} \times \mathbf{H}^*) = \tfrac{1}{2}\left[(\hat{a}_\phi E_\phi) \times (\hat{a}_r H_r^* + \hat{a}_\theta H_\theta^*)\right]$$
$$= \tfrac{1}{2}(-\hat{a}_r E_\phi H_\theta^* + \hat{a}_\theta E_\phi H_r^*) \tag{5-22}$$

is first formed. When (5-22) is integrated over a closed sphere, only its radial component given by

$$W_r = \eta \frac{(ka)^4}{32}|I_0|^2 \frac{\sin^2\theta}{r^2}\left[1 + j\frac{1}{(kr)^3}\right] \tag{5-22a}$$

contributes to the complex power P_r. Thus

$$P_r = \oiint_S \mathbf{W} \cdot d\mathbf{s} = \eta \frac{(ka)^4}{32}|I_0|^2 \int_0^{2\pi}\int_0^\pi \left[1 + j\frac{1}{(kr)^3}\right]\sin^3\theta\,d\theta\,d\phi \tag{5-23}$$

which reduces to

$$P_r = \eta\left(\frac{\pi}{12}\right)(ka)^4|I_0|^2\left[1 + j\frac{1}{(kr)^3}\right] \tag{5-23a}$$

and whose real part is equal to

$$P_{rad} = \eta\left(\frac{\pi}{12}\right)(ka)^4|I_0|^2 \tag{5-23b}$$

For small values of kr ($kr \ll 1$), the second term within the brackets of (5-23a) is dominant which makes the power mainly reactive. In the far-field ($kr \gg 1$), the second term within the brackets diminishes which makes the power real. A comparison between (5-23a) with (4-14) indicates a difference in sign between the terms within the brackets. Whereas for the infinitesimal dipole the radial power density in the near-field is capacitive, for the small loop it is inductive. This indicates that the radial magnetic energy is larger than the electric energy.

The radiation resistance of the loop is found by equating (5-23b) to $|I_0|^2/(2R_r)$. Doing this, the radiation resistance can be written as

$$\boxed{R_r = \eta\left(\frac{\pi}{6}\right)(k^2a^2)^2 = \eta\frac{2\pi}{3}\left(\frac{kS}{\lambda}\right)^2 = 20\pi^2\left(\frac{C}{\lambda}\right)^4} \tag{5-24}$$

where $S = \pi a^2$ is the area and $C = 2\pi a$ is the circumference of the loop.

The radiation resistance as given by (5-24) is only for a single-turn loop. If the loop antenna has N turns wound so that the magnetic field passes through all the loops, the radiation resistance is equal to that of single turn multiplied by N^2. That is,

$$\boxed{R_r = \eta\left(\frac{2\pi}{3}\right)\left(\frac{kS}{\lambda}\right)^2 N^2 = 20\pi^2\left(\frac{C}{\lambda}\right)^4 N^2} \tag{5-24a}$$

Even though the radiation resistance of a single turn loop may be small, the overall value can be increased by including many turns. This is a very desirable and practical mechanism that is not available for the infinitesimal dipole.

Example 5.1

Find the radiation resistance of a single-turn and an 8-turn small circular loop. The radius of the loop is $\lambda/25$ and the medium is free-space.

SOLUTION

$$S = \pi a^2 = \pi \left(\frac{\lambda}{25} \right)^2 = \frac{\pi \lambda^2}{625}$$

$$R_r \text{ (single turn)} = 120\pi \left(\frac{2\pi}{3} \right) \left(\frac{2\pi^2}{625} \right)^2 = 0.788 \text{ ohms}$$

$$R_r \text{ (8 turns)} = 0.788(8)^2 = 50.43 \text{ ohms}$$

The radiation and loss resistances of an antenna determine the radiation efficiency, as defined by (2-86). The loss resistance of a single-turn small loop is, in general, much larger than its radiation resistance; thus the corresponding radiation efficiencies are very low and depend on the loss resistance. To increase the radiation efficiency, multiturn loops are often employed. However, because the current distribution in a multiturn loop is quite complex, great confidence has not yet been placed in analytical methods for determining the radiation efficiency. Therefore greater reliance has been placed on experimental procedures. Two experimental techniques that can be used to measure the radiation efficiency of a small multiturn loop are those that are usually referred to as the Wheeler method and the Q method [1].

Usually it is assumed that the loss resistance of a small loop is the same as that of a straight wire whose length is equal to the circumference of the loop, and it is computed using (2-86b). Although this assumption is adequate for single-turn loops, it is not valid for multiturn loops. In a multiturn loop, the current is not uniformly distributed around the wire but depends on the skin and proximity effects [2]. In fact, for close spacings between turns, the contribution to the loss resistance due to the proximity effect can be larger than that due to the skin effect.

The total ohmic resistance for an N-turn circular loop antenna with loop radius a, wire radius b, and loop separation $2c$, shown in Figure 5.2(a), is given by [3]

$$R_{\text{ohmic}} = \frac{Na}{b} R_s \left(\frac{R_p}{R_0} + 1 \right) \tag{5-25}$$

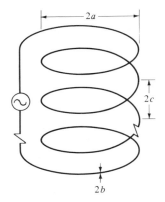

(a) *N*-turn circular loop

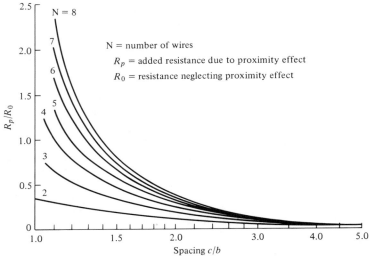

(b) Ohmic resistance due to proximity (after G. N. Smith)

Figure 5.2 *N*-turn circular loop and ohmic resistance due to proximity effect. (SOURCE: G. N. Smith, "Radiation Efficiency of Electrically Small Multiturn Loop Antennas," IEEE Trans. Antennas Propag., Vol. AP-20, No. 5, pp. 656–657, Sept. 1972 © (1972) IEEE)

where

$$R_s = \sqrt{\frac{\omega \mu_0}{2\sigma}} = \text{surface impedance of conductor}$$

$R_p = $ ohmic resistance due to proximity effect

$$R_0 = \frac{NR_s}{2\pi b} = \text{ohmic skin effect resistance per unit length}$$
$$\text{(ohms/m)}$$

The ratio of R_p/R_0 has been computed [3] as a function of the spacing c/b for loops with $2 \leq N \leq 8$ and it is shown plotted in Figure 5.2(b). It is evident that for close spacings the ohmic resistance is twice as large as that in the absence of the proximity effect ($R_p/R_0 = 0$).

Example 5.2

Find the radiation efficiency of a single-turn and an 8-turn small circular loop at $f = 100$ MHz. The radius of the loop is $\lambda/25$, the radius of the wire is $10^{-4}\lambda$, and the turns are spaced $4 \times 10^{-4}\lambda$ apart. Assume the wire is copper with a conductivity of 5.7×10^7 (S/m) and the antenna is radiating into free-space.

SOLUTION
From Example 5.1

$$R_r \text{ (single turn)} = 0.788 \text{ ohms}$$

$$R_r \text{ (8 turns)} = 50.43 \text{ ohms}$$

The loss resistance for a single turn is given, according to (2-86b), by

$$R_L = R_{hf} = \frac{a}{b}\sqrt{\frac{\omega\mu_0}{2\sigma}} = \frac{1}{25(10^{-4})}\sqrt{\frac{\pi(10^8)(4\pi \times 10^{-7})}{5.7 \times 10^7}}$$

$$= 1.053 \text{ ohms}$$

and the radiation efficiency, according to (2-86), by

$$e_{cd} = \frac{0.788}{0.788 + 1.053} = 0.428 = 42.8\%$$

From Figure 5.2(b)

$$\frac{R_p}{R_0} = 0.38$$

and from (5-25)

$$R_L = R_{\text{ohmic}} = \frac{8}{25(10^{-4})}\sqrt{\frac{\pi(10^8)(4\pi \times 10^{-7})}{5.7 \times 10^7}}(1.38) = 11.62$$

Thus

$$e_{cd} = \frac{50.43}{50.43 + 11.62} = 0.813 = 81.3\%$$

5.2.4 Near-Field ($kr \ll 1$) Region

The expressions for the fields, as given by (5-18a)–(5-19b), can be simplified if the observations are made in the near-field ($kr \ll 1$). As for the infinitesimal dipole, the predominant term in each expression for the field in the near-zone region is the last one within the parentheses of (5-18a)–(5-19b).

Thus for $kr \ll 1$

$$H_r \simeq \frac{a^2 I_0 e^{-jkr}}{2r^3} \cos\theta \qquad (5\text{-}26\text{a})$$

$$H_\theta \simeq \frac{a^2 I_0 e^{-jkr}}{4r^3} \sin\theta \qquad (5\text{-}26\text{b})$$

$$H_\phi = E_r = E_\theta = 0 \qquad (5\text{-}26\text{c})$$

$$E_\phi \simeq -j\frac{a^2 k I_0 e^{-jkr}}{4r^2} \sin\theta \qquad (5\text{-}26\text{d})$$

$\left. \right\} kr \ll 1$

The two **H**-field components are in time phase. However they are in time quadrature with those of the electric field. This indicates that the average power (real power) is zero, as for the infinitesimal dipole. The condition of $kr \ll 1$ can be satisfied at moderate distances away from the antenna provided the frequency of operation is very low. The fields of (5-26a)–(5-26d) are usually referred to as *quasistationary*.

5.2.5 Far-Field ($kr \gg 1$) Region

The other space of interest where the fields can be approximated is the far-field ($kr \gg 1$) region. In contrast to the near-field, the dominant term in (5-18a)–(5-19b) for $kr \gg 1$ is the first one within the parentheses. Since for $kr > 1$ the H_r component will be inversely proportional to r^2 whereas H_θ will be inversely proportional to r, for large values of kr ($kr \gg 1$) the H_r component will be small compared to H_θ. Thus it can be assumed that it is approximately equal to zero. Therefore for $kr \gg 1$,

$$H_\theta \simeq -\frac{k^2 a^2 I_0 e^{-jkr}}{4r} \sin\theta = -\frac{\pi S I_0 e^{-jkr}}{\lambda^2 r} \sin\theta \qquad (5\text{-}27\text{a})$$

$$E_\phi \simeq \eta\frac{k^2 a^2 I_0 e^{-jkr}}{4r} \sin\theta = \eta\frac{\pi S I_0 e^{-jkr}}{\lambda^2 r} \sin\theta \qquad (5\text{-}27\text{b})$$

$\left. \right\} kr \gg 1$

$$H_r \simeq H_\phi = E_r = E_\theta = 0 \qquad (5\text{-}27\text{c})$$

where $S = \pi a^2$ is the geometrical area of the loop.

Forming the ratio of $-E_\phi/H_\theta$, the wave impedance can be written as

$$Z_w = -\frac{E_\phi}{H_\theta} \simeq \eta \qquad (5\text{-}28)$$

where

Z_w = wave impedance

η = intrinsic impedance

As for the infinitesimal dipole, the **E**- and **H**-field components of the loop in the far-field ($kr \gg 1$) region are perpendicular to each other and transverse to the direction of propagation. They form a *T*ransverse *E*lectro*M*agnetic (TEM) mode whose wave impedance is equal to the intrinsic impedance of the medium. Equations (5-27a)–(5-27c) can also be derived using the procedure outlined and relationships developed in Section 3.6. This is left as an exercise to the reader (Prob. 5.5).

5.2.6 Radiation Intensity and Directivity

The real power P_{rad} radiated by the loop was found in Section 5.2.3 and is given by (5-23b). The same expression can be obtained by forming the average power density, using (5-27a)–(5-27c), and integrating it over a closed sphere of radius r. This is left as an exercise to the reader (Prob. 5.4). Associated with the radiated power P_{rad} is an average power density $\mathbf{W}_{av}$. It has only a radial component W_r which is related to the radiation intensity U by

$$U = r^2 W_r = \frac{\eta}{2} \left(\frac{k^2 a^2}{4} \right)^2 |I_0|^2 \sin^2 \theta = \frac{r^2}{2\eta} |E_\phi(r, \theta, \phi)|^2 \tag{5-29}$$

and it conforms to (2-12a). The normalized pattern of the loop, as given by (5-29), is identical to that of the infinitesimal dipole shown in Figure 4.2. The maximum value occurs at $\theta = \pi/2$, and it is given by

$$U_{max} = U|_{\theta = \pi/2} = \frac{\eta}{2} \left(\frac{k^2 a^2}{4} \right)^2 |I_0|^2 \tag{5-30}$$

Using (5-30) and (5-23b), the directivity of the loop can be written as

$$\boxed{ D_0 = 4\pi \frac{U_{max}}{P_{rad}} = \frac{3}{2} } \tag{5-31}$$

and its maximum effective aperture as

$$\boxed{ A_{em} = \left(\frac{\lambda^2}{4\pi} \right) D_0 = \frac{3\lambda^2}{8\pi} } \tag{5-32}$$

It is observed that the directivity, and as a result the maximum effective area, of a small loop is the same as that of an infinitesimal dipole. This should be expected since their patterns are identical.

The far-field expressions for a small loop, as given by (5-27a)–(5-27c), will be obtained by another procedure in the next section. In that section a loop of any radius but of constant current will be analyzed. Closed form solutions will be possible only in the far-field region. The small loop far-field expressions will then be obtained as a special case of that problem.

Example 5.3

The radius of a small loop of constant current is $\lambda/25$. Find the physical area of the loop and compare it with its maximum effective aperture.

SOLUTION

$$S \text{ (physical)} = \pi a^2 = \pi \left(\frac{\lambda}{25} \right)^2 = \frac{\pi \lambda^2}{625} = 5.03 \times 10^{-3} \lambda^2$$

$$A_{em} = \frac{3\lambda^2}{8\pi} = 0.119\lambda^2$$

$$\frac{A_{em}}{S} = \frac{0.119\lambda^2}{5.03 \times 10^{-3}\lambda^2} = 23.66$$

Electrically the loop is about 24 times larger than its physical size, which should not be surprising. To be effective, a small loop must be larger electrically than its physical size.

5.3 CIRCULAR LOOP OF CONSTANT CURRENT

Let us now reconsider the loop antenna of Figure 5.1(a) but with a radius that may not necessarily be small. The current in the loop will again be assumed to be constant, as given by (5-1). For this current distribution, the vector potential is given by (5-14). Without using the small radius approximation, the integration in (5-14) cannot be carried out. However, if the observations are restricted in the far-field ($r \gg a$) region, the small radius approximation is not needed to integrate (5-14).

5.3.1 Radiated Fields

To find the fields in the far-field region, the distance R can be approximated by

$$R = \sqrt{r^2 + a^2 - 2ar\sin\theta\cos\phi'} \simeq \sqrt{r^2 - 2ar\sin\theta\cos\phi'} \quad \text{for} \quad r \gg a \tag{5-33}$$

which can be reduced, using the binomial expansion, to

$$\left. \begin{array}{l} R \simeq r\sqrt{1 - \dfrac{2a}{r}\sin\theta\cos\phi'} = r - a\sin\theta\cos\phi' = r - a\cos\psi_0 \\[4pt] \qquad\qquad \text{for phase terms} \\[4pt] R \simeq r \qquad \text{for amplitude terms} \end{array} \right\} \tag{5-34}$$

since

$$\cos\psi_0 = \hat{a}_\rho' \cdot \hat{a}_r \big|_{\phi=0} = \left(\hat{a}_x \cos\phi' + \hat{a}_y \sin\phi' \right)$$

$$\cdot \left(\hat{a}_x \sin\theta\cos\phi + \hat{a}_y \sin\theta\sin\phi + \hat{a}_z \cos\theta \right)_{\phi=0}$$

$$= \sin\theta\cos\phi' \tag{5-34a}$$

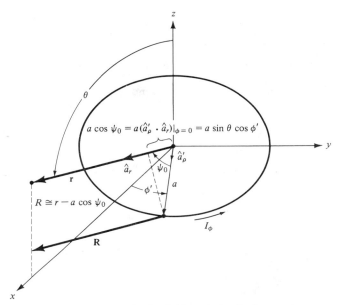

Figure 5.3   Geometry for far-field analysis of a loop antenna.

The geometrical relation between R and r, for any observation angle ϕ in the far-field region, is shown in Figure 5.1(b). For observations at $\phi = 0$, it simplifies to that given by (5-34) and shown in Figure 5.3. Thus (5-14) can be written as

$$A_\phi \simeq \frac{a\mu I_0 e^{-jkr}}{4\pi r} \int_0^{2\pi} \cos\phi' e^{+jka\sin\theta\cos\phi'}\, d\phi' \tag{5-35}$$

and it can be separated into two terms as

$$A_\phi \simeq \frac{a\mu I_0 e^{-jkr}}{4\pi r} \left[\int_0^{\pi} \cos\phi' e^{+jka\sin\theta\cos\phi'}\, d\phi' + \int_\pi^{2\pi} \cos\phi' e^{+jka\sin\theta\cos\phi'}\, d\phi' \right] \tag{5-36}$$

The second term within the brackets can be rewritten by making a change of variable of the form

$$\phi' = \phi'' + \pi \tag{5-37}$$

Thus (5-36) can also be written as

$$A_\phi \simeq \frac{a\mu I_0 e^{-jkr}}{4\pi r} \left[\int_0^{\pi} \cos\phi' e^{+jka\sin\theta\cos\phi'}\, d\phi' - \int_0^{\pi} \cos\phi'' e^{-jka\sin\theta\cos\phi''}\, d\phi'' \right] \tag{5-38}$$

Each of the integrals in (5-38) can be integrated by the formula (see Appendix V)

$$\pi j^n J_n(z) = \int_0^{\pi} \cos(n\phi) e^{+jz\cos\phi}\, d\phi \tag{5-39}$$

where $J_n(z)$ is the Bessel function of the first kind of order n. Using (5-39) reduces (5-38) to

$$A_\phi \simeq \frac{a\mu I_0 e^{-jkr}}{4\pi r} \left[\pi j J_1(ka\sin\theta) - \pi j J_1(-ka\sin\theta) \right] \tag{5-40}$$

The Bessel function of the first kind and order n is defined (see Appendix V) by the infinite series

$$J_n(z) = \sum_{m=0}^{\infty} \frac{(-1)^m (z/2)^{n+2m}}{m!(m+n)!} \tag{5-41}$$

By a simple substitution into (5-41), it can be shown that

$$J_n(-z) = (-1)^n J_n(z) \tag{5-42}$$

which for $n=1$ is equal to

$$J_1(-z) = -J_1(z) \tag{5-43}$$

Using (5-43) we can write (5-40) as

$$A_\phi \simeq j \frac{a\mu I_0 e^{-jkr}}{2r} J_1(ka\sin\theta) \tag{5-44}$$

The next step is to find the **E**- and **H**-fields associated with the vector potential of (5-44). Since (5-44) is only valid for far-field observations, the procedure outlined in Section 3.6 can be used. The vector potential **A**, as given by (5-44), is of the form suggested by (3-56). That is, the r variations are separable from those of θ and ϕ. Therefore according to (3-58a)–(3-58b) and (5-44)

$$E_r \simeq E_\theta = 0 \tag{5-45a}$$

$$E_\phi \simeq \frac{a\omega\mu I_0 e^{-jkr}}{2r} J_1(ka\sin\theta) \tag{5-45b}$$

$$H_r \simeq H_\phi = 0 \tag{5-45c}$$

$$H_\theta \simeq -\frac{E_\phi}{\eta} = -\frac{a\omega\mu I_0 e^{-jkr}}{2\eta r} J_1(ka\sin\theta) \tag{5-45d}$$

This is a much easier way of obtaining the radiated fields.

5.3.2 Power Density, Radiation Intensity, Radiation Resistance, and Directivity

The next objective for this problem will be to find the power density, radiation intensity, radiation resistance, and directivity. To do this, the time-average power density is formed. That is,

$$\mathbf{W}_{av} = \frac{1}{2} \text{Re}[\mathbf{E} \times \mathbf{H}^*] = \frac{1}{2} \text{Re}[\hat{a}_\phi E_\phi \times \hat{a}_\theta H_\theta^*] = \hat{a}_r \frac{1}{2\eta} |E_\phi|^2 \tag{5-46}$$

which can be written using (5-45b) as

$$\mathbf{W}_{av} = \hat{a}_r W_r = \hat{a}_r \frac{(a\omega\mu)^2 |I_0|^2}{8\eta r^2} J_1^2(ka\sin\theta) \tag{5-47}$$

with the radiation intensity given by

$$U = r^2 W_r = \frac{(a\omega\mu)^2 |I_0|^2}{8\eta} J_1^2(ka\sin\theta) \tag{5-48}$$

The radiation patterns for $a = \lambda/10$, $\lambda/5$, and $\lambda/2$ are shown in Figure 5.4. These patterns indicate that the field radiated by the loop along its axis ($\theta = 0°$) is zero. Also the shape of these patterns is similar to that of a linear dipole with $l \leq \lambda$ (a figure-eight shape). As the radius a increases beyond 0.5λ, the field intensity along the plane of the loop ($\theta = 90°$) diminishes and eventually it forms a null when $a \simeq 0.61\lambda$. This is left as an exercise to the reader for verification (Prob. 5.10). Beyond $a = 0.61\lambda$, the radiation along the plane of the loop begins to intensify and the pattern attains a multilobe form.

The patterns represented by (5-48) (some of them are illustrated in Figure 5.4) assume that the current distribution, no matter what the loop size, is constant. This is not a valid assumption if the loop circumference C ($C = 2\pi a$) exceeds about 0.2λ (i.e., $a > 0.032\lambda$) [4]. For radii much greater than about 0.032λ, the current variation along the circumference of the loop begins to attain a distribution that is best represented by a Fourier series [5]. Although a most common assumption is that the current distribution is nearly cosinusoidal, it is not satisfactory particularly near the driving point of the antenna.

It has been shown [6] that when the circumference of the loop is about one wavelength ($C \simeq \lambda$), its maximum radiation is along its axis ($\theta = 0°$) which is perpendicular to the plane of the loop. This feature of the loop antenna has been utilized to design Yagi-Uda arrays whose basic elements (feed, directors, and reflectors) are circular loops [7]. Because of its many applications, the one wavelength circumference circular loop antenna is considered as fundamental as a half-wavelength dipole.

The radiated power can be written using (5-47) as

$$P_{rad} = \iint_S \mathbf{W}_{av} \cdot d\mathbf{s} = \frac{\pi(a\omega\mu)^2 |I_0|^2}{4\eta} \int_0^\pi J_1^2(ka\sin\theta) \sin\theta \, d\theta \tag{5-49}$$

The integral in (5-49) cannot be integrated exactly. However, it can be rewritten [8] as

$$\int_0^\pi J_1^2(ka\sin\theta) \sin\theta \, d\theta = \frac{1}{ka} \int_0^{2ka} J_2(x) \, dx \tag{5-50}$$

Even though (5-50) still cannot be integrated, approximations can be made depending upon the values of the upper limit (the radius of the loop).

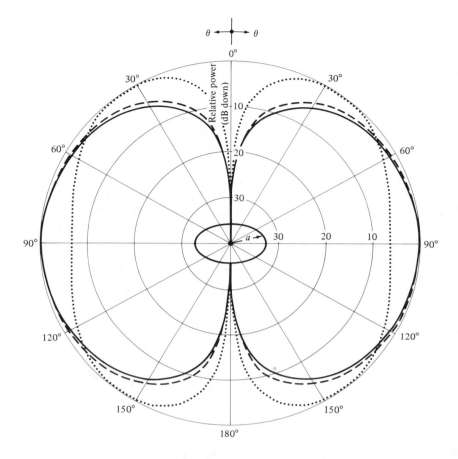

Figure 5.4 Elevation plane amplitude patterns for a circular loop of constant current (a=0.1λ, 0.2λ, and 0.5λ).

———————	$a = 0.1\lambda$
— — — — —	$a = 0.2\lambda$
·············	$a = 0.5\lambda$

LARGE LOOP APPROXIMATION ($a \geq \lambda/2$)

To evaluate (5-50), the first approximation will be to assume that the radius of the loop is large ($a \geq \lambda/2$). For that case, the integral in (5-50) can be approximated by

$$\int_0^\pi J_1^2(ka\sin\theta)\sin\theta\,d\theta = \frac{1}{ka}\int_0^{2ka} J_2(x)\,dx \simeq \frac{1}{ka} \tag{5-51}$$

and (5-49) by

$$P_{\text{rad}} \simeq \frac{\pi(a\omega\mu)^2|I_0|^2}{4\eta(ka)} \tag{5-52}$$

The maximum radiation intensity occurs when $ka\sin\theta=1.84$ so that

$$U|_{max}=\frac{(a\omega\mu)^2|I_0|^2}{8\eta}J_1^{\;2}(ka\sin\theta)|_{ka\sin\theta=1.84}=\frac{(a\omega\mu)^2|I_0|^2}{8\eta}(0.584)^2$$

(5-53)

Thus

$$R_r=\frac{2P_{rad}}{|I_0|^2}=\frac{2\pi(a\omega\mu)^2}{4\eta(ka)}=\eta\left(\frac{\pi}{2}\right)ka=60\pi^2(ka)=60\pi^2\left(\frac{C}{\lambda}\right)\quad\text{(5-54a)}$$

$$D_0=4\pi\frac{U_{max}}{P_{rad}}=4\pi\frac{ka(0.584)^2}{2\pi}=2ka(0.584)^2=0.682\left(\frac{C}{\lambda}\right)\quad\text{(5-54b)}$$

$$A_{em}=\frac{\lambda^2}{4\pi}D_0=\frac{\lambda^2}{4\pi}\left[0.682\left(\frac{C}{\lambda}\right)\right]=5.43\times10^{-2}\lambda C\quad\text{(5-54c)}$$

where C (circumference)$=2\pi a$ and $\eta\simeq120\pi$.

INTERMEDIATE LOOP APPROXIMATION ($\lambda/6\pi\le a<\lambda/2$)
If the radius of the loop is $\lambda/6\pi\le a<\lambda/2$, the integral of (5-50) can be approximated by

$$\int_0^\pi J_1^{\;2}(ka\sin\theta)\sin\theta\,d\theta=\frac{1}{ka}\int_0^{2ka}J_2(x)\,dx$$

$$\simeq\frac{1}{ka}\left[-2J_1(2ka)+\int_0^{2ka}J_0(y)\,dy\right]\quad\text{(5-55)}$$

where $J_0(y)$ is the Bessel function of the first kind of zero order. No further simplifications can be made. The integral of $J_0(y)$ appearing in (5-55) is a tabulated function which is included in Appendix V. The radiation resistance, directivity, and maximum effective area can be found using (5-55) to evaluate the P_{rad} of (5-49).

SMALL LOOP APPROXIMATION ($a<\lambda/6\pi$)
If the radius of the loop is small ($a<\lambda/6\pi$), the expressions for the fields as given by (5-45a)–(5-45d) can be simplified. To do this, the Bessel function $J_1(ka\sin\theta)$ is expanded, by the definition of (5-41), in an infinite series of the form (see Appendix V)

$$J_1(ka\sin\theta)=\tfrac{1}{2}(ka\sin\theta)-\tfrac{1}{8}(ka\sin\theta)^3+\cdots\quad\text{(5-56)}$$

For small values of ka ($ka<\tfrac{1}{3}$), (5-56) can be approximated by its first term, or

$$J_1(ka\sin\theta)\simeq\frac{ka\sin\theta}{2}\quad\text{(5-56a)}$$

Thus (5-45a)–(5-45d) can be written as

$$E_r \simeq E_\theta = 0 \qquad (5\text{-}57\text{a})$$

$$E_\phi \simeq \frac{a^2 \omega \mu k I_0 e^{-jkr}}{4r} \sin\theta = \eta \frac{a^2 k^2 I_0 e^{-jkr}}{4r} \sin\theta \qquad (5\text{-}57\text{b})$$

$$H_r \simeq H_\phi = 0 \qquad \qquad a < \lambda/6\pi \qquad (5\text{-}57\text{c})$$

$$H_\theta \simeq -\frac{a^2 \omega \mu k I_0 e^{-jkr}}{4\eta r} \sin\theta = -\frac{a^2 k^2 I_0 e^{-jkr}}{4r} \sin\theta \qquad (5\text{-}57\text{d})$$

which are identical to those of (5-27a)–(5-27c). Thus the expressions for the radiation resistance, radiation intensity, directivity, maximum effective aperture, and radiation resistance are those given by (5-24), (5-29), (5-31), and (5-32).

To demonstrate the variation of the radiation resistance as a function of the radius a of the loop, it is plotted in Figure 5.5 for $\lambda/100 \leq a \leq \lambda/30$, based on the approximation of (5-56a). It is evident that the values are extremely low (less than 1 ohm), and they are usually smaller than the loss resistances of the wires. These radiation resistances also lead to large mismatch losses when connected to practical transmission lines of 50 or 75 ohms. To increase the radiation resistance, it would require multiple turns as suggested by (5-24a). This, however, also increases the loss resistance which

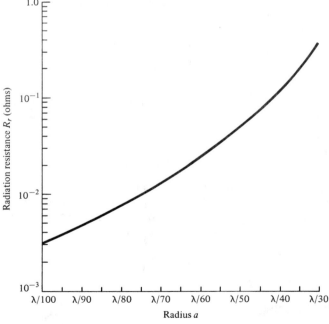

Figure 5.5 Radiation resistance for a constant current circular loop antenna based on the approximation of (5-56a).

contributes to the inefficiency of the antenna. A plot of the radiation resistance for $0 < ka = C/\lambda < 20$, based on the evaluation of (5-50) by numerical techniques, is shown in Figure 5.6. The dashed line represents the values based on the large loop approximation of (5-51) and the dotted ($\cdots\cdots$) represents the values based on the small loop approximation of (5-56a).

In addition to the real part of the input impedance, there is also an imaginary component which would increase the mismatch losses even if the real part is equal to the characteristic impedance of the lossless transmission line. However, the imaginary component can always, in principle at least, be eliminated by connecting a reactive element (capacitive or inductive) across the terminals of the loop to make the antenna a resonant circuit.

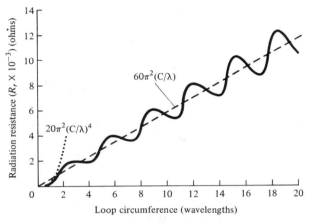

(a) Radiation resistance of circular loop

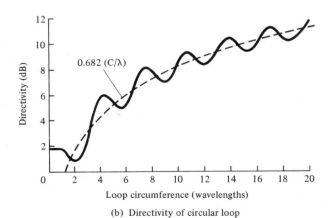

(b) Directivity of circular loop

Figure 5.6 Radiation resistance and directivity for circular loop of constant current. (SOURCE: E. A. Wolff, *Antenna Analysis*, Wiley, New York, 1966)

To facilitate the computations for the directivity and radiation resistance of a circular loop with a constant current distribution, a FORTRAN computer program has been developed. The program utilizes (5-53) and (5-49) to compute the directivity [(5-49) is integrated numerically]. The program requires that the radius of the loop (in wavelengths) is read with a FORMAT as specified by the READ statement. A Bessel function subroutine is contained within the program. A listing of the program is included at the end of this chapter.

5.4   CIRCULAR LOOP WITH NONUNIFORM CURRENT

The analysis in the previous sections was based on a uniform current, which would be a valid approximation when the radius of the loop is small electrically (usually $a < 0.03$–0.04λ). As the dimensions of the loop increase, the current variations along the circumference of the loop must be taken into account. As stated previously, a very common assumption for the current distribution is a cosinusoidal variation [9], [10]. This, however, is not a satisfactory approximation particularly near the driving point of the antenna [4]. A better distribution would be to represent the current by a Fourier series [5].

A complete analysis of the fields radiated by a loop with nonuniform current distribution is somewhat complex, laborious, and quite lengthy. Instead of attempting to include the analytical formulations, which are cumbersome but well documented in the cited references, a number of graphical illustrations of numerical and experimental data will be presented. These curves can be used in facilitating designs.

To illustrate that the current distribution of a wire loop antenna is not uniform unless its radius is very small, the magnitude and phase of it have been plotted in Figure 5.7 as a function of ϕ' (in degrees). The loop circumference C is $ka = C/\lambda = 0.1$, 0.2, 0.3, and 0.4 and the wire size was chosen so that $\Omega = 2\ln(2\pi a/b) = 10$. It is apparent that for $ka = 0.1$ the current is nearly uniform. For $ka = 0.2$ the variations are slightly greater and become even larger as ka increases. On the basis of these results, loops much larger than $ka = 0.2$ (radius much greater than 0.03–0.04λ) cannot be considered small.

Computed impedances, based on the Fourier series representation of the current, are shown plotted in Figure 5.8. The input resistance and reactance are plotted as a function of the circumference C (in wavelengths) for $0 \le ka = C/\lambda \le 2.5$. The diameter of the wire was chosen so that $\Omega = 2\ln(2\pi a/b) = 8$, 9, 10, 11, and 12. It is apparent that the first antiresonance occurs when the circumference of the loop is about $\lambda/2$, and it is extremely sharp. It is also noted that as the loop wire increases in thickness, there is a rapid disappearance of the resonances. As a matter of fact, for $\Omega < 9$ there is only one antiresonance point. These curves (for $C > \lambda$) are similar, both qualitatively and quantitatively, to those of a linear dipole. The major

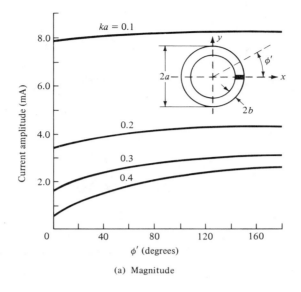

(a) Magnitude

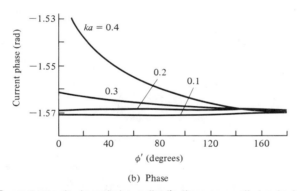

(b) Phase

Figure 5.7 Current magnitude and phase distributions on small circular loop antennas. (SOURCE: J. E. Storer, "Impedance of Thin-Wire Loop Antennas," *AIEE Trans.*, vol. 75, Nov. 1956. © 1956 IEEE)

difference is that the loop is more capacitive (by about 130 ohms) than a dipole. This shift in reactance allows the dipole to have several resonances and antiresonances while moderately thick loops ($\Omega < 9$) have only one antiresonance. Also small loops are primarily inductive while small dipoles are primarily capacitive. The resistance curves for the loop and the dipole are very similar.

To verify the analytical formulations and the numerical computations, loop antennas were built and measurements of impedance were made [4]. The measurements were conducted using a half-loop over an image plane, and it was driven by a two-wire line. An excellent agreement between theory

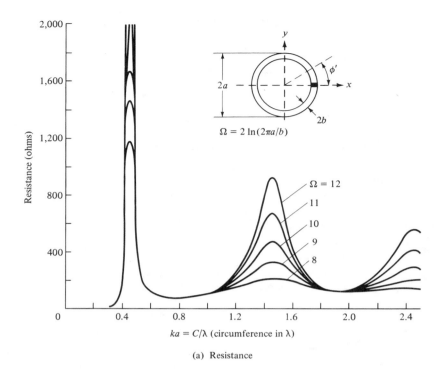

(a) Resistance

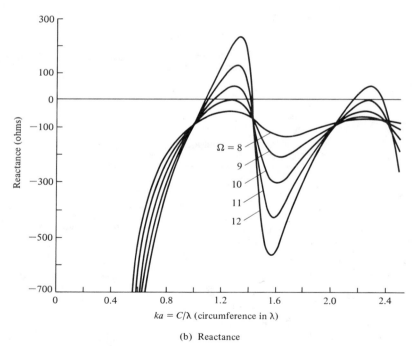

(b) Reactance

Figure 5.8 Input impedance of circular loop antennas. (SOURCE: J. E. Storer, "Impedance of Thin-Wire Loop Antennas," *AIEE Trans.*, vol. 75, Nov. 1956. © 1956 IEEE)

and experiment was indicated everywhere except near resonances where computed conductance curves were slightly higher than those measured. This is expected since ohmic losses were not taken into account in the analytical formulation. It was also noted that the measured susceptance curve was slightly displaced vertically by a constant value. This can be attributed to the "end effect" of the experimental feeding line and the "slice generator" used in the analytical modeling of the feed. For a dipole, the correction to the analytical model is usually a negative capacitance in shunt with the antenna [11]. A similar correction for the loop would result in a better agreement between the computed and measured susceptances. Computations for a half-loop above a ground plane were also performed by J. E. Jones [12] using the Moment Method.

The radiation resistance of a loop antenna, with a cosinusoidal current distribution, was computed [13] by evaluating triple integrals numerically. The results are shown in Figure 5.9 where they are compared with those of a uniform current distribution. It is evident that when the circumference of the loop is less than about 0.8λ, the constant current radiation resistances agree quite well with those of the cosinusoidal distribution.

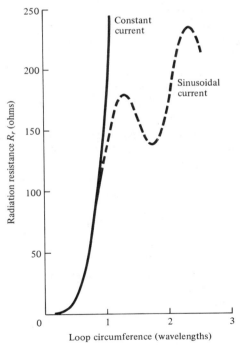

Figure 5.9 Radiation resistance of circular loop with constant and sinusoidal current distributions. (SOURCE: A. Richtscheid, "Calculation of the Radiation Resistance of Loop Antennas with Sinusoidal Current Distribution," *IEEE Trans. Antennas Propag.*, vol. AP-24, Nov. 1976. © 1976 IEEE)

5.5 GROUND AND EARTH CURVATURE EFFECTS FOR CIRCULAR LOOPS

The presence of a lossy medium can drastically alter the performance of a circular loop. The parameters mostly affected are the pattern, directivity, input impedance, and antenna efficiency. The amount of energy dissipated as heat by the lossy medium directly affects the antenna efficiency. As for the linear elements, geometrical optics techniques can be used to analyze the radiation characteristics of loops in the presence of conducting surfaces. The reflections are taken into account by introducing appropriate image (virtual) sources. Divergence factors are introduced to take into account the effects of the ground curvature. Because the techniques are identical to the formulations of Section 4.8, they will not be repeated here. The reader is directed to that section for the details. It should be pointed out, however, that a horizontal loop has horizontal polarization in contrast to the vertical polarization of a vertical electric dipole. Exact boundary-value solutions, based on Sommerfeld integral formulations, are available [14]. However they are too complex to be included in an introductory chapter.

A qualitative criterion that can be used to judge the antenna performance is the ratio of the radiation resistance in free-space to that in the presence of the homogeneous lossy medium [14]. This is a straightforward but very tedious approach. A much simpler method [15] is to find directly the self-impedance changes (real and imaginary) that result from the presence of the conducting medium.

Since a small horizontal circular loop is equivalent to a small vertical magnetic dipole (see Section 5.2.2), computations [16] were carried out for a vertical magnetic dipole placed a height h above a homogeneous lossy half-space. The changes in the self-impedance, normalized with respect to the free-space radiation resistance R_0 given by (5-24), are shown plotted in Figure 5.10. The parameter N_1 is defined by (4-124).

As for the vertical electric dipole, the magnitude changes of $\Delta R / R_0$ in Figure 5.10(a) approach unity as the height h of the antenna above a perfectly conducting ($|N_1| = \infty$) ground plane approaches zero ($2k_0 h \rightarrow 0$). For the magnetic dipole (or the loop) this corresponds to a vanishing resistance. Also, as expected, the magnitude of ΔX approaches infinity as $2k_0 h \rightarrow 0$. Both ΔR and ΔX become oscillatory as $2k_0 h$ exceeds approximately π or when h exceeds about $\lambda_0 / 4$.

The effect the finite conductivity has on the resistance (ΔR) and reactance (ΔX) changes for $|N_1| = 100, 25, 4$ are shown in Figures 5.10(b) and (c). Significant modifications, compared to those of a perfect conductor, are indicated. The effects a stratified lossy half-space have on the characteristics of a horizontal small circular loop have also been investigated and documented [17]. It was found that when a resonant loop is close to the interface, the changes in the input admittance as a function of the antenna height and the electrical properties of the lossy medium were very pronounced. This suggests that a resonant loop could be used effectively to

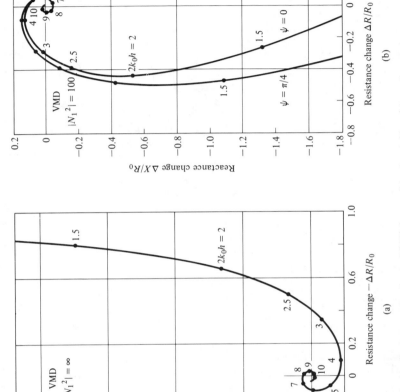

Figure 5.10 Vertical magnetic dipole (VMD) (or small horizontal loop) impedance change as a function of height above a homogeneous lossy half-space. (SOURCE: R. E. Collin and F. J. Zucker (eds.), *Antenna Theory Part 2*, McGraw-Hill, New York, 1969)

189

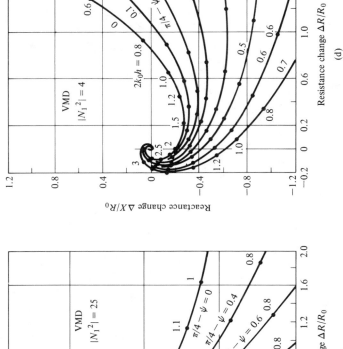

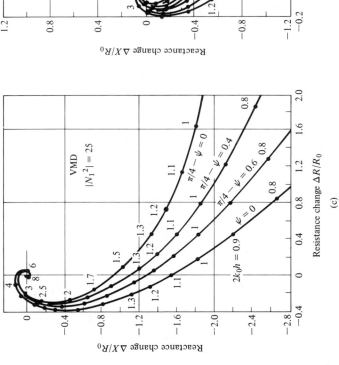

Figure 15.10 (*Continued*)

190

sense and to determine the electrical properties of an unknown geological structure.

5.6 POLYGONAL LOOP ANTENNAS

The most attractive polygonal loop antennas are the square, rectangular, triangular, and rhombic. These antennas can be used for practical applications such as for aircraft, missiles, and communications systems. However, because of their more complex structure, theoretical analyses seem to be unsuccessful [18]. Thus the application of these antennas has received much less attention. However design curves, computed using the Moment Method, do exist [19] and can be used to design polygonal loop antennas for practical applications. Usually the circular loop has been used in the UHF range because of its higher directivity while triangular and square loops have been applied in the HF and UHF bands because of advantages in their mechanical construction. Broadband impedance characteristics can be obtained from the different polygonal loops.

5.6.1 Square Loop

Next to the circular loop, the square loop is the simplest loop configuration. The far-field pattern for a small loop, in each of its principal planes, can be obtained by assuming that each of its sides is a small linear dipole of constant current I_0 and length l. Referring to Figure 5.11, the field in the y-z plane is given according to (4-26a) by

$$E_\phi = E_{\phi 1} + E_{\phi 2} = -j\eta \frac{kI_0 l}{4\pi} \left[\frac{e^{-jkr_1}}{r_1} - \frac{e^{-jkr_2}}{r_2} \right] \tag{5-58}$$

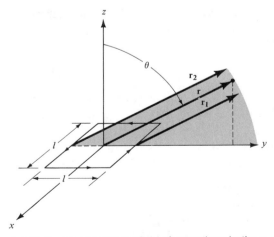

Figure 5.11 Square loop geometry for far-field observations in the y-z plane.

since the pattern of each element is omnidirectional in that plane. Using the far-field approximations of

$$
\left.
\begin{aligned}
r_1 &\simeq r - \frac{l}{2}\sin\theta \\
r_2 &\simeq r + \frac{l}{2}\sin\theta
\end{aligned}
\right\} \quad \text{for phase variations}
\tag{5-58a}
$$

$$
r_1 \simeq r_2 \simeq r \qquad \text{for amplitude variations}
\tag{5-58b}
$$

(5-58) can be written as

$$
E_\phi = \eta \frac{kI_0 l e^{-jkr}}{2\pi r} \sin\left(\frac{kl}{2}\sin\theta\right)
\tag{5-59}
$$

For small values of l ($l < \lambda/50$), (5-59) reduces to

$$
\boxed{\;E_\phi = \eta \frac{(kl)^2 I_0 e^{-jkr}}{4\pi r}\sin\theta = \eta \frac{\pi S I_0 e^{-jkr}}{\lambda^2 r}\sin\theta\;}
\tag{5-60}
$$

where $S = l^2$ is the geometrical area of the loop. The corresponding magnetic field is given by

$$
H_\theta = -\frac{E_\phi}{\eta} = -\frac{\pi S I_0 e^{-jkr}}{\lambda^2 r}\sin\theta
\tag{5-61}
$$

Equations (5-60) and (5-61) are identical to (5-27b) and (5-27a), respectively, for the small circular loop. Thus the far-zone principal-plane fields of a small square loop are identical to those of a small circular loop. The fields in the other planes are more difficult to obtain, and they will not be attempted here. However design curves are included which can be used for practical design applications.

5.6.2 Triangular, Rectangular, and Rhombic Loops

Shown in Figure 5.12 are the polygonal loops for which design data will be presented. They consist of top- and base-driven triangular loops, a rectangular loop, and a rhombic loop. The top-driven triangular loop has its feed at the top corner of the isosceles triangle while the base-driven configuration has its terminals at the base. The rectangular loop has its feed at the center of one of its sides while the rhombic configuration has its terminals at one of its corners.

The parameter β defines the angle of the top corner of the isosceles triangle for the triangular and rhombic loops while $\gamma = W/H$ is used to identify the relative side dimensions of the rectangular loop. The perimeter of each loop is given by P; for the rectangular loop, $P = 2(H + W)$. For all configurations, the radius of the wire is a.

Shown in Figure 5.13 are the input impedance ($Z = R + jX$) variations, as a function of P (in wavelengths), of the four configurations shown

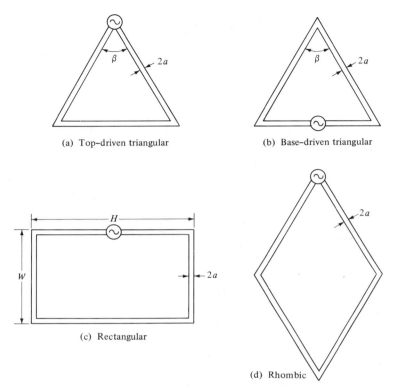

(a) Top–driven triangular   (b) Base–driven triangular

(c) Rectangular

(d) Rhombic

Figure 5.12 Typical configurations of polygonal loop antennas. (SOURCE: T. Tsukiji and S. Tou, "On Polygonal Loop Antennas," *IEEE Trans. Antennas Propag.*, vol. AP-28, No. 4, July 1980. © 1980 IEEE)

in Figure 5.12. The interval between adjacent points on each curve is $\Delta P/\lambda = 0.2$. Depending on the parameters β or γ, the input resistance of polygonal loops near the resonance frequency changes drastically. The impedance goes to zero when a loop approaches a short-circuited $\lambda/2$ long transmission line. In design then, the shape of the loop can be chosen so that the input impedance is equal to the characteristic impedance of the transmission line. Although the curves in Figure 5.13 are for specific wire radii, the impedance variations of the polygonal antennas as a function of the wire diameter are similar to those of the dipole.

Because the radius of the impedance locus for the $\beta = 60°$ of the top-driven triangular loop [Figure 5.13(a)] is smaller than for the other values of β, the $\beta = 60°$ has the broadest impedance bandwidth compared with other triangular shapes or with the same shape but different feed points. Similar broadband impedance characteristics are indicated in Figure 5.13(c) for a rectangular loop with $\gamma = 0.5$ (the side with the feed point is twice as large as the other).

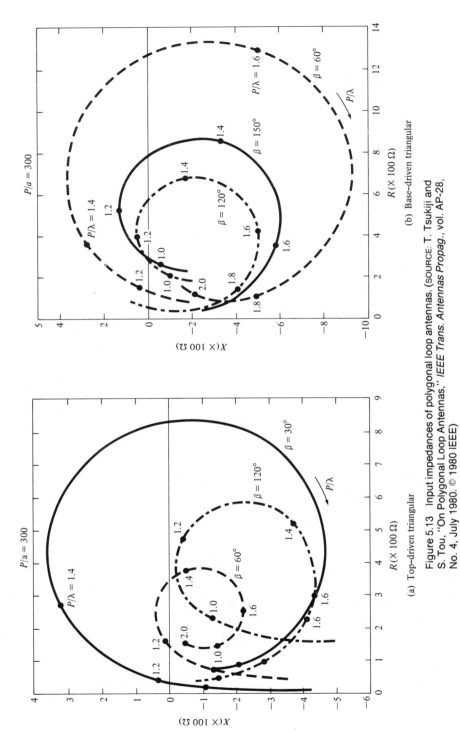

Figure 5.13 Input impedances of polygonal loop antennas. (SOURCE: T. Tsukiji and S. Tou, "On Polygonal Loop Antennas," *IEEE Trans. Antennas Propag.*, vol. AP-28, No. 4, July 1980. © 1980 IEEE)

(a) Top-driven triangular

(b) Base-driven triangular

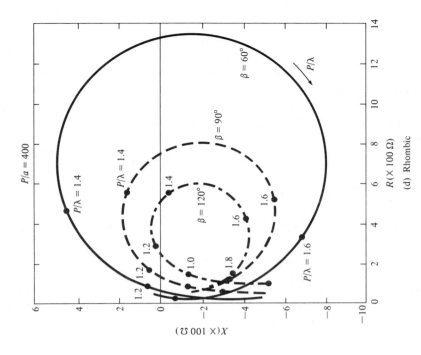

(d) Rhombic

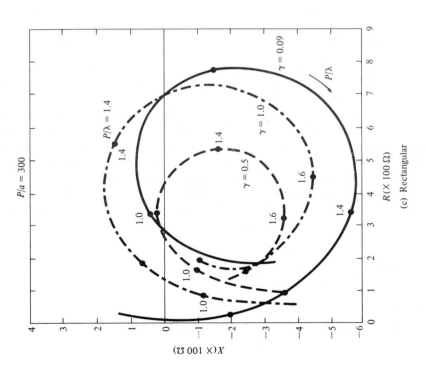

(c) Rectangular

Figure 5.13 *(Continued)*

195

It can then be concluded that if the proper shape and feed point are chosen, a polygonal loop can have broadband impedance characteristics. The most attractive are the top-driven triangular loop with $\beta = 60°$ and the rectangular loop with $\gamma = 0.5$. A 50–70 ohm coaxial cable can be matched with a triangular loop with $\beta = 40°$. Rectangular loops with greater directivities, but with less ideal impedance characteristics, are those with larger values of γ.

The frequency characteristics of a polygonal loop can be estimated by inspecting its current distribution. When the current standing wave pattern has, at its antiresonant frequency, a null at a sharp corner of the loop, the loop has a very low current standing wave and, hence, broadband impedance characteristics.

Radiation patterns for the $\beta = 60°$ top- and base-driven triangular loops and the $\gamma = 4$ rectangular loop, for various values of P (in wavelengths), were also computed [19]. It was noted that for low frequencies near the resonance, the patterns of the top- and base-driven triangular loops were not too different. However, for higher frequencies the base-driven triangular loop had a greater gain than its corresponding top-driven configuration. In general, rectangular loops with larger γ's have greater gains.

5.7 FERRITE LOOP

Because the loss resistance is comparable to the radiation resistance, electrically small loops are very poor radiators and are seldom used in the transmitting mode. However, they are often used for receiving signals, such as in radios, where the signal-to-noise ratio is much more important than the efficiency.

The radiation resistance, and in turn the antenna efficiency, can be raised by increasing the circumference of the loop. Another way to increase the radiation resistance, without increasing the electrical dimensions of the antenna, would be to insert within its circumference a ferrite core that has a tendency to increase the magnetic flux, the magnetic field intensity, and in turn the radiation resistance of the loop [20]–[22]. This is the so-called *ferrite loop* and the ferrite material can be a rod of very few inches in length. The radiation resistance of the ferrite loop is given by

$$\frac{R_f}{R_r} = \left(\frac{\mu_e}{\mu_0} \right)^2 \tag{5-62}$$

where

R_f = radiation resistance of ferrite loop

R_r = radiation resistance of air core loop

μ_e = effective permeability of ferrite core

μ_0 = permeability of free-space

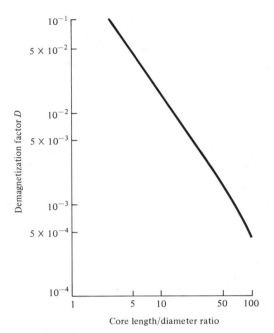

Figure 5.14 Demagnetization factor as a function of core length/diameter ratio. (SOURCE: E. A. Wolff, *Antenna Analysis*, Wiley, New York, 1966)

Using (5-24), the radiation resistance of (5-62) for a single-turn small ferrite loop can be written as

$$R_f = 20\pi^2 \left(\frac{C}{\lambda}\right)^4 \left(\frac{\mu_e}{\mu_0}\right)^2 \tag{5-63}$$

and for a N-turn loop, using (5-24a), as

$$R_f = 20\pi^2 \left(\frac{C}{\lambda}\right)^4 \left(\frac{\mu_e}{\mu_0}\right)^2 N^2 \tag{5-64}$$

The actual permeability of the ferrite material μ_f is related to the effective permeability of the ferrite core by

$$\mu_e = \frac{\mu_f}{1 + D(\mu_f - 1)} \tag{5-65}$$

where D is the demagnetization factor which has been found experimentally for different core geometries, as shown in Figure 5.14.

Because of their smallness, ferrite loop antennas of few turns wound around a small ferrite rod are used as antennas especially in pocket transistor radios. The antenna is usually connected in parallel with the RF amplifier tuning capacitance and, in addition to acting as an antenna, it furnishes the necessary inductance to form a tuned circuit. Because the inductance is obtained with only few turns, the loss resistance is kept small. Thus the Q is usually very high, and it results in high selectivity and greater induced voltage.

References

1. E. H. Newman, P. Bohley, and C. H. Walter, "Two Methods for Measurement of Antenna Efficiency," *IEEE Trans. Antennas Propag.*, vol. AP-23, No. 4, July 1975, pp. 457–461.
2. G. N. Smith, "Radiation Efficiency of Electrically Small Multiturn Loop Antennas," *IEEE Trans. Antennas Propag.*, vol. AP-20, No. 5, September 1972, pp. 656–657.
3. G. Smith, "The Proximity Effect in Systems of Parallel Conductors," *J. Appl. Phys.*, vol. 43, No. 5, May 1972, pp. 2196–2203.
4. J. E. Storer, "Impedance of Thin-Wire Loop Antennas," *AIEE Trans.*, (Part I. Communication and Electronics) vol. 75, Nov. 1956, pp. 606–619.
5. H. C. Pocklington, "Electrical Oscillations in Wire," *Cambridge Philosophical Society Proceedings*, London, England, vol. 9, 1897, p. 324.
6. S. Adachi and Y. Mushiake, "Studies of Large Circular Loop Antenna," Sci. Rep. Research Institute of Tohoku University (RITU), B, 9, 2, 1957, pp. 79–103.
7. S. Ito, N. Inagaki, and T. Sekiguchi, "An Investigation of the Array of Circular-Loop Antennas," *IEEE Trans. Antennas and Propag.*, vol. AP-19, No. 4, July 1971, pp. 469–476.
8. G. N. Watson, *A Treatise on the Theory of Bessel Functions*, Cambridge University Press, London, 1922.
9. J. E. Lindsay, Jr., "A Circular Loop Antenna with Non-Uniform Current Distribution," *IRE Trans. Antennas and Propag.*, vol. AP-8, No. 4, July 1960, pp. 438–441.
10. E. A. Wolff, *Antenna Analysis*, Wiley, New York, 1966.
11. R. King, "Theory of Antennas Driven from Two-Wire Line," *Journal of Applied Physics*, vol. 20, 1949, p. 832.
12. D. G. Fink (ed.), *Electronics Engineers' Handbook*, Section 18, "Antennas" (by W. F. Croswell), McGraw-Hill, New York, pp. 18–22.
13. A. Richtscheid, "Calculation of the Radiation Resistance of Loop Antennas with Sinusoidal Current Distribution," *IEEE Trans. Antennas and Propag.*, vol. AP-24, Nov. 1976, pp. 889–891.
14. R. E. Collin and F. J. Zucher (eds.), *Antenna Theory Part 2*, Chapter 23 (by J. R. Wait), McGraw-Hill, New York, 1969.
15. J. R. Wait, "Possible Influence of the Ionosphere on the Impedance of a Ground-Based Antenna," *J. Res. Natl. Bur. Std.* (U.S.), vol. 66D, September-October 1962, pp. 563–569.
16. L. E. Vogler and J. L. Noble, "Curves of Input Impedance Change Due to Ground for Dipole Antennas," U.S. National Bureau of Standards, Monograph 72, Jan. 31, 1964.
17. D. C. Chang, "Characteristics of a Horizontal Circular Loop Antenna over a

Multilayered, Dissipative Half-Space," *IEEE Trans. Antennas Propag.*, vol. AP-21, No. 6, November 1973, pp. 871–874.

18. R. W. P. King, "Theory of the Center-Driven Square Loop Antenna," *IRE Trans. Antennas Propag.*, vol. AP-4, No. 4, July 1956, p. 393.

19. T. Tsukiji and S. Tou, "On Polygonal Loop Antennas," *IEEE Trans. Antennas Propag.*, vol. AP-28, No. 4, July 1980, pp. 571–575.

20. M. A. Islam, "A Theoretical Treatment of Low-Frequency Loop Antennas with Permeable Cores," *IEEE Trans. Antennas and Propag.*, vol. AP-11, No. 2, March 1963, pp. 162–169.

21. V. H. Rumsey and W. L. Weeks, "Electrically Small Ferrite Loaded Loop Antennas," *IRE Convention Record*, vol. 4, Part 1, 1956, pp. 165–170.

22. E. A. Wolff, *Antenna Analysis*, Wiley, New York, 1966, pp. 75–89.

23. IBM-360 Scientific Subroutine Package, p. 363.

PROBLEMS

5.1. Derive
   (a) (5-18a)–(5-18c) using (5-17) and (3-2a)
   (b) (5-19a)–(5-19b) using (5-18a)–(5-18c)

5.2. Write the fields of an infinitesimal linear magnetic dipole of constant current I_m, length l, and positioned along the z-axis. Use the fields of an infinitesimal electric dipole, (4-8a)–(4-10c), and apply the principle of duality. Compare with (5-20a)–(5-20d).

5.3. Find the radiation efficiency of a single-turn and a 4-turn circular loop each of radius $\lambda/(10\pi)$ and operating at 10 MHz. The radius of the wire is $10^{-3}\lambda$ and the turns are spaced $3 \times 10^{-3}\lambda$ apart. Assume the wire is copper with a conductivity of 5.7×10^7 S/m, and the antenna is radiating into free-space.

5.4. Find the power radiated by a small loop by forming the average power density, using (5-27a)–(5-27c), and integrating over a sphere of radius r. Compare the answer with (5-23b).

5.5. For a small loop of constant current, derive its far-zone fields using (5-17) and the procedure outlined and relationships developed in Section 3.6. Compare the answers with (5-27a)–(5-27b).

5.6. A very small circular loop of radius a ($a < \lambda/6\pi$) and constant current I_0 is symmetrically placed about the origin at $x = 0$ and with the plane of its area parallel to the y-z plane. Find the
   (a) spherical **E**- and **H**-field components radiated by the loop in the far-zone
   (b) directivity of the antenna

5.7. Repeat Problem 5.6 when the plane of the loop is parallel to the x-z plane at $y = 0$.

5.8. Using the computer program at the end of this chapter, compute the radiation resistance and the directivity of a circular loop of constant current with a radius of
   (a) $a = \lambda/50$ (b) $a = \lambda/10$
   (c) $a = \lambda/4$ (d) $a = \lambda/2$

5.9. A constant current circular loop of radius $a = 5\lambda/4$ is placed on the x-y plane. Find the *two* smallest angles (excluding $\theta = 0°$) where a null is formed in the far-field pattern.

5 10. Design a circular loop of constant current such that its field intensity vanishes only at $\theta = 0°$ and $90°$. Find its
   (a) radius
   (b) radiation resistance
   (c) directivity

5.11. Design a constant current circular loop so that its first minimum, aside from $\theta = 0°$, in its far-field pattern is at $30°$ from a normal to the plane of the loop. Find the
   (a) smallest radius of the antenna (in wavelengths)
   (b) relative (to the maximum) radiation intensity (*in dB*) in the plane of the loop

5.12. Design a constant current circular loop so that its pattern has a null in the plane of the loop, and two nulls above and two nulls below the plane of the loop. Find the
   (a) radius of the loop
   (b) angles where the nulls will occur

5.13. A constant current circular loop is placed on the x-y plane. Find the far-field position, relative to that of the loop, that a linearly polarized probe antenna must have so that the polarization loss factor (PLF) is maximized.

5.14. A very small $(a \ll \lambda)$ circular loop of constant current is placed a distance h above an infinite electric ground plane. Assuming z is perpendicular to the ground plane, find the total far-zone field radiated by the loop when its plane is parallel to the
   (a) x-z plane
   (b) y-z plane

5.15. For the loop of Problem 5.14(a), find the smallest height h so that a null is formed in the y-z plane at an angle of $45°$ above the ground plane.

5.16. A circular loop of nonconstant current distribution, with circumference of 1.4λ, is attached to a 300-ohm line. Assuming the radius of the wire is $1.555 \times 10^{-2}\lambda$, find the
   (a) input impedance of the loop
   (b) VSWR of the system
   (c) inductance or capacitance that must be placed across the feed points so that the loop becomes resonant at $f = 100$ MHz

5.17. Design circular loops of wire radius b, which resonate at the first resonance. Find
   (a) four values of a/b where the first resonance occurs (a is the radius of the loop)
   (b) the circumference of the loops and the corresponding radii of the wires for the antennas of part (a)

5.18. A very small circular loop, of constant current and radius of $\lambda_0/25$, is placed a height h above a perfect conductor and it is radiating in free-space.
   (a) Find the smallest height h $(h < \lambda)$ where the changes of its reactance are the smallest.
   (b) At the height from part (a), find the radiation resistance of the loop.

COMPUTER PROGRAM—CIRCULAR LOOP:
DIRECTIVITY AND RADIATION RESISTANCE

```
C  ************************************************************
C    THIS PROGRAM COMPUTES THE DIRECTIVITY (DIMENSIONLESS-
C  AND DB) AND RADIATION RESISTANCE FOR SMALL (CONSTANT CUR-
C  RENT) LOOPS OF RADIUS SPECIFIED BY THE USER.THE LOOP IS
C  RADIATING IN FREE SPACE.THE DIRECTIVITY AND RADIATION
C  RESISTANCE ARE CALCULATED USING THE TRAILING EDGE METHOD
C  IN INCREMENTS OF 1 DEGREE IN THETA.THE INPUT DATA CARDS
C  CONTAIN THE LOOP RADII (IN WAVELENGTHS),ONE TO A CARD.
C  ************************************************************

C
C DEFINE CONTANTS AND INCREMENT TAKEN.
C
      PI=3.14159
      E=120.0*PI
      THETA=PI/180.0
      WRITE(6,65)
   65 FORMAT(1H1)
C
C THE LOOP RADIUS (IN WAVELENGTHS) IS READ IN
C
      DO 30 J=1,1000
   40 READ(5,50,END=1000) A
   50 FORMAT (F7.4)
C
C INITALIZE PRAD AND UMAX TO 0.0 EACH TIME THROUGH
C THE LOOP TO CLEAR PRAD AND UMAX FOR A NEW COMPUTATION
C
      UMAX=0.0
      PRAD=0.0
C
C A SINGLE DO LOOP IS USED TO COMPUTE PRAD(INTEGRAL
C OF THE RADIATION INTENSITY U),SINCE U VARIES ONLY
C IN THETA
C
      DO 60 I=1,180
C
C DEGREE INCREMENTS ARE CHANGE TO RADIANS FOR COMPUTATION
C
      XI=FLOAT(I)*PI/180.0
      X=2.0*PI*A*SIN(XI)
      CALL BESJ(X,1,F,0.0001,IER)
      IF(IER.EQ.2) WRITE(6,102)
  102 FORMAT(10X,'X IS NEGATIVE OR ZERO')
      IF(IER.EQ.3) WRITE(6,103)
  103 FORMAT(10X,'REQUIRED ACCURACY NOT OBTAINED')
      U=A**2*(2.0*PI)**2/8.0*E*F**2
C
C THE MAXIMUM RADIATION INTENSITY OF ALL THE U VALUES
C IS STORED FOR THE DIRECTIVITY CALCULATION.

C
      IF(U.GT.UMAX) UMAX=U
      UA=U*SIN(XI)*THETA*2.0*PI
      PRAD=PRAD+UA
   60 CONTINUE
C
C COMPUTE THE DIRECTIVITY(DIMENSIONLESS AND IN DB)
C AND RADIATION RESISTANCE
C
      D=(4.0*PI*UMAX)/PRAD
      DDB=10.0*ALOG10(D)
C
C NOTE: THE RADIATION RESISTANCE=2*PRAD/IO**2.THE
```

```
C CONSTANCE CURRENT IO CANCELS OUT SINCE IO**2 IS
C CONTAINED IN PRAD ALSO.
C
      RR=2.0*PRAD
   71 WRITE(6,70) A,D,DDB,RR
   70 FORMAT(/////,10X,'THE LOOP RADIUS IS',F9.4,
     1'WAVELENGTHS',/,10X,'THE DIMENSIONLESS DIRECT
     2IVITY IS',F11.7,/,10X,'THE DIRECTIVITY IN DB
     3 IS',F10.5,'DB',/,10X,'THE RADIATION RESIST
     4ANCE IS',F10.5,'OHMS')
   30 CONTINUE
 1000 STOP
      END
C
C ***********************************************************
C
C    SUBROUTINE BESJ [23]
C
C    PURPOSE
C      COMPUTE THE J BESSEL FUNCTION FOR A GIVEN ARGUMENT
C      AND ORDER
C    USAGE
C      CALL BESJ(X,N,BJ,D,IER)
C    DESCRIPTION OF PARAMETERS
C      X - THE ARGUMENT OF THE J BESSEL FUNCTION DESIRED
C      N - THE ORDER OF THE J BESSEL FUNCTION DESIRED
C      BJ - THE RESULTANT J BESSEL FUNCTION
C      D - REQUIRED ACCURACY
C      IER- RESULTANT ERROR CODE WHERE
C         IER=0 NO ERROR
C         IER=1 N IS NEGITIVE
C         IER=2 X IS NEGITIVE OR ZERO
C         IER=3 REQUIRED ACCURACY NOT OBTAINED
C         IER=4 RANGE OF N COMPARED TO X NOT CORRECT (SEE -
C               REMARKS)
C    REMARKS
C      N MUST BE GREATER THAN OR EQUAL TO ZERO,BUT IT
C      MUST BE LESS THAN
C            20+10*X-X**2/3  FOR X LESS THAN OR EQUAL TO 15
C            90+X/2          FOR X GREATER THAN 15
C  SUBROUTINES AND FUNCTION SUBPROGRAMS REQUIRED
C    NONE
C
C  METHOD
C    RECURRENCE RELATION TECHNIQUE DESCRIBED BY H. GOLDSTEIN
C    AND R.M. THALER,'RECURRENCE TECHNIQUES FOR THE CALCULA-
C    TION OF BESSEL FUNCTIONS',M.T.A.V.,V.13,PP.102-108 AND
C    I.A. STEGUN AND M. ABRAMOWITZ,'GENERATION OF BESSEL
C    FUNCTIONS ON HIGH SPEED COMPUTERS',M.T.A.C.,V.11,
C    1957.PP.255-257
C
C ***********************************************************
C
      SUBROUTINE BESJ(X,N,BJ,D,IER)

      BJ=.0
      IF(N)10,20,20
   10 IER=1
      RETURN
   20 IF(X)30,30,31
   30 IER=2
      RETURN
   31 IF(X-15.)32,32,34
   32 NTEST=20.+10.*X-X**2/3
      GO TO 36
   34 NTEST=90.+X/2.
   36 IF(N-NTEST)40,38,38
```

```
   38   IER=4
        RETURN
   40   IER=0
        N1=N+1
        BPREV=.0
C
C       COMPUTE STARTING VALUE OF M
C
        IF(X-5.)50,60,60
   50   MA=X+6.
        GO TO 70
   60   MA=1.4*X+60./X
   70   MB=N+IF IX(X)/4+2
        MZERO=MAXO(MA,MB)
C
C       SET UPPER LIMIT OF M
C
        MMAX=NTEST
  100   DO 190 M=MZERO,MMAX,3
C
C       SET F(M),F(M-1)
C
        FM1=1.0E-28
        FM=.0
        ALPHA=.0

        IF(M-(M/2)*2)120,110,120
  110   JT=-1
        GO TO 130
  120   JT=1
  130   M2=M-2
        DO 160 K=1,M2
        MK=M-K
        BMK=2.*FLOAT(MK)*FM1/X-FM
        FM=FM1
        FM1=BMK
        IF(MK-N-1)150,140,150
  140   BJ=BMK
  150   JT=-JT
        S=1+JT
  160   ALPHA=ALPHA+BMK*S
        BMK=2.*FM1/X-FM
        IF(N)180,170,180
  170   BJ=BMK
  180   ALPHA=ALPHA+BMK
        BJ=BJ/ALPHA
        IF(ABS(BJ-BPREV)-ABS(D*BJ))200,200,190
  190   BPREV=BJ
        IER=3
  200   RETURN
        END
```

Chapter 6
Arrays: Linear, Planar, and Circular

6.1 INTRODUCTION

In the previous chapter, the radiation characteristics of single-element antennas were discussed and analyzed. Usually the radiation pattern of a single element is relatively wide, and each element provides low values of directivity (gain). In many applications it is necessary to design antennas with very directive characteristics (very high gains) to meet the demands of long distance communication. This can only be accomplished by increasing the electrical size of the antenna.

Enlarging the dimensions of single elements often leads to more directive characteristics. Another way to enlarge the dimensions of the antenna, without necessarily increasing the size of the individual elements, is to form an assembly of radiating elements in an electrical and geometrical configuration. This new antenna, formed by multielements, is referred to as an *array*. In most cases, the elements of an array are identical. This is not necessary, but it is often convenient, simpler, and more practical. The individual elements of an array may be of any form (wires, apertures, etc.).

Neglecting coupling between elements, the total field of the array is determined by the vector addition of the fields radiated by the individual elements. To provide very directive patterns, it is necessary that the fields from the elements of the array interfere constructively (add) in the desired directions and interfere destructively (cancel each other) in the remaining space. Ideally this can be accomplished, but practically it is only approached. In an array of identical elements, there are five controls that can be used to shape the overall pattern of the antenna. These are:

1. the geometrical configuration of the overall array (linear, circular, rectangular, spherical, etc.)

2. the relative displacement between the elements
3. the excitation amplitude of the individual elements
4. the excitation phase of the individual elements
5. the relative pattern of the individual elements

The influence that each one of the above has on the overall radiation characteristics will be the subject of this chapter. In many cases the techniques will be illustrated with examples.

The simplest and one of the most practical arrays is formed by placing the elements along a line. To simplify the presentation and give a better physical interpretation of the techniques, a two-element array will first be considered. The analysis of an N-element array will then follow. Two-dimensional analysis will be the subject at first. In latter sections, three-dimensional techniques will be introduced.

6.2 TWO-ELEMENT ARRAY

Let us assume that the antenna under investigation is an array of two infinitesimal horizontal dipoles positioned along the z-axis, as shown in Figure 6.1(a). The field radiated by the two elements, assuming no coupling between the elements, is equal to the sum of the two and in the y-z plane it is given by

$$\mathbf{E}_t = \mathbf{E}_1 + \mathbf{E}_2 = \hat{a}_\theta \, j\eta \frac{kI_0 l}{4\pi} \left\{ \frac{e^{-j[kr_1-(\beta/2)]}}{r_1} |\cos\theta_1| + \frac{e^{-j[kr_2+(\beta/2)]}}{r_2} |\cos\theta_2| \right\}$$

(6-1)

where β is the difference in phase excitation between the elements. The magnitude excitation of the radiators is identical. Assuming far-field observations and referring to Figure 6.1(b),

$$\theta_1 \simeq \theta_2 \simeq \theta \qquad (6\text{-}2a)$$

$$\left. \begin{aligned} r_1 &\simeq r - \frac{d}{2}\cos\theta \\ r_2 &\simeq r + \frac{d}{2}\cos\theta \end{aligned} \right| \begin{aligned} &\text{for phase} \\ &\text{variations} \end{aligned} \qquad (6\text{-}2b)$$

$$r_1 \simeq r_2 \simeq r \qquad \text{for amplitude variations} \qquad (6\text{-}2c)$$

Equation (6-1) reduces to

$$\mathbf{E}_t = \hat{a}_\theta \, j\eta \frac{kI_0 l e^{-jkr}}{4\pi r} |\cos\theta| [e^{+j(kd\cos\theta+\beta)/2} + e^{-j(kd\cos\theta+\beta)/2}]$$

$$\mathbf{E}_t = \hat{a}_\theta \, j\eta \frac{kI_0 l e^{-jkr}}{4\pi r} |\cos\theta| \, 2\cos\left[\frac{1}{2}(kd\cos\theta+\beta) \right]$$

(6-3)

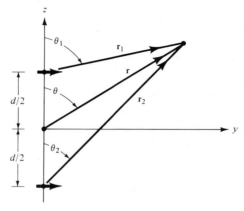

(a) Two infinitesimal dipoles

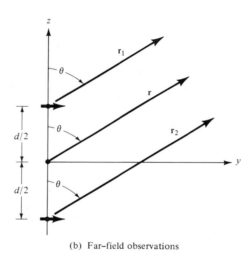

(b) Far–field observations

Figure 6.1 Geometry of a two-element array positioned along the z-axis.

It is apparent from (6-3) that the total field of the array is equal to the field of a single element positioned at the origin multiplied by a factor which is widely referred to as the *array factor*. Thus for the two-element array of constant amplitude, the array factor is given by

$$\text{AF} = 2\cos\left[\tfrac{1}{2}(kd\cos\theta + \beta)\right] \tag{6-4}$$

which in normalized form can be written as

$$(\text{AF})_n = \cos\left[\tfrac{1}{2}(kd\cos\theta + \beta)\right] \tag{6-4a}$$

The array factor is a function of the geometry of the array and the excitation phase. By varying the separation d and/or the phase β between the elements, the characteristics of the array factor and of the total field of the array can be controlled.

It has been illustrated that the far-zone field of a uniform two-element array of identical elements is equal to the *product of the field of a single element, at a selected reference point (usually the origin), and the array factor of that array*. That is,

$$
\boxed{\mathbf{E}(\text{total}) = \left[\mathbf{E}(\text{single element at reference point}) \right] \times \left[\text{array factor} \right]}
$$

(6-5)

This is referred to as *pattern multiplication* for arrays of identical elements. Although it has been illustrated only for an array of two elements, each of identical magnitude, it is also valid for arrays with any number of identical elements which do not necessarily have identical magnitudes, phases, and/or spacings between them. This will be demonstrated in this chapter by a number of different arrays.

Each array has its own array factor. The array factor, in general, is a function of the number of elements, their geometrical arrangement, their relative magnitudes, their relative phases, and their spacings. The array factor will be of simpler form if the elements have identical amplitudes, phases, and spacings. Since the array factor does not depend on the directional characteristics of the radiating elements themselves, it can be formulated by replacing the actual elements with isotropic (point) sources. Once the array factor has been derived using the point-source array, the total field of the actual array is obtained by the use of (6-5). Each point-source is assumed to have the amplitude, phase, and location of the corresponding element it is replacing.

In order to synthesize the total pattern of an array, the designer is not only required to select the proper radiating elements but the geometry (positioning) and excitation of the individual elements. To illustrate the principles, let us consider some examples.

Example 6.1

Given the array of Figures 6.1(a) and (b), find the nulls of the total field when $d = \lambda/4$ and

(a) $\beta = 0$

(b) $\beta = +\dfrac{\pi}{2}$

(c) $\beta = -\dfrac{\pi}{2}$

SOLUTION

(a) $\beta = 0$

The normalized field is given by

$$E_{tn} = |\cos \theta| \cos\left(\frac{\pi}{4} \cos \theta\right)$$

The nulls are obtained by setting the total field equal to zero, or

$$E_{tn} = |\cos \theta| \cos\left(\frac{\pi}{4} \cos \theta\right)\Big|_{\theta=\theta_n} = 0$$

Thus

$$\cos \theta_n = 0 \Rightarrow \theta_n = 90°$$

and

$$\cos\left(\frac{\pi}{4} \cos \theta_n\right) = 0 \Rightarrow \frac{\pi}{4} \cos \theta_n = \frac{\pi}{2}, -\frac{\pi}{2} \Rightarrow \theta_n = \text{does not exist}$$

The only null occurs at $\theta = 90°$ and is due to the pattern of the individual elements. The array factor does not contribute any additional nulls because there is not enough separation between the elements to introduce a phase difference of 180° between the elements, for any observation angle.

(b) $\beta = +\frac{\pi}{2}$

The normalized field is given by

$$E_{tn} = |\cos \theta| \cos\left[\frac{\pi}{4}(\cos \theta + 1)\right]$$

The nulls are found from

$$E_{tn} = |\cos \theta| \cos\left[\frac{\pi}{4}(\cos \theta + 1)\right]\Big|_{\theta=\theta_n} = 0$$

Thus

$$\cos \theta_n = 0 \Rightarrow \theta_n = 90°$$

and

$$\cos\left[\frac{\pi}{4}(\cos \theta + 1)\right]\Big|_{\theta=\theta_n} = 0 \Rightarrow \frac{\pi}{4}(\cos \theta_n + 1) = \frac{\pi}{2} \Rightarrow \theta_n = 0°$$

and

$$\Rightarrow \frac{\pi}{4}(\cos \theta_n + 1) = -\frac{\pi}{2} \Rightarrow \theta_n = \text{does not exist}$$

The nulls of the array occur at $\theta = 90°$ and $0°$. The null at $0°$ is introduced by the arrangement of the elements (array factor). This can also be shown by physical reasoning. The element in the negative z-axis has an initial phase lag of 90° relative to the other element. As the wave from that element travels toward the positive z-axis, it undergoes an additional 90°

phase retardation when it arrives at the other element on the positive z-axis. Thus there is a total of 180° phase difference between the waves of the two elements when travel is toward the positive z-axis ($\theta=0°$). The waves of the two elements are in phase when they travel in the negative z-axis ($\theta=180°$).

(c) $\beta=-\dfrac{\pi}{2}$

The normalized field is given by

$$E_{tn}=|\cos\theta|\cos\left[\frac{\pi}{4}(\cos\theta-1)\right]$$

and the nulls by

$$E_{tn}=|\cos\theta|\cos\left[\frac{\pi}{4}(\cos\theta-1)\right]\Big|_{\theta=\theta_n}=0$$

Thus

$$\cos\theta_n=0\Rightarrow\theta_n=90°$$

and

$$\cos\left[\frac{\pi}{4}(\cos\theta_n-1)\right]=0\Rightarrow\frac{\pi}{4}(\cos\theta_n-1)=\frac{\pi}{2}\Rightarrow\theta_n=\text{does not exist}$$

and

$$\Rightarrow\frac{\pi}{4}(\cos\theta_n-1)=-\frac{\pi}{2}\Rightarrow\theta_n=180°$$

The nulls occur at 90° and 180°. The element at the positive z-axis has a phase lag of 90° relative to the other, and the phase difference is 180° when travel is restricted toward the negative z-axis. There is no phase difference when the waves travel toward the positive z-axis.

To better illustrate the pattern multiplication rule, the normalized patterns of the single element, the array factor, and the total array for each of the above array examples are shown in Figures 6.2, 6.3(a), and 6.3(b). In each figure, the total pattern of the array is obtained by multiplying the pattern of the single element by that of the array factor. Since the array factor for the example of Figure 6.2 is nearly isotropic (within 3 dB), the element pattern and the total pattern are almost identical in shape. The largest magnitude difference between the two is about 3 dB. Because the array factor for Figure 6.3(a) is of cardioid form, its corresponding element and total patterns are considerably different. In the total pattern, the null at $\theta=90°$ is due to the element pattern while that toward $\theta=0°$ is due to the array factor. Similar results are displayed in Figure 6.3(b).

Example 6.2

Consider an array of two identical infinitesimal dipoles oriented as shown in Figures 6.1(a) and (b). For a separation d and phase excitation difference β

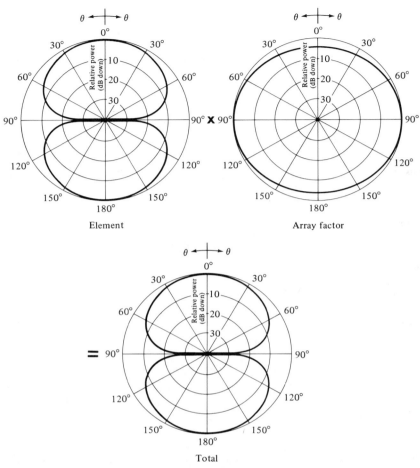

Figure 6.2   Element, array factor, and total field patterns of a two-element array of infinitesimal horizontal dipoles with identical phase excitation ($\beta=0°, d=\lambda/4$).

between the elements, find the angles of observation where the nulls of the array occur. The magnitude excitation of the elements is the same.

SOLUTION

The normalized total field of the array is given by (6-3) as

$$E_{tn}=|\cos\theta|\ \cos\left[\tfrac{1}{2}(kd\cos\theta+\beta)\right]$$

To find the nulls, the field is set equal to zero, or

$$E_{tn}=|\cos\theta|\ \cos\left[\tfrac{1}{2}(kd\cos\theta+\beta)\right]\big|_{\theta=\theta_n}=0$$

Thus

$$\cos\theta_n=0\Rightarrow\theta_n=90°$$

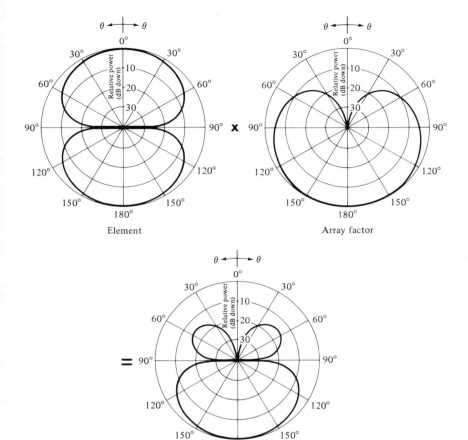

Figure 6.3 (a) Pattern multiplication of element, array factor, and total array patterns of a two-element array of infinitesimal horizontal dipoles with (a) $\beta = +90°$, $d=\lambda/4$. (b) $\beta = -90°$, $d=\lambda/4$.

and

$$\cos\left[\frac{1}{2}(kd\cos\theta_n + \beta)\right] = 0 \Rightarrow \frac{1}{2}(kd\cos\theta_n + \beta) = \pm\left(\frac{2n+1}{2}\right)\pi$$

$$\Rightarrow \theta_n = \cos^{-1}\left(\frac{\lambda}{2\pi d}[-\beta \pm (2n+1)\pi]\right),$$

$$n = 0, 1, 2, \ldots$$

The null at $\theta = 90°$ is attributed to the pattern of the individual elements of the array while the remaining ones are due to the formation of the array. For no phase difference between the elements ($\beta = 0$), the separation d must be equal or greater than half a wavelength ($d \geq \lambda/2$) in order for at least one null, due to the formation of the array, to occur.

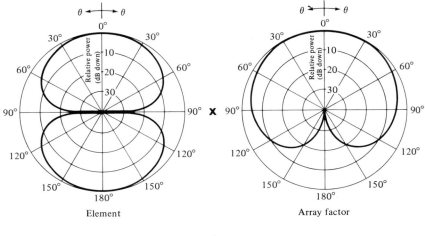

Element   X   Array factor

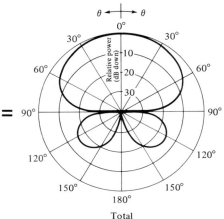

=

Total

Figure 6.3(b) Continued

6.3 *N*-ELEMENT LINEAR ARRAY: UNIFORM AMPLITUDE AND SPACING

Now that the arraying of elements has been introduced and it was illustrated by the two-element array, let us generalize the method to include N elements. Referring to the geometry of Figure 6.4, let us assume that all the elements have identical amplitudes but each succeeding element has a β progressive phase lead current excitation relative to the preceding one (β represents the phase by which the current in each element leads the current of the preceding element). *An array of identical elements all of identical magnitude and each with a progressive phase is referred to as a uniform array.* The array factor can be obtained by considering the elements to be point sources. If the actual elements are not isotropic sources, the total field can

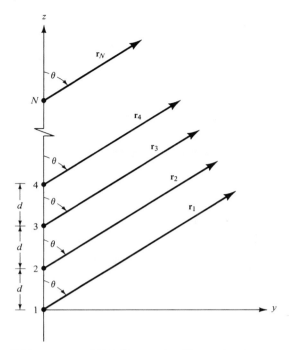

Figure 6.4 Far-field geometry of *N*-element array of isotropic sources positioned along the *z*-axis.

be formed by multiplying the array factor of the isotropic sources by the field of a single element. This is the pattern multiplication rule of (6-5), and it applies only for arrays of identical elements. The array factor is given by

$$AF = 1 + e^{+j(kd\cos\theta + \beta)} + e^{+j2(kd\cos\theta + \beta)} + \cdots + e^{j(N-1)(kd\cos\theta + \beta)}$$

$$AF = \sum_{n=1}^{N} e^{j(n-1)(kd\cos\theta + \beta)} \tag{6-6}$$

which can be written as

$$AF = \sum_{n=1}^{N} e^{j(n-1)\psi} \tag{6-7}$$

$$\text{where} \quad \psi = kd\cos\theta + \beta \tag{6-7a}$$

Multiplying both sides of (6-7) by $e^{j\psi}$, it can be written as

$$(AF)e^{j\psi} = e^{j\psi} + e^{j2\psi} + e^{j3\psi} + \cdots + e^{j(N-1)\psi} + e^{jN\psi} \tag{6-8}$$

Subtracting (6-7) from (6-8) reduces to

$$AF(e^{j\psi} - 1) = (-1 + e^{jN\psi}) \tag{6-9}$$

which can also be written as

$$AF = \left[\frac{e^{jN\psi} - 1}{e^{j\psi} - 1} \right] = e^{j[(N-1)/2]\psi} \left[\frac{e^{j(N/2)\psi} - e^{-j(N/2)\psi}}{e^{j(1/2)\psi} - e^{-j(1/2)\psi}} \right]$$

$$= e^{j[(N-1)/2]\psi} \left[\frac{\sin\left(\dfrac{N}{2}\psi\right)}{\sin\left(\dfrac{1}{2}\psi\right)} \right] \qquad \text{(6-10)}$$

If the reference point is the physical center of the array, the array factor of (6-10) reduces to

$$AF = \left[\frac{\sin\left(\dfrac{N}{2}\psi\right)}{\sin\left(\dfrac{1}{2}\psi\right)} \right] \qquad \text{(6-10a)}$$

For small values of ψ, the above expression can be approximated by

$$AF \simeq \left[\frac{\sin\left(\dfrac{N}{2}\psi\right)}{\dfrac{\psi}{2}} \right] \qquad \text{(6-10b)}$$

The maximum value of (6-10a) or (6-10b) is equal to N. To normalize the array factors so that the maximum value of each is equal to unity, (6-10a) and (6-10b) are written in normalized form as (see Appendix II)

$$\boxed{(AF)_n = \frac{1}{N} \left[\frac{\sin\left(\dfrac{N}{2}\psi\right)}{\sin\left(\dfrac{1}{2}\psi\right)} \right]} \qquad \text{(6-10c)}$$

and (see Appendix I)

$$\boxed{(AF)_n \simeq \left[\frac{\sin\left(\dfrac{N}{2}\psi\right)}{\dfrac{N}{2}\psi} \right]} \qquad \text{(6-10d)}$$

To find the nulls of the array, (6-10c) or (6-10d) are set equal to zero. That is,

$$\sin\left(\frac{N}{2}\psi\right) = 0 \Rightarrow \frac{N}{2}\psi\Big|_{\theta=\theta_n} = \pm n\pi \Rightarrow \theta_n = \cos^{-1}\left[\frac{\lambda}{2\pi d}\left(-\beta \pm \frac{2n}{N}\pi\right)\right]$$

$$\text{(6-11)}$$

$$n = 1, 2, 3, \ldots$$
$$n \neq N, 2N, 3N, \ldots \text{ with } (6\text{-}10c)$$

For $n = N, 2N, 3N, \ldots$, (6-10c) attains its maximum values because it reduces to a $\sin(0)/0$ form. The values of n determine the order of the nulls (first, second, etc.). For a zero to exist, the argument of the arccosine cannot exceed unity. Thus the number of nulls that can exist will be a function of the element separation d and the phase excitation difference β.

The maximum values of (6-10c) occur when

$$\frac{\psi}{2} = \frac{1}{2}(kd\cos\theta + \beta)\Big|_{\theta=\theta_m} = \pm m\pi \Rightarrow \theta_m = \cos^{-1}\left[\frac{\lambda}{2\pi d}(-\beta \pm 2m\pi)\right]$$

$$m = 0, 1, 2, \ldots \tag{6-12}$$

The array factor of (6-10d) has only one maximum and occurs when $m = 0$ in (6-12). That is,

$$\theta_m = \cos^{-1}\left(\frac{\lambda\beta}{2\pi d}\right) \tag{6-13}$$

which is the observation angle that makes $\psi = 0$.

The 3-dB point for the array factor of (6-10d) occurs when (see Appendix I)

$$\frac{N}{2}\psi = \frac{N}{2}(kd\cos\theta + \beta)\Big|_{\theta=\theta_h} = \pm 1.391$$

$$\Rightarrow \theta_h = \cos^{-1}\left[\frac{\lambda}{2\pi d}\left(-\beta \pm \frac{2.782}{N}\right)\right] \tag{6-14}$$

which can also be written as

$$\theta_h = \frac{\pi}{2} - \sin^{-1}\left[\frac{\lambda}{2\pi d}\left(-\beta \pm \frac{2.782}{N}\right)\right] \tag{6-14a}$$

For large values of $d(d \gg \lambda)$, it reduces to

$$\theta_h \simeq \left[\frac{\pi}{2} - \frac{\lambda}{2\pi d}\left(-\beta \pm \frac{2.782}{N}\right)\right] \tag{6-14b}$$

The half-power beamwidth Θ_h can be found once the angles of the first maximum (θ_m) and the half-power point (θ_h) are found. For a symmetrical pattern

$$\Theta_h = 2|\theta_m - \theta_h| \tag{6-14c}$$

For the array factor of (6-10d), there are secondary maxima (maxima of minor lobes) which occur *approximately* when the numerator of (6-10d) attains its maximum value. That is,

$$\sin\left(\frac{N}{2}\psi\right) = \sin\left[\frac{N}{2}(kd\cos\theta + \beta)\right]\Big|_{\theta=\theta_s} \simeq \pm 1 \Rightarrow \frac{N}{2}(kd\cos\theta + \beta)\Big|_{\theta=\theta_s}$$

$$\simeq \pm\left(\frac{2s+1}{2}\right)\pi \Rightarrow \theta_s \simeq \cos^{-1}\left\{\frac{\lambda}{2\pi d}\left[-\beta \pm \left(\frac{2s+1}{N}\right)\pi\right]\right\},$$

$$s = 1, 2, 3, \ldots \tag{6-15}$$

which can also be written as

$$\theta_s \simeq \frac{\pi}{2} - \sin^{-1}\left\{\frac{\lambda}{2\pi d}\left[-\beta \pm \left(\frac{2s+1}{N}\right)\pi\right]\right\}, \qquad s=1,2,3,\ldots \qquad (6\text{-}15a)$$

For large values of $d(d \gg \lambda)$, it reduces to

$$\theta_s \simeq \frac{\pi}{2} - \frac{\lambda}{2\pi d}\left[-\beta \pm \left(\frac{2s+1}{N}\right)\pi\right], \qquad s=1,2,3,\ldots \qquad (6\text{-}15b)$$

The maximum of the first minor lobe of (6-10c) occurs *approximately* when (see Appendix I)

$$\frac{N}{2}\psi = \frac{N}{2}(kd\cos\theta + \beta)\Big|_{\theta=\theta_s} \simeq \pm\left(\frac{3\pi}{2}\right) \qquad (6\text{-}16)$$

or when

$$\theta_s = \cos^{-1}\left\{\frac{\lambda}{2\pi d}\left[-\beta \pm \frac{3\pi}{N}\right]\right\} \qquad (6\text{-}16a)$$

At that point, the magnitude of (6-10d) reduces to

$$(AF)_n \simeq \left[\frac{\sin\left(\frac{N}{2}\right)\psi}{\frac{N}{2}\psi}\right]\Bigg|_{\substack{\theta=\theta_s \\ s=1}} = \frac{2}{3\pi} = 0.212 \qquad (6\text{-}17)$$

which in dB is equal to

$$(AF)_n = 20\log_{10}\left(\frac{2}{3\pi}\right) = -13.46 \text{ dB} \qquad (6\text{-}17a)$$

Thus the maximum of the first minor lobe of the array factor of (6-10d) is 13.46 dB down from the maximum at the major lobe. More accurate expressions for the angle, beamwidth, and magnitude of first minor lobe of the array factor of (6-10d) can be obtained. These will be discussed in Chapter 11.

6.3.1 Broadside Array

In many applications it is desirable to have the maximum radiation of an array directed normal to the axis of the array (broadside; $\theta=90°$ of Figure 6.4). To optimize the design, the maxima of the single element and of the array factor should both be directed toward $\theta=90°$. The requirements of the single elements can be accomplished by the judicious choice of the radiators, and those of the array factor by the proper separation and excitation of the individual radiators. In this section, the requirements that allow the array factor to "radiate" efficiently broadside will be developed.

Referring to (6-10c) or (6-10d), the maximum of the array factor occurs when

$$\psi = kd\cos\theta + \beta = 0 \qquad (6\text{-}18)$$

Since it is desired to have the maximum directed toward $\theta = 90°$, then

$$\boxed{\psi = kd\cos\theta + \beta\big|_{\theta=90°} = \beta = 0} \qquad (6\text{-}18a)$$

Thus to have the maximum of the array factor of a uniform linear array directed broadside to the axis of the array, it is necessary that all the elements have the same phase excitation (in addition to the same amplitude excitation). The separation between the elements can be of any value. To ensure that there are no maxima in other directions, the separation between the elements should not be equal to multiples of a wavelength ($d \neq n\lambda$, $n = 1, 2, 3 \dots$) when $\beta = 0$. If $d = n\lambda$, $n = 1, 2, 3, \dots$ and $\beta = 0$, then

$$\psi = kd\cos\theta + \beta \bigg|_{\substack{d=n\lambda \\ \beta=0 \\ n=1,2,3,\dots}} = 2\pi n\cos\theta \bigg|_{\theta=0°,180°} = \pm 2n\pi \qquad (6\text{-}19)$$

This value of ψ when substituted in (6-10c) makes the array factor attain its maximum value. Thus for a uniform array with $\beta = 0$ and $d = n\lambda$, in addition to having the maxima of the array factor directed broadside ($\theta = 90°$) to the axis of the array, there are additional maxima directed along the axis ($\theta = 0°, 180°$) of the array (end-fire radiation).

To illustrate the method, in Figure 6.5 the pattern of the array factor of a 10-element ($N = 10$) uniform array with $\beta = 0$ and $d = \lambda/4$ is plotted. The only maximum occurs at $\theta = 90°$. To form a comparison, the pattern of the same array but with $d = \lambda$ is also plotted in Figure 6.5. For this pattern, in addition to the maximum at $\theta = 90°$, there are additional maxima directed toward $\theta = 0°, 180°$.

In Tables 6.1 and 6.2 the expressions for the nulls, maxima, half-power points, minor lobe maxima, and beamwidths for broadside arrays have been listed. They are derived from the more general ones given by (6-10c)–(6-16a).

6.3.2 Ordinary End-Fire Array

Instead of having the maximum radiation broadside to the axis of the array, it may be desirable to direct it along the axis of the array (end-fire). As a matter of fact, it may be necessary that it radiate toward only one direction (either $\theta = 0°$ or $180°$ of Figure 6.4).

To direct the maximum toward $\theta = 0°$,

$$\boxed{\psi = kd\cos\theta + \beta\big|_{\theta=0°} = kd + \beta = 0 \Rightarrow \beta = -kd} \qquad (6\text{-}20a)$$

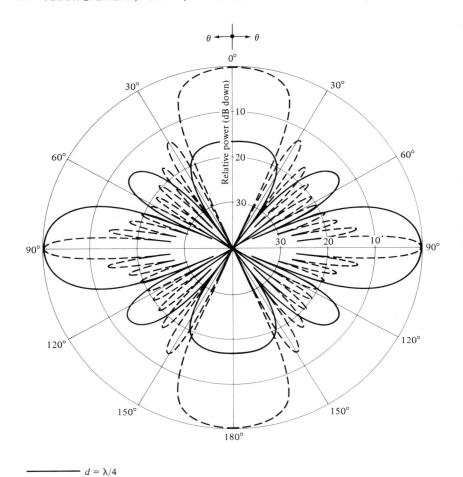

—————— $d = \lambda/4$

— — — — $d = \lambda$

Figure 6.5 Array factor patterns of a 10-element uniform amplitude broadside array ($N=10, \beta=0$).

If the maximum is desired toward $\theta = 180°$, then

$$\psi = kd\cos\theta + \beta\big|_{\theta=180°} = -kd + \beta = 0 \Rightarrow \beta = kd \qquad \text{(6-20b)}$$

Thus end-fire radiation is accomplished when $\beta = -kd$ (for $\theta=0°$) or $\beta = kd$ (for $\theta = 180°$).

If the element separation is a multiple of a wavelength ($d = n\lambda, n = 1, 2, 3, \ldots$), then in addition to having end-fire radiation, there also exist maxima in the broadside directions. In addition, the end-fire radiation is directed toward both directions of the axis of the array ($\theta = 0°$ and $180°$).

Table 6.1 NULLS, MAXIMA, HALF-POWER POINTS, AND MINOR LOBE MAXIMA FOR UNIFORM AMPLITUDE BROADSIDE ARRAYS

NULLS	$\theta_n = \cos^{-1}\left(\pm\dfrac{n}{N}\dfrac{\lambda}{d}\right)$ $n = 1,2,3,\ldots$ $n \neq N, 2N, 3N, \ldots$
MAXIMA	$\theta_m = \cos^{-1}\left(\pm\dfrac{m\lambda}{d}\right)$ $m = 0, 1, 2, \ldots$
HALF-POWER POINTS	$\theta_h \simeq \cos^{-1}\left(\pm\dfrac{1.391\lambda}{\pi N d}\right)$ $\pi d / \lambda \ll 1$
MINOR LOBE MAXIMA	$\theta_s \simeq \cos^{-1}\left[\pm\dfrac{\lambda}{2d}\left(\dfrac{2s+1}{N}\right)\right]$ $s = 1,2,3,\ldots$ $\pi d / \lambda \ll 1$

Table 6.2 BEAMWIDTHS FOR UNIFORM AMPLITUDE BROADSIDE ARRAYS

FIRST NULL BEAMWIDTH (FNBW)	$\Theta_n = 2\left[\dfrac{\pi}{2} - \cos^{-1}\left(\dfrac{\lambda}{Nd}\right)\right]$
HALF-POWER BEAMWIDTH (HPBW)	$\Theta_h \simeq 2\left[\dfrac{\pi}{2} - \cos^{-1}\left(\dfrac{1.391\lambda}{\pi Nd}\right)\right]$ $\pi d / \lambda \ll 1$
FIRST SIDE LOBE BEAMWIDTH (FSLBW)	$\Theta_s \simeq 2\left[\dfrac{\pi}{2} - \cos^{-1}\left(\dfrac{3\lambda}{2dN}\right)\right]$ $\pi d / \lambda \ll 1$

Thus for $d = n\lambda$, $n = 1, 2, 3, \ldots$ there exist four maxima; two in the broadside directions and two along the axis of the array.

The radiation patterns of a 10-element ($N = 10$) array with $d = \lambda/4$, $\beta = \pm kd$ are plotted in Figure 6.6. When $\beta = -kd$, the maximum is directed along $\theta = 0°$. However, when $\beta = kd$, the maximum is oriented toward $\theta = 180°$. To form a comparison, the array factor of the same array ($N = 10$) but with $d = \lambda$ and $\beta = -kd$ has been calculated. Its pattern is identical to that of a broadside array with $N = 10$, $d = \lambda$, and it is shown plotted in Figure 6.5. It is seen that there are four maxima; two broadside and two along the axis of the array.

The expressions for the nulls, maxima, half-power points, minor lobe maxima, and beamwidths, as applied to ordinary end-fire arrays, are listed in Tables 6.3 and 6.4.

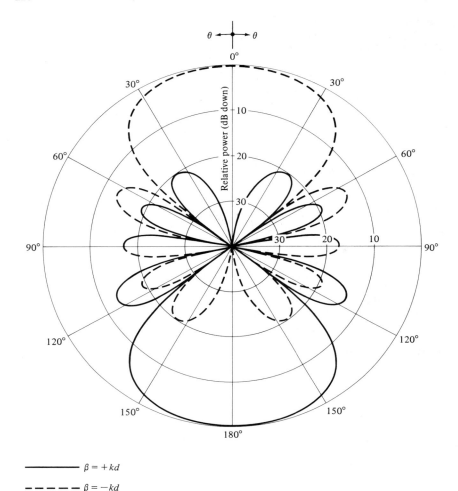

Figure 6.6 Array factor patterns of a 10-element uniform amplitude end-fire array ($N=10, d=\lambda/4$).

6.3.3 Phased (Scanning) Array

In the previous two sections it was shown how to direct the major radiation from an array, by controlling the phase excitation between the elements, in directions normal (broadside) and along the axis (end-fire) of the array. It is then logical to assume that the maximum radiation can be oriented in any direction to form a scanning array. The procedure is similar to that of the previous two sections.

Let us assume that the maximum radiation of the array is required to be oriented at an angle θ_0 ($0° \leq \theta_0 \leq 180°$). To accomplish this, the phase

Table 6.3 NULLS, MAXIMA, HALF-POWER POINTS, AND MINOR LOBE MAXIMA FOR UNIFORM AMPLITUDE ORDINARY END-FIRE ARRAYS

NULLS	$\theta_n = \cos^{-1}\left(1 - \dfrac{n\lambda}{Nd}\right)$ $n = 1,2,3,\ldots$ $n \neq N, 2N, 3N, \ldots$
MAXIMA	$\theta_m = \cos^{-1}\left(1 - \dfrac{m\lambda}{d}\right)$ $m = 0,1,2,\ldots$
HALF-POWER POINTS	$\theta_h \simeq \cos^{-1}\left(1 - \dfrac{1.391\lambda}{\pi d N}\right)$ $\pi d/\lambda \ll 1$
MINOR LOBE MAXIMA	$\theta_s \simeq \cos^{-1}\left[1 - \dfrac{(2s+1)\lambda}{2Nd}\right]$ $s = 1,2,3,\ldots$ $\pi d/\lambda \ll 1$

Table 6.4 BEAMWIDTHS FOR UNIFORM AMPLITUDE ORDINARY END-FIRE ARRAYS

FIRST NULL BEAMWIDTH (FNBW)	$\Theta_n = 2\cos^{-1}\left(1 - \dfrac{\lambda}{Nd}\right)$
HALF-POWER BEAMWIDTH (HPBW)	$\Theta_h \simeq 2\cos^{-1}\left(1 - \dfrac{1.391\lambda}{\pi d N}\right)$ $\pi d/\lambda \ll 1$
FIRST SIDE LOBE BEAMWIDTH (FSLBW)	$\Theta_s \simeq 2\cos^{-1}\left(1 - \dfrac{3\lambda}{2Nd}\right)$ $\pi d/\lambda \ll 1$

excitation β between the elements must be adjusted so that

$$\psi = kd\cos\theta + \beta\big|_{\theta=\theta_0} = kd\cos\theta_0 + \beta = 0 \Rightarrow \beta = -kd\cos\theta_0 \qquad (6\text{-}21)$$

Thus by controlling the progressive phase difference between the elements, the maximum radiation can be squinted in any desired direction to form a scanning array. This is the basic principle of electronic scanning phased array operation. Since in phased array technology the scanning must be continuous, the system should be capable of continuously varying the progressive phase between the elements. In practice, this is accomplished electronically by the use of ferrite phase shifters. The phase shift is controlled by the magnetic field within the ferrite, which in turn is controlled by the amount of current flowing through the wires wrapped around the phase shifter.

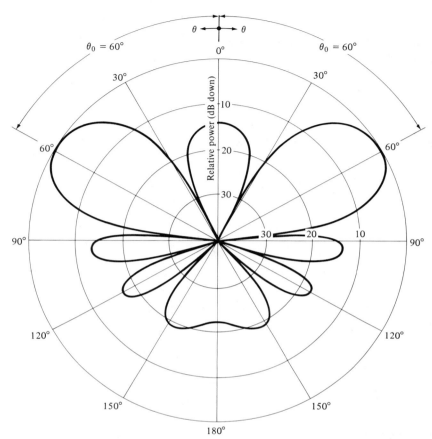

Figure 6.7 Array factor pattern of a 10-element uniform amplitude scanning array ($N=10$, $\beta = -kd\cos\theta_0$, $\theta_0 = 60°$, $d = \lambda/4$.)

To demonstrate the principle of scanning, the radiation pattern of a 10-element array, with a separation of $\lambda/4$ between the elements and with the maximum squinted in the $\theta_0 = 60°$ direction, is plotted in Figure 6.7. The half-power beamwidth of a scanning array is given by [1]

$$\Theta_h = \cos^{-1}\left[\cos\theta_0 - 0.443\frac{\lambda}{(L+d)}\right]$$
$$- \cos^{-1}\left[\cos\theta_0 + 0.443\frac{\lambda}{(L+d)}\right] \tag{6-22}$$

where L is the length of the array. Equation (6-22) can also be used to compute the half-power beamwidth of a broadside array. However, it is not valid for an end-fire array. A plot of the half-power beamwidth (in degrees)

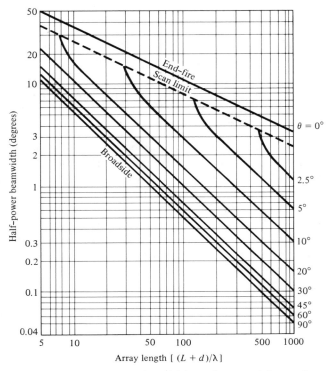

Figure 6.8 Half-power beamwidth for broadside, ordinary end-fire, and scanning uniform linear arrays. (SOURCE: R. S. Elliott, "Beamwidth and Directivity of Large Scanning Arrays,"' First of Two Parts, *The Microwave Journal*, December 1963)

as a function of the array length is shown in Figure 6.8. These curves are valid for broadside, ordinary end-fire, and scanning uniform arrays (constant magnitude but with progressive phase shift). In a later section it will be shown that the curves of Figure 6.8 can be used, in conjunction with a beam broadening factor [1], to compute the directivity of nonuniform amplitude arrays.

6.3.4 Hansen-Woodyard End-Fire Array

The conditions for an ordinary end-fire array were discussed in Section 6.3.2. It was concluded that the maximum radiation can be directed along the axis of the uniform array by allowing the progressive phase shift β between elements to be equal to (6-20a) for $\theta = 0°$ and (6-20b) for $\theta = 180°$.

To enhance the directivity of an end-fire array without destroying any of the other characteristics, Hansen and Woodyard [2] in 1938 proposed that the required phase shift between *closely spaced elements of a very long* *array** should be

$$\beta = -\left(kd + \frac{2.94}{N}\right) \simeq -\left(kd + \frac{\pi}{N}\right) \Rightarrow \text{for maximum in } \theta = 0° \quad \text{(6-23a)}$$

$$\beta = +\left(kd + \frac{2.94}{N}\right) \simeq +\left(kd + \frac{\pi}{N}\right) \Rightarrow \text{for maximum in } \theta = 180°$$

(6-23b)

These requirements are known today as the *Hansen-Woodyard conditions for end-fire radiation*. With this progressive phase shift between the elements of a uniform array, a *larger* directivity can be obtained than by using the ordinary end-fire conditions given by (6-20a) and (6-20b). It should be pointed out, however, that *these conditions do not necessarily yield the maximum possible directivity*.

To realize the increase in directivity as a result of the Hansen-Woodyard conditions, it is necessary that, in addition to the conditions of (6-23a) and (6-23b), $|\psi|$ assumes values of

For Maximum Radiation Along $\theta = 0°$

$$|\psi| = |kd\cos\theta + \beta|_{\theta=0°} = \frac{\pi}{N} \quad \text{and} \quad |\psi| = |kd\cos\theta + \beta|_{\theta=180°} \simeq \pi \quad \text{(6-24a)}$$

For Maximum Radiation Along $\theta = 180°$

$$|\psi| = |kd\cos\theta + \beta|_{\theta=180°} = \frac{\pi}{N} \quad \text{and} \quad |\psi| = |kd\cos\theta + \beta|_{\theta=0°} \simeq \pi \quad \text{(6-24b)}$$

The condition of $|\psi| = \pi/N$ in (6-24a) or (6-24b) is realized by the use of (6-23a) or (6-23b), respectively. Care must be exercised in meeting the requirement of $|\psi| \simeq \pi$ for each array. For an array of N elements, the condition of $|\psi| \simeq \pi$ is satisfied by using (6-23a) for $\theta = 0°$, (6-23b) for $\theta = 180°$, and choosing for each a spacing of

$$d = \left(\frac{N-1}{N}\right)\frac{\lambda}{4} \tag{6-25}$$

If the number of elements is large, (6-25) can be approximated by

$$d \simeq \frac{\lambda}{4} \tag{6-25a}$$

Thus for a large uniform array, the Hansen-Woodyard condition can only yield an improved directivity provided the spacing between the elements is approximately $\lambda/4$.

To illustrate the principles, the patterns of a 10-element ($N = 10$) array with $d = \lambda/4$ ($\beta = -3\pi/5$) and $d = \lambda/2$ ($\beta = -11\pi/10$) have been plotted in

---

*In principle, the Hansen-Woodyard condition was derived for an infinitely long antenna with continuous distribution. It thus gives good results for very long, finite length discrete arrays with closely spaced elements.

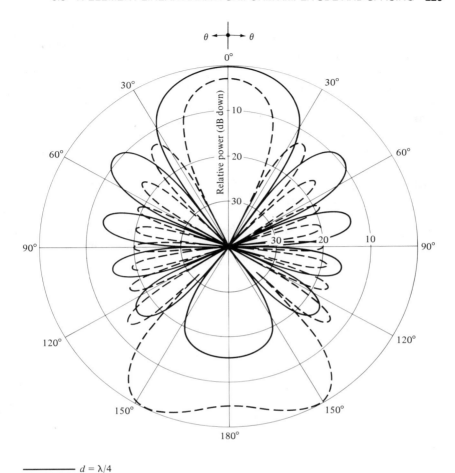

─────── $d = \lambda/4$

───── $d = \lambda/2$

Figure 6.9   Array factor patterns of a 10-element uniform amplitude Hansen-Woodyard end-fire array $[N=10, \beta = -(kd + \pi/N)]$

Figure 6.9. In both cases the desired maximum radiation should be toward $\theta = 0°[\beta \simeq (kd + \pi/N)]$. It is apparent that the main lobe of the $d = \lambda/4$ pattern is much narrower when contrasted to its counterpart of Figure 6.6 using the ordinary end-fire conditions of (6-20a). In fact, the 3-dB beamwidth of the $d = \lambda/4$ pattern in Figure 6.9 is equal to 37° compared to 74° for that of Figure 6.6.

To make the comparisons more meaningful, the directivities for each of the patterns of Figures 6.6 and 6.9 have been calculated, using numerical integration, and it is found that they are equal to 11 and 19, respectively. Thus the Hansen-Woodyard conditions realize a 73% increase in directivity for this case.

To show that (6-23a) and (6-23b) do *not* lead to improved directivities over those of (6-20a) and (6-20b) if (6-24a) and (6-24b) are not satisfied, the pattern for the same array ($N = 10$) but with $d = \lambda/2$ ($\beta = -11\pi/10$) that was plotted in Figure 6.9 will be discussed. Even though this pattern exhibits a very narrow lobe in the $\theta = 0°$ direction, its back lobes are larger than its main lobe. The $d = \lambda/2$ pattern fails to realize a larger directivity because the necessary $|\psi|_{\theta=180°} \simeq \pi$ condition of (6-24a) is not satisfied. That is,

$$|\psi| = |(kd\cos\theta + \beta)|_{\substack{\theta=180° \\ \beta=-(kd+\pi/N)}} = |-(2kd+\pi/N)|_{\substack{d=\lambda/2 \\ N=10}} = 2.1\pi \quad \text{(6-26)}$$

which is not equal to π as required by (6-24a). Similar results occur for spacings other than those specified by (6-25) or (6-25a).

To better understand and appreciate the Hansen-Woodyard conditions, a succinct derivation of (6-23a) will be outlined. The procedure is identical to that reported by Hansen and Woodyard in their classic paper [2].

The array factor of an N-element array is given by (6-10c) as

$$(\text{AF})_n = \frac{1}{N} \left\{ \frac{\sin\left[\frac{N}{2}(kd\cos\theta + \beta)\right]}{\sin\left[\frac{1}{2}(kd\cos\theta + \beta)\right]} \right\} \quad \text{(6-27)}$$

and approximated, for small values of ψ ($\psi = kd\cos\theta + \beta$), by (6-10d) or

$$(\text{AF})_n = \frac{1}{N} \left[\frac{\sin\left(\frac{N}{2}kd\cos\theta\right)}{\sin\left(\frac{1}{2}kd\cos\theta\right)} \right] \quad \text{(6-38)}$$

If the progressive phase shift between the elements is equal to

$$\beta = -pd \quad \text{(6-28)}$$

where p is a constant, (6-27a) can be written as

$$(\text{AF})_n = \left\{ \frac{\sin[q(k\cos\theta - p)]}{q(k\cos\theta - p)} \right\} = \left[\frac{\sin(Z)}{Z} \right] \quad \text{(6-29)}$$

where

$$q = \frac{Nd}{2} \quad \text{(6-29a)}$$

$$Z = q(k\cos\theta - p) \quad \text{(6-29b)}$$

The radiation intensity can be written as

$$U(\theta) = [(\text{AF})_n]^2 = \left[\frac{\sin(Z)}{Z} \right]^2 \quad \text{(6-30)}$$

whose value at $\theta = 0°$ is equal to

$$U(\theta)|_{\theta=0°} = \left\{ \frac{\sin[q(k\cos\theta - p)]}{q(k\cos\theta - p)} \right\}^2 \Bigg|_{\theta=0°} = \left\{ \frac{\sin[q(k-p)]}{q(k-p)} \right\}^2 \quad \text{(6-30a)}$$

Dividing (6-30) by (6-30a), so that the value of the array factor is equal to unity at $\theta=0°$, leads to

$$U(\theta)_n=\left\{\frac{q(k-p)}{\sin[q(k-p)]}\frac{\sin[q(k\cos\theta-p)]}{[q(k\cos\theta-p)]}\right\}^2=\left[\frac{z}{\sin(z)}\frac{\sin(Z)}{Z}\right]^2$$

(6-31)

where

$$z=q(k-p)$$

(6-31a)

$$Z=q(k\cos\theta-p)$$

(6-31b)

The directivity of the array factor can be evaluated using

$$D_0=\frac{4\pi U_{max}}{P_{rad}}=\frac{U_{max}}{U_0}$$

(6-32)

where U_0 is the average radiation intensity and it is given by

$$U_0=\frac{P_{rad}}{4\pi}=\frac{1}{4\pi}\int_0^{2\pi}\int_0^\pi U(\theta)\sin\theta\,d\theta\,d\phi$$

$$=\frac{1}{2}\left[\frac{z}{\sin(z)}\right]^2\int_0^\pi\left[\frac{\sin(Z)}{Z}\right]^2\sin\theta\,d\theta$$

(6-33)

By using (6-31a) and (6-31b), (6-33) can be written as

$$U_0=\frac{1}{2}\left[\frac{q(k-p)}{\sin[q(k-p)]}\right]^2\int_0^\pi\left[\frac{\sin[q(k\cos\theta-p)]}{q(k\cos\theta-p)}\right]^2\sin\theta\,d\theta$$

(6-33a)

To maximize the directivity, as given by (6-32), (6-33a) must be minimized. Performing the integration, (6-33a) reduces to

$$U_0=\frac{1}{2kq}\left[\frac{v}{\sin(v)}\right]^2\left[\frac{\pi}{2}+\frac{[\cos(2v)-1]}{2v}+S_i(2v)\right]=\frac{1}{2kq}g(v)$$

(6-34)

where

$$v=q(k-p)$$

(6-34a)

$$S_i(z)=\int_0^z\frac{\sin t}{t}dt$$

(6-34b)

$$g(v)=\left[\frac{v}{\sin(v)}\right]^2\left[\frac{\pi}{2}+\frac{[\cos(2v)-1]}{2v}+S_i(2v)\right]$$

(6-34c)

The function $g(v)$ is plotted in Figure 6.10 and its minimum value occurs when

$$v=q(k-p)=\frac{Nd}{2}(k-p)=-1.47$$

(6-35)

Thus

$$\beta = -pd = -\left(kd + \frac{2.94}{N}\right) \tag{6-36}$$

which is the condition for end-fire radiation with improved directivity (Hansen-Woodyard condition) along $\theta = 0°$, as given by (6-23a). Similar procedures can be followed to establish (6-23b).

Ordinarily, (6-36) is approximated by

$$\beta = -\left(kd + \frac{2.94}{N}\right) \simeq -\left(kd + \frac{\pi}{N}\right) \tag{6-37}$$

with not too much relaxation in the condition since the curve of Figure 6.10 is very flat around the minimum point $v = 1.47$. Its value at $v = 1.57$ is almost the same as the minimum at $v = 1.47$.

The expressions for the nulls, maxima, half-power points, minor lobe maxima, and beamwidths are listed in Tables 6.5 and 6.6.

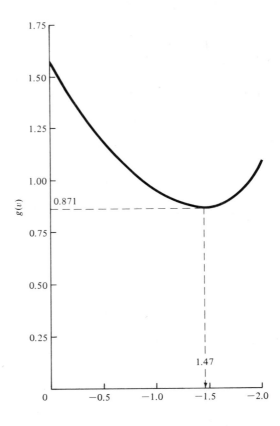

Figure 6.10   Variation of $g(v)$ (see Eq. 6-34c) as a function of v.

Table 6.5 NULLS, MAXIMA, HALF-POWER POINTS, AND MINOR LOBE MAXIMA FOR UNIFORM AMPLITUDE HANSEN-WOODYARD END-FIRE ARRAYS

NULLS	$\theta_n = \cos^{-1}\left[1 + (1-2n)\dfrac{\lambda}{2dN}\right]$ $n = 1,2,3,\dots$ $n \neq N, 2N, 3N, \dots$
SECONDARY MAXIMA	$\theta_m = \cos^{-1}\left\{1 + [1-(2m+1)]\dfrac{\lambda}{2Nd}\right\}$ $m = 1,2,3,\dots$ $\pi d/\lambda \ll 1$
HALF-POWER POINTS	$\theta_h = \cos^{-1}\left(1 - 0.1398\dfrac{\lambda}{Nd}\right)$ $\pi d/\lambda \ll 1$ N large
MINOR LOBE MAXIMA	$\theta_s = \cos^{-1}\left(1 - \dfrac{s\lambda}{Nd}\right)$ $s = 1,2,3,\dots$ $\pi d/\lambda \ll 1$

Table 6.6 BEAMWIDTHS FOR UNIFORM AMPLITUDE HANSEN-WOODYARD END-FIRE ARRAYS

FIRST NULL BEAMWIDTH (FNBW)	$\Theta_n = 2\cos^{-1}\left(1 - \dfrac{\lambda}{2dN}\right)$
HALF-POWER BEAMWIDTH (HPBW)	$\Theta_h = 2\cos^{-1}\left(1 - 0.1398\dfrac{\lambda}{Nd}\right)$ $\pi d/\lambda \ll 1$ N large
FIRST SIDE LOBE BEAMWIDTH (FSLBW)	$\Theta_s = 2\cos^{-1}\left(1 - \dfrac{\lambda}{Nd}\right)$ $\pi d/\lambda \ll 1$

6.4 *N*-ELEMENT LINEAR ARRAY: DIRECTIVITY

The criteria that must be met to achieve broadside and end-fire radiation by a uniform linear array of N elements were discussed in the previous section. It would be instructive to investigate the directivity of each of the arrays, since it represents a figure-of-merit on the operation of the system.

6.4.1 Broadside Array

As a result of the criteria for broadside radiation given by (6-18a), the array factor for this form of the array reduces to

$$(\text{AF})_n = \frac{1}{N}\left[\frac{\sin\left(\dfrac{N}{2}kd\cos\theta\right)}{\sin\left(\dfrac{1}{2}kd\cos\theta\right)}\right] \tag{6-38}$$

which for a small spacing between the elements ($d \ll \lambda$) can be approximated by

$$(AF)_n \simeq \left[\frac{\sin\left(\frac{N}{2}kd\cos\theta\right)}{\left(\frac{N}{2}kd\cos\theta\right)} \right] \tag{6-38a}$$

The radiation intensity can be written as

$$U(\theta) = [(AF)_n]^2 = \left[\frac{\sin\left(\frac{N}{2}kd\cos\theta\right)}{\frac{N}{2}kd\cos\theta} \right]^2 = \left[\frac{\sin(Z)}{Z} \right]^2 \tag{6-39}$$

$$Z = \frac{N}{2}kd\cos\theta \tag{6-39a}$$

The directivity can be obtained using (6-32) where U_{max} of (6-39) is equal to unity ($U_{max} = 1$) and it occurs at $\theta = 90°$. The average value U_0 of the intensity reduces to

$$U_0 = \frac{1}{4\pi}P_{rad} = \frac{1}{2}\int_0^\pi \left[\frac{\sin(Z)}{Z} \right]^2 \sin\theta\, d\theta$$

$$= \frac{1}{2}\int_0^\pi \left[\frac{\sin\left(\frac{N}{2}kd\cos\theta\right)}{\frac{N}{2}kd\cos\theta} \right]^2 \sin\theta\, d\theta \tag{6-40}$$

By making a change of variable, that is,

$$Z = \frac{N}{2}kd\cos\theta \tag{6-40a}$$

$$dZ = -\frac{N}{2}kd\sin\theta\, d\theta \tag{6-40b}$$

(6-40) can be written as

$$U_0 = -\frac{1}{Nkd}\int_{+Nkd/2}^{-Nkd/2}\left[\frac{\sin Z}{Z}\right]^2 dZ = \frac{1}{Nkd}\int_{-Nkd/2}^{+Nkd/2}\left[\frac{\sin Z}{Z}\right]^2 dZ \tag{6-41}$$

For a large array ($Nkd/2 \to$ large), (6-41) can be approximated by extending the limits to infinity. That is,

$$U_0 = \frac{1}{Nkd}\int_{-Nkd/2}^{+Nkd/2}\left[\frac{\sin Z}{Z}\right]^2 dZ \simeq \frac{1}{Nkd}\int_{-\infty}^{+\infty}\left[\frac{\sin Z}{Z}\right]^2 dZ \tag{6-41a}$$

Since

$$\int_{-\infty}^{+\infty}\left[\frac{\sin(Z)}{Z}\right]^2 dZ = \pi \tag{6-41b}$$

(6-41a) reduces to

$$U_0 \simeq \frac{\pi}{Nkd} \tag{6-41c}$$

The directivity of (6-32) can now be written as

$$D_0 = \frac{U_{max}}{U_0} \simeq \frac{Nkd}{\pi} = 2N\left(\frac{d}{\lambda}\right) \tag{6-42}$$

Using

$$L = (N-1)d \tag{6-43}$$

where L is the overall length of the array, (6-42) can be expressed as

$$D_0 \simeq 2N\left(\frac{d}{\lambda}\right) \simeq 2\left(1+\frac{L}{d}\right)\left(\frac{d}{\lambda}\right) \tag{6-44}$$

which for a large array ($L \gg d$) reduces to

$$D_0 \simeq 2N\left(\frac{d}{\lambda}\right) = 2\left(1+\frac{L}{d}\right)\left(\frac{d}{\lambda}\right) \overset{L \gg d}{\simeq} 2\left(\frac{L}{\lambda}\right) \tag{6-44a}$$

Example 6.3

Given a linear, broadside, uniform array of 10 isotropic elements, ($N = 10$) with a separation of $\lambda/4$ ($d = \lambda/4$) between the elements, find the directivity of the array.

SOLUTION
Using (6-44a)

$$D_0 \simeq 2N\left(\frac{d}{\lambda}\right) = 5 \quad \text{(dimensionless)} = 10\log_{10}(5) = 6.99 \quad \text{(dB)}$$

6.4.2 Ordinary End-Fire Array

For an end-fire array, with the maximum radiation in the $\theta = 0°$ direction, the array factor is given by

$$(AF)_n = \left[\frac{\sin\left[\frac{N}{2}kd(\cos\theta - 1)\right]}{N\sin\left[\frac{1}{2}kd(\cos\theta - 1)\right]}\right] \tag{6-45}$$

which, for a small spacing between the elements ($d \ll \lambda$), can be approximated by

$$(AF)_n \simeq \left[\frac{\sin\left[\frac{N}{2}kd(\cos\theta - 1)\right]}{\left[\frac{N}{2}kd(\cos\theta - 1)\right]}\right] \tag{6-45a}$$

The corresponding radiation intensity can be written as

$$U(\theta)=\left[(AF)_n\right]^2=\left[\frac{\sin\left[\dfrac{N}{2}kd(\cos\theta-1)\right]}{\dfrac{N}{2}kd(\cos\theta-1)}\right]^2=\left[\frac{\sin(Z)}{Z}\right]^2 \tag{6-46}$$

$$Z=\frac{N}{2}kd(\cos\theta-1) \tag{6-46a}$$

whose maximum value is unity ($U_{max}=1$) and it occurs at $\theta=0$. The average value of the radiation intensity is given by

$$U_0=\frac{1}{4\pi}\int_0^{2\pi}\int_0^{\pi}\left[\frac{\sin\left[\dfrac{N}{2}kd(\cos\theta-1)\right]}{\dfrac{N}{2}kd(\cos\theta-1)}\right]^2\sin\theta\,d\theta\,d\phi$$

$$=\frac{1}{2}\int_0^{\pi}\left[\frac{\sin\left[\dfrac{N}{2}kd(\cos\theta-1)\right]}{\dfrac{N}{2}kd(\cos\theta-1)}\right]^2\sin\theta\,d\theta \tag{6-47}$$

By letting

$$Z=\frac{N}{2}kd(\cos\theta-1) \tag{6-47a}$$

$$dZ=-\frac{N}{2}kd\sin\theta\,d\theta \tag{6-47b}$$

(6-47) can be written as

$$U_0=-\frac{1}{Nkd}\int_0^{-Nkd}\left[\frac{\sin(Z)}{Z}\right]^2dZ=\frac{1}{Nkd}\int_0^{Nkd}\left[\frac{\sin(Z)}{Z}\right]^2dZ \tag{6-48}$$

For a large array ($Nkd\rightarrow$large), (6-48) can be approximated by extending the limits to infinity. That is,

$$U_0=\frac{1}{Nkd}\int_0^{Nkd}\left[\frac{\sin(Z)}{Z}\right]^2dZ\simeq\frac{1}{Nkd}\int_0^{\infty}\left[\frac{\sin(Z)}{Z}\right]^2dZ \tag{6-48a}$$

Using (6-41b) reduces (6-48a) to

$$U_0\simeq\frac{\pi}{2Nkd} \tag{6-48b}$$

and the directivity to

$$D_0=\frac{U_{max}}{U_0}\simeq\frac{2Nkd}{\pi}=4N\left(\frac{d}{\lambda}\right) \tag{6-49}$$

Another form of (6-49), using (6-43), is

$$D_0 \simeq 4N\left(\frac{d}{\lambda}\right) = 4\left(1 + \frac{L}{d}\right)\left(\frac{d}{\lambda}\right) \tag{6-49a}$$

which for a large array $(L \gg d)$ reduces to

$$D_0 \simeq 4N\left(\frac{d}{\lambda}\right) = 4\left(1 + \frac{L}{d}\right)\left(\frac{d}{\lambda}\right) \overset{L \gg d}{\simeq} 4\left(\frac{L}{\lambda}\right) \tag{6-49b}$$

It should be noted that the directivity of the end-fire array, as given by (6-49)–(6-49b), is twice that for the broadside array as given by (6-42)–(6-44a).

Example 6.4

Given a linear, end-fire, uniform array of 10 elements $(N = 10)$ with a separation of $\lambda/4$ $(d = \lambda/4)$ between the elements, find the directivity of the array factor. This array is identical to the broadside of Example 6.3.

SOLUTION
Using (6-49)

$$D_0 \simeq 4N\left(\frac{d}{\lambda}\right) = 10 \quad \text{(dimensionless)} = 10\log_{10}(10) = 10\,\text{dB}$$

This value for the directivity $(D_0 = 10)$ is approximate, based on the validity of (6-48a). However, it compares very favorably with the value of $D_0 = 10.05$ obtained by numerically integrating (6-45) using the computer program at the end of Chapter 2.

6.4.3   Hansen-Woodyard End-Fire Array

For an end-fire array with improved directivity (Hansen-Woodyard conditions) and maximum radiation in the $\theta = 0°$ direction, the radiation intensity (for small spacing between the elements, $d \ll \lambda$) is given by (6-31)–(6-31b). The maximum radiation intensity is unity $(U_{\max} = 1)$, and the average radiation intensity is given by (6-34) where q and v are defined, respectively, by (6-29a) and (6-34a). Using (6-29a), (6-34a), (6-35), and (6-37), the radiation intensity of (6-34) reduces to

$$U_0 = \frac{1}{Nkd}\left(\frac{\pi}{2}\right)^2\left[\frac{\pi}{2} + \frac{2}{\pi} - 1.8515\right] = \frac{0.878}{Nkd} \tag{6-50}$$

which can also be written as

$$U_0 = \frac{0.878}{Nkd} = \frac{1.756}{2Nkd} = 0.559\left(\frac{\pi}{2Nkd}\right) \tag{6-50a}$$

The average value of the radiation intensity as given by (6-50a) is 0.559 times that for the ordinary end-fire of (6-48b). Thus the directivity can be expressed, using (6-50a), as

$$D_0 = \frac{U_{max}}{U_0} = \frac{1}{0.559}\left[\frac{2Nkd}{\pi}\right] = 1.789\left[4N\left(\frac{d}{\lambda}\right)\right] \tag{6-51}$$

which is 1.789 times that of the ordinary end-fire as given by (6-49). Using (6-43), (6-51) can also be written as

$$D_0 = 1.789\left[4N\left(\frac{d}{\lambda}\right)\right] = 1.789\left[4\left(1+\frac{L}{d}\right)\frac{d}{\lambda}\right] \tag{6-51a}$$

which for a large array ($L \gg d$) reduces to

$$D_0 = 1.789\left[4N\left(\frac{d}{\lambda}\right)\right] = 1.789\left[4\left(1+\frac{L}{d}\right)\left(\frac{d}{\lambda}\right)\right]$$

$$\simeq 1.789\left[4\left(\frac{L}{\lambda}\right)\right] \tag{6-51b}$$

Example 6.5

Given a linear, end-fire (with improved directivity) Hansen-Woodyard, uniform array of 10 elements ($N = 10$) with a separation of $\lambda/4$ ($d = \lambda/4$) between the elements, find the directivity of the array factor. This array is identical to that of Examples 6.3 (broadside) and 6.4 (ordinary end-fire) and it is used for comparison.

SOLUTION
Using (6.51b)

$$D_0 = 1.789\left[4N\left(\frac{d}{\lambda}\right)\right] = 17.89 \quad \text{(dimensionless)} = 10\log_{10}(17.89)$$

$$= 12.53 \quad \text{(dB)}$$

The value of this directivity ($D_0 = 17.89$) is 1.789 times greater than that of Example 6.4 (ordinary end-fire) and 3.578 times greater than that found in Example 6.3 (broadside).

Table 6.7 lists the directivities for broadside, ordinary end-fire, and Hansen-Woodyard arrays.

Table 6.7 DIRECTIVITIES FOR BROADSIDE AND END-FIRE ARRAYS

ARRAY	DIRECTIVITY
Broadside	$D_0 = 2N\left(\frac{d}{\lambda}\right) = 2\left(1+\frac{L}{d}\right)\frac{d}{\lambda} \simeq 2\left(\frac{L}{\lambda}\right)$ $N\pi d/\lambda \to \infty, L \gg d$
End-Fire (Ordinary)	$D_0 = 4N\left(\frac{d}{\lambda}\right) = 4\left(1+\frac{L}{d}\right)\frac{d}{\lambda} \simeq 4\left(\frac{L}{\lambda}\right)$ $2N\pi d/\lambda \to \infty, L \gg d$
End-Fire (Hansen-Woodyard)	$D_0 = 1.789\left[4N\left(\frac{d}{\lambda}\right)\right] = 1.789\left[4\left(1+\frac{L}{d}\right)\frac{d}{\lambda}\right] = 1.789\left[4\left(\frac{L}{\lambda}\right)\right]$ $2N\pi d/\lambda \to \infty, L \gg d$

6.5 N-ELEMENT LINEAR ARRAY: THREE-DIMENSIONAL CHARACTERISTICS

Up to now, the two-dimensional array factor of an N-element linear array has been investigated. Although in practice only two-dimensional patterns can be measured, a collection of them can be used to reconstruct the three-dimensional characteristics of an array. It would then be instructive to examine the three-dimensional patterns of an array of elements. Emphasis will be placed on the array factor.

6.5.1 N-Elements Along Z-Axis

A linear array of N isotropic elements are positioned along the z-axis and are separated by a distance d, as shown in Figure 6.4. The amplitude excitation of each element is a_n and there exists a progressive phase excitation β between the elements. For far-field observations, the array factor can be written according to (6-6) as

$$\text{AF} = \sum_{n=1}^{N} a_n e^{j(n-1)(kd\cos\gamma + \beta)} = \sum_{n=1}^{N} a_n e^{j(n-1)\psi} \tag{6-52}$$

$$\psi = kd\cos\gamma + \beta \tag{6-52a}$$

where the a_n's are the amplitude excitation coefficients and γ is the angle between the axis of the array (z-axis) and the vector from the origin to the observation point.

In general, the angle γ can be obtained from the dot product of a unit vector along the axis of the array with a unit vector directed toward the observation point. For the geometry of Figure 6.4

$$\cos\gamma = \hat{a}_z \cdot \hat{a}_r = \hat{a}_z \cdot (\hat{a}_x \sin\theta\cos\phi + \hat{a}_y \sin\theta\sin\phi + \hat{a}_z \cos\theta) = \cos\theta \Rightarrow \gamma = \theta$$
$$\tag{6-53}$$

Thus (6-52) along with (6-53) is identical to (6-6), because the system of Figure 6.4 possesses a symmetry around the z-axis (no ϕ variations). This is not the case when the elements are placed along any of the other axes, as will be shown next.

6.5.2 N-Elements Along X- or Y-Axis

To demonstrate the facility that a "sound" coordinate system and geometry can provide in the solution of a problem, let us consider an array of N isotropic elements along the x-axis, as shown in Figure 6.11. The far-zone array factor for this array is identical in form to that of Figure 6.4 except for the phase factor ψ. For this geometry

$$\cos\gamma = \hat{a}_x \cdot \hat{a}_r = \hat{a}_x \cdot (\hat{a}_x \sin\theta\cos\phi + \hat{a}_y \sin\theta\sin\phi + \hat{a}_z \cos\theta) = \sin\theta\cos\phi$$
$$\tag{6-54}$$

$$\cos\gamma = \sin\theta\cos\phi \Rightarrow \gamma = \cos^{-1}(\sin\theta\cos\phi) \tag{6-54a}$$

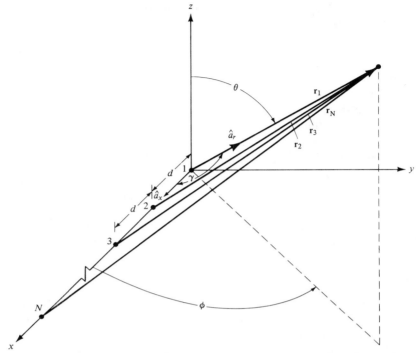

Figure 6.11   Linear array of N isotropic elements positioned along the x-axis.

The array factor of this array is also given by (6-52) but with γ defined by (6-54a). For this system, the array factor is a function of both angles (θ and ϕ) because there is no symmetry about the x-axis.

In a similar manner, the array factor for N isotropic elements placed along the y-axis is that of (6-52) but with γ defined by

$$\cos\gamma = \hat{a}_y \cdot \hat{a}_r = \sin\theta\sin\phi \Rightarrow \gamma = \cos^{-1}(\sin\theta\sin\phi) \qquad (6\text{-}55)$$

Physically placing the elements along the z-, x-, or y-axis does not change the characteristics of the array. Numerically they yield identical patterns even though their mathematical forms are different.

Example 6.6

Two half-wavelengths dipoles ($l=\lambda/2$) are positioned along the x-axis and are separated by a distance d, as shown in Figure 6.12. The lengths of the dipoles are parallel to the z-axis. Find the total field of the array. Assume uniform amplitude excitation and a progressive phase difference of β.

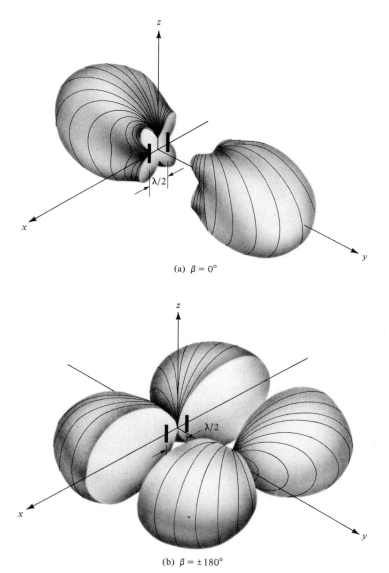

(a) $\beta = 0°$

(b) $\beta = \pm 180°$

Figure 6.12   Three-dimensional patterns of two $\lambda/2$ dipoles spaced $\lambda/2$ apart. (SOURCE: P. Lorrain and D. R. Corson, *Electromagnetic Fields and Waves*, 2nd ed., W. H. Freeman and Co. Copyright © 1970)

SOLUTION

The field pattern of a single element placed at the origin is given by (4-85) as

$$E_\theta = j\eta \frac{I_0 e^{-jkr}}{2\pi r} \left[\frac{\cos\left(\frac{\pi}{2}\cos\theta\right)}{\sin\theta} \right]$$

Using (6-52), (6-54a), and (6-10c), the array factor can be written as

$$(\text{AF})_n = \frac{\sin(kd\sin\theta\cos\phi + \beta)}{2\sin\left[\frac{1}{2}(kd\sin\theta\cos\phi + \beta)\right]}$$

The total field of the array is then given, using the pattern multiplication rule of (6-5), by

$$E_{\theta t} = E_\theta \cdot (\text{AF})_n = j\eta \frac{I_0 e^{-jkr}}{2\pi r} \frac{\cos\left(\frac{\pi}{2}\cos\theta\right)}{\sin\theta} \left[\frac{\sin(kd\sin\theta\cos\phi + \beta)}{2\sin\left[\frac{1}{2}(kd\sin\theta\cos\phi + \beta)\right]} \right]$$

To illustrate the techniques, the three-dimensional patterns of the two-element array of Example 6.6 have been sketched in Figures 6.12(a) and (b). For both, the element separation is $\lambda/2$ $(d = \lambda/2)$. For the pattern of Figure 6.12(a), the phase excitation between the elements is identical $(\beta = 0)$. In addition to the nulls in the $\theta = 0°$ direction, provided by the individual elements of the array, there are additional nulls along the x-axis $(\theta = \pi/2, \phi = 0, \text{ and } \phi = \pi)$ provided by the formation of the array. The 180° phase difference required to form the nulls along the x-axis is a result of the separation of the elements $[kd = (2\pi/\lambda)(\lambda/2) = \pi]$.

To form a comparison, the three-dimensional pattern of the same array but with a 180° phase excitation $(\beta = 180°)$ between the elements is sketched in Figure 6.12(b). The overall pattern of this array is quite different from that shown in Figure 6.12(a). In addition to the nulls along the z-axis $(\theta = 0°)$ provided by the individual elements, there are nulls along the y-axis formed by the 180° excitation phase difference.

6.6 RECTANGULAR-TO-POLAR GRAPHICAL SOLUTION

In antenna theory, many solutions are of the form

$$f(\zeta) = f(C\cos\gamma + \delta) \tag{6-56}$$

where C, γ, and δ are constants. For example, the approximate array factor of an N-element, uniform amplitude linear array [Equation (6-10d)] is that of a $\sin(\zeta)/\zeta$ form with

$$\zeta = C\cos\gamma + \delta = \frac{N}{2}\psi = \frac{N}{2}(kd\cos\theta + \beta) \tag{6-57}$$

where

$$C = \frac{N}{2} kd \tag{6-57a}$$

$$\delta = \frac{N}{2} \beta \tag{6-57b}$$

Usually the $f(\zeta)$ function can be sketched as a function of ζ in rectilinear coordinates. Since ζ in (6-57) has no physical analog, in many instances it is desired that a graphical representation of $|f(\zeta)|$ be obtained as a function of the physically observable angle θ. This can be constructed graphically from the rectilinear graph, and it forms a polar plot.

The procedure that must be followed in the construction of the polar graph is as follows:

1. Plot, using rectilinear coordinates, the function $|f(\zeta)|$.
2. a. Draw a circle with radius equal to C and with its center on the abscissa at $\zeta = \delta$.
   b. Draw vertical lines to the abscissa so that they will intersect the circle.
   c. From the center of the circle, draw radial lines through the points on the circle intersected by the vertical lines.
   d. Along the radial lines, mark off corresponding magnitudes from the linear plot.
   e. Connect all points to form a continuous graph.

To better illustrate the procedure, the polar graph of the function

$$f(\zeta) = \frac{\sin\left(\frac{N}{2}\psi\right)}{N \sin\left(\frac{\psi}{2}\right)}, \qquad \zeta = \frac{5\pi}{2}\cos\theta - \frac{5\pi}{4} \tag{6-58}$$

has been constructed in Figure 6.13. The function $f(\zeta)$ of (6-58) represents the array factor of a 10-element ($N=10$) uniform linear array with a spacing of $\lambda/4$ ($d=\lambda/4$) and progressive phase shift of $-\pi/4$ ($\beta=-\pi/4$) between the elements. The constructed graph can be compared with its exact form shown in Figure 6.7.

From the construction of Figure 6.13, it is evident that the angle at which the maximum is directed is controlled by the radius of the circle C and the variable δ. For the array factor of Figure 6.13, the radius C is a function of the number of elements (N) and the spacing between the elements (d). In turn, δ is a function of the number of elements (N) and the progressive phase shift between the elements (β). Making $\delta=0$ directs the maximum toward $\theta=90°$ (broadside array). The part of the linear graph that is used to construct the polar plot is determined by the radius of the circle and the relative position of its center along the abscissa. The usable

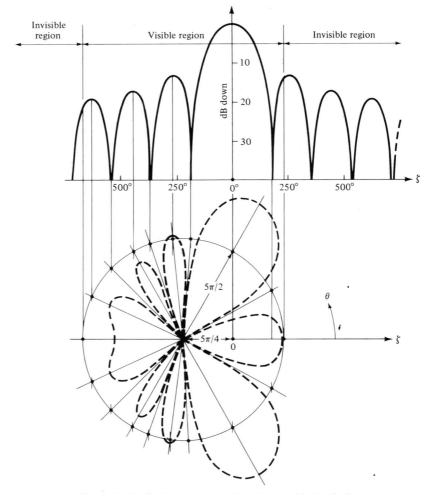

Figure 6.13   Rectangular-to-polar plot graphical solution.

part of the linear graph is referred to as the "visible" region and the remaining part as the "invisible" region. Only the "visible" region of the linear graph is related to the physically observable angle θ (hence its name).

6.7   *N*-ELEMENT LINEAR ARRAY: UNIFORM SPACING, NONUNIFORM AMPLITUDE

The theory to analyze linear arrays with uniform spacing, uniform amplitude, and a progressive phase between the elements was introduced in the previous sections of this chapter. A number of numerical and graphical solutions were used to illustrate some of the principles. In this section, broadside arrays with uniform spacing but nonuniform amplitude distribution will be considered. Most of the discussion will be directed toward binomial [3] and Dolph-Tschebyscheff [4] broadside arrays (also spelled Tchebyscheff or Chebyshev).

Of the three distributions (uniform, binomial, and Tschebyscheff), a uniform amplitude array yields the smallest half-power beamwidth. It is followed, in order, by the Dolph-Tschebyscheff and binomial arrays. In contrast, binomial arrays usually possess the smallest side lobes followed, in order, by the Dolph-Tschebyscheff and uniform arrays. As a matter of fact, binomial arrays with element spacing equal or less than $\lambda/2$ have no side lobes. It is apparent that the designer must compromise between side lobe level and beamwidth.

A criterion that can be used to judge the relative beamwidth and side lobe level of one design to another is the amplitude distribution (tapering) along the source. It has been shown analytically that for a given side lobe level the Dolph-Tschebyscheff array produces the smallest beamwidth between the first nulls. Conversely, for a given beamwidth between the first nulls, the Dolph-Tschebyscheff design leads to the smallest possible side lobe level.

Uniform arrays usually possess the largest directivity. However, superdirective (or super gain as most people call them) antennas possess directivities higher than those of a uniform array [5]. Although a certain amount of superdirectivity is practically possible, superdirective arrays require very large currents with opposite phases between adjacent elements. Thus the net total current and efficiency of each array are very small compared to the corresponding values of an individual element.

Before introducing design methods for specific nonuniform amplitude distributions, let us first derive the array factor.

6.7.1 Array Factor

An array of an even number of isotropic elements ($2M$ where M is an integer) is positioned symmetrically along the z-axis, as shown in Figure 6.14(a). The separation between the elements is d, and M elements are placed on each side of the origin. Assuming that the amplitude excitation is symmetrical about the origin, the array factor for a nonuniform amplitude broadside array can be written as

$$(\text{AF})_{2M} = a_1 e^{+j(1/2)kd\cos\theta} + a_2 e^{+j(3/2)kd\cos\theta} + \cdots$$

$$+ a_M e^{+j[(2M-1)/2]kd\cos\theta}$$

$$+ a_1 e^{-j(1/2)kd\cos\theta} + a_2 e^{-j(3/2)kd\cos\theta} + \cdots$$

$$+ a_M e^{-j[(2M-1)/2]kd\cos\theta}$$

$$(\text{AF})_{2M} = 2 \sum_{n=1}^{M} a_n \cos\left[\frac{(2n-1)}{2}kd\cos\theta\right] \tag{6-59}$$

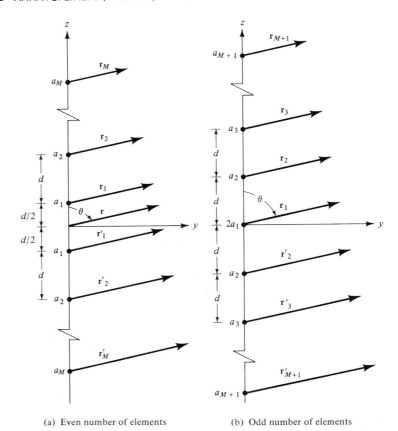

(a) Even number of elements   (b) Odd number of elements

Figure 6.14   Nonuniform amplitude arrays of even and odd number of elements.

which in normalized form reduces to

$$(AF)_{2M} = \sum_{n=1}^{M} a_n \cos\left[\frac{(2n-1)}{2} kd \cos\theta\right] \tag{6-59a}$$

where a_n are the excitation coefficients of the array elements.

If the total number of isotropic elements of the array is odd $(2M+1$ where M is an integer), as shown in Figure 6.14(b), the array factor can be written as

$$(AF)_{2M+1} = 2a_1 + a_2 e^{+jkd\cos\theta} + a_3 e^{j2kd\cos\theta} + \cdots + a_{M+1} e^{jMkd\cos\theta}$$
$$+ a_2 e^{-jkd\cos\theta} + a_3 e^{-j2kd\cos\theta} + \cdots + a_{M+1} e^{-jMkd\cos\theta}$$

$$(AF)_{2M+1} = 2 \sum_{n=1}^{M+1} a_n \cos\left[(n-1)kd\cos\theta\right] \tag{6-60}$$

which in normalized form reduces to

$$(\text{AF})_{2M+1} = \sum_{n=1}^{M+1} a_n \cos[(n-1)kd\cos\theta] \qquad (6\text{-}60a)$$

The amplitude excitation of the center element is $2a_1$.
Equations (6-59a) and (6-60a) can be written as

$$(\text{AF})_{2M}(\text{even}) = \sum_{n=1}^{M} a_n \cos[(2n-1)u] \qquad (6\text{-}61a)$$

$$(\text{AF})_{2M+1}(\text{odd}) = \sum_{n=1}^{M+1} a_n \cos[2(n-1)u] \qquad (6\text{-}61b)$$

where

$$u = \frac{\pi d}{\lambda}\cos\theta \qquad (6\text{-}61c)$$

The next step will be to determine the values of the excitation coefficients (a_n).

6.7.2 Binomial Array

To determine the excitation coefficients of a binomial array, John Stone Stone [3] suggested that the function $(1+x)^{m-1}$ be written in a series, using the binomial expansion, as

$$(1+x)^{m-1} = 1 + (m-1)x + \frac{(m-1)(m-2)}{2!}x^2$$
$$+ \frac{(m-1)(m-2)(m-3)}{3!}x^3 + \cdots \qquad (6\text{-}62)$$

The positive coefficients of the series expansion for different values of m are

$m=1$									1									
$m=2$								1		1								
$m=3$							1		2		1							
$m=4$						1		3		3		1						
$m=5$					1		4		6		4		1					(6-63)
$m=6$				1		5		10		10		5		1				
$m=7$			1		6		15		20		15		6		1			
$m=8$		1		7		21		35		35		21		7		1		
$m=9$		1	8		28		56		70		56		28		8		1	
$m=10$	1	9	36		84		126		126		84		36		9		1	

The above represents Pascal's triangle. If the values of m are used to represent the number of elements of the array, then the coefficients of the expansion represent the relative amplitudes of the elements. Since the coefficients are determined from a binomial series expansion, the array is known as a *binomial array*.

Referring to (6-61a), (6-61b), and (6-63), the amplitude coefficients for the following arrays are:

1. Two elements $(2M=2)$
   $$a_1=1$$
2. Three elements $(2M+1=3)$
   $$2a_1=2 \Rightarrow a_1=1$$
   $$a_2=1$$
3. Four elements $(2M=4)$
   $$a_1=3$$
   $$a_2=1$$
4. Five elements $(2M+1=5)$
   $$2a_1=6 \Rightarrow a_1=3$$
   $$a_2=4$$
   $$a_3=1$$

The coefficients for other arrays can be determined in a similar manner.

To illustrate the method, the patterns of a 10-element binomial array $(2M=10)$ with spacings between the elements of $\lambda/4$, $\lambda/2$, $3\lambda/4$, and λ, respectively, have been plotted in Figure 6.15. The patterns are plotted using (6-61a) and (6-61c) with the coefficients of $a_1=126$, $a_2=84$, $a_3=36$, $a_4=9$, and $a_5=1$. It is observed that there are no minor lobes for the arrays with spacings of $\lambda/4$ and $\lambda/2$ between the elements. While binomial arrays have very low level minor lobes, they exhibit larger beamwidths (compared to uniform and Dolph-Tschebyscheff designs). A major practical disadvantage of binomial arrays is the wide variations between the amplitudes of the different elements of an array, especially for an array with a large number of elements. This leads to very low efficiencies, and it makes the method not very desirable in practice. For example, the relative amplitude coefficient of the end elements of a 10-element array is 1 while that of the center element is 126. Practically, it would be difficult to obtain and maintain such large amplitude variations among the elements. They would also lead to very inefficient antennas. Because the magnitude distribution is monotonically decreasing from the center toward the edges and the magnitude of the extreme elements is negligible compared to those toward the center, a very low side lobe level is expected.

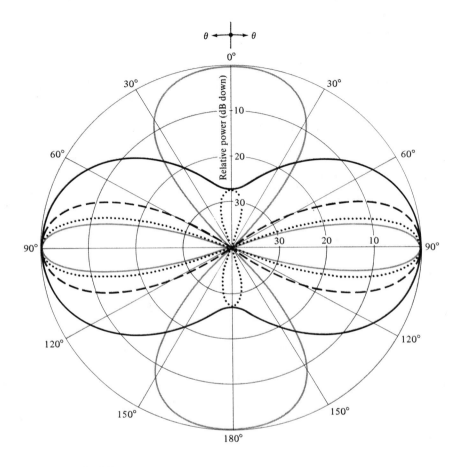

Figure 6.15   Array factor power patterns for a 10-element broadside binomial array with $N = 10$ and $d = \lambda/4$, $\lambda/2$, $3\lambda/4$, and λ.

6.7.3 Dolph-Tschebyscheff Array

Another array, with many practical applications, is the *Dolph-Tschebyscheff array*. The method was originally introduced by Dolph [4] and investigated afterward by others [6]–[9]. It is primarily a compromise between uniform and binomial arrays. Its excitation coefficients are related to Tschebyscheff polynomials. A Dolph-Tschebyscheff array with no side lobes (or side lobes of $-\infty$ dB) reduces to the binomial design. The excitation coefficients for this case, as obtained by both methods, would be identical.

ARRAY FACTOR

Referring to (6-61a) and (6-61b), the array factor of an array of even or odd number of elements with symmetric amplitude excitation is nothing more than a summation of M or $M+1$ cosine terms. The largest harmonic of the cosine terms is one less than the total number of elements of the array. Each cosine term, whose argument is an integer times a fundamental frequency, can be rewritten as a series of cosine functions with the fundamental frequency as the argument. That is,

$$
\begin{array}{lll}
m=0 & \cos(mu)=1 \\
m=1 & \cos(mu)=\cos u \\
m=2 & \cos(mu)=\cos(2u)= & 2\cos^2 u-1 \\
m=3 & \cos(mu)=\cos(3u)= & 4\cos^3 u-3\cos u \\
m=4 & \cos(mu)=\cos(4u)= & 8\cos^4 u-8\cos^2 u+1 \\
m=5 & \cos(mu)=\cos(5u)= & 16\cos^5 u-20\cos^3 u+5\cos u \quad (6\text{-}64) \\
m=6 & \cos(mu)=\cos(6u)= & 32\cos^6 u-48\cos^4 u+18\cos^2 u-1 \\
m=7 & \cos(mu)=\cos(7u)= & 64\cos^7 u-112\cos^5 u+56\cos^3 u-7\cos u \\
m=8 & \cos(mu)=\cos(8u)= & 128\cos^8 u-256\cos^6 u+160\cos^4 u \\
& & \qquad -32\cos^2 u+1 \\
m=9 & \cos(mu)=\cos(9u)= & 256\cos^9 u-576\cos^7 u+432\cos^5 u \\
& & \qquad -120\cos^3 u+9\cos u
\end{array}
$$

The above are obtained by the use of Euler's formula

$$
[e^{ju}]^m=(\cos u+j\sin u)^m=e^{jmu}=\cos(mu)+j\sin(mu) \qquad (6\text{-}65)
$$

and the trigonometric identity $\sin^2 u=1-\cos^2 u$.

If we let

$$
z=\cos u \qquad (6\text{-}66)
$$

(6-64) can be written as

$$
\begin{array}{ll}
m=0 & \cos(mu)=1=T_0(z) \\
m=1 & \cos(mu)=z=T_1(z) \\
m=2 & \cos(mu)=2z^2-1=T_2(z) \\
m=3 & \cos(mu)=4z^3-3z=T_3(z) \\
m=4 & \cos(mu)=8z^4-8z^2+1=T_4(z) \\
m=5 & \cos(mu)=16z^5-20z^3+5z=T_5(z) \qquad (6\text{-}67) \\
m=6 & \cos(mu)=32z^6-48z^4+18z^2-1=T_6(z) \\
m=7 & \cos(mu)=64z^7-112z^5+56z^3-7z=T_7(z) \\
m=8 & \cos(mu)=128z^8-256z^6+160z^4-32z^2+1=T_8(z) \\
m=9 & \cos(mu)=256z^9-576z^7+432z^5-120z^3+9z=T_9(z)
\end{array}
$$

and each is related to a Tschebyscheff (Chebyshev) polynomial $T_m(z)$. These relations between the cosine functions and the Tschebyscheff polynomials are valid only in the $-1 \leq z \leq +1$ range. Because $|\cos(mu)| \leq 1$, each Tschebyscheff polynomial is $|T_m(z)| \leq 1$ for $-1 \leq z \leq +1$. For $|z| > 1$, the Tschebyscheff polynomials are related to the hyperbolic cosine functions.

The recursion formula for Tschebyscheff polynomials is

$$T_m(z) = 2zT_{m-1}(z) - T_{m-2}(z) \qquad (6\text{-}68)$$

It can be used to find one Tschebyscheff polynomial if the polynomials of the previous two orders are known. Each polynomial can also be computed using

$$
\begin{array}{lll}
T_m(z) = \cos\left[m\cos^{-1}(z)\right] & -1 \leq z \leq +1 & (6\text{-}69a) \\
T_m(z) = \cosh\left[m\cosh^{-1}(z)\right]^* & z < -1, \quad z > +1 & (6\text{-}69b)
\end{array}
$$

In Figure 6.16 the first six Tschebyscheff polynomials have been plotted. The following properties of the polynomials are of interest:

1. All polynomials, of any order, pass through the point $(1, 1)$.
2. Within the range $-1 \leq z \leq 1$, the polynomials have values within -1 to $+1$.
3. All roots occur within $-1 \leq z \leq 1$, and all maxima and minima have values of $+1$ and -1, respectively.

Since the array factor of an even or odd number of elements is a summation of cosine terms whose form is the same as the Tschebyscheff polynomials, the unknown coefficients of the array factor can be determined by equating the series representing the cosine terms of the array factor to the appropriate Tschebyscheff polynomial. *The order of the polynomial should be one less than the total number of elements of the array.*

The design procedure will be outlined first, and it will be illustrated with an example. In outlining the procedure, it will be assumed that the number of elements, spacing between the elements, and ratio of major-to-minor lobe intensity (R_0) are known. The requirements will be to determine the excitation coefficients and the array factor of a Dolph-Tschebyscheff array.

ARRAY DESIGN

• *Statement.* Design a broadside Dolph-Tschebyscheff array of $2M$ or $2M + 1$ elements with spacing d between the elements. The side lobes are R_0 dB below the maximum of the major lobe. Find the excitation coefficients and form the array factor.

$^*x = \cosh^{-1}(y) = \ln[y \pm (y^2 - 1)^{1/2}]$

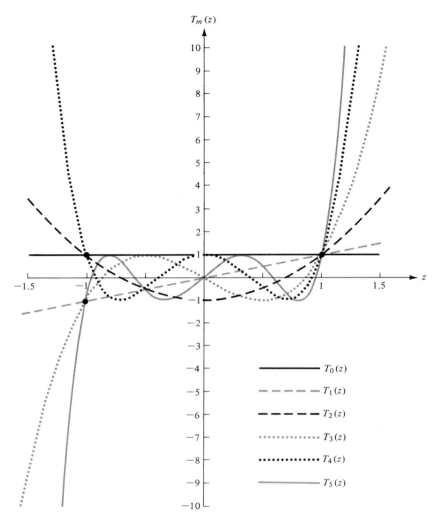

Figure 6.16   Tschebyscheff polynomials of orders zero through five.

Procedure

1. Select the appropriate array factor as given by (6-61a) or (6-61b).
2. Expand the array factor. Replace each $\cos(mu)$ function ($m = 0, 1, 2, 3, \ldots$) by its appropriate series expansion found in (6-64).
3. Determine the point $z = z_0$ such that $T_m(z_0) = R_0$ (dimensionless). *The order m of the Tschebyscheff polynomial is always one less than the total number of elements.* The design procedure requires that the Tschebyscheff polynomial in the $-1 \leq z \leq z_1$, where z_1 is the null nearest to $z = +1$, be used to represent the minor lobes of the array.

The major lobe of the pattern is formed from the remaining part of the polynomial up to point z_0 ($z_1 < z \le z_0$).

4. Substitute

$$\cos(u) = \frac{z}{z_0} \qquad (6\text{-}70)$$

in the array factor of step 2. The $\cos(u)$ is replaced by z/z_0, *and not by z*, so that (6-70) would be valid for $|z| \le |z_0|$. At $|z| = |z_0|$, (6-70) attains its maximum value of unity.

5. Equate the array factor from step 2, after substitution of (6-70), to a $T_m(z)$ from (6-67). The $T_m(z)$ chosen should be of order m where m is an integer equal to one less than the total number of elements of the designed array. This will allow the determination of the excitation coefficients a_n.

6. Write the array factor of (6-61a) or (6-61b) using the coefficients found in step 5.

Example 6.7

Design a broadside Dolph-Tschebyscheff array of 10 elements with spacing d between the elements and with a major-to-minor lobe ratio of 26 dB. Find the excitation coefficients and form the array factor.

SOLUTION

1. The array factor is given by (6-61a) and (6-61c). That is,

$$(AF)_{2M} = \sum_{n=1}^{M=5} a_n \cos[(2n-1)u]$$

$$u = \frac{\pi d}{\lambda} \cos\theta$$

2. When expanded, the array factor can be written as

$$(AF)_{10} = a_1 \cos(u) + a_2 \cos(3u)$$

$$+ a_3 \cos(5u) + a_4 \cos(7u) + a_5 \cos(9u)$$

Replace $\cos(u)$, $\cos(3u)$, $\cos(5u)$, $\cos(7u)$, and $\cos(9u)$ by their series expansions found in (6-67).

3. R_0 (dB) $= 26 = 20 \log_{10}(R_0)$ or R_0 (voltage ratio) $= 20$. Determine z_0 by equating R_0 to $T_9(z)$. Thus

$$R_0 = 20 = T_9(z_0) = \cosh[9 \cosh^{-1}(z_0)]$$

or

$$z_0 = \cosh[\tfrac{1}{9} \cosh^{-1}(20)] = 1.0851$$

Another equation which can, in general, be used to find z_0 and does not require hyperbolic functions is [6]

$$z_0 = \frac{1}{2}\left[\left(R_0 + \sqrt{R_0^2 - 1}\right)^{1/P} + \left(R_0 - \sqrt{R_0^2 - 1}\right)^{1/P}\right]$$

where P is an integer equal to one less than the number of array elements (in this case $P=9$). $R_0 = H_0/H_1$ and z_0 are identified in Figure 6.17.

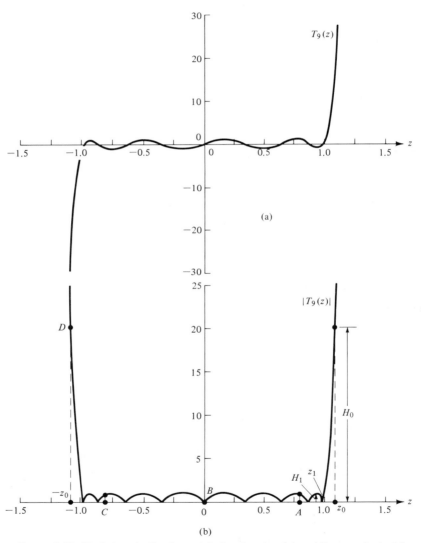

Figure 6.17   Tschebyscheff polynomial of order nine (a) and its magnitude (b).

4. Substitute

$$\cos(u) = \frac{z}{z_0} = \frac{z}{1.0851}$$

in the array factor found in step 2.
5. Equate the array factor of step 2, after the substitution from step 4, to $T_9(z)$. The polynomial $T_9(z)$ is shown plotted in Figure 6.17. Thus

$$
\begin{aligned}
(AF)_{10} = \ & z[(a_1 - 3a_2 + 5a_3 - 7a_4 + 9a_5)/z_0] \\
& + z^3[(4a_2 - 20a_3 + 56a_4 - 120a_5)/z_0{}^3] \\
& + \quad z^5[(16a_3 - 112a_4 + 432a_5)/z_0{}^5] \\
& + \quad \quad \quad z^7[(64a_4 - 576a_5)/z_0{}^7] \\
& + \quad \quad \quad \quad \quad z^9[(256a_5)/z_0{}^9] \\
= \ & 9z - 120z^3 + 432z^5 - 576z^7 + 256z^9
\end{aligned}
$$

Matching similar terms allows the determination of the a_n's. That is,

$$256a_5/z_0{}^9 = 256 \qquad\qquad \Rightarrow a_5 = 2.0860$$

$$(64a_4 - 576a_5)/z_0{}^7 = -576 \qquad\qquad \Rightarrow a_4 = 2.8308$$

$$(16a_3 - 112a_4 + 432a_5)/z_0{}^5 = 432 \qquad\qquad \Rightarrow a_3 = 4.1184$$

$$(4a_2 - 20a_3 + 56a_4 - 120a_5)/z_0{}^3 = -120 \Rightarrow a_2 = 5.2073$$

$$(a_1 - 3a_2 + 5a_3 - 7a_4 + 9a_5)/z_0 = 9 \qquad \Rightarrow a_1 = 5.8377$$

In normalized form, the a_n coefficients can be written as

$a_5 = 1$		$a_5 = 0.357$
$a_4 = 1.357$		$a_4 = 0.485$
$a_3 = 1.974$	or	$a_3 = 0.706$
$a_2 = 2.496$		$a_2 = 0.890$
$a_1 = 2.798$		$a_1 = 1$

The first (left) set is normalized with respect to the amplitude of the elements at the edge while the other (right) is normalized with respect to the amplitude of the center elements.
6. Using the first (left) set of normalized coefficients, the array factor can be written as

$$(AF)_{10} = 2.798\cos(u) + 2.496\cos(3u) + 1.974\cos(5u)$$
$$+ 1.357\cos(7u) + \cos(9u)$$

where $u = [(\pi d/\lambda)\cos\theta]$.

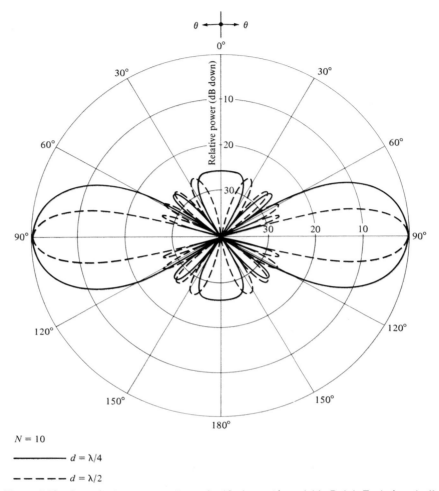

$N = 10$

——————— $d = \lambda/4$

— — — — $d = \lambda/2$

Figure 6.18 Array factor power pattern of a 10-element broadside Dolph-Tschebyscheff array.

The array factor patterns of Example 6.7 for $d=\lambda/4$ and $\lambda/2$ are shown plotted in Figure 6.18. Since the spacing is less than $\lambda(d<\lambda)$, maxima exist only at broadside ($\theta=90°$). However when the spacing is equal to $\lambda(d=\lambda)$, two more maxima appear (one toward $\theta=0°$ and the other toward $\theta=180°$). For $d=\lambda$ the array has four maxima, and it acts as an end-fire as well as a broadside array.

To better illustrate how the pattern of a Dolph-Tschebyscheff array is formed from the Tschebyscheff polynomial, let us again consider the 10-element array whose corresponding Tschebyscheff polynomial is of order 9 and is shown plotted in Figure 6.17. The abscissa of Figure 6.17, in terms of the spacing between the elements (d) and the angle θ, is given by (6-70)

Table 6.8 VALUES OF THE ABSCISSA z AS A FUNCTION OF θ FOR A 10-ELEMENT DOLPH-TSCHEBYSCHEFF ARRAY WITH $R_0 = 20$

θ	$d = \lambda/4$ z (EQ. 6-70a)	$d = \lambda/2$ z (EQ. 6-70a)	$d = 3\lambda/4$ z (EQ. 6-70a)	$d = \lambda$ z (EQ. 6-70a)
0°	0.7673	0.0	−0.7673	−1.0851
10°	0.7764	0.0259	−0.7394	−1.0839
20°	0.8028	0.1026	−0.6509	−1.0657
30°	0.8436	0.2267	−0.4912	−0.9904
40°	0.8945	0.3899	−0.2518	−0.8049
50°	0.9497	0.5774	0.0610	−0.4706
60°	1.0025	0.7673	0.4153	0.0
70°	1.0462	0.9323	0.7514	0.5167
80°	1.0750	1.0450	0.9956	0.9276
90°	1.0851	1.0851	1.0851	1.0851
100°	1.0750	1.0450	0.9956	0.9276
110°	1.0462	0.9323	0.7514	0.5167
120°	1.0025	0.7673	0.4153	0.0
130°	0.9497	0.5774	0.0610	−0.4706
140°	0.8945	0.3899	−0.2518	−0.8049
150°	0.8436	0.2267	−0.4912	−0.9904
160°	0.8028	0.1026	−0.6509	−1.0657
170°	0.7764	0.0259	−0.7394	−1.0839
180°	0.7673	0.0	−0.7673	−1.0851

or

$$z = z_0 \cos u = z_0 \cos\left(\frac{\pi d}{\lambda} \cos\theta\right) = 1.0851 \cos\left(\frac{\pi d}{\lambda} \cos\theta\right) \qquad (6\text{-}70a)$$

For $d = \lambda/4, \lambda/2, 3\lambda/4$, and λ the values of z for angles from $\theta = 0°$ to 90° to 180° are shown tabulated in Table 6.8. Referring to Table 6.8 and Figure 6.17, it is interesting to discuss the pattern formation for the different spacings.

1. $d = \lambda/4$, $N = 10$, $R_0 = 20$

At $\theta = 0°$ the value of z is equal to 0.7673 (point A). As θ attains larger values, z increases until it reaches its maximum value of 1.0851 for $\theta = 90°$. Beyond 90°, z begins to decrease and reaches its original value of 0.7673 for $\theta = 180°$. Thus for $d = \lambda/4$, only the Tschebyscheff polynomial between the values $0.7673 \leq z \leq 1.0851$ ($A \leq z \leq z_0$) is used to form the pattern of the array factor.

2. $d = \lambda/2$, $N = 10$, $R_0 = 20$

At $\theta = 0°$ the value of z is equal to 0 (point B). As θ becomes larger, z increases until it reaches its maximum value of 1.0851 for $\theta = 90°$. Beyond that angle, z decreases and comes back to the original point for $\theta = 180°$. For $d = \lambda/2$, a larger part of the Tschebyscheff polynomial is used ($0 \leq z \leq 1.0851$; $B \leq z \leq z_0$).

3. $d = 3\lambda/4$, $N = 10$, $R_0 = 20$

For this spacing, the value of z for $\theta=0°$ is -0.7673 (point C), and it increases as θ becomes larger. It attains its maximum value of 1.0851 at $\theta=90°$. Beyond that, it traces back to its original value ($-0.7673 \leq z \leq z_0$; $C \leq z \leq z_0$).

4. $d=\lambda$, $N=10$, $R_0=20$

As the spacing increases, a larger portion of the Tschebyscheff polynomial is used to form the pattern of the array factor. When $d=\lambda$, the value of z for $\theta=0°$ is equal to -1.0851 (point D) which in magnitude is equal to the maximum value of z. As θ attains values larger than $0°$, z increases until it reaches its maximum value of 1.0851 for $\theta=90°$. At that point the polynomial (and thus the array factor) again reaches its maximum value. Beyond $\theta=90°$, z and in turn the polynomial and array factor retrace their values ($-1.0851 \leq z \leq +1.0851$; $D \leq z \leq z_0$). For $d=\lambda$ there are four maxima, and a broadside and an end-fire array have been formed simultaneously.

The excitation coefficients of a Dolph-Tschebyscheff array can be derived using various documented techniques [7]–[9] and others. One method, whose results are suitable for computer calculations, is that by Barbiere [7]. The coefficients using this method can be obtained using

$$a_n = \begin{cases} \displaystyle\sum_{q=n}^{M} (-1)^{M-q}(z_0)^{2q-1} \frac{(q+M-2)!(2M-1)}{(q-n)!(q+n-1)!(M-q)!} \\ \qquad\qquad\qquad\qquad\qquad\qquad\qquad \text{for even } 2M \text{ elements} \\[4pt] \displaystyle\sum_{q=n}^{M+1} (-1)^{M-q+1}(z_0)^{2(q-1)} \frac{(q+M-2)!(2M)}{\varepsilon_n(q-n)!(q+n-2)!(M-q+1)!} \\ \qquad\qquad\qquad\qquad\qquad\qquad\qquad \text{for odd } 2M+1 \text{ elements} \\ \qquad\qquad\qquad\qquad\qquad\qquad\qquad\qquad n=1,2,\ldots M+1 \end{cases}$$

$$\text{(6-71a)}$$
$$\text{(6-71b)}$$

$$\text{where } \varepsilon_n = \begin{cases} 2 & n=1 \\ 1 & n\neq 1 \end{cases}$$

BEAMWIDTH AND DIRECTIVITY

For large Dolph-Tschebyscheff arrays scanned not too close to end-fire and with side lobes in the range from -20 to -60 dB, the half-power beamwidth and directivity can be found by introducing a beam broadening factor given approximately by [1]

$$f = 1 + 0.636 \left\{ \frac{2}{R_0} \cosh\left[\sqrt{(\cosh^{-1} R_0)^2 - \pi^2} \right] \right\}^2 \qquad\qquad \text{(6-72)}$$

where R_0 is the major-to-side lobe voltage ratio. The beam broadening factor is plotted in Figure 6.19(a) as a function of side lobe level (in dB).

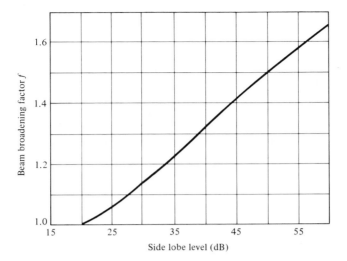

(a) Beam broadening factor

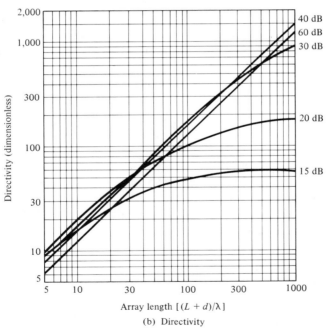

(b) Directivity

Figure 6.19   Beam broadening factor and directivity of Tschebyscheff arrays. (SOURCE: R. S. Elliott, "Beamwidth and Directivity of Large Scanning Arrays," First of Two Parts, *The Microwave Journal*, December 1963)

The half-power beamwidth of a Dolph-Tschebyscheff array can be determined by

1. calculating the beamwidth of a uniform array (of the same number of elements and spacing) using (6-22) or reading it off Figure 6.8
2. multiplying the beamwidth of part (1) by the appropriate beam broadening factor f computed using (6-72) or reading it off Figure 6.19(a)

The same procedure can be used to determine the beamwidth of arrays with a cosine-on-pedestal distribution [1].

The beam broadening factor f can also be used to determine the directivity of large Dolph-Tschebyscheff arrays, scanned near broadside, with side lobes in the -20 to -60 dB range [1]. That is,

$$D_0 = \frac{2R_0^2}{1 + (R_0^2 - 1)f\dfrac{\lambda}{(L+d)}} \tag{6-73}$$

which is shown plotted in Figure 6.19(b) as a function of $L+d$ in wavelengths.

From the data in Figure 6.19(b) it can be concluded that:

1. The directivity of a Dolph-Tschebyscheff array, with a given side lobe level, increases as the array size or number of elements increases.
2. For a given array length, or a given number of elements in the array, the directivity does not necessarily increase as the side lobe level decreases. As a matter of fact, a -15-dB side lobe array has smaller directivity than a -20-dB side lobe array. This may not be the case for all other side lobe levels.

The beamwidth and the directivity of an array depend linearly, but not necessarily at the same rate, on the overall length or total number of elements of the array. Therefore, the beamwidth and directivity must be related to each other. For a uniform broadside array this relation is [1]

$$D_0 = \frac{101.5}{\Theta_d} \tag{6-74}$$

where Θ_d is the 3-dB beamwidth (in degrees). The above relation can be used as a good approximation between beamwidth and directivity for most linear broadside arrays with practical distributions (including the Dolph-Tschebyscheff array). Equation (6-74) states that for a linear broadside array the product of the 3-dB beamwidth and the directivity is approximately equal to 100. This is analogous to the product of the gain and bandwidth for electronic amplifiers.

Example 6.8

Calculate the half-power beamwidth and the directivity for the Dolph-Tschebyscheff array of Example 6.7 for a spacing of $\lambda/2$ between the elements.

SOLUTION
From Example 6.7,

$$R_0 = 26 \text{ dB} \Rightarrow R_0 = 20 \quad \text{(voltage ratio)}$$

Using (6-72) or Figure 6.19(a), the beam broadening factor f is equal to

$$f = 1.079$$

According to (6-22) or Figure 6.8, the beamwidth of a broadside array with $L + d = 5\lambda$ is equal to

$$\Theta_h = 10.17°$$

Thus the beamwidth of a Dolph-Tschebyscheff array is equal to

$$\Theta_h = 10.17f = 10.17(1.079) = 10.97°$$

The directivity can be obtained using (6-73), and it is equal to

$$D_0 = \frac{2(20)^2}{1 + \left[(20)^2 - 1\right]\dfrac{1.079}{5}} = 9.18 = 9.63 \text{ dB}$$

which closely agrees with the results of Figure 6.19(b).

6.8 SUPERDIRECTIVITY

Antennas whose directivities are much larger than the directivity of a reference antenna of the same size are known as superdirective antennas. Thus a superdirective array is one whose directivity is larger than that of a reference array (usually a uniform array of the same length). In an array, superdirectivity is accomplished by inserting more elements within a fixed length (decreasing the spacing). Doing this leads eventually to very large magnitudes and rapid changes of phase in the excitation coefficients of the elements of the array. Thus adjacent elements have very large and oppositely directed currents. This necessitates a very precise adjustment of their values. Associated with this are increases in reactive power (relative to the radiated power) and the Q of the array.

Because of the very large currents in the elements, the ohmic losses increase and the antenna efficiency decreases very sharply. Although practically the ohmic losses can be reduced by the use of superconductive materials, there is no easy solution for the precise adjustment of the amplitudes and phases of the array elements. High radiation efficiency superdirective arrays can be designed utilizing array functions that are insensitive to changes in element values [10].

In practice, superdirective arrays are usually called *supergain*. However, supergain is a misnomer because such antennas have actual overall gains (because of very low efficiencies) less than uniform arrays of the same length. Although significant superdirectivity is very difficult and usually very impractical, a moderate amount can be accomplished. Superdirective antennas are very intriguing, and they have received much attention in the literature.

The length of the array is usually the limiting factor to the directivity of an array. Schelkunoff [11] pointed out that theoretically very high directivities can be obtained from linear end-fire arrays. Bowkamp and de Bruijn [12], however, concluded that theoretically there is no limit in the directivity of a linear antenna. More specifically, Riblet [6] showed that Dolph-Tschebyscheff arrays with element spacing less than $\lambda/2$ can yield any desired directivity. A numerical example of a Dolph-Tschebyscheff array of nine elements, $\lambda/38$ spacing between the elements (total length of $\lambda/4$), and a $1/19.5$ side lobe level was carried out by Yaru [5]. It was found that to produce a directivity of 8.5 times greater than that of a single element, the currents on the individual elements must be on the order of 14×10^6 A and their values adjusted to an accuracy of better than one part in 10^{11}. The maximum radiation intensity produced by such an array is equivalent to that of a single element with a current of only 19.5×10^{-3} A. If the elements of such an array are 1-cm-diameter copper $\lambda/2$ dipoles operating at 10 MHz, the efficiency of the array is less than $10^{-14}\%$.

DESIGNS WITH CONSTRAINTS

To make the designs more practical, applications that warrant some superdirectivity should incorporate constraints. One constraint is based on the sensitivity factor, and it was utilized for the design of superdirective arrays [13]. The sensitivity factor (designated as K) is an important parameter which is related to the electrical and mechanical tolerances of an antenna, and it can be used to describe its performance (especially its practical implementation). For an N-element array, such as that shown in Figure 6.4, it can be written as [13]

$$K = \frac{\sum_{n=1}^{N} |a_n|^2}{\left| \sum_{n=1}^{N} a_n e^{-jkr_n'} \right|}$$

(6-75)

where a_n is the current excitation of the nth element, and r_n' is the distance from the nth element to the far-field observation point (*in the direction of maximum radiation*).

In practice, the excitation coefficients and the positioning of the elements, which result in a desired pattern, cannot be achieved as specified. A certain amount of error, both electrical and mechanical, will always be present. Therefore the desired pattern will not be realized exactly, as required. However, if the design is accomplished based on specified constraints, the realized pattern will approximate the desired one within a specified deviation.

To derive design constraints, the realized current excitation coefficients c_n's are related to the desired ones a_n's by

$$c_n = a_n + \alpha_n a_n = a_n(1 + \alpha_n) \qquad (6\text{-}75\text{a})$$

where $\alpha_n a_n$ represents the error in the nth excitation coefficient. The mean square value of α_n is denoted by

$$\varepsilon^2 = \langle |\alpha_n| \rangle^2 \qquad (6\text{-}75\text{b})$$

To take into account the error associated with the positioning of the elements, we introduce

$$\delta^2 = \frac{(k\sigma)^2}{3} \qquad (6\text{-}75\text{c})$$

where σ is the root mean square value of the element position error. Combining (6-75b) and (6-75c) reduces to

$$\Delta^2 = \delta^2 + \varepsilon^2 \qquad (6\text{-}75\text{d})$$

where Δ is a measure of the combined electrical and mechanical errors.

For uncorrelated errors [13]

$$K\Delta^2 = \frac{\text{average radiation intensity of realized pattern}}{\text{maximum radiation intensity of desired pattern}}$$

If the realized pattern is to be very close to the desired one, then

$$K\Delta^2 \ll 1 \Rightarrow \Delta \ll \frac{1}{\sqrt{K}} \qquad (6\text{-}75\text{e})$$

Equation (6-75e) can be rewritten, by introducing a safety factor S, as

$$\boxed{\Delta = \frac{1}{\sqrt{SK}}} \qquad (6\text{-}75\text{f})$$

S is chosen large enough so that (6-75e) is satisfied. When Δ is multiplied by 100, 100Δ represents the percent tolerance for combined electrical and mechanical errors.

The choice of the value of S depends largely on the required accuracy between the desired and realized patterns. For example, if the focus is primarily on the realization of the main beam, a value of $S = 10$ will probably be satisfactory. For side lobes of 20 dB down, S should be about

1000. In general, an approximate value of S should be chosen according to

$$S \simeq 10 \times 10^{b/10} \tag{6-75g}$$

where b represents the pattern level (in dB down) whose shape is to be accurately realized.

The above method can be used to design, with the safety factor K constrained to a certain value, arrays with maximum directivity. Usually one first plots, for each selected excitation distribution and positioning of the elements, the directivity D of the array under investigation versus the corresponding sensitivity factor K (using 6-75) of the same array. The design usually begins with the excitation and positioning of a uniform array (i.e., uniform amplitudes, a progressive phase, and equally spaced elements). The directivity associated with it is designated as D_0 while the corresponding sensitivity factor, computed using (6-75), is equal to $K_0 = 1/N$.

As the design deviates from that of the uniform array and becomes superdirective, the values of the directivity increase monotonically with increases in K. Eventually a maximum directivity is attained (designated as D_{max}), and it corresponds to a $K = K_{max}$; beyond that point ($K > K_{max}$), the directivity decreases monotonically. The antenna designer should then select the design for which $D_0 < D < D_{max}$ and $K_0 = 1/N < K < K_{max}$.

The value of D is chosen subject to the constraint that K is a certain number whose corresponding tolerance error Δ of (6-75f), for the desired safety factor S, can be achieved practically. Tolerance errors of less than about 0.3 percent are usually not achievable in practice. In general, the designer must trade-off between directivity and sensitivity factor; larger D's (provided $D \leq D_{max}$) result in larger K's ($K \leq K_{max}$), and vice-versa.

A number of constrained designs can be found in [13]. For example, an array of cylindrical monopoles above an infinite and perfectly conducting ground plane was designed for optimum directivity at $f = 30$ MHz, with a constraint on the sensitivity factor. The spacing d between the elements was maintained uniform.

For a four-element array, it was found that for $d = 0.3\lambda$ the maximum directivity was 14.5 dB and occurred at a sensitivity factor of $K = 1$. However for $d = 0.1\lambda$ the maximum directivity was up to 15.8 dB with the corresponding sensitivity factor up to about 10^3. At $K_0 = 1/N = 1/4$, the directivities for $d = 0.3\lambda$ and 0.1λ were about 11.3 and 8 dB, respectively. When the sensitivity factor was maintained constant and equal to $K = 1$, the directivity for $d = 0.3\lambda$ was 14.5 dB and only 11.6 dB for $d = 0.1\lambda$. It should be noted that the directivity of a single monopole above an infinite ground plane is twice that in free-space and equal to about 3.25 (or about 5.1 dB).

6.9 PLANAR ARRAY

In addition to placing elements along a line (to form a linear array), individual radiators can be positioned along a rectangular grid to form a rectangular or planar array. Planar arrays provide additional variables which can be used to control and shape the pattern of the array. Planar arrays are more versatile and can provide more symmetrical patterns with lower side lobes. In addition, they can be used to scan the main beam of the antenna toward any point in space.

6.9.1 Array Factor

To derive the array factor for a planar array, let us refer to Figure 6.20. If M elements are initially placed along the x-axis, as shown in Figure 6.20(a), the array factor of it can be written according to (6-52) and (6-54) as

$$\text{AF} = \sum_{m=1}^{M} I_{m1} e^{j(m-1)(kd_x \sin\theta\cos\phi + \beta_x)} \tag{6-76}$$

where I_{m1} is the excitation coefficient of each element. The spacing and progressive phase shift between the elements along the x-axis are represented, respectively, by d_x and β_x. If N such arrays are placed next to each other in the y-direction, a distance d_y apart and with a progressive phase β_y, a rectangular array will by formed as shown in Figure 6.20(b). The array factor for the entire planar array can be written as

$$\text{AF} = \sum_{n=1}^{N} I_{1n} \left[\sum_{m=1}^{M} I_{m1} e^{j(m-1)(kd_x \sin\theta\cos\phi + \beta_x)} \right] e^{j(n-1)(kd_y \sin\theta\sin\phi + \beta_y)} \tag{6-76a}$$

or

$$\text{AF} = S_{xm} S_{yn} \tag{6-77}$$

where

$$S_{xm} = \sum_{m=1}^{M} I_{m1} e^{j(m-1)(kd_x \sin\theta\cos\phi + \beta_x)} \tag{6-77a}$$

$$S_{yn} = \sum_{n=1}^{N} I_{1n} e^{j(n-1)(kd_y \sin\theta\sin\phi + \beta_y)} \tag{6-77b}$$

Equation (6-77) indicates that the pattern of a rectangular array is the product of the array factors of the arrays in the x- and y-directions.

    If the amplitude excitation coefficients of the elements of the array in the y-direction are proportional to those along the x, the amplitude of the (m, n)th element can be written as

$$I_{mn} = I_{m1} I_{1n} \tag{6-78}$$

If in addition the amplitude excitation of the entire array is uniform ($I_{mn} = I_0$), (6-76a) can be expressed as

$$\text{AF} = I_0 \sum_{m=1}^{M} e^{j(m-1)(kd_x \sin\theta\cos\phi + \beta_x)} \sum_{n=1}^{N} e^{j(n-1)(kd_y \sin\theta\sin\phi + \beta_y)} \tag{6-79}$$

According to (6-6), (6-10), and (6-10c), the normalized form of (6-79) can

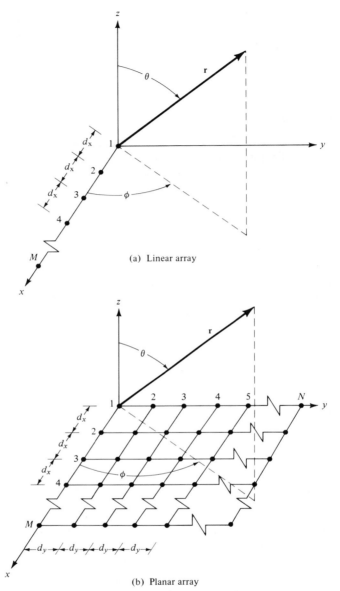

(a) Linear array

(b) Planar array

Figure 6.20   Linear and planar array geometries.

also be written as

$$AF_n(\theta, \phi) = \left\{ \frac{1}{M} \frac{\sin\left(\dfrac{M}{2}\psi_x\right)}{\sin\left(\dfrac{\psi_x}{2}\right)} \right\} \left\{ \frac{1}{N} \frac{\sin\left(\dfrac{N}{2}\psi_y\right)}{\sin\left(\dfrac{\psi_y}{2}\right)} \right\} \tag{6-80}$$

where

$$\psi_x = kd_x \sin\theta \cos\phi + \beta_x \tag{6-80a}$$

$$\psi_y = kd_y \sin\theta \sin\phi + \beta_y \tag{6-80b}$$

When the spacing between the elements is equal or greater than λ, multiple maxima of equal magnitude are formed. The principal maximum is referred to as the major lobe and the remaining as the *grating lobes*. To form or avoid grating lobes in a rectangular array, the same principles must be satisfied as for a linear array. To avoid grating lobes in the x-z and y-z planes, the spacing between the elements in the x- and y-directions, respectively, must be less than λ ($d_x < \lambda$ and $d_y < \lambda$).

For a rectangular array, the major lobe and grating lobes of S_{xm} and S_{yn} in (6-77a) and (6-77b) are located at

$$kd_x \sin\theta \cos\phi + \beta_x = \pm 2m\pi \qquad m = 0, 1, 2, \dots \tag{6-81a}$$

$$kd_y \sin\theta \sin\phi + \beta_y = \pm 2n\pi \qquad n = 0, 1, 2, \dots \tag{6-81b}$$

The phases β_x and β_y are independent of each other, and they can be adjusted so that the main beam of S_{xm} is not the same as that of S_{yn}. However, in most practical applications it is required that the conical main beams of S_{xm} and S_{yn} intersect and their maxima be directed toward the same direction. If it is desired to have only one main beam that is directed along $\theta = \theta_0$ and $\phi = \phi_0$, the progressive phase shift between the elements in the x- and y-directions must be equal to

$$\beta_x = -kd_x \sin\theta_0 \cos\phi_0 \tag{6-82a}$$

$$\beta_y = -kd_y \sin\theta_0 \sin\phi_0 \tag{6-82b}$$

When solved simultaneously, (6-82a) and (6-82b) can also be expressed as

$$\tan\phi_0 = \frac{\beta_y d_x}{\beta_x d_y} \tag{6-83a}$$

$$\sin^2\theta_0 = \left(\frac{\beta_x}{kd_x}\right)^2 + \left(\frac{\beta_y}{kd_y}\right)^2 \tag{6-83b}$$

The principal maximum ($m=n=0$) and the grating lobes can be located by

$$kd_x(\sin\theta\cos\phi - \sin\theta_0\cos\phi_0) = \pm 2m\pi, \qquad m=0,1,2,\ldots \qquad (6\text{-}84a)$$

$$kd_y(\sin\theta\sin\phi - \sin\theta_0\sin\phi_0) = \pm 2n\pi, \qquad n=0,1,2,\ldots \qquad (6\text{-}84b)$$

or

$$\sin\theta\cos\phi - \sin\theta_0\cos\phi_0 = \pm\frac{m\lambda}{d_x}, \qquad m=0,1,2,\ldots \qquad (6\text{-}85a)$$

$$\sin\theta\sin\phi - \sin\theta_0\sin\phi_0 = \pm\frac{n\lambda}{d_y}, \qquad n=0,1,2,\ldots \qquad (6\text{-}85b)$$

which, when solved simultaneously, reduce to

$$\phi = \tan^{-1}\left[\frac{\sin\theta_0\sin\phi_0 \pm n\lambda/d_y}{\sin\theta_0\cos\phi_0 \pm m\lambda/d_x}\right] \qquad (6\text{-}86a)$$

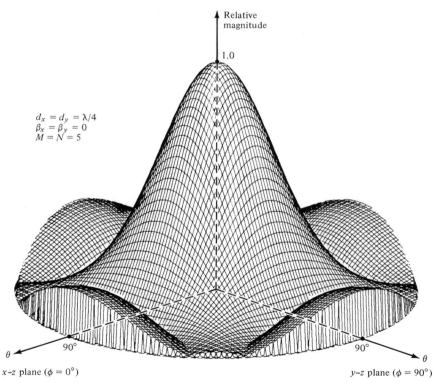

$d_x = d_y = \lambda/4$
$\beta_x = \beta_y = 0$
$M = N = 5$

x–z plane ($\phi = 0°$) y–z plane ($\phi = 90°$)

Figure 6.21 Three-dimensional antenna pattern of a planar array of isotropic elements with a spacing of $d_x = d_y = \lambda/4$, and equal amplitude and phase excitations.

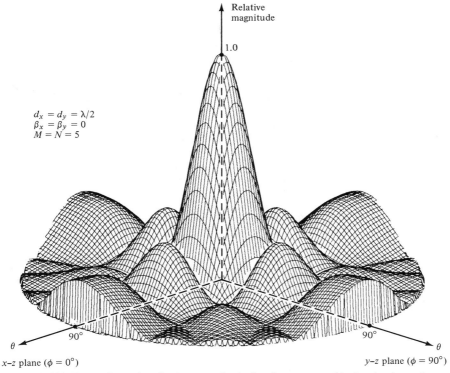

Relative
magnitude

1.0

$d_x = d_y = \lambda/2$
$\beta_x = \beta_y = 0$
$M = N = 5$

90°   90°

θ θ

x–z plane ($\phi = 0°$)   y–z plane ($\phi = 90°$)

Figure 6.22   Three-dimensional antenna pattern of a planar array of isotropic elements with a spacing of $d_x = d_y = \lambda/2$, and equal amplitude and phase excitations.

and

$$\theta = \sin^{-1}\left[\frac{\sin\theta_0\cos\phi_0 \pm m\lambda/d_x}{\cos\phi}\right] = \sin^{-1}\left[\frac{\sin\theta_0\sin\phi_0 \pm n\lambda/d_y}{\sin\phi}\right]$$

(6-86b)

To demonstrate the principles of planar array theory, the three-dimensional pattern of a 5×5 element array of uniform amplitude, $\beta_x = \beta_y = 0$, and $d_x = d_y = \lambda/4$ is shown in Figure 6.21. The maximum is oriented along $\theta_0 = 0°$ and only the pattern above the x-y plane is shown. An identical pattern is formed in the lower hemisphere which can be diminished by the use of a ground plane.

To examine the pattern variation as a function of the element spacing, the three-dimensional pattern of the same 5×5 element array of isotropic sources with $d_x = d_y = \lambda/2$ and $\beta_x = \beta_y = 0$ is displayed in Figure 6.22. As contrasted with Figure 6.21, the pattern of Figure 6.22 exhibits complete minor lobes in all planes. Figure 6.23 displays the corresponding two-

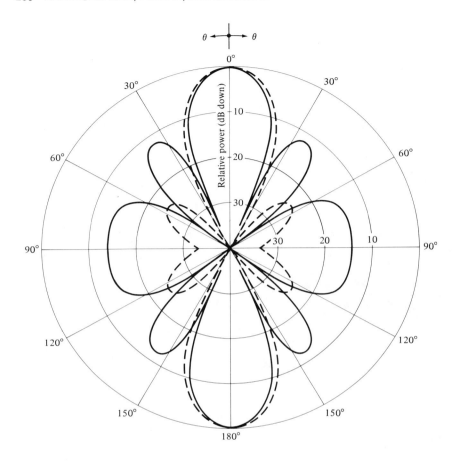

Figure 6.23 Two-dimensional antenna patterns of a planar array of isotropic elements with a spacing of $d_x = d_y = \lambda/2$, and equal amplitude and phase excitations.

dimensional elevation patterns with cuts at $\phi = 0°$ (x-z plane), $\phi = 90°$ (y-z plane), and $\phi = 45°$. The two principal patterns ($\phi = 0°$ and $\phi = 90°$) are identical. The patterns of Figures 6.21 and 6.22 display a four-fold symmetry.

As discussed previously, arrays possess wide versatility in their radiation characteristics. The most common characteristic of an array is its scanning mechanism. To illustrate that, the three-dimensional pattern of the same 5×5 element array, with its maximum oriented along the $\theta_0 = 30°$,

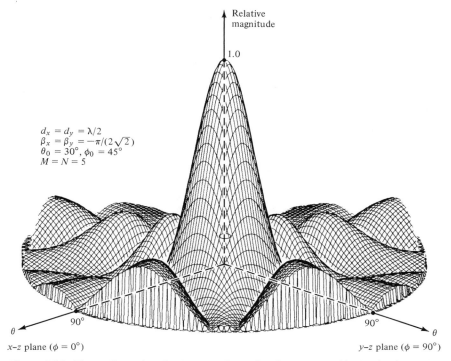

Relative
magnitude

1.0

$d_x = d_y = \lambda/2$
$\beta_x = \beta_y = -\pi/(2\sqrt{2})$
$\theta_0 = 30°, \phi_0 = 45°$
$M = N = 5$

θ

90°   90°

θ

x-z plane $(\phi = 0°)$ y-z plane $(\phi = 90°)$

Figure 6.24   Three-dimensional antenna pattern of a planar array of isotropic elements with a spacing of $d_x = d_y = \lambda/2$, equal amplitude, and progressive phase excitation.

$\phi_0 = 45°$, is plotted in Figure 6.24. The element spacing is $d_x = d_y = \lambda/2$. The maximum is found in the first quadrant of the upper hemisphere. The small ring around the vertical axis indicates the maximum value of the pattern along that axis ($\theta = 0°$). The two-dimensional patterns are shown in Figure 6.25, and they exhibit only a two-fold symmetry. The principal plane pattern ($\phi = 0°$ or $\phi = 90°$) is normalized relative to the maximum which occurs at $\theta = 30°, \phi_0 = 45°$. Its maximum along the principal planes ($\phi = 0°$ or $\phi = 90°$) occurs when $\theta = 21°$ and it is 17.37 dB down from the maximum at $\theta_0 = 30°$, $\phi_0 = 45°$.

To illustrate the formation of the grating lobes, when the spacing between the elements is large, the three-dimensional pattern of the 5×5 element array with $d_x = d_y = \lambda$ and $\beta_x = \beta_y = 0$ are displayed in Figure 6.26. Its corresponding two-dimensional elevation patterns at $\phi = 0°$ ($\phi = 90°$) and $\phi = 45°$ are exhibited in Figure 6.27. Besides the maxima along $\theta = 0°$ and $\theta = 180°$, additional maxima with equal intensity, referred to as *grating lobes*, appear along the principal planes (x-z and y-z planes) when $\theta = 90°$. Further increase of the spacing to $d_x = d_y = 2\lambda$ would result in additional grating lobes.

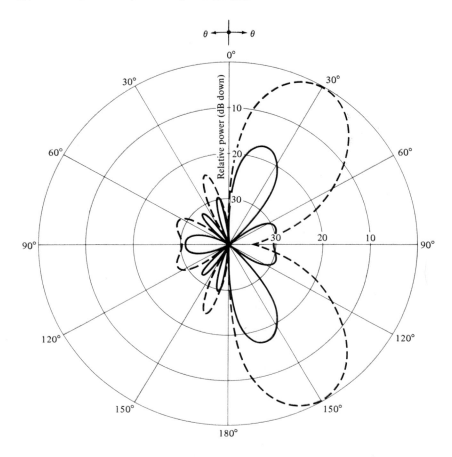

Figure 6.25 Two-dimensional antenna patterns of a planar array of isotropic elements with a spacing of $d_x = d_y = \lambda/2$, equal amplitude, and progressive phase excitation.

The array factor of the planar array has been derived assuming that each element is an isotropic source. If the antenna is an array of *identical* elements, the total field can be obtained by applying the pattern multiplication rule of (6-5) in a manner similar as for the linear array.

When only the central element of a large planar array is excited and the others are passively terminated, it has been observed experimentally that additional nulls in the pattern of the element are developed which are not accounted for by theory. The nulls were observed to become deeper and

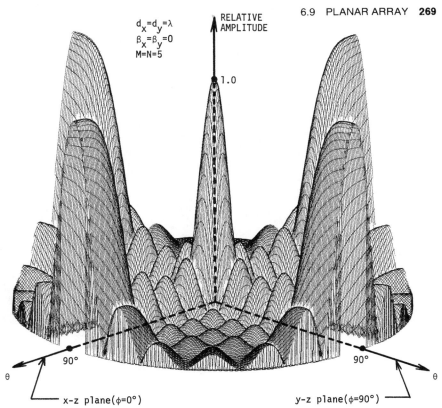

$d_x = d_y = \lambda$
$\beta_x = \beta_y = 0$
$M = N = 5$

RELATIVE
AMPLITUDE

1.0

90°   90°

θ   θ

x-z plane($\phi = 0°$)   y-z plane($\phi = 90°$)

Figure 6.26 Three-dimensional antenna pattern of a planar array of isotropic elements with a spacing of $d_x = d_y = \lambda$, and equal amplitude and phase excitations.

narrower [14] as the number of elements surrounding the excited element increased and approached a large array. These effects became more noticeable for arrays of open waveguides. It has been demonstrated [15] that dips at angles interior to grating lobes are formed by coupling through surface wave propagation. The coupling decays very slowly with distance, so that even distant elements from the driven elements experience substantial parasitic excitation. The angles where these large variations occur can be placed outside scan angles of interest by choosing smaller element spacing than would be used in the absence of such coupling. Because of the complexity of the problem, it will not be pursued here any further but the interested reader is referred to the published literature.

6.9.2 Beamwidth

The task of finding the beamwidth of nonuniform amplitude planar arrays is quite formidable. Instead, a very simple procedure will be outlined which can be used to compute these parameters for large arrays whose maximum is not scanned too far off broadside. The method [16] utilizes results of a

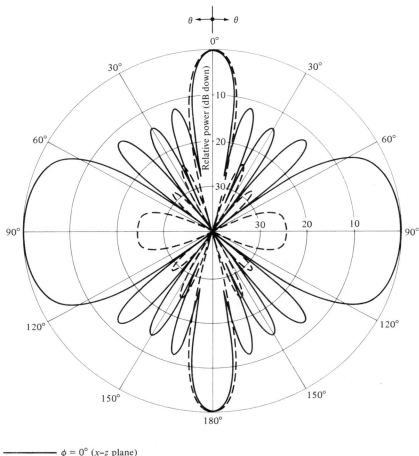

Figure 6.27 Two-dimensional antenna patterns of a planar array of isotropic elements with a spacing of $d_x = d_y = \lambda$, and equal amplitude and phase excitations.

uniform linear array and the beam broadening factor of the amplitude distribution.

The maximum of the conical main beam of the array is assumed to be directed toward θ_0, ϕ_0 as shown in Figure 6.28. To define a beamwidth, two planes are chosen. One is the elevation plane defined by the angle $\phi = \phi_0$ and the other is a plane that is perpendicular to it. The corresponding half-power beamwidth of each is designated, respectively, by Θ_h and Ψ_h. For example, if the array maximum is pointing along $\theta_0 = \pi/2$ and $\phi_0 = \pi/2$,

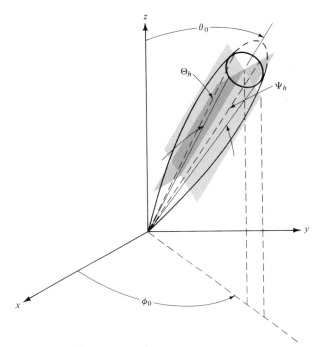

Figure 6.28 Half-power beamwidths for a conical main beam oriented toward $\theta=\theta_0, \phi=\phi_0$. (SOURCE: R. S. Elliott, "Beamwidth and Directivity of Large Scanning Arrays," Last of Two Parts, *The Microwave Journal*, January 1964)

Θ_h represents the beamwidth in the *y-z* plane and Ψ_h, the beamwidth in the *x-y* plane.

For a large array, with its maximum near broadside, the elevation plane half-power beamwidth Θ_h is given approximately by [16]

$$\Theta_h = \sqrt{\frac{1}{\cos^2\theta_0\left[\Theta_{x0}^{-2}\cos^2\phi_0 + \Theta_{y0}^{-2}\sin^2\phi_0\right]}} \qquad (6\text{-}87)$$

where Θ_{x0} represents the half-power beamwidth of a *broadside* linear array of *M* elements. Similarly, Θ_{y0} represents the half-power beamwidth of a *broadside* array of *N* elements.

The values of Θ_{x0} and Θ_{y0} can be obtained by using previous results. For a uniform distribution, for example, the values of Θ_{x0} and Θ_{y0} can be obtained by using, respectively, the lengths $(L_x+d_x)/\lambda$ and $(L_y+d_y)/\lambda$ and reading the values from the broadside curve of Figure 6.8. For a Tschebyscheff distribution, the values of Θ_{x0} and Θ_{y0} are obtained by multiplying each uniform distribution value by the beam broadening factor of (6-72) or Figure 6.19(a). The same concept can be used to obtain the beamwidth of other distributions as long as their corresponding beam broadening factors are available.

For a square array ($M = N$, $\Theta_{x0} = \Theta_{y0}$), (6-87) reduces to

$$\Theta_h = \Theta_{x0} \sec \theta_0 = \Theta_{y0} \sec \theta_0 \tag{6-87a}$$

Equation (6-87a) indicates that for $\theta_0 > 0$ the beamwidth increases proportionally to $\sec \theta_0 = 1/\cos \theta_0$. The broadening of the beamwidth by $\cos \theta_0$ is consistent with the reduction by $\sec \theta_0$ of the projected area of the array in the pointing direction.

The half-power beamwidth Ψ_h, in the plane that is perpendicular to the $\phi = \phi_0$ elevation, is given by [16]

$$\Psi_h = \sqrt{\frac{1}{\Theta_{x0}^{-2} \sin^2 \phi_0 + \Theta_{y0}^{-2} \cos^2 \phi_0}} \tag{6-88}$$

and it does not depend on θ_0. For a square array, (6-88) reduces to

$$\Psi_h = \Theta_{x0} = \Theta_{y0} \tag{6-88a}$$

The values of Θ_{x0} and Θ_{y0} are the same as in (6-87) and (6-87a).

For a planar array, it is useful to define a beam solid angle Ω_A by

$$\Omega_A = \Theta_h \Psi_h \tag{6-89}$$

as it was done in (2-23), (2-24), and (2-27). Using (6-87) and (6-88), (6-89) can be expressed as

$$\Omega_A = \frac{\Theta_{x0} \Theta_{y0} \sec \theta_0}{\left[\sin^2 \phi_0 + \dfrac{\Theta_{y0}^2}{\Theta_{x0}^2} \cos^2 \phi_0 \right]^{1/2} \left[\sin^2 \phi_0 + \dfrac{\Theta_{x0}^2}{\Theta_{y0}^2} \cos^2 \phi_0 \right]^{1/2}} \tag{6-90}$$

6.9.3 Directivity

The directivity of the array factor $AF(\theta, \phi)$ whose major beam is pointing in the $\theta = \theta_0$ and $\phi = \phi_0$ direction, can be obtained by employing the definition of (2-22) and writing it as

$$D_0 = \frac{4\pi [AF(\theta_0, \phi_0)][AF(\theta_0, \phi_0)]^* \big|_{max}}{\displaystyle\int_0^{2\pi} \int_0^{\pi} [AF(\theta, \phi)][AF(\theta, \phi)]^* \sin \theta \, d\theta \, d\phi} \tag{6-91}$$

A novel method has been introduced [17] for integrating the terms of the directivity expression for isotropic and conical patterns.

As in the case of the beamwidth, the task of evaluating (6-91) for nonuniform amplitude distribution is formidable. Instead, a very simple procedure will be outlined to compute the directivity of a planar array using data from linear arrays.

For large planar arrays, which are nearly broadside, the directivity reduces to [16]

$$D_0 = \pi \cos \theta_0 D_x D_y$$ (6-92)

where D_x and D_y are the directivities of broadside linear arrays each, respectively, of length and number of elements L_x, M and L_y, N. The factor $\cos \theta_0$ accounts for the decrease of the directivity because of the decrease of the projected area of the array. Each of the values, D_x and D_y, can be obtained by using (6-73) with the appropriate beam broadening factor f. For Tschebyscheff arrays, D_x and D_y can be obtained using (6-72) or Figure 6-19(a) and (6-73). Alternatively, they can be obtained using the graphical data of Figure 6.19(b).

For most practical amplitude distributions, the directivity of (6-92) is related to the beam solid angle of the same array by

$$D_0 \simeq \frac{\pi^2}{\Omega_A(\text{rads}^2)} = \frac{32,400}{\Omega_A(\text{degrees}^2)}$$ (6-93)

where Ω_A is expressed in square radians or square degrees. Equation (6-93) should be compared with (2-26) or (2-28) given by Kraus.

Example 6.9

Compute the half-power beamwidths, beam solid angle, and directivity of a planar square array of 100 isotropic elements (10×10). Assume a Tschebyscheff distribution, $\lambda/2$ spacing between the elements, -26-dB side lobe level, and the maximum oriented along $\theta_0 = 30°$, $\phi_0 = 45°$.

SOLUTION

Since in the x- and y-directions

$$L_x + d_x = L_y + d_y = 5\lambda$$

and each is equal to $L + d$ of Example 6.8, then

$$\Theta_{x0} = \Theta_{y0} = 10.97°$$

According to (6-87a)

$$\Theta_h = \Theta_{x0} \sec \theta_0 = 10.17° \sec(30°) = 12.67°$$

and (6-88a)

$$\Psi_h = \Theta_{x0} = 10.97°$$

and (6-89)

$$\Omega_A = \Theta_h \Psi_h = 12.67(10.97) = 138.96 \quad (\text{degrees}^2)$$

The directivity can be obtained using (6-92). Since the array is square, $D_x = D_y$ and each is equal to the directivity of Example 6.8. Thus

$$D_0 = \pi \cos(30°)(9.18)(9.18) = 229.28 = 23.60 \text{ dB}$$

Using (6-93)

$$D_0 \simeq \frac{32,400}{\Omega_A(\text{degrees}^2)} = \frac{32,400}{138.96} = 233.16 = 23.67 \text{ dB}$$

Obviously we have an excellent agreement.

6.10 CIRCULAR ARRAY

The circular array, in which the elements are placed in a circular ring, is an array configuration of very practical interest. Its applications span radio direction finding, air and space navigation, underground propagation, radar, sonar, and many other systems.

6.10.1 Array Factor

Referring to Figure 6.29, let us assume that N isotropic elements are equally spaced on the x-y plane along a circular ring of the radius a. The field of the array can be written as

$$E(r, \theta, \phi) = \sum_{n=1}^{N} a_n \frac{e^{-jkR_n}}{R_n} \tag{6-94}$$

where R_n is the distance from the nth element to the observation point. In general

$$R_n = (r^2 + a^2 - 2ar\cos\psi)^{1/2} \tag{6-94a}$$

which for $r \gg a$ reduces to

$$R_n \simeq r - a\cos\psi_n = r - a(\hat{a}_\rho \cdot \hat{a}_r) = r - a\sin\theta\cos(\phi - \phi_n) \tag{6-94b}$$

where

$$\hat{a}_\rho \cdot \hat{a}_r = (\hat{a}_x \cos\phi_n + \hat{a}_y \sin\phi_n) \cdot (\hat{a}_x \sin\theta\cos\phi + \hat{a}_y \sin\theta\sin\phi + \hat{a}_z \cos\theta)$$

$$= \sin\theta\cos(\phi - \phi_n) \tag{6-94c}$$

Thus (6-94) reduces, assuming that for amplitude variations $R_n \simeq r$, to

$$E(r, \theta, \phi) = \frac{e^{-jkr}}{r} \sum_{n=1}^{N} a_n e^{+jka\sin\theta\cos(\phi - \phi_n)} \tag{6-95}$$

where

a_n = excitation coefficients (amplitude and phase) of nth element

$\phi_n = 2\pi\left(\dfrac{n}{N}\right)$ = angular position of nth element on x-y plane

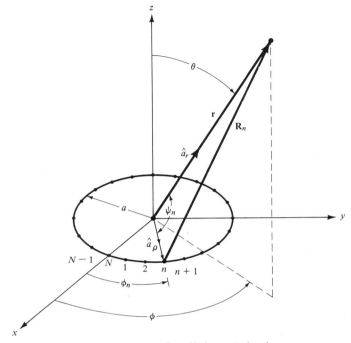

Figure 6.29   Geometry of an *N*-element circular array.

In general, the excitation coefficient of the nth element can be written as

$$a_n = I_n e^{j\alpha_n} \qquad (6\text{-}96)$$

where

I_n = amplitude excitation of the nth element

α_n = phase excitation (relative to the array center) of the nth element

With (6-96), (6-95) can be expressed as

$$E(r, \theta, \phi) = \frac{e^{-jkr}}{r} \big[\text{AF}(\theta, \phi) \big] \qquad (6\text{-}97)$$

where

$$\text{AF}(\theta, \phi) = \sum_{n=1}^{N} I_n e^{j[ka\sin\theta\cos(\phi - \phi_n) + \alpha_n]} \qquad (6\text{-}97a)$$

Equation (6-97a) represents the array factor of a circular array of N equally spaced elements. To direct the peak of the main beam in the (θ_0, ϕ_0) direction, the phase excitation of the nth element can be chosen to be

$$\alpha_n = -ka\sin\theta_0\cos(\phi_0 - \phi_n) \qquad (6\text{-}98)$$

Thus the array factor of (6-97a) can be written as

$$AF(\theta, \phi) = \sum_{n=1}^{N} I_n e^{jka[\sin\theta\cos(\phi-\phi_n) - \sin\theta_0\cos(\phi_0-\phi_n)]}$$

$$= \sum_{n=1}^{N} I_n e^{jka(\cos\psi - \cos\psi_0)} \tag{6-99}$$

To reduce (6-99) to a simpler form, we define ρ_0 as

$$\rho_0 = a\left[(\sin\theta\cos\phi - \sin\theta_0\cos\phi_0)^2 + (\sin\theta\sin\phi - \sin\theta_0\sin\phi_0)^2\right]^{1/2}$$

$$\tag{6-100}$$

Then the exponential in (6-99) can take the form of

$$ka(\cos\psi - \cos\psi_0)$$

$$= \frac{k\rho_0[\sin\theta\cos(\phi-\phi_n) - \sin\theta_0\cos(\phi_0-\phi_n)]}{\left[(\sin\theta\cos\phi - \sin\theta_0\cos\phi_0)^2 + (\sin\theta\sin\phi - \sin\theta_0\sin\phi_0)^2\right]^{1/2}}$$

$$\tag{6-101}$$

which when expanded reduces to

$$ka(\cos\psi - \cos\psi_0)$$

$$= k\rho_0 \left\{ \frac{\cos\phi_n(\sin\theta\cos\phi - \sin\theta_0\cos\phi_0) + \sin\phi_n(\sin\theta\sin\phi - \sin\theta_0\sin\phi_0)}{\left[(\sin\theta\cos\phi - \sin\theta_0\cos\phi_0)^2 + (\sin\theta\sin\phi - \sin\theta_0\sin\phi_0)^2\right]^{1/2}} \right\}$$

$$\tag{6-101a}$$

Defining

$$\cos\xi = \frac{\sin\theta\cos\phi - \sin\theta_0\cos\phi_0}{\left[(\sin\theta\cos\phi - \sin\theta_0\cos\phi_0)^2 + (\sin\theta\sin\phi - \sin\theta_0\sin\phi_0)^2\right]^{1/2}}$$

$$\tag{6-102}$$

then

$$\sin\xi = \left[1 - \cos^2\xi\right]^{1/2}$$

$$= \frac{\sin\theta\sin\phi - \sin\theta_0\sin\phi_0}{\left[(\sin\theta\cos\phi - \sin\theta_0\cos\phi_0)^2 + (\sin\theta\sin\phi - \sin\theta_0\sin\phi_0)^2\right]^{1/2}}$$

$$\tag{6-103}$$

Thus (6-101a) and (6-99) can be rewritten, respectively, as

$$ka(\cos\psi - \cos\psi_0) = k\rho_0(\cos\phi_n\cos\xi + \sin\phi_n\sin\xi) = k\rho_0\cos(\phi_n - \xi)$$

$$\tag{6-104}$$

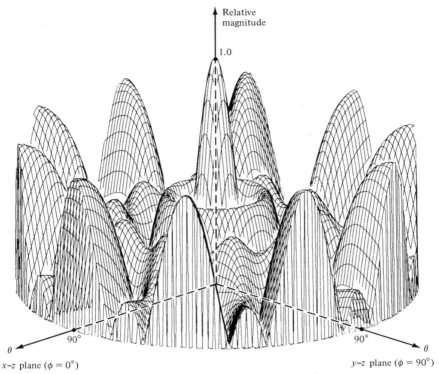

Figure 6.30   Three-dimensional amplitude pattern of the array factor for a uniform circular array of 10 elements ($ka = 10$).

$$\mathrm{AF}(\theta,\phi) = \sum_{n=1}^{N} I_n e^{jka(\cos\psi - \cos\psi_0)} = \sum_{n=1}^{N} I_n e^{jk\rho_0\cos(\phi_n - \xi)} \qquad \text{(6-105)}$$

where

$$\xi = \tan^{-1}\left[\frac{\sin\theta\sin\phi - \sin\theta_0\sin\phi_0}{\sin\theta\cos\phi - \sin\theta_0\cos\phi_0}\right] \qquad \text{(6-105a)}$$

and ρ_0 is defined by (6-100).

Equations (6-105), (6-100), and (6-105a) can be used to calculate the array factor once N, I_n, a, θ_0, and ϕ_0 are specified. This is usually very time consuming, even for moderately large values of N. The three-dimensional pattern of the array factor for a 10-element uniform circular array of $ka = 10$ is shown in Figure 6.30. The corresponding two-dimensional principal plane patterns are displayed in Figure 6.31. As the radius of the array becomes very large, the directivity of a uniform circular array approaches the value of N, where N is equal to the number of elements. An excellent discussion on circular arrays can be found in [18].

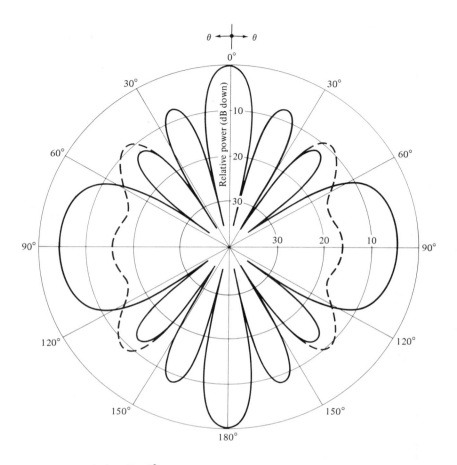

$x-z$ plane ($\phi = 0°$)

$y-z$ plane ($\phi = 90°$)

Figure 6.31 Principal plane amplitude patterns of the array factor for a uniform circular array of 10 elements ($ka=10$).

For a uniform amplitude excitation of each element ($I_n = I_0$), (6-105) can be written as

$$AF(\theta, \phi) = NI_0 \sum_{m=-\infty}^{+\infty} J_{mN}(k\rho_0) e^{jmN(\pi/2-\xi)}$$

(6-106)

where $J_p(x)$ is the Bessel function of the first kind (see Appendix V). The part of the array factor associated with the zero order Bessel function $J_0(k\rho_0)$ is called the principal term and the remaining terms are noted as the residuals. For a circular array with a large number of elements, the term $J_0(k\rho_0)$ alone can be used to approximate the two-dimensional principal plane patterns. The remaining terms in (6-106) contribute negligibly because Bessel functions of larger orders are very small.

References

1. R. S. Elliott, "Beamwidth and Directivity of Large Scanning Arrays," First of Two Parts, *The Microwave Journal*, December 1963, pp. 53–60.
2. W. W. Hansen and J. R. Woodyard, "A New Principle in Directional Antenna Design," *Proceedings of the Institute of Radio Engineers*, vol. 26, No. 3, March 1938, pp. 333–345.
3. J. S. Stone, United States Patents No. 1,643,323 and No. 1,715,433.
4. C. L. Dolph, "A Current Distribution for Broadside Arrays Which Optimizes the Relationship Between Beamwidth and Side-Lobe Level," *Proceedings of the I.R.E. and Waves and Electrons*, June 1946.
5. N. Yaru, "A Note on Super-Gain Arrays," *Proc. IRE*, vol. 39, Sept. 1951, pp. 1081–1085.
6. H. J. Riblet, Discussion on "A Current Distribution for Broadside Arrays Which Optimizes the Relationship Between Beamwidth and Side-Lobe Level," *Proceedings of the I.R.E.*, May 1947, pp. 489–492.
7. D. Barbiere, "A Method for Calculating the Current Distribution of Tschebyscheff Arrays," *Proceedings of the I.R.E.*, January 1952, pp. 78–82.
8. R. J. Stegen, "Excitation Coefficients and Beamwidths of Tschebyscheff Arrays," *Proceedings of the I.R.E.*, November 1953, pp. 1671–1674.
9. C. J. Drane, Jr., "Useful Approximations for the Directivity and Beamwidth of Large Scanning Dolph-Chebyshev Arrays," *Proceedings of the IEEE*, November 1968, pp. 1779–1787.
10. M. M. Dawond and A. P. Anderson, "Design of Superdirective Arrays with High Radiation Efficiency," *IEEE Trans. Antennas Propag.*, vol. AP-26, No. 6, Jan. 1978, pp. 819–823.
11. S. A. Schelkunoff, "A Mathematical Theory of Linear Arrays," *Bell System Tech. Journal*, vol. 22, January 1943, pp. 80–87.
12. C. J. Bowkamp and N. G. de Bruijn, "The Problem of Optimum Antenna Current Distribution," *Phillips Res. Rept.*, vol. 1, January 1946, pp. 135–158.
13. E. H. Newman, J. H. Richmond, and C. H. Walter, "Superdirective Receiving Arrays," *IEEE Trans. Antennas Propag.*, vol. AP-26, No. 5, Sept. 1978, pp. 629–635.
14. J. L. Allen, "On Surface-Wave Coupling Between Elements of Large Arrays," *IEEE Transactions on Antennas and Propagation*, vol. AP-13, July 1965, pp. 638–639.
15. R. H. T. Bates, "Mode Theory Approach to Arrays," *IEEE Transactions on Antennas and Propagation*, vol. AP-13, March 1965, pp. 321–322.
16. R. S. Elliott, "Beamwidth and Directivity of Large Scanning Arrays," Last of Two Parts, *The Microwave Journal*, January 1964, pp. 74–82.
17. B. J. Forman, "A Novel Directivity Expression for Planar Antenna Arrays," *Radio Science*, vol. 5, July 1970, pp. 1077–1083.
18. M. T. Ma, *Theory and Application of Antenna Arrays*, Wiley, 1974, Chapter 3, pp. 191–202.
19. P. Lorrain and D. R. Corson, *Electromagnetic Fields and Waves*, Second Edition, W. H. Freeman and Co., San Francisco, 1970.

PROBLEMS

6.1. Three isotropic sources, with spacing d between them, are placed along the z-axis. The excitation coefficient of each outside element is unity while that of the center element is 2. For a spacing of $d = \lambda/4$ between the elements, find the
(a) array factor
(b) angles (in degrees) where the nulls of the pattern occur ($0 \le \theta \le 180°$)
(c) angles (in degrees) where the maxima of the pattern occur ($0 \le \theta \le 180°$)

6.2. Design a two-element uniform array of isotropic sources, positioned along the z-axis a distance $\lambda/4$ apart, so that its only maximum occurs along $\theta = 0°$. Assuming ordinary end-fire conditions, find the
(a) relative phase excitation of each element
(b) array factor of the array
(c) directivity using Kraus' approximate formula

6.3. Repeat the design of Problem 6.2 so that its only maximum occurs along $\theta = 180°$.

6.4. An array of 10 isotropic elements are placed along the z-axis a distance d apart. Assuming uniform distribution, find the progressive phase (in degrees), half-power beamwidth, first null beamwidth, first side lobe level maximum beamwidth, relative side lobe level maximum (in dB), and directivity (using equations and the computer program at the end of Chapter 2, and compare) for
(a) broadside
(b) ordinary end-fire
(c) Hansen-Woodyard end-fire
arrays when the spacing between the elements is $d = \lambda/4$.

6.5. Find the beamwidth and directivity of a 10-element uniform scanning array of isotropic sources placed along the z-axis. The spacing between the elements is $\lambda/4$ and the maximum is directed at $45°$ from its axis.

6.6. Show that in order for a uniform array of N elements not to have any minor lobes, the spacing and the progressive phase shift between the elements must be
(a) $d = \lambda/N$, $\beta = 0$ for a broadside array.
(b) $d = \lambda/(2N)$, $\beta = \pm kd$ for an ordinary end-fire array.

6.7. An array of four isotropic sources is formed by placing one at the origin, and one along the x-, y-, and z-axes a distance d from the origin. Find the array factor for all space. The excitation coefficient of each element is identical.

6.8. Design a three-element binomial array of isotropic elements positioned along the z-axis a distance d apart. Find the
(a) normalized excitation coefficients
(b) array factor
(c) nulls of the array factor for $d = \lambda$
(d) maxima of the array factor for $d = \lambda$

6.9. Show that a three-element binomial array with a spacing of $d \le \lambda/2$ between the element does not have a side lobe.

6.10. Four isotropic sources are placed symmetrically along the z-axis a distance d apart. Design a binomial array. Find the
(a) normalized excitation coefficients

(b) array factor

(c) angles (in degrees) where the array factor nulls occur when $d = 3\lambda/4$

6.11. Design a four-element binomial array of $\lambda/2$ dipoles, placed symmetrically along the x-axis a distance d apart. The length of each dipole is parallel to the z-axis.

(a) Find the normalized excitation coefficients.

(b) Write the array factor for all space.

(c) Write expressions for E-fields for all space.

6.12. Repeat the design of Problem 6.11 when the $\lambda/2$ dipoles are placed along the y-axis.

6.13. Five isotropic elements, with spacing d between them, are placed along the z-axis. For a binomial amplitude distribution,

(a) write the array factor in its most simplified form

(b) compute the directivity (in dB) using the computer program at the end of Chapter 2 $(d = \lambda/2)$

(c) find the nulls of the array when $d = \lambda (0° \leq \theta \leq 180°)$

6.14. Repeat the design of Problem 6.8 for a Dolph-Tschebyscheff array with a side lobe level of -20 dB.

6.15. Design a three-element, -40-dB side lobe level Dolph-Tshebyscheff array of isotropic elements placed symmetrically along the z-axis. Find the

(a) amplitude excitation coefficients

(b) array factor

(c) angles where the nulls occur for $d = 3\lambda/4$ $(0° \leq \theta \leq 180°)$

(d) directivity for $d = 3\lambda/4$

(e) half-power beamwidth for $d = 3\lambda/4$

6.16. Repeat the design of Problem 6.11 for a Dolph-Tschebyscheff distribution of -40-dB side lobe level and $\lambda/4$ spacing between the elements. In addition, find the

(a) directivity of the entire array

(b) half-power beamwidths of the entire array in the x-y and y-z planes

6.17. Repeat the design of Problem 6.12 for a Dolph-Tschebyscheff distribution of -40-dB side lobe level and $\lambda/4$ spacing between the elements. In addition, find the

(a) directivity of the entire array

(b) half-power beamwidths of the entire array in the x-y and x-z planes

6.18. Design a five-element, -40-dB side lobe level Dolph-Tschebyscheff array of isotropic elements. The elements are placed along the x-axis with a spacing of $\lambda/4$ between them. Determine the

(a) normalized amplitude coefficients

(b) array factor

(c) directivity

(d) half-power beamwidth

6.19. The total length of a discrete-element array is 4λ. For a -30-dB side lobe level Dolph-Tschebyscheff design and a spacing of $\lambda/2$ between the elements along the z-axis, find the

(a) number of elements

(b) excitation coefficients

(c) directivity

(d) half-power beamwidth

6.20. Determine the azimuthal and elevation angles of the grating lobes for a 10×10 element uniform planar array when the spacing between the elements is λ. The maximum of the main beam is directed toward $\theta_0 = 60°$, $\phi_0 = 90°$ and the array is located on the x-y plane.

6.21. Design a 10×8 (10 in the x direction and 8 in the y) element uniform planar array so that the main maximum is oriented along $\theta_0 = 10°$, $\phi_0 = 90°$. For a spacing of $d_x = d_y = \lambda/8$ between the elements, find the
   (a) progressive phase shift between the elements in the x and y directions
   (b) directivity of the array
   (c) half-power beamwidths (in two perpendicular planes) of the array

6.22. The main beam maximum of a 10×10 planar array of isotropic elements (100 elements) is directed toward $\theta_0 = 10°$ and $\phi_0 = 45°$. Find the directivity, beamwidths (in two perpendicular planes), and beam solid angle for a Tschebyscheff distribution design with side lobes of -26 dB. The array is placed on the x-y plane and the elements are equally spaced with $d = \lambda/4$.

6.23. Repeat Problem 6.21 for a Tschebyscheff distribution array of -30-dB side lobes.

Chapter 7
Self- and Mutual
Impedances of
Linear Elements and Arrays,
and Finite Diameter Effects

(MOMENT METHOD)

7.1 INTRODUCTION

In Chapter 2 it was shown, by the Thévenin and Norton equivalent circuits of Figures 2.18 and 2.19, that an antenna can be represented by an equivalent impedance Z_A [$Z_A = (R_r + R_L) + jX_A$]. The equivalent impedance is attached across two terminals (terminals a-b in Figures 2.18 and 2.19) which are used to connect the antenna to a generator, receiver, or transmission line. In general, this impedance is called the *driving-point* impedance. However, when the antenna is radiating in an unbounded medium, in the absence of any other interfering elements or objects, the driving-point impedance is the same as the *self-impedance* of the antenna. In practice, however, there is always the ground whose presence must be taken into account in determining the antenna driving-point impedance. The self- and driving point impedances each have, in general, a real and an imaginary part. The real part is designated as the resistance and the imaginary part is called the reactance.

The impedance of an antenna depends on many factors including its frequency of operation, its geometry, its method of excitation, and its proximity to the surrounding objects. Because of their complex geometries, only a limited number of practical antennas have been investigated analytically. For many others, the input impedance has been determined experimentally.

The impedance of an antenna at a point is defined as the ratio of the electric to the magnetic fields at that point; alternatively, at a pair of terminals it is defined as the ratio of the voltage to the current across those terminals. There are many methods that can be used to calculate the impedance of an antenna [1]. Generally these can be classified into three categories: (1) the boundary-value method, (2) the transmission-line method, and (3) the Poynting vector method. Extensive and brief discussions and comparisons of these methods have been reported [1], [2].

The boundary-value approach is the most basic, and it treats the antenna as a boundary-value problem. The solution to this is obtained by enforcing the boundary conditions (usually that the tangential electric field components vanish at the conducting surface). In turn the current distribution and finally the impedance (ratio of applied emf to current) are determined, with no assumptions as to their distribution, as solutions to the problem. The principal disadvantage of this method is that it has limited applications. It can only be applied and solved exactly on simplified geometrical shapes where the scalar wave equation is separable.

The transmission-line method, which has been used extensively by Schelkunoff [3], treats the antenna as a transmission line, and it is most convenient for the biconical antenna. Since it utilizes tangential electric field boundary conditions for its solution, this technique may also be classified as a boundary-value method.

The basic approach to the Poynting vector method is to integrate the Poynting vector (power density) over a closed surface. The closed surface chosen is usually either a sphere of a very large radius r ($r \geq 2D^2/\lambda$ where D is the largest dimension of the antenna) or a surface that coincides with the surface of the antenna. The large sphere closed surface method has been introduced in Chapters 4 and 5, but it lends itself to calculations only of the real part of the antenna impedance (radiation resistance). The method that utilizes the antenna surface has been designated as the induced emf method, and it has been utilized [4]–[6] for the calculation of antenna impedances.

The impedance of an antenna can also be found using a numerical technique which is widely referred to as the *Method of Moments* [7]. This method, which in the late 1960s was extended to include electromagnetic problems, is analytically simple, it is versatile, but it requires large amounts of computation. The limitation of this technique is usually the speed and storage capacity of the computer.

The induced emf method is used in this chapter to derive expressions and compute values for the self- and driving-point impedances of linear dipoles and arrays of such. However, before this is attempted, it will be necessary to derive the near-field radiated by a linear dipole.

In addition, the current distribution on a finite diameter linear dipole will be formulated using the Moment Method [7]. To accomplish this,

Hallén's and Pocklington's integral equations will be derived first. Techniques for computing the input impedance and radiation pattern, and modeling the source-gap will be outlined.

7.2 NEAR-FIELDS OF DIPOLE

In Chapter 4, the far-zone electric and magnetic fields radiated by a finite length dipole with a sinusoidal current distribution were found. The observations were restricted in the far-field in order to reduce the mathematical complexities. The expressions of these fields were then used to derive the radiation resistance and the input resistance of the dipole. However, when the input reactance and/or the mutual impedance between elements are

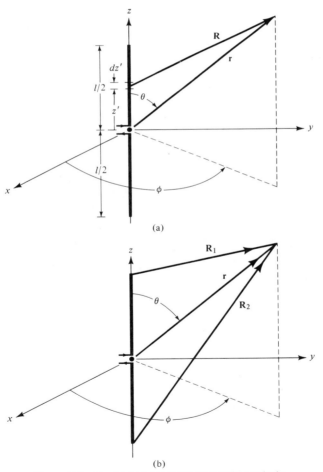

Figure 7.1 Dipole geometry for near-field analysis.

desired, the near-fields of the element must be known. It is the intent here to highlight the derivation.

Referring to Figure 7.1(a) and assuming a sinusoidal current distribution along the element, as given by (4-56), or

$$\mathbf{I}_e(x', y', z') = \begin{cases} \hat{a}_z I_0 \sin\left[k\left(\dfrac{l}{2} - z'\right)\right], & 0 \le z' \le l/2 \\ \hat{a}_z I_0 \sin\left[k\left(\dfrac{l}{2} + z'\right)\right], & -l/2 \le z' \le 0 \end{cases} \tag{7-1}$$

the vector potential $\mathbf{A}$ of (4-2) can be written as

$$\mathbf{A} = \hat{a}_z A_z$$

$$= \hat{a}_z \frac{\mu I_0}{4\pi} \left\{ \int_{-l/2}^{0} \sin\left[k\left(\frac{l}{2} - z'\right)\right] \frac{e^{-jkR}}{R} dz' \right.$$

$$\left. + \int_{0}^{l/2} \sin\left[k\left(\frac{l}{2} + z'\right)\right] \frac{e^{-jkR}}{R} dz' \right\} \tag{7-2}$$

where for $x' = y' = 0$

$$R = \sqrt{(x-x')^2 + (y-y')^2 + (z-z')^2}$$
$$= \sqrt{x^2 + y^2 + (z-z')^2} = \sqrt{\rho^2 + (z-z')^2} \tag{7-2a}$$

According to (3-2a)

$$\mathbf{H} = \frac{1}{\mu} \nabla \times \mathbf{A} \tag{7-3}$$

which for an A_z component with no ϕ variations reduces, in cylindrical coordinates, to

$$\mathbf{H} = -\hat{a}_\phi \frac{1}{\mu} \frac{\partial A_z}{\partial \rho} \tag{7-3a}$$

Since the field is not a function of ϕ, because of the azimuthal symmetry, the observations can be made at any angle ϕ. Choosing $\phi = \pi/2$ reduces x and y to

$$\left. \begin{aligned} x &= \rho\cos\phi = 0 \\ y &= \rho\sin\phi = \rho \\ \frac{\partial}{\partial \rho} &= \frac{\partial}{\partial y} \end{aligned} \right\} \tag{7-4}$$

and (7-3a), in conjunction with (7-2), to

$$\mathbf{H} = -\hat{a}_\phi \frac{I_0}{4\pi} \frac{\partial}{\partial y} \left\{ \int_{-l/2}^{0} \sin\left[k\left(\frac{l}{2} + z'\right)\right] \frac{e^{-jkR}}{R} dz' \right.$$

$$\left. + \int_{0}^{l/2} \sin\left[k\left(\frac{l}{2} - z'\right)\right] \frac{e^{-jkR}}{R} dz' \right\} \tag{7-5}$$

Using Euler's relation

$$\sin\left[k\left(\frac{l}{2}\pm z'\right)\right]=\frac{e^{jk(l/2\pm z')}-e^{-jk(l/2\pm z')}}{2j} \tag{7-6}$$

reduces (7-5) to

$$H_\phi=-\frac{I_0}{8\pi j}\left\{e^{+j(kl/2)}\int_{-l/2}^{0}\frac{\partial}{\partial y}\left[\frac{e^{-jk(R-z')}}{R}\right]dz'\right.$$

$$-e^{-j(kl/2)}\int_{-l/2}^{0}\frac{\partial}{\partial y}\left[\frac{e^{-jk(R+z')}}{R}\right]dz'$$

$$+e^{+j(kl/2)}\int_{0}^{l/2}\frac{\partial}{\partial y}\left[\frac{e^{-jk(R+z')}}{R}\right]dz'$$

$$\left.-e^{-j(kl/2)}\int_{0}^{l/2}\frac{\partial}{\partial y}\left[\frac{e^{-jk(R-z')}}{R}\right]dz'\right\} \tag{7-7}$$

The third term within the brackets can be written as

$$e^{+j(kl/2)}\int_{0}^{l/2}\frac{\partial}{\partial y}\left[\frac{e^{-jk(R+z')}}{R}\right]dz'$$

$$=e^{+j(kl/2)}\int_{0}^{l/2}\left\{\frac{1}{R}\frac{\partial}{\partial y}\left[e^{-jk(R+z')}\right]+e^{-jk(R+z')}\frac{\partial}{\partial y}\left(\frac{1}{R}\right)\right\}dz' \tag{7-8}$$

The two terms of (7-8) can be expanded, using (7-2a), to

$$\frac{\partial}{\partial y}\left[e^{-jk(R+z')}\right]=\frac{\partial}{\partial y}\left[e^{-jk\left(\sqrt{x^2+y^2+(z-z')^2}+z'\right)}\right]=-jk\frac{y}{R}e^{-jk(R+z')} \tag{7-8a}$$

$$\frac{\partial}{\partial y}\left(\frac{1}{R}\right)=\frac{\partial}{\partial y}\left\{\left[x^2+y^2+(z-z')^2\right]^{-1/2}\right\}=-\frac{y}{R^3} \tag{7-8b}$$

Thus (7-8) can be expressed as

$$e^{+j(kl/2)}\int_{0}^{l/2}\frac{\partial}{\partial y}\left[\frac{e^{-jk(R+z')}}{R}\right]dz'$$

$$=ye^{+j(kl/2)}\int_{0}^{l/2}\left[-jk\frac{e^{-jk(R+z')}}{R^2}-\frac{e^{-jk(R+z')}}{R^3}\right]dz' \tag{7-9}$$

Consider now the differential of

$$d\left[\frac{e^{-jk(R+z')}}{R(R+z'-z)}\right]=d\left[R^{-1}(R+z'-z)^{-1}e^{-jk(R+z')}\right]$$

$$=e^{-jk(R+z')}\left[\frac{dR^{-1}}{(R+z'-z)}+\frac{d(R+z'-z)^{-1}}{R}\right.$$

$$\left.-jk\frac{d(R+z')}{R(R+z'-z)}\right] \tag{7-10}$$

Each term of (7-10) can be written as

$$\frac{dR^{-1}}{(R+z'-z)} = \left[\frac{z-z'}{R^3(R+z'-z)}\right] dz' \tag{7-10a}$$

$$\frac{d(R+z'-z)^{-1}}{R} = -\left[\frac{(R+z'-z)^{-2}d(R+z'-z)}{R}\right]$$

$$= -\left[\frac{1}{R^2(R+z'-z)}\right] dz' \tag{7-10b}$$

$$-jk\left[\frac{d(R+z')}{R(R+z'-z)}\right] = -jk\left(\frac{1}{R^2}\right) dz' \tag{7-10c}$$

Adding (7-10a)–(7-10c) reduces (7-10) to

$$d\left[\frac{e^{-jk(R+z')}}{R(R+z'-z)}\right] = e^{-jk(R+z')}\left[-\frac{1}{R^3} -jk\frac{1}{R^2}\right] dz' \tag{7-11}$$

which is an exact differential.

With the aid of (7-11), (7-9) can be integrated and expressed as

$$e^{+j(kl/2)}\int_0^{l/2}\frac{\partial}{\partial y}\left[\frac{e^{-jk(R+z')}}{R}\right] dz' = ye^{+j(kl/2)}\int_0^{l/2}d\left[\frac{e^{-jk(R+z')}}{R(R+z'-z)}\right]$$

$$= ye^{+j(kl/2)}\left[\frac{e^{-jk(R_1+l/2)}}{R_1(R_1+l/2-z')} - \frac{e^{-jkr}}{r(r-z)}\right] \tag{7-12}$$

where according to Figure 7.1(b) for $\phi = \pi/2$

$$R_1 = \sqrt{x^2+y^2+\left(z-\frac{l}{2}\right)^2} = \sqrt{y^2+\left(z-\frac{l}{2}\right)^2} \tag{7-12a}$$

$$r = \sqrt{x^2+y^2+z^2} = \sqrt{y^2+z^2} \tag{7-12b}$$

Because

$$\left.\begin{aligned} R_1^2 - \left(\frac{l}{2}-z\right)^2 &= y^2 \\[2mm] r^2 - z^2 &= y^2 \end{aligned}\right\} \tag{7-13}$$

(7-12) can be placed into the form of

$$e^{+j(kl/2)}\int_0^{l/2}\frac{\partial}{\partial y}\left[\frac{e^{-jk(R+z')}}{R}\right] dz' = \frac{e^{+j(kl/2)}}{y}\left[\left(1-\frac{l/2-z}{R_1}\right)e^{-jk(R_1+l/2)}\right.$$

$$\left. -\left(1+\frac{z}{r}\right)e^{-jkr}\right] \tag{7-14}$$

In a similar manner, the other terms of (7-7) can be written as

$$+e^{+j(kl/2)} \int_{-l/2}^{0} \frac{\partial}{\partial y} \left[\frac{e^{-jk(R-z')}}{R} \right] dz'$$

$$= \frac{e^{+j(kl/2)}}{y} \left[\left(1 - \frac{l/2+z}{R_2} \right) e^{-jk(R_2+l/2)} - \left(1 - \frac{z}{r} \right) e^{-jkr} \right] \qquad (7\text{-}14a)$$

$$-e^{-j(kl/2)} \int_{-l/2}^{0} \frac{\partial}{\partial y} \left[\frac{e^{-jk(R+z')}}{R} \right] dz'$$

$$= \frac{e^{-j(kl/2)}}{y} \left[\left(1 + \frac{l/2+z}{R_2} \right) e^{-jk(R_2-l/2)} - \left(1 + \frac{z}{r} \right) e^{-jkr} \right] \qquad (7\text{-}14b)$$

$$-e^{-j(kl/2)} \int_{0}^{l/2} \frac{\partial}{\partial y} \left[\frac{e^{-jk(R-z')}}{R} \right] dz'$$

$$= \frac{e^{-j(kl/2)}}{y} \left[\left(1 + \frac{l/2-z}{R_1} \right) e^{-jk(R_1-l/2)} - \left(1 - \frac{z}{r} \right) e^{-jkr} \right] \qquad (7\text{-}14c)$$

where

$$R_2 = \sqrt{x^2+y^2+\left(z+\frac{l}{2}\right)^2} = \sqrt{\rho^2+\left(z+\frac{l}{2}\right)^2} \qquad (7\text{-}14d)$$

Using (7-14)–(7-14c) reduces (7-7) to

$$H_\phi = -\frac{I_0}{4\pi j} \frac{1}{y} \left[e^{-jkR_1} + e^{-jkR_2} - 2\cos\left(\frac{kl}{2}\right) e^{-jkr} \right] \qquad (7\text{-}15)$$

The next step will be to find the corresponding electric field components. Assuming an H_ϕ and no ϕ variations, Maxwell's equation

$$\mathbf{E} = \frac{1}{j\omega\varepsilon} \nabla \times \mathbf{H} \qquad (7\text{-}16)$$

simplifies in the y-z plane to

$$E_\rho = E_y = -\frac{1}{j\omega\varepsilon} \frac{\partial H_\phi}{\partial z} \qquad (7\text{-}16a)$$

$$E_z = \frac{1}{j\omega\varepsilon} \frac{1}{\rho} \frac{\partial}{\partial \rho} (\rho H_\phi) = \frac{1}{j\omega\varepsilon} \frac{1}{y} \frac{\partial}{\partial y} (y H_\phi) \qquad (7\text{-}16b)$$

since $y = \rho$ in that plane.

Equations (7-16a) and (7-16b) reduce, using (7-15), to

$$E_\rho = E_y = j\frac{\eta I_0}{4\pi y} \left[\left(z - \frac{l}{2} \right) \frac{e^{-jkR_1}}{R_1} + \left(z + \frac{l}{2} \right) \frac{e^{-jkR_2}}{R_2} - 2z\cos\left(\frac{kl}{2}\right) \frac{e^{-jkr}}{r} \right]$$

$$\qquad (7\text{-}17a)$$

$$E_z = -j\frac{\eta I_0}{4\pi} \left[\frac{e^{-jkR_1}}{R_1} + \frac{e^{-jkR_2}}{R_2} - 2\cos\left(\frac{kl}{2}\right) \frac{e^{-jkr}}{r} \right] \qquad (7\text{-}17b)$$

where R_1, r, and R_2 are given, respectively, by (7-12a), (7-12b), and (7-14d). It should be noted that the last term in (7-15), (7-17a), and (7-17b) vanishes when the overall length of the element is an integral number of odd half wavelengths $(l=nl/2, n=1,3,5,\ldots)$ because $\cos(kl/2)=\cos(n\pi/2)=0$ for $n=1,3,5,\ldots$.

7.3 INPUT IMPEDANCE OF DIPOLE

The input impedance of an antenna is a very important parameter, and it is used to determine the efficiency of the antenna. In Section 4.5 the real part of the impedance (referred either to the current at the feed terminals or to the current maximum) was found. At that time, because of mathematical complexities, no attempt was made to find the imaginary part (reactance) of the impedance.

From the analysis of the infinitesimal dipole in Section 4.2, it was shown that the imaginary part of the power density, which contributes to the imaginary power, is dominant in the near-zone of the element and becomes negligible in the far-field. Thus near-zone fields of an antenna are required to find its input reactance.

The fields for a dipole, as given by (7-15), (7-17a), and (7-17b), were derived assuming a zero radius wire. In practice all wire antennas have a finite radius which in most cases is very small electrically. Therefore the fields of (7-15), (7-17a), and (7-17b) would be good approximations for finite, but small, radius dipoles.

The technique, which will be used in this chapter to derive expressions for the self- and driving-point impedances of finite linear dipoles, is known as the *induced emf method*. The general approach of this method is to form the Poynting vector using (7-15), (7-17a), and (7-17b), and to integrate it over the surface that coincides with the surface of the antenna (linear dipole) itself. The expressions derived using this method will be more valid for small radius dipoles. Expressions, which are more accurate for larger radius dipoles, can be derived using the Moment Method techniques of Section 7.5.

7.3.1 Induced emf Method

To find the input impedance of a linear dipole, shown in Figure 7.2, the fields on the surface of the wire are needed. Let us assume that an emf, applied at the terminals of the antenna, produces a current I_z. The current I_z produces an electric field E_z which in turn induces a field E_{zi} at the conductor surface such that the boundary conditions are satisfied. For a perfect conductor, the total tangential electric field E_{zt} must vanish at its surface. That is,

$$E_{zt}(\rho=a, z=z')= E_z(\rho=a, z=z')+ E_{zi}(\rho=a, z=z')=0 \qquad (7\text{-}18)$$

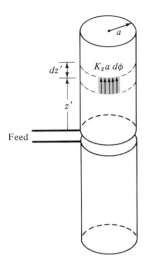

Figure 7.2   Uniform linear current density over cyclindrical surface of wire.

Thus

$$E_{zi}(\rho = a, z = z') = - E_z(\rho = a, z = z') \tag{7-18a}$$

The potential difference dV_z on an incremental length dz' of the dipole is given by

$$dV_z(\rho = a, z = z') = - E_z(\rho = a, z = z')\, dz' \tag{7-19}$$

In reference to the current maximum I_m, this voltage is related by a transfer impedance Z_t. That is,

$$Z_t = \frac{dV_z}{dI_m} \tag{7-20}$$

Because of reciprocity, the voltage V_m at the current maximum is related to the current at $z = z'$ by the same transfer impedance Z_t as

$$Z_t = \frac{V_m}{I_z(\rho = a, z = z')} \tag{7-21}$$

Equating (7-20) and (7-21) leads to

$$I_z(\rho = a, z = z')\, dV_z(\rho = a, z = z') = V_m\, dI_m \tag{7-22}$$

The radiation impedance (*referred to the current maximum*) is defined as

$$Z_m = \frac{V_m}{I_m} = \frac{dV_m}{dI_m} \tag{7-23}$$

or

$$V_m\, dI_m = I_m\, dV_m \tag{7-23a}$$

Equation (7-22) can be written using (7-23a) as

$$I_z(\rho = a, z = z') \, dV_z(\rho = a, z = z') = V_m \, dI_m = I_m \, dV_m \tag{7-24}$$

or

$$dV_m = \frac{1}{I_m} I_z(\rho = a, z = z') \, dV_z(\rho = a, z = z') \tag{7-24a}$$

Using (7-19), (7-24a) reduces to

$$V_m = \int_{-l/2}^{+l/2} dV_m = -\frac{1}{I_m} \int_{-l/2}^{+l/2} I_z(\rho = a, z - z') E_z(\rho = a, z = z') \, dz' \tag{7-25}$$

7.3.2 Finite Dipole Input Impedance

With the aid of (7-25), (7-23) can be written as

$$Z_m = -\frac{1}{I_m^2} \int_{-l/2}^{l/2} I_z(\rho = a, z = z') E_z(\rho = a, z = z') \, dz' \tag{7-26}$$

Equation (7-25) can also be obtained by forming the complex power density, integrating it over the surface of the antenna, and then relating the complex power to the terminal and induced voltages [2]. The integration can be performed either over the gap at the terminals or over the surface of the conducting wire.

For a wire dipole, the total current I_z is uniformly distributed around the surface of wire, and it forms a linear current sheet K_z. The current is concentrated primarily over a very small thickness of the conductor, as shown in Figure 7.2, and it is given by

$$I_z = 2\pi a K_z = I_m \sin\left[k\left(\frac{l}{2} - |z'| \right) \right] \tag{7-27}$$

Therefore (7-26) can be written as

$$Z_m = -\frac{1}{I_m} \int_{-l/2}^{l/2} \sin\left(k\frac{l}{2} - |z'| \right) E_z(\rho = a, z = z') \, dz' \tag{7-28}$$

For simplicity, it will be assumed that the E-field produced on the surface of the wire by a current sheet is the same as if the current were concentrated along a filament placed along the axis of the wire. Then the E-field used in (7-28) would be the one obtained along a line parallel to the wire at a distance $\rho = a$ from the filament. Thus (7-28) can be written, using

(7-17b) with $I_m = I_0$, as

$$Z_m = R_m + jX_m = +j\frac{\eta}{4\pi}\left\{\int_{-l/2}^{0}\sin\left[k\left(\frac{l}{2}+z'\right)\right]\left[\frac{e^{-jkR_1}}{R_1}+\frac{e^{-jkR_2}}{R_2}\right.\right.$$

$$\left.-2\cos\left(\frac{kl}{2}\right)\frac{e^{-jkr}}{r}\right]dz'$$

$$+\int_{0}^{l/2}\sin\left[k\left(\frac{l}{2}-z'\right)\right]$$

$$\left.\times\left[\frac{e^{-jkR_1}}{R_1}+\frac{e^{-jkR_2}}{R_2}-2\cos\left(\frac{kl}{2}\right)\frac{e^{-jkr}}{r}\right]\right\}dz'$$

(7-29)

which can be separated into its real (R_m) and imaginary parts (X_m) as

$$R_m = R_r = \frac{\eta}{4\pi}\left\{\int_{-l/2}^{0}\sin\left[k\left(\frac{l}{2}+z'\right)\right]\right.$$

$$\times\left[-2\cos\left(\frac{kl}{2}\right)\frac{\sin(kr)}{r}+\frac{\sin(kR_1)}{R_1}+\frac{\sin(kR_2)}{R_2}\right]dz'$$

$$+\int_{0}^{l/2}\sin\left[k\left(\frac{l}{2}-z'\right)\right]$$

$$\left.\times\left[-2\cos\left(\frac{kl}{2}\right)\frac{\sin(kr)}{r}+\frac{\sin(kR_1)}{R_1}+\frac{\sin(kR_2)}{R_2}\right]dz'\right\}$$

(7-29a)

$$X_m = \frac{\eta}{4\pi}\left\{\int_{-l/2}^{0}\sin\left[k\left(\frac{l}{2}+z'\right)\right]\right.$$

$$\times\left[-2\cos\left(\frac{kl}{2}\right)\frac{\cos(kr)}{r}+\frac{\cos(kR_1)}{R_1}+\frac{\cos(kR_2)}{R_2}\right]dz'$$

$$+\int_{0}^{l/2}\sin\left[k\left(\frac{l}{2}-z'\right)\right]$$

$$\left.\times\left[-2\cos\left(\frac{kl}{2}\right)\frac{\cos(kr)}{r}+\frac{\cos(kR_1)}{R_1}+\frac{\cos(kR_2)}{R_2}\right]dz'\right\}$$

(7-29b)

Equations (7-29a) and (7-29b) represent, respectively, the resistance and reactance *referred to the current maximum*. The input resistance and input reactance (*referred to the current at the input terminals*) can be obtained by a transfer relation given by (4-79) or

$$R_{in} = \left(\frac{I_0}{I_{in}}\right)^2 R_r = \frac{R_r}{\sin^2(kl/2)} \qquad (7\text{-}30a)$$

$$X_{in} = \left(\frac{I_0}{I_{in}}\right)^2 X_m = \frac{X_m}{\sin^2(kl/2)} \qquad (7\text{-}30b)$$

In evaluating (7-29a) it can be assumed that the radius of the wire is negligible, provided that $l \gg a$, and it has little effect on the overall answer. This can be confirmed by examining the terms of the integrand in (7-29a). It is evident that the radius a will have very little effect on the values of r, R_1, and R_2 except when each approaches a value of zero. For that case, each of the terms in the integrand are of the form $\sin(kR_i)/kR_i$ which approaches a value of unity as $R_i \to 0$. This of course is not the case in (7-29b). For that reason, the radius a will not be set equal to zero in (7-29b). For a zero wire radius ($a = 0$), the values of r, R_1, and R_2 are given by

$$r = z'$$
$$R_1 = \frac{l}{2} - z' \qquad (7\text{-}31)$$
$$R_2 = \frac{l}{2} + z'$$

Substituting (7-31) into (7-29a) and carrying out the integrations reduces it to (4-70).

To evaluate (7-29b), it is recognized that the terms with R_1 and R_2 contribute equally. Thus (7-29b) reduces to

$$X_m = \frac{\eta}{2\pi} \left\{ \int_{-l/2}^{0} \sin\left[k\left(\frac{l}{2} + z'\right)\right]\left[-\cos\left(\frac{kl}{2}\right)\frac{\cos(kr)}{r} + \frac{\cos(kR_1)}{R_1}\right] dz' \right.$$
$$\left. + \int_{0}^{l/2} \sin\left[k\left(\frac{l}{2} - z'\right)\right]\left[-\cos\left(\frac{kl}{2}\right)\frac{\cos(kr)}{r} + \frac{\cos(kR_1)}{R_2}\right] dz' \right\}$$

$$(7\text{-}32)$$

where R_1, r, and R_2 are defined by (7-12a), (7-12b), and (7-14d) with $\rho = a$. After some tedious but straightforward manipulations, (7-32) reduces to

$$X_m = \frac{\eta}{4\pi} \left\{ 2S_i(kl) + \cos(kl)[2S_i(kl) - S_i(2kl)] \right.$$
$$\left. - \sin(kl)\left[2C_i(kl) - C_i(2kl) - C_i\left(\frac{2ka^2}{l}\right)\right] \right\}$$

$$(7\text{-}33)$$

which represents the antenna reactance referred to the current maximum. $S_i(x)$ and $C_i(x)$ are the sine and cosine integrals of Appendix III. The input reactance is obtained by using (7-30b). For a small dipole of length l and radius a, the input reactance is given by [8]

$$X_{in}=X_m=-120\frac{[\ln(l/a)-1]}{\tan(kl)} \tag{7-33a}$$

while its input resistance and radiation resistance is given by (4-37).

To examine the effect the radius has on the values of the reactance, its values as given by (7-33) have been plotted in Figure 7.3 for $a=10^{-5}\lambda$, $10^{-4}\lambda$, $10^{-3}\lambda$, and $10^{-2}\lambda$. The overall length of the wire is taken to be $0\le l\le 3\lambda$. It is apparent that the reactance can be reduced to zero provided the overall length is slightly less than $n\lambda/2$, $n=1,2,3,\dots$. This is commonly done in practice for $l\simeq\lambda/2$ because the input resistance is close to 50 ohms, an almost ideal match for the widely used 50-ohm lines. For small radii, the reactance for $l=\lambda/2$ is equal to 42.5 ohms.

From (7-33) it is also evident that when $l=n\lambda/2$, $n=1,2,3,\dots$, the terms within the last bracket do not contribute because $\sin(kl)=\sin(n\pi)=0$. Thus for dipoles whose overall length is an integral number of half-wavelengths, the radius has no effect on the antenna reactance. This is illustrated in Figure 7.3 by the intersection points of the curves. These values are equal to 42.5 for $\lambda/2$, 125.4 for λ, 45.5 for $3\lambda/2$, 133.1 for 2λ, 46.2 for $5\lambda/2$, and 135.8 for 3λ.

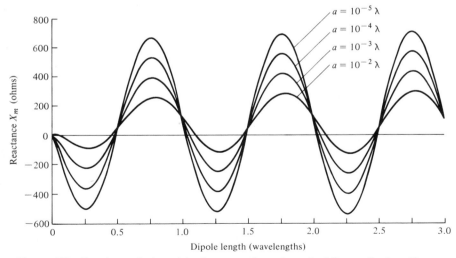

Figure 7.3 Reactance (referred to the current maximum) of linear dipole with sinusoidal current distribution for different wire radii.

7.4 MUTUAL IMPEDANCE BETWEEN LINEAR ELEMENTS

In the previous section, the input impedance of a linear dipole was derived when the element was radiating into an unbounded medium. The presence of an obstacle, which could be another element, would alter the current distribution, the field radiated, and in turn the input impedance of the antenna. Thus the antenna performance depends not only on its own current but also on the current of neighboring elements. For resonant elements with no current excitation of their own, there could be a substantial current induced by radiation from another source. These are known as parasitic elements, as in the case of a Yagi-Uda antenna, and play an important role in the overall performance of the entire antenna system. The antenna designer, therefore, must take into account the interaction, and mutual effects between elements. The input impedance of the antenna in the presence of the other elements or obstacles, which will be referred to as driving-point impedance, will depend upon the self-impedance (input impedance in the absence of any obstacle or other element) and the mutual impedance between the driven element and the other obstacles or elements.

To simplify the analysis, it will be assumed that the antenna system consists of two elements. The system can be represented by a two-port (four-terminal) network, as shown in Figure 7.4, and by the voltage-current relations

$$V_1 = Z_{11}I_1 + Z_{12}I_2 \Big\rbrace$$
$$V_2 = Z_{21}I_1 + Z_{22}I_2 \Big\rbrace \tag{7-34}$$

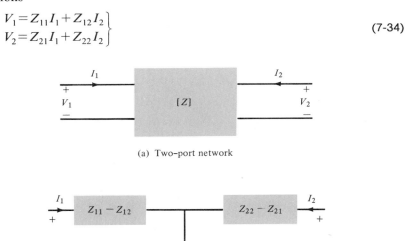

(a) Two-port network

(b) T-network equivalent

Figure 7.4 Two-port network and its T-equivalent.

where

$$Z_{11} = \frac{V_1}{I_1}\bigg|_{I_2=0} = \text{input impedance at port \#1 with port \#2 open-circuited} \qquad (7\text{-}34\text{a})$$

$$Z_{12} = \frac{V_1}{I_2}\bigg|_{I_1=0} = \text{mutual impedance at port \#1 due to a current at port \#2 (with port \#1 open-circuited)} \qquad (7\text{-}34\text{b})$$

$$Z_{21} = \frac{V_2}{I_1}\bigg|_{I_2=0} = \text{mutual impedance at port \#2 due to a current in port \#1 (with port \#2 open-circuited)} \qquad (7\text{-}34\text{c})$$

$$Z_{22} = \frac{V_2}{I_2}\bigg|_{I_1=0} = \text{input impedance at port \#2 with port \#1 open-circuited} \qquad (7\text{-}34\text{d})$$

For a reciprocal network arrangement $Z_{12} = Z_{21}$.

The impedances Z_{11} and Z_{22} are the input impedances of antennas 1 and 2, respectively, when each is radiating in an unbounded medium. The presence of an other element would modify the input impedance and the extent and nature of the effects will depend upon (1) the antenna type, (2) the relative placement of the elements, and (3) the type of feed used to excite the elements.

Equation (7-34) can also be written as

$$Z_{1d} = \frac{V_1}{I_1} = Z_{11} + Z_{12}\left(\frac{I_2}{I_1}\right) \qquad (7\text{-}35\text{a})$$

$$Z_{2d} = \frac{V_2}{I_2} = Z_{22} + Z_{21}\left(\frac{I_1}{I_2}\right) \qquad (7\text{-}35\text{b})$$

Z_{1d} and Z_{2d} represent the driving point impedances of antennas 1 and 2, respectively. Each driving point impedance depends upon the current ratio I_1/I_2, the mutual impedance, and the self-input impedance (when radiating into an unbounded medium). When attempting to match any antenna, it is the driving point impedance that must be matched. It is, therefore, apparent that the mutual impedance plays an important role in the performance of an antenna and should be investigated. However, the analysis associated with it is usually quite complex and only simplified models will be examined. Moment Method techniques can be used for more complex geometries.

Referring to Figure 7.5, the induced open-circuit voltage in antenna 2, *referred to its current at the input terminals*, due to radiation from antenna 1 is given by

$$V_{21} = -\frac{1}{I_{2i}} \int_{-l_2/2}^{l_2/2} E_{z21}(z) I_2(z)\, dz \qquad (7\text{-}36)$$

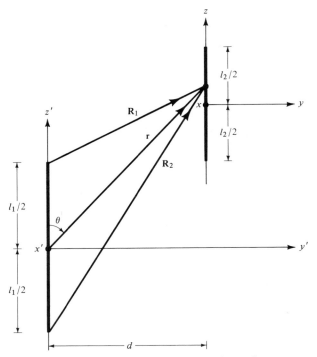

Figure 7.5   Dipole positioning for mutual coupling.

E_{z21} is the **E**-field component radiated by antenna 1 which is parallel to antenna 2. It would be calculated as if antenna 2 were absent. $I_2(z)$ represents the current distribution along antenna 2. Using forms of (7-1) for $I_2(z)$ and (7-17b) for E_{z21}, (7-36) can be written as

$$V_{21} = j\frac{\eta I_{1m}I_{2m}}{4\pi I_{2i}} \int_{-l_2/2}^{+l_2/2} \sin\left[k\left(\frac{l_2}{2}-|z|\right)\right]$$

$$\times \left[\frac{e^{-jkR_1}}{R_1} + \frac{e^{-jkR_2}}{R_2} - 2\cos\left(\frac{kl_1}{2}\right)\frac{e^{-jkr}}{r}\right] dz \qquad (7\text{-}37)$$

and the mutual impedance of (7-34c), *referred to the input current I_{1i} of antenna 1*, as

$$Z_{21i} = \frac{V_{21}}{I_{1i}} = j\frac{\eta I_{1m}I_{2m}}{4\pi I_{1i}I_{2i}} \int_{-l_2/2}^{l_2/2} \sin\left[k\left(\frac{l_2}{2}-|z|\right)\right]$$

$$\times \left[\frac{e^{-jkR_1}}{R_1} + \frac{e^{-jkR_2}}{R_2} - 2\cos\left(k\frac{l_1}{2}\right)\frac{e^{-jkr}}{r}\right] dz \qquad (7\text{-}38)$$

where R_1, r, and R_2 are given, respectively, by (7-12a), (7-12b), and (7-14d) but with $y = d$ and $l = l_1$. I_{1m}, I_{2m}, and I_{1i}, I_{2i} represent, respectively, the maximum and input currents for antennas 1 and 2.

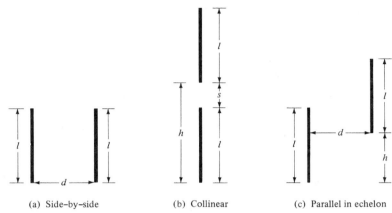

(a) Side–by–side   (b) Collinear   (c) Parallel in echelon

Figure 7.6   Dipole configurations of two identical elements for mutual impedance computations.

The mutual impedance, as given by (7-38), is referred to the current at the input terminals and can be translated to the current maxima by

$$Z_{21m} = Z_{21i} \frac{I_{1i} I_{2i}}{I_{1m} I_{2m}} \tag{7-39}$$

or

$$Z_{21m} = j \frac{\eta}{4\pi} \int_{-l_2/2}^{l_2/2} \sin\left[k\left(\frac{l_2}{2} - |z| \right) \right]$$

$$\times \left[\frac{e^{-jkR_1}}{R_1} + \frac{e^{-jkR_2}}{R_2} - 2\cos\left(k\frac{l_1}{2} \right) \frac{e^{-jkr}}{r} \right] dz \tag{7-39a}$$

For two identical antennas (each of length $l = n\lambda/2$, $n = 1, 2, 3, \ldots$), (7-39a) can be written in a simplified form. For each of the arrangements of Figure 7.6, (7-39a) reduces to

Side-by-Side Configuration [Figure 7.6(a)]

$$R_{21m} = \frac{\eta}{4\pi} \left[2C_i(u_0) - C_i(u_1) - C_i(u_2) \right] \tag{7-40a}$$

$$X_{21m} = -\frac{\eta}{4\pi} \left[2S_i(u_0) - S_i(u_1) - S_i(u_2) \right] \tag{7-40b}$$

$$u_0 = kd \tag{7-40c}$$

$$u_1 = k\left(\sqrt{d^2 + l^2} + l \right) \tag{7-40d}$$

$$u_2 = k\left(\sqrt{d^2 + l^2} - l \right) \tag{7-40e}$$

Collinear Configuration [Figure 7.6(b)]

$$R_{21m} = -\frac{\eta}{8\pi}\cos(v_0)\left[-2C_i(2v_0)+C_i(v_2)+C_i(v_1)-\ln(v_3)\right]$$
$$+\frac{\eta}{8\pi}\sin(v_0)\left[2S_i(2v_0)-S_i(v_2)-S_i(v_1)\right] \qquad (7\text{-}41a)$$

$$X_{21m} = -\frac{\eta}{8\pi}\cos(v_0)\left[2S_i(2v_0)-S_i(v_2)-S_i(v_1)\right]$$
$$+\frac{\eta}{8\pi}\sin(v_0)\left[2C_i(2v_0)-C_i(v_2)-C_i(v_1)-\ln(v_3)\right] \qquad (7\text{-}41b)$$

$$v_0 = kh \qquad (7\text{-}41c)$$
$$v_1 = 2k(h+l) \qquad (7\text{-}41d)$$
$$v_2 = 2k(h-l) \qquad (7\text{-}41e)$$
$$v_3 = (h^2 - l^2)/h^2 \qquad (7\text{-}41f)$$

Parallel in Echelon Configuration [Figure 7.6(c)]

$$R_{21m} = -\frac{\eta}{8\pi}\cos(w_0)\left[-2C_i(w_1)-2C_i(w_1')+C_i(w_2)+C_i(w_2')\right.$$
$$\left.+C_i(w_3)+C_i(w_3')\right]$$
$$+\frac{\eta}{8\pi}\sin(w_0)\left[2S_i(w_1)-2S_i(w_1')\right.$$
$$\left.-S_i(w_2)+S_i(w_2')-S_i(w_3)+S_i(w_3')\right] \qquad (7\text{-}42a)$$

$$X_{21m} = -\frac{\eta}{8\pi}\cos(w_0)\left[2S_i(w_1)+2S_i(w_1')-S_i(w_2)-S_i(w_2')\right.$$
$$\left.-S_i(w_3)-S_i(w_3')\right]$$
$$+\frac{\eta}{8\pi}\sin(w_0)\left[2C_i(w_1)-2C_i(w_1')-C_i(w_2)+C_i(w_2')\right.$$
$$\left.-C_i(w_3)+C_i(w_3')\right] \qquad (7\text{-}42b)$$

$$w_0 = kh \qquad (7\text{-}42c)$$
$$w_1 = k\left(\sqrt{d^2+h^2}+h\right) \qquad (7\text{-}42d)$$
$$w_1' = k\left(\sqrt{d^2+h^2}-h\right) \qquad (7\text{-}42e)$$
$$w_2 = k\left[\sqrt{d^2+(h-l)^2}+(h-l)\right] \qquad (7\text{-}42f)$$
$$w_2' = k\left[\sqrt{d^2+(h-l)^2}-(h-l)\right] \qquad (7\text{-}42g)$$
$$w_3 = k\left[\sqrt{d^2+(h+l)^2}+(h+l)\right] \qquad (7\text{-}42h)$$
$$w_3' = k\left[\sqrt{d^2+(h+l)^2}-(h+l)\right] \qquad (7\text{-}42i)$$

where $C_i(x)$ and $S_i(x)$ are the cosine and sine integrals of (4-68a) and (4-68b) which are found tabulated in Appendix III.

The impedance of (7-39a) can be referred to the input terminals by

$$Z_{21i} = Z_{21m} \left(\frac{I_{1m}}{I_{1i}} \right) \left(\frac{I_{2m}}{I_{2i}} \right) = Z_{21m} \left[\frac{1}{\sin(kl_1/2)} \right] \left[\frac{1}{\sin(kl_2/2)} \right] \qquad (7\text{-}43)$$

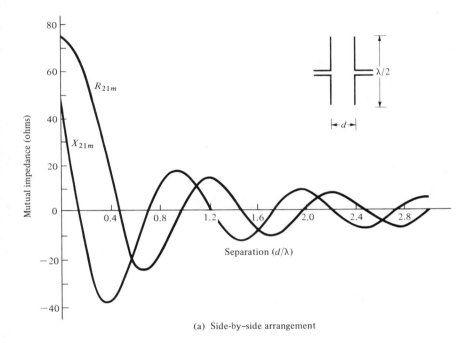

(a) Side-by–side arrangement

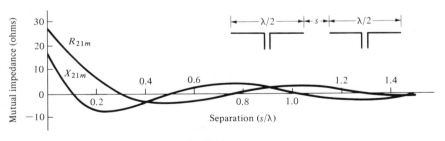

(b) Collinear arrangement

Figure 7.7 Mutual impedance of side-by-side and collinear arrangements of half-wavelength dipoles. (SOURCE: W. L. Weeks, *Antenna Engineering*, McGraw-Hill, New York, 1968)

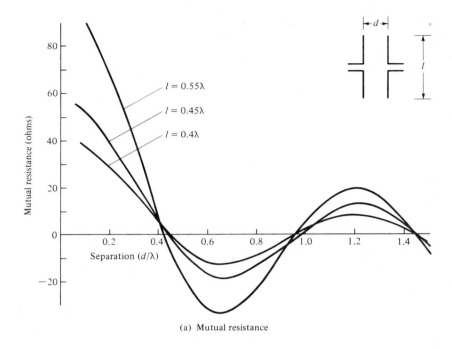

(a) Mutual resistance

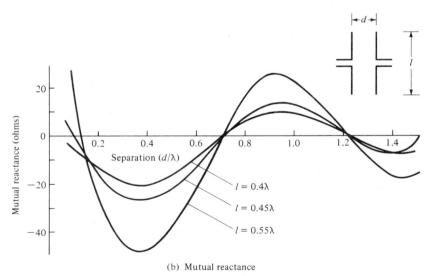

(b) Mutual reactance

Figure 7.8   Mutual impedance for side-by-side arrangement of two dipoles. (SOURCE: W. L. Weeks, *Antenna Engineering*, McGraw-Hill, New York, 1968)

For identical lengths ($l_1=l_2=l$), (7-43) reduces to

$$R_{21i} = \frac{R_{21m}}{\sin^2(kl/2)} \tag{7-43a}$$

$$X_{21i} = \frac{X_{21m}}{\sin^2(kl/2)} \tag{7-43b}$$

where R_{21m} and X_{21m} are, respectively, the resistance and reactance as given by (7-39a).

The mutual impedance, referred to the current maximum and given by (7-39a), of a side-by-side and a collinear arrangement of two half-wavelength dipoles is shown plotted in Figure 7.7. It is apparent that the side-by-side arrangement exhibits larger mutual effects since the antennas are placed in the direction of maximum radiation. Figure 7.8 illustrates the variations of the mutual resistance and reactance for a side-by-side arrangement, as a function of spacing, when the overall length of each antenna in $l=0.4\lambda$, 0.45λ, and 0.55λ. It is observed that the mutual impedances increase as the length of the antennas increases.

Example 7.1

Two identical linear half-wavelength dipoles are placed in a side-by-side arrangement, as shown in Figure 7.6(a). Assuming that the separation between the elements is $d=0.35\lambda$, find the driving point impedance of each.

SOLUTION
Using (7-35a)

$$Z_{1d} = \frac{V_1}{I_1} = Z_{11} + Z_{12}\left(\frac{I_2}{I_1}\right)$$

Since the dipoles are identical, $I_1=I_2$. Thus

$$Z_{1d} = Z_{11} + Z_{12}$$

From Figure 7.7(a)

$$Z_{12} \simeq 25 - j38$$

Since

$$Z_{11} = 73 + j42.5$$

Z_{1d} reduces to

$$Z_{1d} \simeq 98 + j4.5$$

which is also equal to Z_{2d} of (7-35b).

The mutual impedance produced an almost resonant antenna system. A slight length reduction of one or both of the dipoles can produce a nearly ideal resonance. The amount of length reduction will be a function of the wire radius.

7.5 FINITE DIAMETER WIRES: THE MOMENT METHOD

For thin wire antennas, the current distribution was assumed to be of sinusoidal form as given by (4-56). For a finite diameter wire (usually $d > 0.05\lambda$), the sinusoidal current distribution is representative but not exact. To find the current distribution for a cylindrical antenna, an integral equation is usually derived and solved. Previously, solutions to the integral equation were obtained using iterative methods [10]; presently, it is most convenient to use Moment Method techniques [7]. A brief discussion of the Moment Method will be included here.

Knowing the voltage as the feed terminals and determining the current distribution, the input impedance and the radiation pattern can then be obtained. While the linear dipole is conceptually simple, most of the information presented here can be readily extended to more complicated structures.

7.5.1 Integral Equation

Two of the most popular integral equations that are used to determine the current distribution of a finite radius wire are Hallén's integral equation [11], [12] and Pocklington's integral equation [12], [13]. Hallén's equation is usually restricted to the use of a delta-gap voltage source model at the feed. Pocklington's equation is more general, and it is adaptable to many types of feed sources (through alteration of its excitation function or excitation matrix) including a magnetic frill [12]. In addition, Hallén's equation requires the inversion of a $N+1$ order matrix (where N is the number of division of the wire) while Pocklington's equation requires the inversion of an N order matrix. These and other advantages and disadvantages are found in [14], [15] from which most of the material of this section is drawn.

HALLÉN'S INTEGRAL EQUATION
Referring to Figure 7.9(a), let us assume that a finite radius wire of length l is center-fed by an applied delta-gap V_i. If the length of the cylinder is much larger than its radius ($l \gg a$) and its radius is much smaller than the wavelength ($a \ll \lambda$), the effects of the end faces of the cylinder can be neglected. Therefore, the boundary conditions for a wire with infinite conductivity are those of vanishing tangential **E**-fields on the surface of the cylinder and vanishing current at the ends of the cylinder $[I_z(z') = \pm l/2 = 0]$.

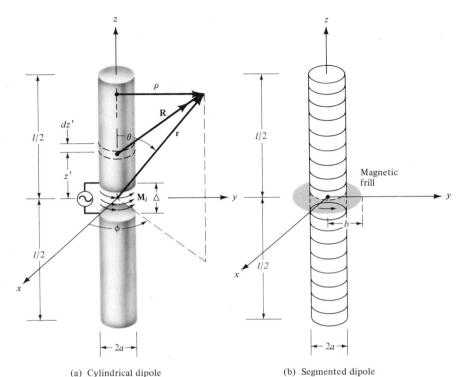

(a) Cylindrical dipole   (b) Segmented dipole

Figure 7.9   Cylindrical dipole and its subdivisions.

Since only an electric current flows on the cylinder and it is directed along the z-axis ($\mathbf{J} = \hat{a}_z J_z$), (3-29) reduces for $\mathbf{F} = 0$ to

$$\frac{d^2 A_z}{dz^2} + k^2 A_z = 0 \tag{7-44}$$

The right-hand side of (7-44) is equal to zero because of the vanishing tangential **E**-field on the surface of the cylinder. Since the current density on the cylinder is symmetrical [$J_z(z') = J_z(-z')$], the potential function A_z is also symmetrical [i.e., $A_z(z') = A_z(-z')$]. Thus the solution of (7-44) is given by

$$A_z(z) = -j\sqrt{\mu\varepsilon}\left[A_1 \cos(kz) + B_1 \sin(k|z|)\right] \tag{7-45}$$

where A_1 and B_1 are constants. For a current carrying wire, its potential function is also given by (3-53). Equating (7-45) to (3-53) reduces to

$$\boxed{\int_{-l/2}^{l/2} I(z') \frac{e^{-jkR}}{4\pi R} dz' = -\frac{j}{\eta}\left[A_1 \cos(kz) + B_1 \sin(k|z|)\right]} \tag{7-46}$$

where η is the intrinsic impedance of the medium. If the applied voltage at the input terminals is V_i, it can be shown that the constant B_1 is equal to $B_1 = V_i/2$. The constant A_1 is determined from the boundary condition which requires the current to vanish at the end points of the wire.

Equation (7-46) is referred to as Hallén's integral equation for a perfectly conducting wire. It was derived by solving the differential equation of (3-29) or (7-44) with the enforcement of the appropriate boundary conditions.

POCKLINGTON'S INTEGRAL EQUATION

In deriving Pocklington's integral equation, an integral equation approach (in contrast to the differential approach for Hallén's) is taken. The appropriate boundary conditions are incorporated in the integral equation itself.

For a current density $\mathbf{J} = \hat{a}_z J_z$ (with $\mathbf{M} = 0$), (3-29) reduces to

$$\frac{\partial^2 A_z}{\partial z^2} + k^2 A_z = j\omega\mu\varepsilon E_z \tag{7-47}$$

whose solution is given by

$$\iiint J_z(x', y', z')\left(\frac{\partial^2}{\partial z^2} + k^2\right)\frac{e^{-jkR}}{4\pi R}\,dv' = j\omega\varepsilon E_z \tag{7-48}$$

where

$$R = \sqrt{(x-x')^2 + (y-y')^2 + (z-z')^2} \tag{7-48a}$$

If

1. the current density J_z is restricted on the surface of a perfectly conducting wire of length l ($J_z \Rightarrow K_z$, as shown in Figure 7.2)
2. the current density K_z circumferentially is uniformly distributed on the surface of the wire [$I_z(z') = 2\pi a K_z(z')$; this is a good approximation for thin wires]
3. E_z in (7-48) represents the scattered field E_z^s radiated by the current I_z

then (7-48) can be written as

$$\int_{-l/2}^{l/2} I_z(z')\left[\left(\frac{\partial^2}{\partial z^2} + k^2\right)\frac{e^{-jkR}}{R}\right]dz' = j\omega\varepsilon E_z^s(z)$$

$$= -j\omega\varepsilon E_z^i(z) \tag{7-49}$$

where

$$R = \sqrt{(x-x')^2 + (y-y')^2 + (z-z')^2}$$

$$\overset{x' \to 0}{\underset{y' \to 0}{\simeq}} \sqrt{\rho^2 + (z-z')^2} \tag{7-49a}$$

since $E_z(\text{total})=0=E_z^i+E_z^s$ or $E_z^s=-E_z^i$. E_z^i is the field incident or impressed on the surface of the wire, and for small radii, it is assumed to be circumferentially uniformly distributed.

Equation (7-49) is referred to as Pocklington's integral equation, and it has been presented in many other different forms [12]. A more convenient form of (7-49) is that by Richmond [16] given by

$$\int_{-l/2}^{l/2} I_z(z')\frac{e^{-jkR}}{4\pi R^5}\left[(1+jkR)(2R^2-3a^2)+(kaR)^2\right]dz'$$

$$=j\omega\varepsilon E_z^s(z)=-j\omega\varepsilon E_z^i(z)$$

(7-50)

7.5.2 Moment Method Solution

Equations (7-46), (7-48), and (7-50) each has the form of

$$F(g)=h$$

(7-51)

where F is a known linear (integral) operator, h is a known excitation function, and g is the response function. The objective here is to determine g once F and h are specified.

While the inverse problem is often intractable in closed form, the linearity of the operator F makes a numerical solution possible. One technique, known as the Moment Method [7], requires that the unknown response function is expanded as a linear combination of N terms and written as

$$g(z')\simeq c_1g_1(z')+c_2g_2(z')+\cdots+c_Ng_N(z')=\sum_{n=1}^{N}c_ng_n(z')$$

(7-52)

Each c_n is an unknown constant and each $g_n(z')$ is a known function usually referred to as a *basis* or *expansion* function. The domain of the $g_n(z')$ functions is the same as that of $g(z')$. Substituting (7-52) into (7-51), and using the linearity of the F operator, reduces (7-51) to

$$\sum_{n=1}^{N}c_nF(g_n)=h$$

(7-53)

The basis functions g_n are chosen so that each $F(g_n)$ in (7-53) can be evaluated conveniently; preferably in closed form or at the very least numerically. The only task remaining then is to find the c_n unknown constants.

7.5.3 Basis Functions

One very important step in any numerical solution is the choice of basis functions. In general, one chooses as basis functions the set which has the ability to accurately represent and resemble the anticipated unknown function, while minimizing the computational effort required to employ it.

Theoretically, there are infinitely many possible basis sets. However, only a limited number are used in practice. These sets may be divided into two general classes. The first is the subdomain functions, which are nonzero only over a part of the domain of the function $g(z')$ (its domain being the surface of the structure). The second class contains entire-domain functions, those that are nonzero for the entire domain of the unknown function.

SUBDOMAIN BASES
Of the two types, subdomain functions are the most commonly used. Unlike entire-domain bases, they may be used without prior knowledge of the nature of the function they must represent.

The subdomain approach involves subdivision of the structure into N nonoverlapping segments, as illustrated on the axis in Figure 7.10(a). For clarity, the segments are here shown to be collinear and of equal length, although neither condition is necessary. The basis functions are defined in conjunction with the limits of one or more of the segments.

Perhaps the most common of these basis functions is the conceptually simple piecewise constant, or "pulse" function, shown in Figure 7.10(b). It is defined by

Piecewise Constant

$$g_n(z') = \begin{cases} 1 & z'_{n-1} \leq z' \leq z'_n \\ 0 & \text{elsewhere} \end{cases} \tag{7-54}$$

Once the associated coefficients are determined, this function will produce a staircase representation of the unknown function, similar to that in Figure 7.10(c).

Another common basis set is that of piecewise linear, or "triangle" functions, seen in Figure 7.10(d). These are defined by

Piecewise Linear

$$g_n(z') = \begin{cases} \dfrac{z' - z'_{n-1}}{z'_n - z'_{n-1}} & z'_{n-1} \leq z' \leq z'_n \\[2mm] \dfrac{z'_{n+1} - z'}{z'_{n+1} - z'_n} & z'_n \leq z' \leq z'_{n+1} \\[2mm] 0 & \text{elsewhere} \end{cases} \tag{7-55}$$

and are seen to cover two segments, and overlap adjacent functions. The

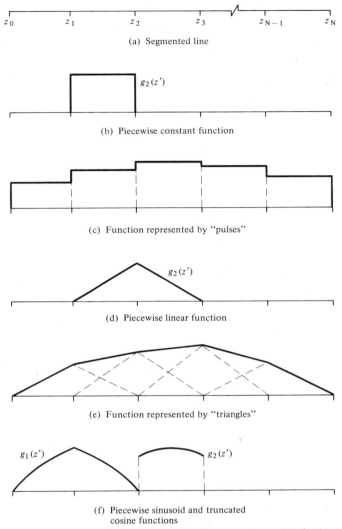

(a) Segmented line

$g_2(z')$

(b) Piecewise constant function

(c) Function represented by "pulses"

$g_2(z')$

(d) Piecewise linear function

(e) Function represented by "triangles"

$g_1(z')$ $g_2(z')$

(f) Piecewise sinusoid and truncated
     cosine functions

Figure 7.10   Typical basis functions and representative distributions.

resulting representation [Figure 7.10(e)] is smoother than that for "pulses," but at the cost of increased computational complexity.

Increasing the sophistication of subdomain basis functions beyond the level of the "triangle" is seldom warranted by the possible improvement in representation accuracy. However, there are cases where more specialized functions are useful for other reasons. For example, some integral operators may be evaluated without numerical integration when their integrands are multiplied by a $\sin(kz')$ or $\cos(kz')$ function (where z' is the variable of integration). In such a case, considerable advantages in computation time and resistance to errors would be gained by using basis functions like the piecewise sinusoid or truncated cosine of Figure 7.10(f). These functions are defined by

Piecewise Sinusoid

$$g_n(z') = \begin{cases} \dfrac{\sin[k(z'-z'_{n-1})]}{\sin[k(z'_n-z'_{n-1})]} & z'_{n-1} \leq z' \leq z'_n \\[2mm] \dfrac{\sin[k(z'_{n+1}-z')]}{\sin[k(z'_{n+1}-z'_n)]} & z'_n \leq z' \leq z'_{n+1} \\[2mm] 0 & \text{elsewhere} \end{cases} \qquad (7\text{-}56)$$

Truncated Cosine

$$g_n(z') = \begin{cases} \cos\left[k\left(z'-\dfrac{z'_n-z'_{n-1}}{2}\right)\right] & z'_{n-1} \leq z' \leq z'_n \\[2mm] 0 & \text{elsewhere} \end{cases} \qquad (7\text{-}57)$$

ENTIRE DOMAIN BASES

Entire-domain basis functions, as their name implies, are defined and nonzero over the entire length of the structure being considered. Thus, no segmentation as before is involved in their use.

A common entire-domain basis set is that of sinusoidal functions, where

Entire Domain

$$g_n(z') = \cos\left[\frac{(2n-1)\pi z'}{l}\right] \qquad -\frac{l}{2} \leq z' \leq \frac{l}{2} \qquad (7\text{-}58)$$

Note that this basis set would be particularly useful for modeling the current distribution on a wire dipole, which is known to have primarily sinusoidal distribution. The main advantage of entire-domain bases lies in problems where the unknown function is assumed *a priori* to follow a known pattern. In such cases, entire-domain functions may render an acceptable representation of the unknown while using far fewer terms in the expansion of (7-52) than would be necessary for subdomain bases.

Because we are constrained to use a finite number of functions (or modes, as they are sometimes called), entire-domain bases usually have difficulty in modeling arbitrary or complicated unknown functions.

As examples of other entire-domain basis functions, sets like (7-58) can be generated using Tschebyscheff, Maclaurin, Legendre, and Hermite polynomials, or other convenient functions.

7.5.4 Weighting (Testing) Functions

Expansion of (7-53) leads to one equation with N unknowns. It alone is not sufficient to determine the N unknown c_n $(n=1,2,...,N)$ constants. To resolve the N constants, it is necessary to have N linearly independent equations. To accomplish this, an inner product $\langle w, g \rangle$ is defined which is a scalar operation satisfying the laws

$$\langle w, g \rangle = \langle g, w \rangle \tag{7-59a}$$

$$\langle af + bg, w \rangle = a \langle f, w \rangle + b \langle g, w \rangle \tag{7-59b}$$

$$\langle g^*, g \rangle > 0 \text{ if } g \neq 0 \tag{7-59c}$$

$$\langle g^*, g \rangle = 0 \text{ if } g = 0 \tag{7-59d}$$

where a and b are scalars and (*) indicates complex conjugation. A typical, but not unique, inner product is

$$\langle \mathbf{w}, \mathbf{g} \rangle = \iint_S \mathbf{w} \cdot \mathbf{g} \, ds \tag{7-60}$$

where S is the surface of the structure being analyzed. Note that the functions w and g can be vectors.

The Moment Method is a numerical technique whose solutions satisfy the electromagnetic boundary conditions (e.g., vanishing tangential electric fields on the surface of an electric conductor) only at discrete points. Between these points the boundary conditions may not be satisfied, and we define the deviation as a residual [e.g., residual $= \Delta \mathbf{E}|_{\text{tan}} = \mathbf{E}(\text{scattered})|_{\text{tan}} + \mathbf{E}(\text{incident})|_{\text{tan}} \neq 0$ on the surface of an electric conductor]. To minimize the residual in such a way that its overall average over the entire structure approaches zero, the method of weighted residuals is utilized in conjunction with the inner product of (7-60). This technique does not lead to a vanishing residual at every point on the surface of a conductor, for example, but forces the boundary conditions to be satisfied in an average sense over the entire surface.

To accomplish this, we define a set of N weighting (or *testing*) functions $\{w_m\} = w_1, w_2, ..., w_N$ in the domain of the operator F. Forming the inner product between each of these functions, (7-53) results in

$$\sum_{n=1}^{N} c_n \langle w_m, F(g_n) \rangle = \langle w_m, h \rangle \qquad m = 1, 2, ..., N \tag{7-61}$$

This set of N equations may be written in matrix form as

$$[F_{mn}][c_n] = [h_m] \tag{7-62}$$

where

$$[F_{mn}] = \begin{bmatrix} \langle w_1, F(g_1) \rangle & \langle w_1, F(g_2) \rangle & \cdots \\ \langle w_2, F(g_1) \rangle & \langle w_2, F(g_2) \rangle & \\ \vdots & & \vdots \end{bmatrix}$$ (7-62a)

$$[c_n] = \begin{bmatrix} c_1 \\ c_2 \\ \vdots \\ c_N \end{bmatrix} \qquad h_m = \begin{bmatrix} \langle w_1, h \rangle \\ \langle w_2, h \rangle \\ \vdots \\ \langle w_N, h \rangle \end{bmatrix}$$ (7-62b)

The matrix of (7-62) may be solved for the c_n's by inversion, and it can be written as

$$[c_n] = [F_{mn}]^{-1}[h_m]$$ (7-63)

The choice of weighting functions is important in that the elements of $\{w_n\}$ must be linearly independent, so that the N equations in (7-61) will be linearly independent. Further, it will generally be advantageous to choose weighting functions that minimize the computations required to evaluate the inner product.

The condition of linear independence between elements and the advantage of computational simplicity are also important characteristics of basis functions. Because of this, similar types of functions are often used for both weighting and expansion.

A particular choice of functions may be to let the weighting and basis function be the same; that is, $w_n = g_n$. This technique is known as *Galerkin's method* [17].

POINT MATCHING (COLLOCATION)
It should be noted that there are N^2 terms to be evaluated in (7-62a). Each term usually may require two or more integrations; at least one to evaluate each $F(g_n)$, and one to perform the inner product (7-60). When these integrations are to be done numerically, as is often the case, vast amounts of computation may be necessary.

There is, however, a unique set of weighting functions which reduce the number of required integrations. This is the set of Dirac delta weighting functions

$$w_m = \delta(p - p_m) = \delta(p - p_1), \delta(p - p_2), \ldots \qquad (7\text{-}64)$$

where p specifies a position with respect to some reference (origin), and p_m represents a point at which the boundary condition is enforced. Using (7-60) and (7-64) reduces (7-61) to

$$\sum_n c_n \langle \delta(p - p_m), F(g_n) \rangle = \langle w_m, h \rangle \qquad m = 1, 2, \ldots, N$$

$$\sum_n c_n \iint_S \delta(p - p_m) \cdot F(g_n)\, ds = \iint_S \delta(p - p_m) \cdot h\, ds \qquad m = 1, 2, \ldots, N$$

$$\sum_n c_n F(g_n)\big|_{p=p_m} = h\big|_{p=p_m} \qquad m = 1, 2, \ldots, N \qquad (7\text{-}65)$$

Hence, the only remaining integrations are those specified by $F(g_n)$. This simplification may make possible some solutions that would be impractical if other weighting functions were used.

Physically, the use of Dirac delta weighting functions is seen as the relaxation of boundary conditions so that they are enforced only at discrete points on the surface of the structure, hence the name *point-matching*.

An important consideration when using point-matching is the positioning of the N points (p_m's). While equally spaced points often yield good results, much depends upon the basis functions used. When using subsectional bases in conjunction with point matching, one match point should be placed on each segment (to maintain linear independence). Placing the points at the center of the segments usually produces good results. It is important that a match point does not coincide with the "peak" of a triangle or a similar discontinuous function (where the basis function is not differentiably continuous). This may cause errors in some situations.

Because it provides acceptable accuracy along with its obvious computational advantages, point-matching (sometimes called *collocation*) is easily the most popular testing technique for Moment Method solutions to electromagnetics problems. The analysis presented here, along with most problems considered in the literature, proceed via point-matching.

7.5.5 Current Distribution

In setting up a Moment Method (MM) solution based upon (7-46), the dipole of Figure 7.9(a) is subdivided into N segments as shown in Figure 7.9(b). To ensure good results, several points should be noted. When the current (I_z) is expanded in terms of N basis functions, the corresponding matrix equations will be of order $N + 1$, to include the unknown variable A_1.

For point-matching, (7-46) takes the form

$$
\begin{bmatrix}
& & \vdots & \dfrac{j}{\eta}\cos(kz_1) \\
& & & \vdots \\
F_{mn} & & \vdots & \dfrac{j}{\eta}\cos(kz_m) \\
(N+1)\times N & & & \vdots \\
& & \vdots & \dfrac{j}{\eta}\cos(kz_{N+1})
\end{bmatrix}
\begin{bmatrix}
c_1 \\ \vdots \\ c_n \\ \vdots \\ \dfrac{c_N}{A_1}
\end{bmatrix}
\begin{bmatrix}
-\dfrac{j}{\eta}\dfrac{V_i}{2}\sin(k|z_1|) \\
\vdots \\
-\dfrac{j}{\eta}\dfrac{V_i}{2}\sin(k|z_m|) \\
\vdots \\
-\dfrac{j}{\eta}\dfrac{V_i}{2}\sin(k|z_{N+1}|)
\end{bmatrix}
\qquad (7\text{-}66)
$$

where

$$
F_{mn}=\int_{-l/2}^{l/2}g_n(z')\frac{e^{-jkR_m}}{4\pi R_m}dz' \qquad (7\text{-}66a)
$$

$$
R_m=\sqrt{\rho^2+(z-z_m')^2} \qquad (7\text{-}66b)
$$

If symmetrical subdomain basis functions are used, they need to be evaluated only on one-half of the dipole, because of current symmetry. Similarly, match points (or other subdomain weighting functions) will be placed on only one-half of the dipole.

Note that all quantities (matrix elements) involved in this solution are (in general) complex, and must be treated accordingly. Such quantities may be specified either by their real and imaginary components, or by their magnitude and phase. The latter form will be used to represent current distributions.

To illustrate the solution outlined here, an example will be taken. Consider a straight wire dipole (Figure 7.9) having a length of 0.5λ, with a length-to-diameter ratio of 50 [$l/d=l/(2a)=50$, $a=0.005\lambda$]. The feed is represented by two nonzero excitation matrix elements at the center (a finite feed gap). The normalized current distribution is as seen in Figure 7.11(a) in comparison with an ideal sinusoid. While the current magnitude bears a general resemblance to the sinusoidal distribution which is often assumed for wire antennas, there are noticeable differences between the two, especially near the dipole center. Such differences may have a significant effect upon near-field calculations (e.g., input impedance). It may be noted that this current distribution compares well with measurements made by Mack [18].

As a second example, let us analyze a $l=\lambda$ dipole by the same technique. The current distribution calculated for this case is presented in Figure 7.11(b), and it is again compared to a sinusoidal distribution. Note the peak at the center of the MM solution, a characteristic that has been predicted by King and Harrison [10] through an iterative solution to

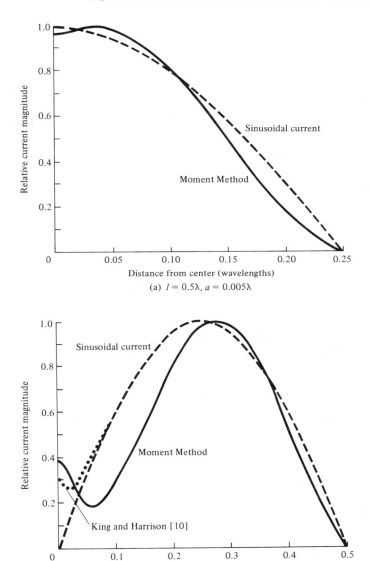

(a) $l = 0.5\lambda$, $a = 0.005\lambda$

(b) $l = \lambda$, $a = 0.01\lambda$

Figure 7.11   Current distribution of finite radius center-fed dipole.

Hallén's equation. This difference between the MM and sinusoidal distributions becomes very important when the input impedance is calculated, since the zero current at the center of the sinusoid predicts an infinite impedance (which is not at all the case).

A computer program, based on Hallén's integral equation and using entire domain basis functions, is included at the end of this chapter. It computes the current distribution, input impedance, and pattern of a linear wire dipole of length l and radius a. Two or three modes usually give the best results.

7.5.6 Input Impedance

For efficient design or utilization of an antenna, it is important that the input impedance be considered. This quantity largely determines the structure's radiation efficiency, and must be known before specifying the transmission line and matching networks to be used.

The input impedance of a dipole may be calculated from a current distribution determined by MM. It can be found using

$$\boxed{Z_{\text{in}} = \frac{V_i}{I_i}}$$ (7-67)

where I_i is the complex input current and V_i is the impressed voltage at the antenna feed (input terminals). For a distributed feed, V_i is found by multiplying the electric field strength used to excite the system by the distance over which that field is impressed. Computed results can be found in Section 8.4.2. The computer program at the end of this chapter can be used for impedance calculations.

7.5.7 Radiation Pattern

Once the current distribution has been determined, the field radiated by the wire can be found using the techniques of Chapter 4. For far-field observations, the field can be computed using (4-58a). Since the current will be in a digitized form, the integration required in (4-58a) must be performed numerically. Computed patterns can be found in Section 8.4.4. The computer program at the end of this chapter can also be used for pattern calculations.

7.5.8 Source Modeling

For the Hallén integral equation of (7-46), the dipole feed was modeled by a *delta-gap* voltage source. This model assumes that the field generated within the gap is uniform; it is a good approximation for small spacings. For the Pocklington integral equation of (7-49) or (7-50), the field can be modeled by a delta-gap source or by an equivalent magnetic ring current which is usually referred to as a *frill generator* [12]. Thus the incident electric field $\mathbf{E}_i$ required in (7-49) or (7-50) can be found using either one of these two models. Although the delta-gap is used most widely, the frill generator usually gives better results (especially for impedances).

For the delta-gap model, the feed-gap Δ of Figure 7.9(a) is replaced by narrow strips of equivalent magnetic current density

$$\boxed{\mathbf{M}_i = -\hat{n} \times \mathbf{E}_i = -\hat{a}_\rho \times \hat{a}_z \frac{V_i}{\Delta} = \hat{a}_\phi \frac{V_i}{\Delta} \qquad -\Delta/2 \le z' \le \Delta/2} \qquad (7\text{-}68)$$

where V_i is the applied gap voltage. The magnetic current density $\mathbf{M}_i$ is sketched in Figure 7.9(a).

The frill-generator model was introduced to calculate the near-zone, as well as the far-zone, fields from coaxial apertures [19]. To use this model, the aperture is replaced with a circumferentially directed magnetic current. The fields generated from this model can be computed using simple analytical expressions [12], [19]. For the dipole problem of Figure 7.9(a), the feed-gap is replaced by an equivalent magnetic frill, as shown in Figure 7.9(b). The inner radius a of the annular ring is usually the radius of the dipole wire. Since the dipole is fed by transmission lines, the outer radius b of the equivalent annular ring is found using the expression for the characteristic impedance of the transmission line.

References

1. R. E. Burgess, "Aerial Characteristics," *Wireless Engr.*, vol. 21, pp. 154–160, April 1944.
2. J. D. Kraus, *Antennas*, McGraw-Hill, New York, 1950, Chapter 10, pp. 251–278.
3. S. A. Schelkunoff and H. T. Friis, *Antennas: Theory and Practice*, Wiley, New York, 1952, pp. 213–242.
4. A. A. Pistolkors, "The Radiation Resistance of Beam Antennas," *Proc. IRE*, vol. 17, pp. 562–579, March 1929.
5. R. Bechmann, "On the Calculation of Radiation Resistance of Antennas and Antenna Combinations," *Proc. IRE*, vol. 19, pp. 461–466, March 1931.
6. P. S. Carter, "Circuit Relations in Radiating Systems and Applications to Antenna Problems," *Proc. IRE*, vol. 20, pp. 1004–1041, June 1932.
7. R. F. Harrington, *Field Computation by Moment Methods*, Macmillan, New York, 1968.
8. R. C. Hansen, "Fundamental Limitations in Antennas," *Proc. IEEE*, vol. 69, No. 2, pp. 170–182, February 1981.
9. W. L. Weeks, *Antenna Engineering*, McGraw-Hill, New York, 1968, pp. 189–190.
10. R. King and C. W. Harrison, Jr., "The Distribution of Current Along a Symmetrical Center-Driven Antenna," *Proc. IRE*, vol. 31, pp. 548–567, October 1943.
11. E. Hallén, "Theoretical Investigations into the Transmitting and Receiving Qualities of Antennae," *Nova Acta Regiae Soc. Sci. Upsaliensis*, Ser. IV, 11, No. 4, pp. 1–44, 1938.
12. R. Mittra (ed.), *Computer Techniques for Electromagnetics*, Pergamon Press, New York, 1973, pp. 7–70.
13. H. C. Pocklington, "Electrical Oscillations in Wire," *Cambridge Philosophical Society Proceedings*, London, England, vol. 9, pp. 324–332, 1897.

14. J. D. Lilly, "Application of the Moment Method to Antenna Analysis," MSEE Thesis, Department of Electrical Engineering, West Virginia University, 1980.

15. J. D. Lilly and C. A. Balanis, "Current distributions, input impedances, and radiation patterns of wire antennas," North American Radio Science (URSI) Meeting, Universite Laval, Quebec, Canada, June 2–6, 1980.

16. J. H. Richmond, "Digital Computer Solutions of the Rigorous Equations for Scattering Problems," *Proceedings IEEE*, pp. 796–804, August 1965.

17. L. Kantorovich and G. Akilov, *Functional Analysis in Normed Spaces*, Pergamon Press, Oxford, 1964, pp. 586–587.

18. R. P. King, R. Mack, and S. Sandler, *Arrays of Cylindrical Dipoles*, Cambridge University Press, New York, 1968, pp. 56–59.

19. L. T. Tsai, "A numerical solution for the near and far fields of an annular ring of magnetic current," *IEEE Trans. Antennas Propag.*, vol. AP-20, no. 5, pp. 569–576, Sept. 1972.

PROBLEMS

7.1. Derive (7-17a)–(7-17b) using (7-16), (7-17a), and (7-16b).

7.2. For a linear dipole with sinusoidal current distribution, radiating in free-space, find the radiation Z_{im} and the input Z_{in} impedances when ($a = \lambda/20$)
   (a) $l = \lambda/4$ (b) $l = \lambda/2$
   (c) $l = 3\lambda/4$ (d) $l = \lambda$

7.3. A $\lambda/2$ dipole of finite radius is not self-resonant. However, if the dipole is somewhat less than $\lambda/2$, it becomes self-resonant. For a dipole with radius of $a = \lambda/200$ radiating in free-space, find the
   (a) nearest length by which the $\lambda/2$ dipole becomes self-resonant
   (b) radiation resistance (referred to the current maximum) of the new resonant dipole
   (c) input resistance
   (d) VSWR when the dipole is connected to a 50-ohm line

7.4. Find the length, at the first resonance, of linear dipoles with wire radii of
   (a) $10^{-5}\lambda$ (b) $10^{-4}\lambda$
   (c) $10^{-3}\lambda$ (d) $10^{-2}\lambda$
   Compute the radiation resistance of each.

7.5. For two half-wavelength dipoles radiating in free-space, compute (using equations, *not* curves) the mutual impedance Z_{21m} referred to the current maxima for
   (a) side-by-side arrangement with $d = \lambda/4$
   (b) collinear configuration with $s = \lambda/4$

7.6. Two identical linear $\lambda/2$ dipoles are placed in a collinear arrangement a distance $s = 0.35\lambda$ apart. Find the driving point impedance of each.

7.7. Two identical linear $\lambda/2$ dipoles are placed in a collinear arrangement. Find the spacings between them so that the driving point impedance of each has the smallest reactive part.

7.8. Derive (7-45), (7-48), (7-49), and (7-50).

7.9. Using the computer program at the end of the chapter, compute the input impedance of a $\lambda/4$ and $3\lambda/4$ dipole with a l/d ratio of $l/d = 50$ and 25 (use three modes). Compare the results with the impedances of a dipole with $l/d = 10^9$. Plot the current distribution and the far-field pattern of each dipole.

COMPUTER PROGRAM—FINITE DIAMETER DIPOLE:
CURRENT DISTRIBUTION, INPUT IMPEDANCE,
AND RADIATION PATTERN

```
C **************************************************************
C THIS PROGRAM USES HALLEN'S EQUATION ON SYMMETRICAL DIPOLES
C [EQU.(7-46)] AND COMPUTES THE CURRENT DISTRIBUTION,INPUT
C  IMPEDANCE,AND RADIATION PATTERN OF A FINITE DIAMETER
C  DIPOLE.EQUATION (7-46) IS SOLVED FOR THE DIPOLE CURR-
C  ENT DISTRIBUTION USING MOMENT METHOD TECHNIQUES,WITH
C  ENTIRE DOMAIN BASIS FUNCTIONS,AND POINT MATCHING,AS
C  OUTLINED IN SECTION 7.5.2.
C **************************************************************
      EXTERNAL GE,BMODE,POWER
      COMPLEX OP(50,50),EFRIL(50),ZIN
      DIMENSION CRL(100),CIM(100),ZE(100),PWR(181),PHI(181)
     1,PHID(181)
      COMMON RA,POINT,EL,N,N1,NMODE,CRL,CIM,ZE
      DIMENSION PIVOT(50),NPT(1),ICR(1),ICI(1)
      DATA NPT/100/,ICR/'RRRR'/,ICI/'IIII'/
      PI=3.1415927
C EACH DATA INPUT CARD HAS: NUMBER OF MODES TO BE USED (I2),
C RADIUS (E10.3) AND LENGTH OF WIRE (F5.2) IN WAVELENGTHS.
    5 READ (5,100,END=500) NMODE,RA,EL
  100 FORMAT(I2,E10.3,F5.2)
      WRITE(6,101) NMODE,RA,EL
  101 FORMAT(1H1,I3,' MODES, RADIUS=',E10.3,' LENGTH=',F5.2)
C A AND B ARE LIMITS OF NUMERICAL INTEGRATION
      A=-EL/2.
      B=EL/2.
      DEL=EL*.05
      KK=NMODE+1
      DO 20 M=1,KK
      POINT=EL*FLOAT(M-1)/FLOAT(NMODE)/2.
C OP IS THE N X N OPERATOR MATRIX OF "MUTUAL IMPEDANCES"
      OP(M,KK)=(0.,1.)*(COS(2.*PI*POINT))/120./PI
C EFRIL IS THE EXCITATION MATRIX (CURRENT MATRIX AFTER SOLN)
      EFRIL(M)=(0.,-1.)*(SIN(2.*PI*ABS(POINT)))/240./PI
C LIMITS ARE DIVIDED INTO 3 PARTS FOR SEPARATE INTEGRATION
      C=POINT-DEL
      D=POINT+DEL
      IF(C.LT.A) C=A
      IF(D.GT.B) D=B
      DO 10 N=1,NMODE
C SEPARATE INTEGRATIONS DONE FOR REAL AND IMAGINARY PARTS
      N1=1
      CALL QG32A (A,C,GE,ANS1)
      CALL QG32A (C,D,GE,ANS2)
      CALL QG32A (D,B,GE,ANS3)
      ANSR=ANS1+ANS2+ANS3
      N1=2
      CALL QG32A (A,C,GE,ANS1)
      CALL QG32A (C,D,GE,ANS2)
      CALL QG32A (D,B,GE,ANS3)
      ANSI=ANS1+ANS2+ANS3
   10 OP(M,N)=CMPLX(ANSR,ANSI)
   20 CONTINUE
C LEQT1C IS AN IMSL ROUTINE FOR COMPLEX MATRIX EQN SOLN
      CALL LEQT1C (OP,KK,50,EFRIL,1,50,0,PIVOT,IER)
C SET UP TWO (100 ELMT) ARRAYS HAVING REAL AND IMAG
C CURRENTS
      DO 30 J=1,100
      CRL(J)=0.
      CIM(J)=0.
      ZE(J)=FLOAT(J-1)*EL/198.
```

```
                DO 30 I=1,NMODE
                N=I
                CRL(J)=CRL(J)+REAL(EFRIL(I))*BMODE(ZE(J))
           30   CIM(J)=CIM(J)+AIMAG(EFRIL(I))*BMODE(ZE(J))
      C
      C CALCULATE THE INPUT IMPEDANCE
      C ZIN IS GAP VOLTAGE (1 V) DIVIDED BY GAP CURRENT
                ZIN=(1.,0.)/CMPLX(CRL(1),CIM(1))
                WRITE(6,104) ZIN
          104   FORMAT (/,' THE INPUT IMPEDANCE IS (COMPLEX OHMS)'
               1,2F7.2)
      C
      C PRINT OUT CURRENTS ALONG ONE HALF OF DIPOLE
                WRITE(6,107)
                DO 40 J=1,100,3
                CMAG=SQRT(CRL(J)**2+CIM(J)**2)
           40   WRITE (6,108) ZE(J),CRL(J),CIM(J),CMAG
      C
      C CALCULATE THE POWER PATTERN OF THE ANTENNA
                WRITE(6,110)
                PMAX=0.
                DO 35 I=1,181
                PHID(I)=1.0*FLOAT(I)-0.9999
                PHI(I)=PHID(I)*PI/180.
                PWR(I)=POWER(PHI(I))*60.*PI/SIN(PHI(I))
           35   IF (PWR(I).GT.PMAX) PMAX=PWR(I)
      C PUT PATTERN IN DB
                DO 36 I=1,181
                PWR(I)=10.*ALOG10(PWR(I)/PMAX)
                IF (PWR(I).LT.-40.) PWR(I)=-40.
           36   WRITE(6,111) PHID(I),PWR(I)
          107   FORMAT(//,' CURRENT: Z',6X,'REAL',6X,'IMAGINARY',
               &4X,'MAGNITUDE')
          108   FORMAT(F12.3,E11.3,2E13.3)
          110   FORMAT(//,' POWER PATTERN:    THETA    POWER(DB)')
          111   FORMAT(T17,F6.1,F11.2)
      C REPEAT PROGRAM AS LONG AS DATA CARDS REMAIN
                GO TO 5
          500   STOP
                END


      C       FUNCTION SUBROUTINE NO.1

                FUNCTION BMODE(Z)

      C BMODE EVALUATES THE NTH MODE AT DISTANCE Z FROM CENTER
                COMMON RA,POINT,EL,N,N1,NMODE
                BMODE=SIN((FLOAT(N)*3.1415927/EL)*(EL/2.-ABS(Z)))
                RETURN
                END


      C       FUNCTION SUBROUTINE NO.2

                FUNCTION GE(Z)
      C GE PROVIDES THE KERNEL OF HALLENS EQN FOR INTEGRATION
      C REAL OR IMAG PART CHOSEN BY PARAMETER N1 EQUAL TO 1 OR 2
                EXTERNAL BMODE
                COMMON RA,POINT,EL,N,N1,NMODE
                COMPLEX G
                PI=3.1415927
                R=SQRT(RA**2+(POINT-Z)**2)
                K=2.*PI
                G=CEXP((0.,-1.)*K*R)*BMODE(Z)/4./PI/R
                IF (N1.EQ.2) GO TO 10
                GE=REAL(G)
                GO TO 20
           10   GE=AIMAG(G)
           20   RETURN
                END
```

```
C     FUNCTION SUBROUTINE NO.3

      FUNCTION POWER(THETA)
C POWER CALCULATES THE RADIATED POWER LEVEL AT ANGLE THETA
C RADIANS TO THE DIPOLE AXIS.  CURRENT DISTRIBUTION GIVEN BY
C ARRAYS CRL, CIM, AT POSITIONS GIVEN BY ARRAY ZE
      DIMENSION CRL(100),CIM(100),ZE(100)
      COMMON RA,POINT,EL,N,N1,NMODE,CRL,CIM,ZE
      PI=3.1415927
      PRR=0.0
      PRI=0.0
      DO 10 I=1,99
      K=I+1
      PHAS=PI*COS(THETA)*(ZE(I)+ZE(K))
      PRR=PRR+(CRL(I)+CRL(K))*COS(PHAS)
   10 PRI=PRI+(CIM(I)+CIM(K))*COS(PHAS)
      POWER=((SIN(THETA))**3)*((EL/396.)**2)*(PRR**2+PRI**2)
      RETURN
      END


C     NUMERICAL INTEGRATION SUBROUTINE

      SUBROUTINE QG32A(XL,XU,FCT,Y)
C QG32A DOES 32 POINT GAUSSIAN QUADRATURE INTEGRATION OF
C FCT OVER THE LIMITS XL TO XU, AND RETURNS THE ANSWER
C IN Y.
      A=.5*(XL+XU)
      B=XU-XL
      C=.4986319*B
      Y=.003509305*(FCT(A+C)+FCT(A-C))
      C=.4928058*B
      Y=Y+.008137197*(FCT(A+C)+FCT(A-C))
      C=.4823811*B
      Y=Y+.01269603*(FCT(A+C)+FCT(A-C))
      C=.4674530*B
      Y=Y+.01713693*(FCT(A+C)+FCT(A-C))
      C=.4481606*B
      Y=Y+.02141795*(FCT(A+C)+FCT(A-C))
      C=.4246838*B
      Y=Y+.02549903*(FCT(A+C)+FCT(A-C))
      C=.3972419*B
      Y=Y+.02934205*(FCT(A+C)+FCT(A-C))
      C=.3660911*B
      Y=Y+.03291111*(FCT(A+C)+FCT(A-C))
      C=.3315221*B
      Y=Y+.03617290*(FCT(A+C)+FCT(A-C))
      C=.2938579*B
      Y=Y+.03909695*(FCT(A+C)+FCT(A-C))
      C=.2534500*B
      Y=Y+.04165596*(FCT(A+C)+FCT(A-C))
      C=.2106756*B
      Y=Y+.04382605*(FCT(A+C)+FCT(A-C))
      C=.1659343*B
      Y=Y+.04558694*(FCT(A+C)+FCT(A-C))
      C=.1196437*B
      Y=Y+.04692220*(FCT(A+C)+FCT(A-C))
      C=.07223598*B
      Y=Y+.04781936*(FCT(A+C)+FCT(A-C))
      C=.02415383*B
      Y=B*(Y+.04827004*(FCT(A+C)+FCT(A-C)))
      RETURN
      END
```

Chapter 8
Broadband Dipoles
and Matching Techniques

8.1 INTRODUCTION

In Chapter 4 the radiation properties (pattern, directivity, input impedance, mutual impedance, etc.) of very thin wire antennas were investigated by assuming that the current distribution, which in most cases is sinusoidal, is known. In practice, infinitely thin (electrically) wires are not realizable but can be approximated. In addition, their radiation characteristics (such as pattern, impedance, gain, etc.) are very sensitive to frequency. The degree to which they change as a function of frequency depends on the antenna bandwidth. For applications that require coverage of a broad range of frequencies, such as television reception of all channels, wide-band antennas are needed. There are numerous antenna configurations, especially of arrays, that can be used to produce wide bandwidths. Some simple and inexpensive dipole configurations, including the conical and cylindrical dipoles, can be used to accomplish this to some degree.

For a finite diameter wire (usually $d > 0.05\lambda$) the current distribution may not be sinusoidal and its effect on the radiation pattern of the antenna is usually negligible. However, it has been shown that the current distribution has a pronounced effect on the input impedance of the wire antenna, especially when its length is such that a near null in current occurs at its input terminals. The effects are much less severe when a near current maximum occurs at the input terminals.

Historically there have been three methods that were used to take into account the finite conductor thickness. The first method treats the problem as boundary-value problem [1], the second as a tapered transmission line or electromagnetic horn [2], and the third finds the current distribution on the wire from an integral equation [3]. The boundary-value approach is well suited for idealistic symmetrical geometries (e.g., ellipsoids, prolate spheroids) which cannot be used effectively to approximate more practical geometries such as the cylinder. The method expresses the fields in terms of an infinite series of free oscillations or natural modes whose coefficients are chosen to satisfy the conditions of the driving source. For the assumed idealized configurations, the method does lead to very reliable data, but it is very difficult to know how to approximate more practical geometries (such as a cylinder) by the more idealized configurations (such as the prolate spheroid). For these reasons the boundary-value method is not very practical and will not be pursued any further in this text.

In the second method Schelkunoff represents the antenna as a two-wire uniformly tapered transmission line, each wire of conical geometry, to form a biconical antenna. Its solution is obtained by applying transmission line theory (incident and reflected waves), so well known to the average engineer. The analysis begins by first finding the radiated fields which in turn are used, in conjunction with transmission line theory, to find the input impedance.

For the third technique, the main objectives are to find the current distribution on the antenna and in turn the input impedance. These were accomplished by Hallén by deriving an integral equation for the current distribution whose approximate solution, of different orders, was obtained by iteration and application of boundary conditions. Once a solution for the current is formed, the input impedance is determined by knowing the applied voltage at the feed terminals.

The details of the second method will follow in summary form. The integral equation technique of Hallén, along with that of Pocklington, form the basis of Moment Method techniques which were discussed in Section 7.5.

8.2 BICONICAL ANTENNA

One simple configuration that can be used to achieve broadband characteristics is the biconical antenna formed by placing two cones of infinite extent together, as shown in Figure 8.1(a). This can be thought to represent a uniformly tapered transmission line. The application of a voltage V_i at the input terminals will produce outgoing spherical waves, as shown in Figure 8.1(b), which in turn produce at any point $(r, \theta = \theta_c, \phi)$ a current I along the surface of the cone and voltage V between the cones (Figure 8.2). These can then be used to find the characteristic impedance of the transmission line, which is also equal to the input impedance of an infinite geometry. Modifications to this expression, to take into account the finite lengths of the cones, will be made using transmission line analogy.

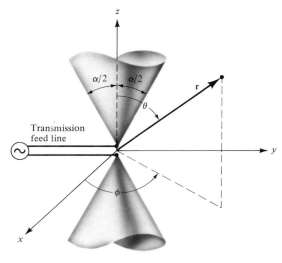

(a) Biconical geometry

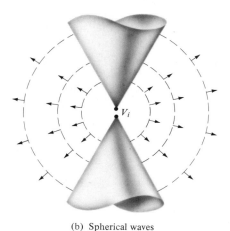

(b) Spherical waves

Figure 8.1 Biconical antenna geometry and radiated spherical waves.

8.2.1 Radiated Fields

The analysis begins by first finding the radiated **E**- and **H**-fields between the cones, assuming dominant TEM mode excitation (**E** and **H** are transverse to the direction of propagation). Once these are determined for any point (r, θ, ϕ), the voltage V and current I at any point on the surface of the cone $(r, \theta = \theta_c, \phi)$ will be formed. From Faraday's law we can write that

$$\nabla \times \mathbf{E} = - j\omega\mu\mathbf{H} \qquad (8\text{-}1)$$

which when expanded in spherical coordinates and assuming that the

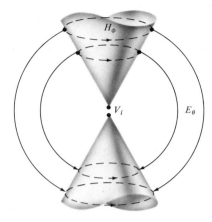

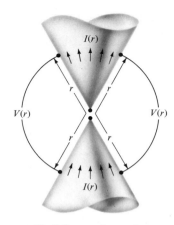

(a) Electric and magnetic fields   (b) Voltages and currents

Figure 8.2   Electric and magnetic fields, and associated voltages and currents, for a biconical antenna.

E-field has only a E_θ component independent of ϕ, reduces to

$$\nabla \times \mathbf{E} = \hat{a}_\phi \frac{1}{r} \frac{\partial}{\partial r} (rE_\theta) = -j\omega\mu(\hat{a}_r H_r + \hat{a}_\theta H_\theta + \hat{a}_\phi H_\phi) \tag{8-2}$$

Since **H** only has an H_ϕ component, necessary to form the TEM mode with E_θ, (8-2) can be written as

$$\frac{1}{r} \frac{\partial}{\partial r} (rE_\theta) = -j\omega\mu H_\phi \tag{8-2a}$$

From Ampere's law we have that

$$\nabla \times \mathbf{H} = -j\omega\varepsilon\mathbf{E} \tag{8-3}$$

which when expanded in spherical coordinates, and assuming only E_θ and H_ϕ components independent of ϕ, reduces to

$$\hat{a}_r \frac{1}{r^2 \sin\theta} \left[\frac{\partial}{\partial\theta} (r\sin\theta H_\phi) \right] - \hat{a}_\theta \frac{1}{r\sin\theta} \left[\frac{\partial}{\partial r} (r\sin\theta H_\phi) \right] = -j\omega\varepsilon(\hat{a}_\theta E_\theta) \tag{8-4}$$

which can also be written as

$$\frac{\partial}{\partial\theta} (r\sin\theta H_\phi) = 0 \tag{8-4a}$$

$$\frac{1}{r\sin\theta} \frac{\partial}{\partial r} (r\sin\theta H_\phi) = -j\omega\varepsilon E_\theta \tag{8-4b}$$

Rewriting (8-4b) as

$$\frac{1}{r} \frac{\partial}{\partial r} (rH_\phi) = -j\omega\varepsilon E_\theta \tag{8-5}$$

and substituting it into (8-2a) we form a differential equation for H_ϕ as

$$-\frac{1}{j\omega\varepsilon r}\frac{\partial}{\partial r}\left[\frac{\partial}{\partial r}(rH_\phi)\right]=-j\omega\mu H_\phi \tag{8-6}$$

or

$$\frac{\partial^2}{\partial r^2}(rH_\phi)=-\omega^2\mu\varepsilon(rH_\phi)=-k^2(rH_\phi) \tag{8-6a}$$

A solution for (8-6a) must be obtained to satisfy (8-4a). To meet the condition of (8-4a), the θ variations of H_ϕ must be of the form

$$H_\phi=\frac{f(r)}{\sin\theta} \tag{8-7}$$

A solution of (8-6a), which also meets the requirements of (8-7) and represents an outward traveling wave, is

$$H_\phi=\frac{H_0}{\sin\theta}\frac{e^{-jkr}}{r} \tag{8-8}$$

where

$$f(r)=H_0\frac{e^{-jkr}}{r} \tag{8-8a}$$

An inward traveling wave is also a solution but does not apply to the infinitely long structure.

Since the field is of TEM mode, the electric field is related to the magnetic field by the intrinsic impedance, and we can write it as

$$E_\theta=\eta H_\phi=\eta\frac{H_0}{\sin\theta}\frac{e^{-jkr}}{r} \tag{8-9}$$

In Figure 8.2(a) we have sketched the electric and magnetic field lines in the space between the two conical structures. The voltage produced between two corresponding points on the cones, a distance r from the origin, is found by

$$V(r)=\int_{\alpha/2}^{\pi-\alpha/2}\mathbf{E}\cdot d\mathbf{l}=\int_{\alpha/2}^{\pi-\alpha/2}(\hat{a}_\theta E_\theta)\cdot(\hat{a}_r r\,d\theta)=\int_{\alpha/2}^{\pi-\alpha/2}E_\theta r\,d\theta \tag{8-10}$$

or by using (8-9)

$$V(r)=\eta H_0 e^{-jkr}\int_{\alpha/2}^{\pi-\alpha/2}\frac{d\theta}{\sin\theta}=\eta H_0 e^{-jkr}\ln\left[\frac{\cot(\alpha/4)}{\tan(\alpha/4)}\right]$$

$$V(r)=2\eta H_0 e^{-jkr}\ln\left[\cot\left(\frac{\alpha}{4}\right)\right] \tag{8-10a}$$

The current on the surface on the cones, a distance r from the origin, is found by using (8-8) as

$$I(r)=\int_0^{2\pi}H_\phi r\sin\theta\,d\phi=H_0 e^{-jkr}\int_0^{2\pi}d\phi=2\pi H_0 e^{-jkr} \tag{8-11}$$

In Figure 8.2(b) we have sketched the voltage and current at a distance r from the origin.

8.2.2 Input Impedance

INFINITE CONES
Using the voltage of (8-10a) and the current of (8-11), we can write the characteristic impedance as

$$Z_c = \frac{V(r)}{I(r)} = \frac{\eta}{\pi} \ln\left[\cot\left(\frac{\alpha}{4}\right)\right] \tag{8-12}$$

Since the characteristic impedance is not a function of the radial distance r, it also represents the input impedance at the antenna feed terminals of the infinite structure. For a free-space medium, (8-12) reduces to

$$\boxed{Z_c = Z_{in} = 120 \ln\left[\cot\left(\frac{\alpha}{4}\right)\right]} \tag{8-12a}$$

which is a pure resistance. For small cone angles

$$Z_{in} = \frac{\eta}{\pi} \ln\left[\cot\left(\frac{\alpha}{4}\right)\right] = \frac{\eta}{\pi} \ln\left[\frac{1}{\tan(\alpha/4)}\right] \simeq \frac{\eta}{\pi} \ln\left(\frac{4}{\alpha}\right) \tag{8-12b}$$

Variations of Z_{in} as a function of the half-cone angle $\alpha/2$ are shown plotted in Figure 8.3(a) for $0° < \alpha/2 \leq 90°$ and in Figure 8.3(b) in an expanded scale for $0° \leq \alpha/2 \leq 2°$. Although the half-cone angle is not very critical in the design, it is usually chosen so that the characteristic impedance of the biconical configuration is nearly the same as that of the transmission line to which it will be attached. Small angle biconical antennas are not very practical but wide-angle configurations ($30° < \alpha/2 < 60°$) are frequently used as broadband antennas.

The radiation resistance of (8-12) can also be obtained by first finding the total radiated power

$$P_{rad} = \oiint_S \mathbf{W}_{av} \cdot d\mathbf{s} = \int_0^{2\pi} \int_{\alpha/2}^{\pi-\alpha/2} \frac{|E|^2}{2\eta} r^2 \sin\theta\, d\theta\, d\phi = \pi\eta|H_0|^2 \int_0^{\alpha/2} \frac{d\theta}{\sin\theta}$$

$$P_{rad} = 2\pi\eta|H_0|^2 \ln\left[\cot\left(\frac{\alpha}{4}\right)\right] \tag{8-13}$$

and by using (8-11) evaluated at $r=0$ we form

$$\boxed{R_r = \frac{2P_{rad}}{[I(o)]^2} = \frac{\eta}{\pi} \ln\left[\cot\left(\frac{\alpha}{4}\right)\right]} \tag{8-14}$$

which is identical to (8-12).

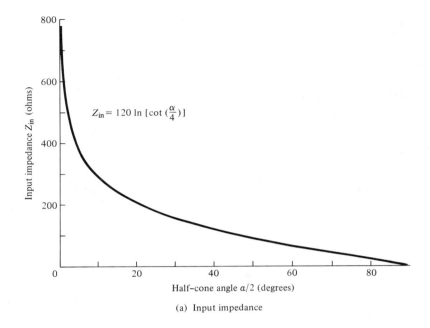

(a) Input impedance

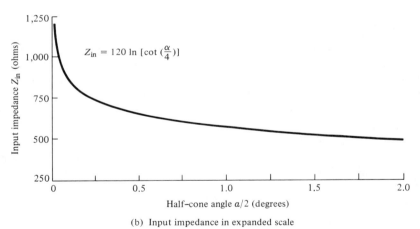

(b) Input impedance in expanded scale

Figure 8.3 Input impedance of an infinitely long biconical antenna radiating in free-space.

FINITE CONES

The input impedance of (8-12) or (8-14) is for an infinitely long structure. To take into account the finite dimensions in determining the input impedance, Schelkunoff [2] has devised an ingenious method where he assumes that for a finite length cone $(r = l/2)$ some of the energy along the surface of the cone is reflected while the remaining is radiated. Near the equator most of the energy is radiated. This can be viewed as a load impedance connected

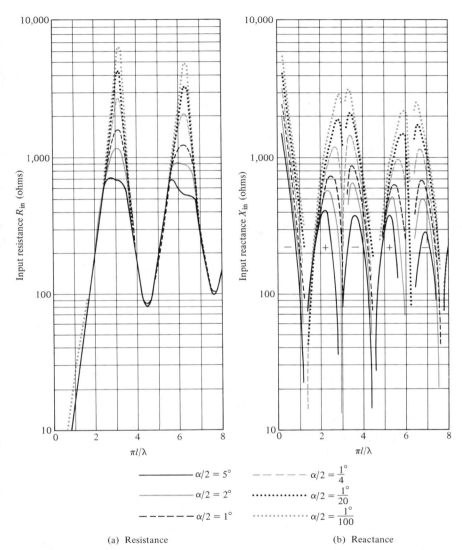

(a) Resistance   (b) Reactance

Figure 8.4 Input impedance (at feed terminals) of finite length biconical antenna. (SOURCE: H. Jasik (ed.), *Antenna Engineering Handbook*, McGraw-Hill, New York, 1961, Chapter 3)

across the ends of the cones. The electrical equivalent is a transmission line of characteristic impedance Z_c terminated in a load impedance Z_L. Computed values [4] for the input resistance and reactance of small angle cones are shown in Figure 8.4. It is apparent that the antenna becomes more broadband (its resistance and reactance variations are less severe) as the cone angle increases.

The biconical antenna represents one of the canonical problems in antenna theory, and its model is well suited for examining general characteristics of dipole-type antennas.

UNIPOLE

Whenever one of the cones is mounted on an infinite plane conductor (i.e., the lower cone is replaced by a ground plane), it forms a unipole and its input impedance is one-half of the two-cone structure. Input impedances for unipoles of various cone angles as a function of the antenna length l have been measured [5]. Radiation patterns of biconical dipoles fed by coaxial lines have been computed by Papas and King [6].

8.3 TRIANGULAR SHEET, BOW-TIE, AND WIRE SIMULATION

Because of their broadband characteristics, biconical antennas have been employed for many years in the VHF and UHF frequency ranges. However, the solid or shell biconical structure is so massive for most frequencies of operation that it is impractical to use. Because of its attractive radiation characteristics, compared to those of other single antennas, realistic variations to its mechanical structure have been sought while retaining as much of the desired electrical features as possible.

Geometrical approximations to the solid or shell conical unipole or biconical antenna are the triangular sheet and bow-tie antennas shown in Figures 8.5(a) and (b), respectively, each fabricated from sheet metal. The triangular sheet has been investigated experimentally by Brown and Woodward [5]. Each of these antennas can also be simulated by a wire along the periphery of its surface which reduces significantly the weight and wind resistance of the structure. The computed input impedances and radiation

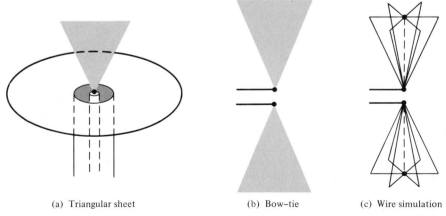

(a) Triangular sheet   (b) Bow–tie   (c) Wire simulation

Figure 8.5 Triangular sheet, bow-tie, and wire simulation of biconical antenna.

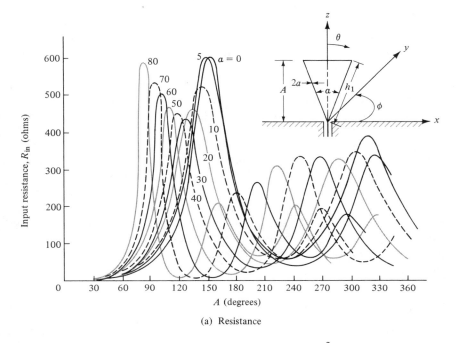

(a) Resistance

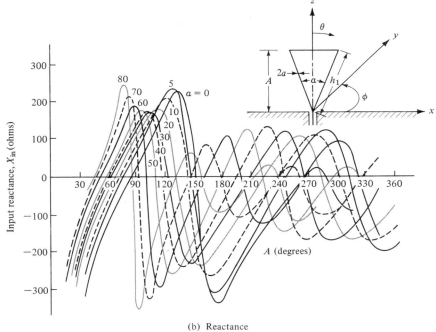

(b) Reactance

Figure 8.6 Computed impedance of wire bow-tie (or wire unipole) as a function of length for various included angles. (SOURCE: C. E. Smith, C. M. Butler, and K. R. Umashankar, "Characteristics of a Wire Biconical Antenna," *Microwave Journal*, pp. 37–40, September 1979)

patterns of wire bow-tie antennas, when mounted above a ground plane, have been computed using the Moment Method [7]. The impedance is shown plotted in Figure 8.6. A comparison of the results of Figure 8.6 with those of reference [5] reveals that the bow-tie antenna does not exhibit as broadband characteristics (i.e., nearly constant resistance and essentially zero reactance over a large frequency range) as the corresponding solid biconical antenna for $30° < \alpha < 90°$. Also for a given flare angle the resistance and reactance of the bow-tie wire structure fluctuate more than for a triangular sheet antenna. Thus the wire bow-tie is very narrowband as compared to the biconical surface of revolution or triangular sheet antenna.

In order to simulate better the attractive surface of revolution of a biconical antenna by low-mass structures, multielement intersecting wire bow-ties were employed as shown in Figure 8.5(c). It has been shown that eight or more intersecting wire-constructed bow-ties can approximate reasonably well the radiation characteristics of a conical body-of-revolution antenna.

8.4 CYLINDRICAL DIPOLE

Another simple and inexpensive antenna which has broadband frequency characteristics is a cylindrical dipole (i.e., a wire of finite diameter and length) of the form shown in Figure 8.7. This geometry can be considered to

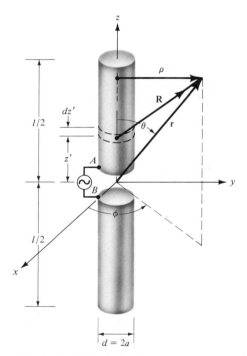

Figure 8.7   Center-fed cylindrical antenna configuration.

be a special form of the biconical antenna when $\alpha = 0°$. A very thorough analysis of the current, impedance, pattern, and other radiation characteristics can be performed using the Moment Method. With that technique the antenna is analyzed in terms of integral formulations of the Hallén and Pocklington type which can be evaluated quite efficiently by the Moment Method. The analytical formulation of the Moment Method has been presented in Section 7.5. In this section we want to present, in summary form, some of its performance characteristics.

8.4.1 Bandwidth

As has been pointed out previously, a very thin linear dipole has very narrowband radiation characteristics. Any small perturbations in the operating frequency will result in large changes in its operational behavior. One method by which its acceptable operational bandwidth can be enlarged will be to decrease the l/d ratio. For a given antenna, this can be accomplished by holding the length the same and increasing the diameter of the wire. For example, an antenna with a $l/d \simeq 5,000$ has an acceptable bandwidth of about 3%, which is a small fraction of the center frequency. An antenna of the same length but with a $l/d \simeq 260$ has a bandwidth of about 30%.

8.4.2 Input Impedance

The input impedance (resistance and reactance) of a very thin dipole of length l and diameter d can be computed using (4-70), (4-79) and (7-30b), (7-33), respectively. As the radius of the wire increases these equations become inaccurate. However, using integral equation analyses such as the Moment of Method of Section 7.5, input impedances can be computed for wires with different l/d ratios. In general, it has been observed that for a given length wire its impedance variations become less sensitive as a function of frequency as the l/d ratio decreases. Thus more broadband characteristics can be obtained by increasing the diameter of a given wire. To demonstrate this, in Figures 8.8(a) and (b) we have plotted, as a function of length, the input resistance and reactance of dipoles with $l/d = 10^4(\Omega = 19.81)$, $50(\Omega = 9.21)$, and $25(\Omega = 6.44)$ where $\Omega = 2\ln(2l/d)$. For $l/d = 10^4$ the values were computed using (4-70) and (7-33) and then transferred to the input terminals by (4-79) and (7-30b), respectively. The others were computed using the Moment Method techniques of Section 7.5.6. It is noted that the variations of each are less pronounced as the l/d ratio decreases, thus providing greater bandwidth.

Measured input resistances and reactances for a wide range of constant l/d ratios have been reported [8]. These curves are for a cylindrical antenna driven by a coaxial cable mounted on a large ground plane on the earth's surface. Thus they represent half of the input impedance of a center-fed cylindrical dipole radiating in free-space. The variations of the antenna's electrical length were obtained by varying the frequency while the length-to-diameter (l/d) ratio was held constant.

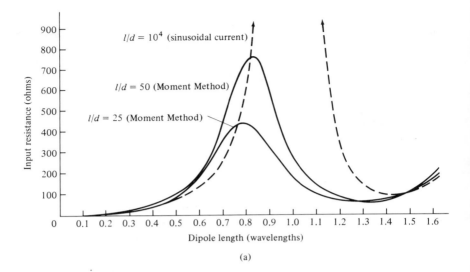

(a)

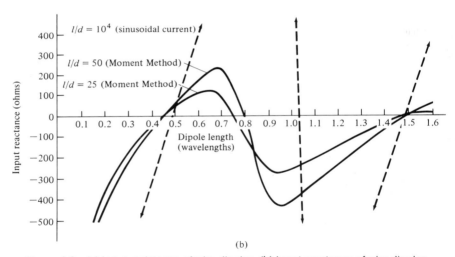

(b)

Figure 8.8   (a) Input resistance of wire dipoles. (b) Input reactance of wire dipoles.

8.4.3   Resonance and Ground Plane Simulation

The imaginary part of the input impedance of a linear dipole can be eliminated by making the total length, l of the wire slightly less than an integral number of half-wavelengths (i.e., l slightly less than $n\lambda/2, n = 1, 2, 3, 4, \ldots$). The amount of reduction in length, is a function of the radius of the wire, and it can be determined for thin wires iteratively using (7-33). At the resonance length, the resistance can then be determined using (4-70).

Table 8.1 CYLINDRICAL DIPOLE RESONANCES

	FIRST RESONANCE	SECOND RESONANCE	THIRD RESONANCE	FOURTH RESONANCE
LENGTH	$0.48\lambda F$	$0.96\lambda F$	$1.44\lambda F$	$1.92\lambda F$
RESISTANCE (ohms)	67	$\dfrac{R_n^{\,2}}{67}$	95	$\dfrac{R_n^{\,2}}{95}$

$$F = \frac{l/2a}{1 + l/2a}; \quad R_n = 150\log_{10}(l/2a)$$

Table 8.2 CYLINDRICAL STUB RESONANCES

	FIRST RESONANCE	SECOND RESONANCE	THIRD RESONANCE	FOURTH RESONANCE
LENGTH	$0.24F'$	$0.48F'$	$0.72F'$	$0.96F'$
RESISTANCE (ohms)	34	$\dfrac{(R_n')^{2}}{34}$	48	$\dfrac{(R_n')^{2}}{48}$

$$F' = \frac{l/a}{1 + l/a}; \quad R_n' = 75\log_{10}(l/a)$$

Empirical equations for approximating the length, impedance, and the order of resonance of the cylindrical dipoles are found in Table 8.1 [9]. R_n is called the natural resistance and represents the geometric mean resistance at an odd resonance and at the next higher even resonance. For a cylindrical stub above a ground plane, as shown in Figure 8.9, the corresponding values are listed in Table 8.2 [9].

To reduce the wind resistance, to simplify the design, and to minimize the costs, a ground plane is often simulated, especially at low frequencies, by crossed wires as shown in Figure 8.9(b). Usually only two crossed wires (four radials) are employed. A larger number of radials results in a better simulation of the ground plane. Ground planes are also simulated by fence wire. The spacing between the wires is usually selected to be equal or smaller than $\lambda/10$. Reflector antennas for UHF educational TV are usually simulated by fence wire.

8.4.4 Radiation Patterns

The theory for the patterns of infinitesimally thin wires was developed in Chapter 4. Although accurate patterns for finite diameter wires can be computed using current distributions obtained by the Moment Method of Section 7.5, the patterns calculated using ideal sinusoidal current distributions, valid for infinitely small diameters, provide a good first-order approximation even for relatively thick cylinders. To illustrate this, in Figure 8.10 we have plotted the relative patterns for $l = 3\lambda/2$ with $l/d = 10^4(\Omega = 19.81)$, $50(\Omega = 9.21)$, $25(\Omega = 6.44)$, and $8.7(\Omega = 5.71)$, where $\Omega = 2\ln(2l/d)$.

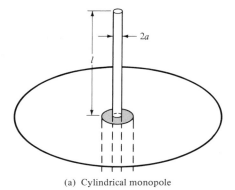

(a) Cylindrical monopole

(b) Wire simulation of ground plane

Figure 8.9 Cylindrical monopole above circular solid and wire-simulated ground planes.

For $l/d = 10^4$ the current distribution was assumed to be purely sinusoidal, as given by (4-56); for the others, the Moment Method techniques of Section 7.5.5 were used. The patterns were computed using the Moment Method formulations outlined in Section 7.5.7. It is noted that the pattern is essentially unaffected by the thickness of the wire in regions of intense radiation. However, as the radius of the wire increases, the minor lobes diminish in intensity and the nulls are replaced by low level radiation. The same characteristics have been observed for other length dipoles such as $l = \lambda/2$, λ and 2λ. The input impedance for the $l = \lambda/2$ and $l = 3\lambda/2$ dipoles, with $l/d = 10^4$, 50, and 25, is equal to

$l = \lambda/2$	$l = 3\lambda/2$	
$Z_{in}(l/d = 10^4) = 73 + j42.5$	$Z_{in}(l/d = 10^4) = 105.49 + j45.54$	
$Z_{in}(l/d = 50) = 85.8 + j54.9$	$Z_{in}(l/d = 50) = 103.3 + j9.2$	(8-15)
$Z_{in}(l/d = 25) = 88.4 + j27.5$	$Z_{in}(l/d = 25) = 106.8 + j4.9$	

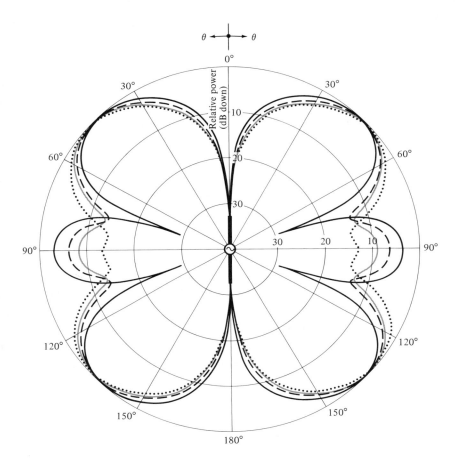

—————— $l/d = \infty$

— — — — — $l/d = 50$

—————— $l/d = 25$

············· $l/d = 8.7$

Figure 8.10 Amplitude radiation patterns of a $3\lambda/2$ dipole of various thicknesses.

8.4.5 Equivalent Radii

The formulations in this section for the current distribution and the input impedance assume that the cross section of the wire is constant and of radius a. An electrical equivalent radius can be obtained for some uniform wires of noncircular cross section. This is demonstrated in Table 8.3 where the actual cross sections and their equivalent radii are illustrated.

Table 8.3 CONDUCTOR GEOMETRICAL SHAPES AND THEIR EQUIVALENT CIRCULAR CYLINDER RADII

GEOMETRICAL SHAPE	ELECTRICAL EQUIVALENT RADIUS
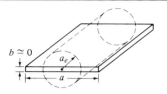	$a_e = 0.25a$
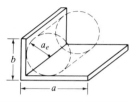	$a_e \simeq 0.2(a+b)$
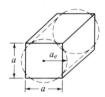	$a_e = 0.59a$
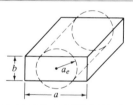 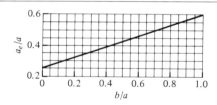	
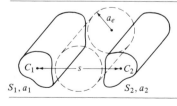	$a_e = \frac{1}{2}(a+b)$
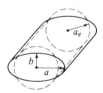	$\ln a_e \simeq \dfrac{1}{(S_1 + S_2)^2}$ $\times [S_1^2 \ln a_1 + S_2^2 \ln a_2 + 2S_1 S_2 \ln s]$ $S_1, S_2 = \text{peripheries of conductors } C_1, C_2$ $a_1, a_2 = \text{equivalent radii of conductors } C_1, C_2$

The equivalent radius concept can be used to obtain the antenna or scattering characteristics of electrically small wires of arbitrary cross sections. It is accomplished by replacing the noncircular cross section wire with a circular wire whose radius is the "equivalent" radius of the noncircular cross section. In electrostatics, the equivalent radius represents the radius of a circular wire whose capacitance is equal to that of the noncircular geometry. This definition can be used at all frequencies provided the wire remains electrically small. The circle with equivalent radius lies between the circles which circumscribe and inscribe the geometry and which together bound the noncircular cross section.

8.4.6 Dielectric Coating

Up to now it has been assumed that the wire antennas are radiating into free-space. The radiation characteristics of a wire antenna (current distribution, far-field pattern, input impedance, bandwidth, radiation efficiency, and effective length) will be affected if the antenna is coated with a thin layer of electrically and magnetically lossless [10] or lossy [11] medium as shown in Figure 8.11. The problem was investigated analytically by the Moment Method and the effects on the radiation characteristics can be

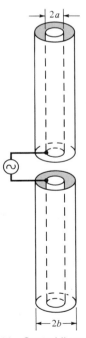

Figure 8.11   Coated linear dipole.

presented by defining the two parameters

$$P = \left(\frac{\dot{\varepsilon}_r - 1}{\dot{\varepsilon}_r} \right) \ln \left(\frac{b}{a} \right) \tag{8-16}$$

$$Q = (\dot{\mu}_r - 1) \ln \left(\frac{b}{a} \right) \tag{8-17}$$

where

$\dot{\varepsilon}_r$ = relative (to the ambient medium) complex permittivity

$\dot{\mu}_r$ = relative (to the ambient medium) complex permeability

a = radius of the conducting wire

$b - a$ = thickness of coating

In general:

1. Increasing the real part of either P or Q
   a. increases the peak input admittance
   b. increases the electrical length (lowers the resonant frequency)
   c. narrows the bandwidth
2. Increasing the imaginary part of P or Q
   a. decreases the peak input admittance
   b. decreases the electrical length (increases the resonant frequency)
   c. increases the bandwidth
   d. accentuates the power dissipated (decreases the radiation efficiency)
   e. accentuates the traveling wave component of the current distribution

Thus the optimum bandwidth of the antenna can be achieved by choosing a lossy dielectric material with maximum imaginary parts of P and Q and minimum real parts. However, doing this decreases the radiation efficiency. In practice, a trade-off between bandwidth and efficiency is usually required. This is not a very efficient technique to broadband the antenna.

8.5 FOLDED DIPOLE

To achieve good directional pattern characteristics and at the same time provide good matching to practical coaxial lines with 50- or 75-ohm characteristic impedances, the length of a single wire element is usually chosen to be $\lambda/4 \leq l < \lambda$. The most widely used dipole is that whose overall length is $l \simeq \lambda/2$, and which has an input impedance of $Z_{in} \simeq 73 + j42.5$ and directivity of $D_0 \simeq 1.643$. In practice, there are other very common transmission lines whose characteristic impedance is much higher than 50 or 75 ohms. For example, a "twin lead" transmission line (usually two parallel wires separated by about $\frac{5}{16}$ in. and embedded in a low-loss plastic material used for support and spacing) is widely used for TV applications and has a characteristic impedance of about 300 ohms.

In order to provide good matching characteristics, variations of the single dipole element must be used. One simple geometry that can achieve this is a folded wire which forms a very thin ($s \ll \lambda$) rectangular loop as shown in Figure 8.12(a). This antenna, when the spacing between the two larger sides is very small (usually $s < 0.05\lambda$), is known as a folded dipole and it serves as a step-up impedance transformer (approximately by a factor of 4 when $l = \lambda/2$) of the single element impedance. Thus when $l = \lambda/2$ and the antenna is resonant, impedances on the order of about 300 ohms can be achieved, and it would be ideal for connections of "twin-lead" transmission lines.

A folded dipole operates basically as an unbalanced transmission line, and it can be analyzed by assuming that its current is decomposed into two distinct modes: a transmission line mode [Figure 8.12(b)] and an antenna mode [Figure 8.12(c)]. This type of an analytic model can be used to predict accurately the input impedance provided the longer parallel wires are close together electrically ($s \ll \lambda$).

To derive an equation for the input impedance, let us refer to the modeling of Figure 8.12. For the transmission line mode of Figure 8.12(b), the input impedance at the terminals $a - b$ or $e - f$, looking toward the shorted ends, is obtained from the impedance transfer equation

$$Z_t = Z_0 \left[\frac{Z_L + jZ_0 \tan(kl')}{Z_0 + jZ_L \tan(kl')} \right]_{\substack{l' = l/2 \\ Z_L = 0}} = jZ_0 \tan \left(k\frac{l}{2} \right) \qquad (8\text{-}18)$$

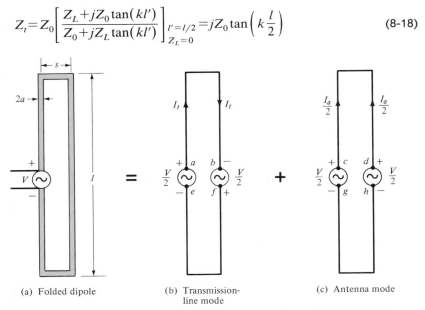

(a) Folded dipole   (b) Transmission-line mode   (c) Antenna mode

Figure 8.12 Folded dipole and its equivalent transmission line and antenna mode models. (SOURCE: G. A. Thiele, E. P. Ekelman, Jr., and L. W. Henderson, "On the Accuracy of the Transmission Line Model for Folded Dipole," *IEEE Trans. Antennas Propag.*, vol. AP-28, No. 5, pp. 700–703, Sept. 1980. © (1980) IEEE)

where Z_0 is the characteristic impedance of a two-wire transmission line

$$Z_0 = \frac{\eta}{\pi} \cosh^{-1}\left(\frac{s/2}{a}\right) = \frac{\eta}{\pi} \ln\left[\frac{s/2 + \sqrt{(s/2)^2 - a^2}}{a}\right] \tag{8-19}$$

which can be approximated for $s/2 \gg a$ by

$$Z_0 = \frac{\eta}{\pi} \ln\left[\frac{s/2 + \sqrt{(s/2)^2 - a^2}}{a}\right] \simeq \frac{\eta}{\pi} \ln\left(\frac{s}{a}\right) = 0.733\eta \log_{10}\left(\frac{s}{a}\right) \tag{8-19a}$$

Since the voltage between the points a and b is $V/2$, and it is applied to a transmission line of length $l/2$, the transmission line current is given by

$$I_t = \frac{V/2}{Z_t} \tag{8-20}$$

For the antenna mode of Figure 8.12(c), the generator points $c-d$ and $g-h$ are each at the same potential and can be connected, without loss of generality, to form a dipole. Each leg of the dipole is formed by a pair of closely spaced wires ($s \ll \lambda$) extending from the feed ($c-d$ or $g-h$) to the shorted end. Thus the current for the antenna mode is given by

$$I_a = \frac{V/2}{Z_d} \tag{8-21}$$

where Z_d is the input impedance of a linear dipole of length l and diameter d computed using (4-70), (4-79), (7-33), and (7-30b). For the configuration of Figure 8.12(c), the radius that is used to compute Z_d for the dipole can be either the half-spacing between the wires ($s/2$) or an equivalent radius a_e. The equivalent radius a_e is related to the actual wire radius a by (from Table 8.1)

$$\ln(a_e) = \tfrac{1}{2}\ln(a) + \tfrac{1}{2}\ln(s) = \ln(a) + \tfrac{1}{2}\ln\left(\frac{s}{a}\right) = \ln\sqrt{as} \tag{8-22}$$

or

$$a_e = \sqrt{as} \tag{8-22a}$$

It should be expected that the equivalent radius would yield the most accurate results.

The total current on the feed leg (left side) of the folded dipole of Figure 8.12(a) is given by

$$I_{in} = I_t + \frac{I_a}{2} = \frac{V}{2Z_t} + \frac{V}{4Z_d} = \frac{V(2Z_d + Z_t)}{4Z_t Z_d} \tag{8-23}$$

and the input impedance at the feed by

$$\boxed{Z_{in} = \frac{V}{I_{in}} = \frac{2Z_t(4Z_d)}{2Z_t + 4Z_d} = \frac{4Z_t Z_d}{2Z_d + Z_t}} \tag{8-24}$$

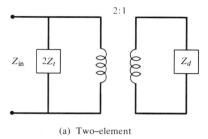

(a) Two-element

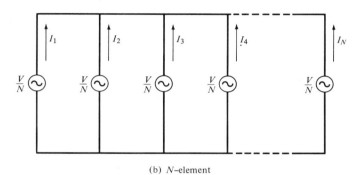

(b) N-element

Figure 8.13 Equivalent circuits for two-element and N-element (with equal radii elements) folded dipoles.

Based on (8-24), the folded dipole behaves as the equivalent of Figure 8.13(a) in which the antenna mode impedance is stepped up by a ratio of four. The transformed impedance is then placed in shunt with twice the impedance of the nonradiating (transmission line) mode to result in the input impedance.

When $l=\lambda/2$, it can be shown that (8-24) reduces to

$$Z_{in}=4Z_d \qquad (8\text{-}25)$$

or that the impedance of the folded dipole is four times greater than that of an isolated dipole of the same length as one of its sides. This is left as an exercise for the reader (Prob. 8.7).

To better understand the impedance transformation of closely spaced conductors (of equal diameter) and forming a multielement folded dipole, let us refer to its equivalent circuit in Figure 8.13(b). For N elements, the equivalent voltage at the center of each conductor is V/N and the current in each is I_n, $n=1,2,3,\ldots,N$. Thus the voltage across the first conductor can be represented by

$$\frac{V}{N}=\sum_{n=1}^{N} I_n Z_{1n} \qquad (8\text{-}26)$$

where Z_{1n} represents the self- or mutual impedance between the first and nth element. Because the elements are closely spaced

$$I_n \simeq I_1 \quad \text{and} \quad Z_{1n} \simeq Z_{11} \tag{8-27}$$

for all values of $n = 1, 2, \ldots, N$. Using (8-27), we can write (8-26) as

$$\frac{V}{N} = \sum_{n=1}^{N} I_n Z_{1n} \simeq I_1 \sum_{n=1}^{N} Z_{1n} \simeq N I_1 Z_{11} \tag{8-28}$$

or

$$\boxed{Z_{\text{in}} = \frac{V}{I_1} \simeq N^2 Z_{11} = N^2 Z_r} \tag{8-28a}$$

since the self-impedance Z_{11} of the first element is the same as its imped-ance Z_r in the absence of the other elements. Hence additional step-up of a single dipole impedance can be obtained by introducing more elements. For a three-element folded dipole with elements of identical diameters and of $l \simeq \lambda/2$, the input impedance would be about nine times greater than that of an isolated element or about 650 ohms. Greater step-up transformations can be obtained by adding more elements; in practice, they are seldom needed. Many other geometrical configurations of a folded dipole can be obtained which would contribute different values of input impedances. Small varia-tions in impedance can be obtained by using elements of slightly different diameters and/or lengths.

To test the validity of the transmission line model for the folded dipole, a number of computations were made [12] and compared with data ob-tained by the Moment Method. In Figures 8.14(a) and (b) the input resistance and reactance for a two-element folded dipole is plotted as a function of l/λ when the diameter of each wire is $d = 2a = 0.001\lambda$ and the spacing between the elements is $s = 0.00613\lambda$. The characteristic impedance of such a transmission line is 300 ohms. The equivalent radius was used in the calculations of Z_d. An excellent agreement is indicated between the results of the transmission line model and the Moment Method. Computa-tions and comparisons for other spacings ($s = 0.0213\lambda$, $Z_0 = 450$ ohms and $s = 0.0742\lambda$, $Z_0 = 600$ ohms) but with elements of the same diameter ($d = 0.001\lambda$) have been made [12]. It has been shown that as the spacing between the wires increased, the results of the transmission line mode began to disagree with those of the Moment Method. For a given spacing, the accuracy for the characteristic impedance, and in turn for the input imped-ance, can be improved by increasing the diameter of the wires. The characteristic impedance of a transmission line, as given by (8-19) or (8-19a), depends not on the spacing but on the spacing-to-diameter (s/d) ratio, which is more accurate for smaller s/d. Computations were also made whereby the equivalent radius was not used. The comparisons of these results indicated larger disagreements, thus concluding the necessity of the equivalent radius, especially for the larger wire-to-wire spacings.

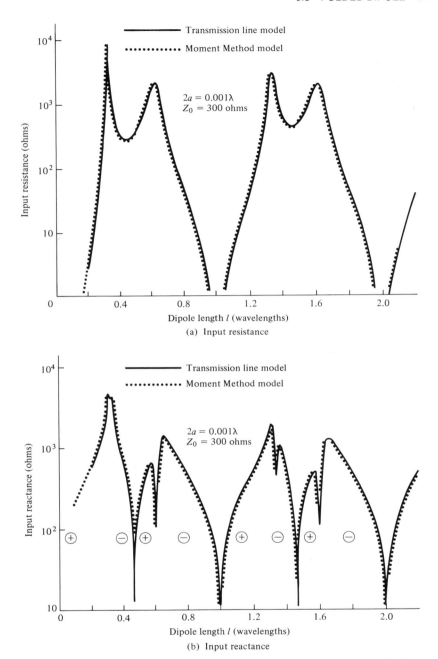

Figure 8.14   Input resistance and reactance of folded dipole. (SOURCE: G. A. Thiele, E. P. Ekelman, Jr., and L. W. Henderson, "On the Accuracy of the Transmission Line Model for Folded Dipole," *IEEE Trans. Antennas Propag.*, vol. AP-28, No. 5, pp. 700–703, Sept. 1980. © (1980) IEEE)

A two-element folded dipole is widely used as feed elements of TV antennas such as Yagi-Uda antennas. Although the impedance of an isolated folded dipole may be around 300 ohms, its value will be somewhat different when it is used as an element in an array or with a reflector. The folded dipole has better bandwidth characteristics than a single dipole of the same size. Its geometrical arrangement tends to behave as a short parallel stub line which attempts to cancel the off resonance reactance of a single dipole. The folded dipole can be thought to have a bandwidth which is the same as that of a single dipole but with an equivalent radius ($a < a_e < s/2$).

8.6 DISCONE AND CONICAL SKIRT MONOPOLE

There are innumerable variations to the basic geometrical configurations of cones and dipoles, some of which have already been discussed, to obtain broad band characteristics. Two other common radiators that meet this characteristic are the conical skirt monopole and the discone antenna [13] shown in Figures 8.15(a) and (b), respectively.

For each antenna, the overall pattern is essentially the same as that of a linear dipole of length $l < \lambda$ (i.e., a solid of revolution formed by the rotation of a figure-eight) whereas in the horizontal (azimuthal) plane it is nearly omnidirectional. The polarization of each is vertical. Each antenna because of its simple mechanical design, ease of installation, and attractive broadband characteristics has wide applications in the VHF (30–300 MHz) and UHF (300 MHz–3 GHz) spectrum for broadcast, television, and communication applications.

The discone antenna is formed by a disk and a cone. The disk is attached to the center conductor of the coaxial feed line, and it is perpendicular to its axis. The cone is connected at its apex to the outer shield of the

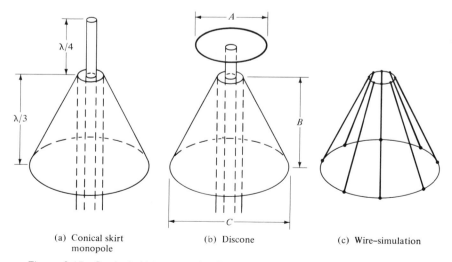

(a) Conical skirt monopole   (b) Discone   (c) Wire–simulation

Figure 8.15 Conical skirt monopole, discone, and wire-simulated cone surface.

Table 8.4 FREQUENCY AND DIMENSIONS OF TWO DESIGNS

FREQUENCY (MHz)	A (cm)	B (cm)	C (cm)
90	45.72	60.96	50.80
200	22.86	31.75	35.56

coaxial line. The geometrical dimensions and the frequency of operation of two designs [13] are shown in Table 8.4.

In general, the impedance and pattern variations of a discone as a function of frequency are much less severe than those of a dipole of fixed length l. The performance of this antenna as a function of frequency is similar to a high-pass filter. Below an effective cutoff frequency it becomes inefficient, and it produces severe standing waves in the feed line. At cutoff, the slant height of the cone is approximately $\lambda/4$.

Measured elevation (vertical) plane radiation patterns from 250 to 650 MHz, at 50-MHz intervals, have been published [13] for a discone with a cutoff frequency of 200 MHz. No major changes in the "figure-eight" shape of the patterns were evident other than at the high-frequency range where the pattern began to turn upward somewhat.

The conical skirt monopole is similar to the discone except that the disk is replaced by a monopole of length usually $\lambda/4$. Its general behavior also resembles that of the discone. Another way to view the conical skirt monopole is with a $\lambda/4$ monopole mounted above a finite ground plane. The plane has been tilted downward to allow more radiation toward and below the horizontal plane.

To reduce the weight and wind resistance of the cone, its solid surface can be simulated by radial wires, as shown in Figure 8.15(c). This is a usual practice in the simulation of finite size ground for monopole antennas. The lengths of the wires used to simulate the ground plane are on the order of about $\lambda/4$ or greater.

8.7 SLEEVE DIPOLE

The radiation patterns of asymmetrically driven wire antennas, with overall length less than a half-wavelength ($l < \lambda/2$), will almost be independent of the point of feed along the wire. However for lengths greater than $\lambda/2$ ($l > \lambda/2$) the current variation along the wire will undergo a phase reversal while maintaining almost sinusoidal amplitude current distribution forced by the boundary conditions at its ends. It would then seem that the input impedance would largely be influenced by the feed point. Even the patterns may be influenced by the point of excitation for antennas with lengths greater than $\lambda/2$.

The input impedance Z_{as} of an asymmetric (off-center) driven dipole is related approximately to the input impedance Z_s at its center by

$$Z_{as} \simeq \frac{Z_s}{\cos^2(k\,\Delta l)} \tag{8-29}$$

where Δl represents the displacement of the feed from the center. Better accuracy can be obtained using more complicated formulas [14].

An antenna that closely resembles an asymmetric dipole and can be analyzed in a similar manner is a sleeve dipole, shown in Figure 8.16(a). This radiator is essentially the same as that of a base-driven monopole above a ground plane. The outer shield of the coaxial line, which is also connected to the ground plane, has been extended a distance l along the axis of the wire to provide mechanical strength, impedance variations, and extended broadband characteristics.

By introducing the outer sleeve, the excitation gap voltage maintained by the feeding transmission line has been moved upward from the conducting plate ($z=0$) to $z=h$. The theory of images yields the equivalent symmetrical structure of Figure 8.16(b) in which two generators maintain each equal voltage at $z=\pm h$.

Because of the linearity of Maxwell's equations, the total current in the system will be equal to the sum of the currents maintained independently by each generator in each of the two asymmetric excited radiators [15] shown in Figure 8.16(c). Thus the antenna can be analyzed as the sum of two asymmetrically fed radiators, ignoring the diameter change in each as in Figure 8.16(d). Since the two structures in Figure 8.16(d) are identical at their feed, the input current is

$$I_{\text{in}} \simeq I_{as}(z=h) + I_{as}(z=-h) \tag{8-30}$$

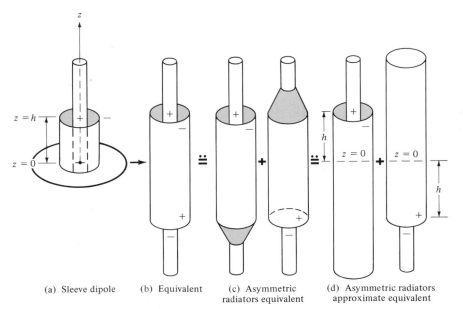

(a) Sleeve dipole   (b) Equivalent   (c) Asymmetric radiators equivalent   (d) Asymmetric radiators approximate equivalent

Figure 8.16   Sleeve dipole and its equivalents. (SOURCE: W. L. Weeks, *Antenna Engineering*, McGraw-Hill, New York, 1968)

where

I_{in} = input current at the feed of the sleeve dipole
[Figure 8.16(a)]

$I_{as}(z=h)$ = current of asymmetric structure at $z=h$
[Figure 8.16(d)]

$I_{as}(z=-h)$ = current of asymmetric structure at $z=-h$
[Figure 8.16(d)]

and the input admittance is

$$Y_{in} = \frac{I_{as}(z=h)+I_{as}(z=-h)}{V_{in}} = \frac{I_{as}(z=h)}{V_{in}}\left[1+\frac{I_{as}(z=-h)}{I_{as}(z=h)}\right]$$

$$= Y_{as}\left[1+\frac{I_{as}(z=-h)}{I_{as}(z=h)}\right] \tag{8-31}$$

where $Y_{as}=1/Z_{as}$ as given by (8-29).

Through a number of computations [15], the frequency response of a sleeve dipole has been shown to be much superior than either that of a half-wavelength or full-wavelength dipole. Also the standing wave inside the feed line can be maintained reasonably constant by the use of a properly designed reactive matching network.

8.8 MATCHING TECHNIQUES

The operation of an antenna system over a frequency range is not completely dependent upon the frequency response of the antenna element itself but rather on the frequency characteristics of the transmission line-antenna element combination. In practice, the characteristic impedance of the transmission line is usually real whereas that of the antenna element is complex. Also the variation of each as a function of frequency is not the same. Thus efficient coupling-matching networks must be designed which attempt to couple-match the characteristics of the two elements over the desired frequency range.

There are many coupling-matching networks that can be used to connect the transmission line to the antenna element and which can be designed to provide acceptable frequency characteristics. Only a limited number will be introduced here.

8.8.1 Stub-Matching

Ideal matching at a given frequency can be accomplished by placing a short- or open-circuited shunt stub a distance s from the transmission line-antenna element connection, as shown in Figure 8.17(a). Assuming a real characteristic impedance, the length s is controlled so as to make the real part of the

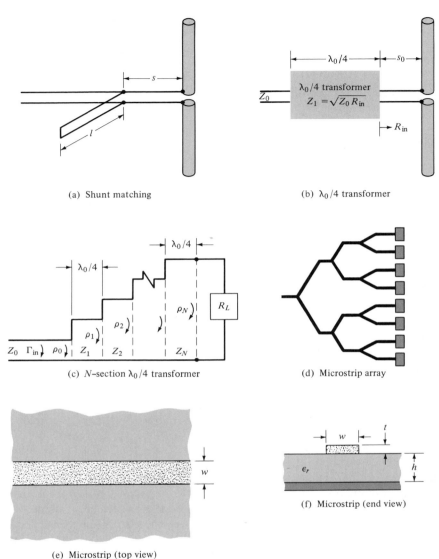

(a) Shunt matching

(b) $\lambda_0/4$ transformer

(c) N–section $\lambda_0/4$ transformer

(d) Microstrip array

(e) Microstrip (top view)

(f) Microstrip (end view)

Figure 8.17   Matching and microstrip techniques.

antenna element impedance equal to the characteristic impedance. The length l of the shunt line is varied until the susceptance of the stub is equal in magnitude but opposite in phase to the line input susceptance at the point of the transmission line-shunt element connection. The matching procedure is illustrated best graphically with the use of a Smith chart. Analytical methods, on which the Smith chart graphical solution is based, can also be used. The short-circuited stub is more practical because an equivalent short can be created by a pin connection in a coaxial cable or a slider in a waveguide. This preserves the overall length of the stub line for matchings which may require longer length stubs.

A single stub with a variable length l cannot always match all antenna (load) impedances. A double-stub arrangement positioned a fixed distance s from the load, with the length of each stub variable and separated by a constant length d, will match a greater range of antenna impedances. However a triple-stub configuration will always match all loads.

An excellent treatment of the analytical and graphical methods for the single-, double-, triple-stub, and other matching techniques is presented by Collin [16]. The higher-order stub arrangements provide more broad and less sensitive matchings (to frequency variations) but are more complex to implement. Usually a compromise is chosen, such as the double-stub.

8.8.2 Quarter-Wavelength Transformer

SINGLE SECTION
Another technique that can be used to match the antenna to the transmission line is to use a $\lambda/4$ transformer. If the impedance of the antenna is real, the transformer is attached directly to the load. However if the antenna impedance is complex, the transformer is placed a distance s_0 away from the antenna, as shown in Figure 8.17(b). The distance s_0 is chosen so that the input impedance toward the load at s_0 is real and designated as R_{in}. To provide a match, the transformer characteristic impedance Z_1 should be $Z_1 = \sqrt{R_{in}Z_0}$, where Z_0 is the characteristic impedance (real) of the input transmission line. The transformer is usually another transmission line with the desired characteristic impedance.

Because the characteristic impedances of most off-the-shelf transmission lines are limited in range and values, the technique is most suitable when used with microstrip transmission lines. In microstrips, the characteristic impedance can be changed by simply varying the width of the center conductor.

MULTIPLE SECTIONS
Matchings which are less sensitive to frequency variations and which provide broader bandwidths require multiple $\lambda/4$ sections. In fact the number and characteristic impedance of each section can be designed so that the reflection coefficient follows, within the desired frequency bandwidth, prescribed variations which are symmetrical about the center frequency. The antenna (load) impedance will again be assumed to be real; if not, the antenna element must be connected to the transformer at a point s_0 along the transmission line where the input impedance is real.

Referring to Figure 8.17(c), the total input reflection coefficient Γ_{in} for an N-section quarter-wavelength transformer with $R_L > Z_0$ can be written approximately as [16]

$$\Gamma_{in}(f) \simeq \rho_0 + \rho_1 e^{-j2\theta} + \rho_2 e^{-j4\theta} + \cdots + \rho_n e^{-j2N\theta}$$

$$= \sum_{n=0}^{N} \rho_n e^{-j2n\theta} \tag{8-32}$$

where

$$\rho_n = \frac{Z_{n+1} - Z_n}{Z_{n+1} + Z_n} \tag{8-32a}$$

$$\theta = k\,\Delta l = \frac{2\pi}{\lambda}\left(\frac{\lambda_0}{4}\right) = \frac{\pi}{2}\left(\frac{f}{f_0}\right) \tag{8-32b}$$

In (8-32), ρ_n represents the reflection coefficient at the junction of two infinite lines with characteristic impedances Z_n and Z_{n+1}, f_0 represents the designed center frequency, and f the operating frequency. Equation (8-32) is valid provided the ρ_n's at each junction are small ($R_L \simeq Z_0$). If $R_L < Z_0$, the ρ_n's should be replaced by $-\rho_n$'s. For a real load impedance, the ρ_n's and Z_n's will also be real.

For a symmetrical transformer ($\rho_0 = \rho_N$, $\rho_1 = \rho_{N-1}$, etc.), (8-32) reduces to

$$\Gamma_{in}(f) \simeq 2e^{-jN\theta}\left[\rho_0 \cos N\theta + \rho_1 \cos(N-2)\theta + \rho_2 \cos(N-4)\theta + \cdots\right] \tag{8-33}$$

The last term in (8-33) should be

$$\rho_{[(N-1)/2]} \cos\theta \qquad \text{for } N = \text{odd integer} \tag{8-33a}$$

$$\tfrac{1}{2}\rho_{(N/2)} \qquad\qquad \text{for } N = \text{even integer} \tag{8-33b}$$

BINOMIAL DESIGN

One technique, used to design an N-section $\lambda/4$ transformer, requires that the input reflection coefficient of (8-32) have maximally flat passband characteristics. For this method, the junction reflection coefficients (ρ_n's) are derived using the binomial expansion. Doing this, we can equate (8-32) to

$$\Gamma_{in}(f) = \sum_{n=0}^{N} \rho_n e^{-j2n\theta} = \frac{Z_L - Z_0}{Z_L + Z_0}\cos^N(\theta)$$

$$= 2^{-N}\frac{R_L - Z_0}{R_L + Z_0}\sum_{n=0}^{N} C_n^N e^{-j2n\theta} \tag{8-34}$$

where

$$C_n^N = \frac{N!}{(N-n)!n!}, \qquad n = 0, 1, 2, \ldots, N \tag{8-34a}$$

From (8-32)

$$\rho_n = 2^{-N} \frac{R_L - Z_0}{R_L + Z_0} C_n^N \tag{8-35}$$

For this type of design, the fractional bandwidth $\Delta f/f_0$ is given by

$$\frac{\Delta f}{f_0} = 2 \frac{(f_0 - f_m)}{f_0} = 2 \left(1 - \frac{f_m}{f_0} \right) = 2 \left(1 - \frac{2}{\pi} \theta_m \right) \tag{8-36}$$

Since

$$\theta_m = \frac{2\pi}{\lambda_m} \left(\frac{\lambda_0}{4} \right) = \frac{\pi}{2} \left(\frac{f_m}{f_0} \right) \tag{8-37}$$

(8-36) reduces to

$$\frac{\Delta f}{f_0} = 2 - \frac{4}{\pi} \cos^{-1} \left[\frac{\rho_m}{(R_L - Z_0)/(R_L + Z_0)} \right]^{1/N} \tag{8-38}$$

where ρ_m is the maximum value of reflection coefficient which can be tolerated within the bandwidth.

The usual design procedure is to specify the

1. load impedance (R_L)
2. input characteristic impedance (Z_0)
3. number of sections (N)
4. maximum tolerable reflection coefficient (ρ_m) [or fractional bandwidth ($\Delta f/f_0$)]

and to find the

1. characteristic impedance of each section
2. fractional bandwidth [or maximum tolerable reflection coefficient (ρ_m)]

To illustrate the principle let us consider an example.

Example 8.1

A linear dipole with an input impedance of $70 + j37$ is to be connected to a 50-ohm line. Design a two-section $\lambda/4$ binomial transformer by specifying the characteristic impedance of each section to match at $f = f_0$ the antenna to the line. If the input impedance (at the point the transformer is connected) is assumed to remain constant as a function of frequency, determine the maximum reflection coefficient and VSWR within a fractional bandwidth of 0.375.

SOLUTION
Since the antenna impedance is not real, the antenna must be connected to the transformer through a transmission line of length s_0. Assuming a 50-ohm characteristic impedance for that section of the transmission line, the input impedance at $s_0 = 0.062\lambda$ is real and equal to 100 ohms. Using (8-34a) and (8-35)

$$\rho_n = 2^{-N} \frac{R_L - Z_0}{R_L + Z_0} C_n^N = 2^{-N} \frac{R_L - Z_0}{R_L + Z_0} \frac{N!}{(N-n)!n!}$$

which for $N = 2$, $R_L = 100$, $Z_0 = 50$

$$n = 0: \quad \rho_0 = \frac{Z_1 - Z_0}{Z_1 + Z_0} = \frac{1}{12} \Rightarrow Z_1 = 1.182 Z_0 = 59.09$$

$$n = 1: \quad \rho_1 = \frac{Z_2 - Z_1}{Z_2 + Z_1} = \frac{1}{6} \Rightarrow Z_2 = 1.399 Z_1 = 82.73$$

For a fractional bandwidth of 0.375 ($\theta_m = 1.276 = 73.12°$) we can write it, using (8-38), as

$$\frac{\Delta f}{f_0} = 0.375 = 2 - \frac{4}{\pi} \cos^{-1} \left[\frac{\rho_m}{(R_L - Z_0)/(R_L + Z_0)} \right]^{1/2}$$

which for $R_L = 100$ and $Z_0 = 50$ gives

$$\rho_m = 0.028$$

The maximum voltage standing wave ratio is

$$VSWR_m = \frac{1 + \rho_m}{1 - \rho_m} = 1.058$$

The magnitude of the reflection coefficient is given by (8-34) as

$$\Gamma_{in} = \rho_{in} = \left| \frac{R_L - Z_0}{R_L + Z_0} \right| \cos^2 \theta = \frac{1}{3} \cos^2 \left[\frac{2\pi}{\lambda} \left(\frac{\lambda_0}{4} \right) \right] = \frac{1}{3} \cos^2 \left[\frac{\pi}{2} \left(\frac{f}{f_0} \right) \right]$$

which is shown plotted in Figure 8.18, and it is compared with the response of a single section $\lambda/4$ transformer.

Microstrip designs are ideally suited for antenna arrays as shown in Figure 8.17(d). In general the characteristic impedance of a microstrip line, whose top and end views are shown in Figures 8.17(e) and (f), is given by [17]

$$Z_c = \frac{87}{\sqrt{\varepsilon_r + 1.41}} \ln \left(\frac{5.98h}{0.8w + t} \right) \qquad \text{for } h < 0.8w \tag{8-39}$$

where

$\varepsilon_r =$ dielectric constant of dielectric substrate
   (board material)
$h =$ distance between center conductor and ground plane

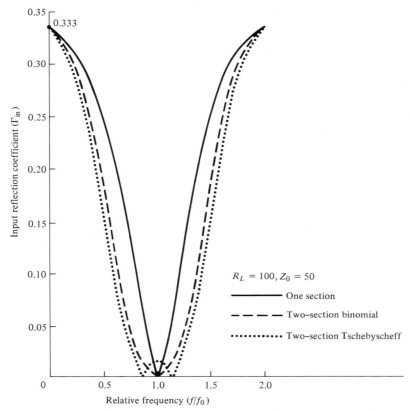

Figure 8.18 Responses of single-section, and two-section binomial and Tschebyscheff quarter-wavelength transformers.

w = width of microstrip center conductor

t = thickness of microstrip center conductor

Thus for constant values of ε_r, h, and t, the characteristic impedance can be changed by simply varying the width (w) of the center conductor.

TSCHEBYSCHEFF DESIGN

The reflection coefficient can be made to vary within the bandwidth in an oscillatory manner and have equal-ripple characteristics. This can be accomplished by making Γ_{in} behave according to a Tschebyscheff polynomial. For the Tschebyscheff design, the equation that corresponds to (8-34) is

$$\Gamma_{in}(f) = e^{-jN\theta} \frac{Z_L - Z_0}{Z_L + Z_0} \frac{T_N(\sec\theta_m \cos\theta)}{T_N(\sec\theta_m)} \tag{8-40}$$

where $T_N(x)$ is the Tschebyscheff polynomial of order N.

The maximum allowable reflection coefficient occurs at the edges of the passband where $\theta = \theta_m$ and $T_N(\sec \theta_m \cos \theta)|_{\theta = \theta_m} = 1$. Thus

$$\rho_m = \left| \frac{Z_L - Z_0}{Z_L + Z_0} \frac{1}{T_N(\sec \theta_m)} \right| \tag{8-41}$$

The first few Tschebyscheff polynomials are given by (6-67). For $z = \sec \theta_m \cos \theta$, the first three polynomials reduce to

$$T_1(\sec \theta_m \cos \theta) = \sec \theta_m \cos \theta$$

$$T_2(\sec \theta_m \cos \theta) = 2(\sec \theta_m \cos \theta)^2 - 1 = \sec^2 \theta_m \cos 2\theta + (\sec^2 \theta_m - 1)$$

$$\tag{8-42}$$

$$T_3(\sec \theta_m \cos \theta) = 4(\sec \theta_m \cos \theta)^3 - 3(\sec \theta_m \cos \theta)$$

$$= \sec^3 \theta_m \cos 3\theta + 3(\sec^3 \theta_m - \sec \theta_m)\cos \theta$$

The remaining details of the analysis are found in [16].

The design of Example 8.1 using a Tschebyscheff transformer is assigned as an exercise to the reader (Prob. 8.11). However its response is shown plotted in Figure 8.18 for comparison.

In general, the multiple sections (either binomial or Tschebyscheff) provide greater bandwidths than a single section. As the number of sections increases the bandwidth also increases. The advantage of the binomial design is that the reflection coefficient values within the bandwidth monotonically decrease from both ends toward the center. Thus the values are always smaller than an acceptable and designed value that occurs at the "skirts" of the bandwidth. For the Tschebyscheff design, the reflection coefficient values within the designed bandwidth are equal or smaller than an acceptable and designed value. The number of times the reflection coefficient reaches the maximum value within the bandwidth is determined by the number of sections. In fact, for an even number of sections the reflection coefficient at the designed center frequency is equal to the maximum allowable value while for an odd number of sections it is zero. For a maximum tolerable reflection coefficient, the N-section Tschebyscheff transformer provides a larger bandwidth than a corresponding N-section binomial design, or for a given bandwidth the maximum tolerable reflection coefficient is smaller for a Tschebyscheff design.

8.8.3 T-Match

Another effective shunt-matching technique is the T-match connection shown in Figure 8.19(a). With this method the dipole of length l and radius a is connected to the transmission line by another dipole of length l' ($l' < l$) and radius a'. The smaller dipole is tapped to the larger one at distances $l'/2$ from the center and the two are separated by a small distance s. The transmission line is connected to the smaller dipole at its center. The

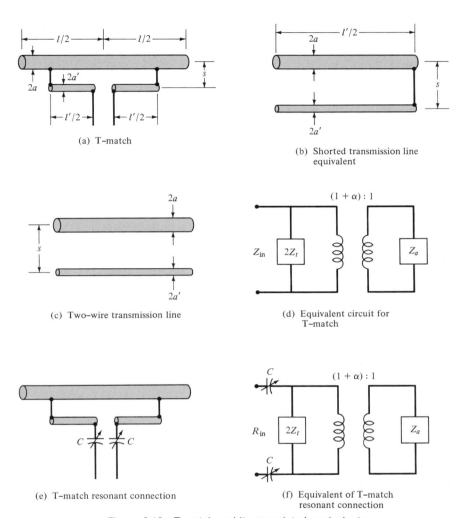

(a) T-match

(b) Shorted transmission line equivalent

(c) Two-wire transmission line

(d) Equivalent circuit for T-match

(e) T-match resonant connection

(f) Equivalent of T-match resonant connection

Figure 8.19 T-match and its associated equivalents.

T-match connection is a general form of a folded dipole since the two legs are usually not of the same length or diameter. Since the T-match is a symmetrical and balanced system, it is well suited for use with parallel-conductor transmission lines such as the "twin lead." Coaxial lines, which are unsymmetrical and unbalanced lines, should be connected to dipoles using the gamma match.

The design procedure for the T-match is developed similarly to that of the folded dipole. The T-match is also modeled by transmission line and antenna modes, as shown in Figure 8.12 for the folded dipole. The total current at the input terminals is divided between the two conductors in a way that depends on the relative radii of the two conductors and the spacing between them. Since the two conductors are not in general of the same radius, the antenna mode current division is not unity. Instead a current division factor is assigned which also applies to the voltage division of the transmission line mode.

Instead of including all of the details of the analysis, only the steps that are applicable to a T-match design will be included.

DESIGN

1. Calculate the current division factor α by

$$\alpha = \frac{\cosh^{-1}\left(\dfrac{v^2-u^2+1}{2v}\right)}{\cosh^{-1}\left(\dfrac{v^2+u^2-1}{2vu}\right)} \simeq \frac{\ln(v)}{\ln(v)-\ln(u)} \tag{8-43}$$

$$u=\frac{a}{a'} \tag{8-43a}$$

$$v=\frac{s}{a'} \tag{8-43b}$$

2. From Table 8.1, the "equivalent" radius of the two-wire arrangement can be written as

$$\ln(a_e) \simeq \frac{1}{(a'+a)^2}[a'^2\ln a' + a^2\ln a + 2a'a\ln s] \tag{8-44}$$

since $S_1 = 2\pi a'$, $S_2 = 2\pi a$. It can be shown that (8-44) reduces to

$$\ln(a_e) \simeq \ln a' + \frac{1}{(1+u)^2}(u^2\ln u + 2u\ln v) \tag{8-44a}$$

3. Calculate the impedance at the input terminals for the transmission line mode [i.e., two-wire shorted transmission line of length $l'/2$ with radii a, a' and separation s shown in Figure 8.19(b)]

$$Z_t = jZ_0\tan\left(k\frac{l'}{2}\right) \tag{8-45}$$

where

$$Z_0 = 60\cosh^{-1}\left(\frac{s^2-a^2-a'^2}{2aa'}\right) \simeq 276\log_{10}\left(\frac{s}{\sqrt{aa'}}\right) \tag{8-45a}$$

Z_0 is the characteristic impedance of the two-wire transmission line with radii a, a' and separation s, as shown in Figure 8.19(c).

4. The total input impedance, which is a combination of the antenna (radiating) and the transmission (nonradiating) modes, can be written as

$$\boxed{Z_{in} = R_{in} + jX_{in} = \frac{2Z_t[(1+\alpha)^2 Z_a]}{2Z_t + (1+\alpha)^2 Z_a}} \tag{8-46}$$

and the input admittance as

$$Y_{in} = \frac{1}{Z_{in}} = \frac{Y_a}{(1+\alpha)^2} + \frac{1}{2Z_t} \qquad (8\text{-}47)$$

$Z_a = 1/Y_a$ is the center point free-space input impedance of the antenna in the absence of the T-match connection.

Based upon (8-46) or (8-47), the T-match behaves as the equivalent circuit of Figure 8.19(d) in which the antenna impedance is stepped up by a ratio of $1+\alpha$, and it is placed in shunt with twice the impedance of the nonradiating mode (transmission line) to result in the input impedance. When the current division factor is unity ($\alpha=1$), the T-match equivalent of Figure 8.19(d) reduces to that of Figure 8.13(a) for the folded dipole.

For $l' \simeq \lambda/2$, the transmission line impedance Z_t is much greater than $(1+\alpha)^2 Z_a$ and the input impedance of (8-46) reduces to

$$Z_{in} \simeq (1+\alpha)^2 Z_a \qquad (8\text{-}48)$$

For two equal radii conductors, the current division factor is unity and (8-48) becomes

$$Z_{in} \simeq 4Z_a \qquad (8\text{-}49)$$

a relation obtained previously.

The impedance of (8-46) is generally complex. Because each of the lengths ($l'/2$) of the T-match rods are usually selected to be very small (0.03 to 0.06λ), Z_{in} is inductive. To eliminate the reactance (resonate the antenna) at a given center frequency and keep a balanced system, two variable series capacitors are usually used, as shown in Figure 8.19(e). The value of each capacitor is selected so that Z_{in} of (8-46) is equal to $R_{in}(Z_{in}=R_{in})$. To accomplish this

$$C = 2C_{in} = \frac{1}{\pi f X_{in}} \qquad (8\text{-}50)$$

where f is the center frequency, and C_{in} is the series combination of the two C capacitors. The resonant circuit equivalent is shown in Figure 8.19(f).

The T-match connection of 8.19(e) is used not only to resonate the circuit, but also to make the total input impedance equal to the characteristic impedance of the feed transmission line. This is accomplished by properly selecting the values of $l'/2$ and C (s is not usually varied because the impedance is not very sensitive to it). In most cases a trial and error procedure is followed. An orderly graphical method using the Smith chart is usually more convenient, and it is demonstrated in the following section for the gamma match.

8.8.4 Gamma Match

Frequently dipole antennas are fed by coaxial cables which are unbalanced transmission lines. A convenient method to connect the dipole or other antennas (Yagi-Uda, log-periodic, etc.) to 50- or 75-ohm "coaxs" and to obtain a match is to use the gamma match arrangement shown in Figure 8.20. This arrangement is equivalent to half of the T-match, and it also requires a capacitor in series with the gamma rod. The equivalent is shown in Figure 8.20(b), and its input impedance is equal to

$$Z_{in} = -jX_c + \frac{Z_g\left[(1+\alpha)^2 Z_a\right]}{2Z_g + (1+\alpha)^2 Z_a} \tag{8-51}$$

where Z_a is the center point free-space impedance of the antenna in the absence of the gamma match connection. The second term of (8-51) is similar in form to that of (8-46).

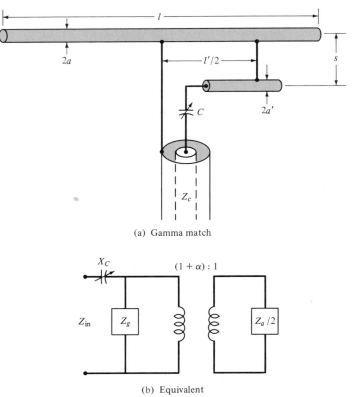

(a) Gamma match

(b) Equivalent

Figure 8.20 Gamma match and its equivalent.

The usual problem encountered is that the length of the wire antenna (l) and the characteristic impedance of the feed coax (Z_c) are known. What is required are the values of the radii a and a', the length $l'/2$, and the capacitance C which will achieve a match. Since the arrangement is similar to the T-match or folded dipole, its analysis is based on the same theory.

To accomplish the match, a graphical design technique, which is different from that reported in [18] and [19], will be demonstrated. This procedure utilizes the Smith chart, and it is based on the equivalent of Figure 8.20(b). A purely mathematical procedure is also available [20], but it will not be included here.

Because the input impedance is not very sensitive to a, a', and s, the usual procedure is to select their values and keep them fixed. The parameters that are usually varied are then $l'/2$ and C. In practice $l'/2$ is varied by simply using a sliding clamp to perform the shorted connection at the end of the gamma rod.

The graphical design method assumes that $l'/2$ is given, and C that resonates the circuit is found. If the input resistance is not equal to the characteristic impedance Z_c of the feed line, another value of $l'/2$ is selected, and the procedure is repeated until $R_{in} = Z_c$. The graphical method is suggestive as to how the length $l'/2$ should be changed (smaller or larger) to accomplish the match.

DESIGN

1. Determine the current division factor α by using (8-43)–(8-43b).
2. Find the free-space impedance (in the absence of the gamma match) of the driven element at the center point. Designate it as Z_a.
3. Divide Z_a by 2 and multiply it by the step-up ratio $(1+\alpha)^2$. Designate the result as Z_2.

$$Z_2 = R_2 + jX_2 = (1+\alpha)^2 \frac{Z_a}{2} \qquad (8\text{-}52)$$

4. Determine the characteristic impedance Z_0 of the transmission line formed by the driven element and the gamma rod using (8-45a).
5. Normalize Z_2 of (8-52) by Z_0 and designate it as z_2.

$$z_2 = \frac{Z_2}{Z_0} = \frac{R_2 + jX_2}{Z_0} = r_2 + jx_2 \qquad (8\text{-}53)$$

and enter on the Smith chart.

6. Invert z_2 of (8-53) and obtain its equivalent admittance $y_2 = g_2 + jb_2$. On the Smith chart this is accomplished by moving z_2 diagonally across from its position.
7. In shunt with the admittance y_2 from step 6 is an inductive reactance due to the short-circuited transmission line formed by the antenna element and the gamma rod. This is an inductive reactance

because the length of the gamma rod is very small (usually 0.03 to 0.06λ), but always much smaller than $\lambda/2$. Obtain its normalized value using

$$z_g = j\tan\left(k\frac{l'}{2}\right) \tag{8-54}$$

and place on Smith chart. The impedance z_g of (8-54) can also be obtained by using exclusively the Smith chart. You begin by locating the short-circuited load at $Z_s = 0 + j0$. Then you move this point a distance $l'/2$ toward the generator, along the outside perimeter of the Smith chart. The new point represents the normalized impedance z_g of (8-54).

8. Invert the impedance from step 7 (z_g) to obtain its equivalent admittance $y_g = g_g + jb_g$. On the Smith chart this is accomplished by moving z_g diagonally across from its position.

9. Add the two parallel admittances (from steps 6 and 8) to obtain the total input admittance at the gamma feed. That is,

$$y_{in} = y_2 + y_g = (g_2 + g_g) + j(b_2 + b_g) \tag{8-55}$$

and locate it on the Smith chart.

10. Invert the normalized input admittance y_{in} of (8-55) to obtain the equivalent normalized input impedance

$$z_{in} = r_{in} + jx_{in} \tag{8-56}$$

11. Obtain the unnormalized input impedance by multiplying z_{in} by Z_0.

$$Z_{in} = R_{in} + jX_{in} = Z_0 z_{in} \tag{8-57}$$

12. Select the capacitor C so that its reactance is equal in magnitude to X_{in}.

$$\frac{1}{\omega C} = \frac{1}{2\pi f_0 C} = X_{in} \tag{8-58}$$

If all the dimensions were chosen properly for a perfect match, the real part R_{in} of (8-57) should be equal to Z_c. If not, change one or more of the dimensions (usually the length of the rod) and repeat the procedure until $R_{in} = Z_c$. Practically the capacitor C is chosen to be variable so adjustments can be made with ease to obtain the best possible match.

Example 8.2

The driven element impedance of a 20-m ($f \approx 15$ MHz; see Appendix VIII) Yagi-Uda antenna has a free-space impedance at its center point of $25 - j25$ ohms [19]. It is desired to connect it to a 50-ohm coaxial line using a gamma match. The driven element and the gamma rod are made of tubing with diameters of $1.9 \times 10^{-3}\lambda$ (1.5 in.) and $6.35 \times 10^{-4}\lambda$ (0.5 in.), respectively. The center-to-center separation between the driven element and the rod is $3.81 \times 10^{-3}\lambda$ (3 in.). Determine the required capacitance to achieve a match. Begin with a gamma rod length of 0.036λ (28.35 in.).

SOLUTION

1. Using (8-43)–(8-43b)

$$u = \frac{a}{a'} = 3 \qquad v = \frac{s}{a'} = \frac{3.81}{0.3175} = 12$$

$$\alpha \simeq \frac{\ln(12)}{\ln(12) - \ln(3)} = 1.79$$

and the step-up ratio

$$(1+\alpha)^2 = (1+1.79)^2 = 7.78$$

2. $Z_a = 25 - j25$, as given.
3. Using (8-52)

$$Z_2 = (1+1.79)^2 \frac{25 - j25}{2} = 97.25(1-j)$$

4. $Z_0 = 276 \log_{10}\left[\dfrac{2(3.81)}{\sqrt{0.95(0.3175)}}\right] = 315.25 \simeq 315$

5. $z_2 = \dfrac{97.25}{315}(1-j) = 0.31(1-j)$

6. On the Smith chart in Figure 8.21 locate z_2 and invert it. It leads to

$$y_2 = \frac{1}{z_2} = 1.6(1+j)$$

7. On the Smith chart locate $z_s = 0 + j0$ and advance it toward the generator a distance 0.036λ to obtain

$$z_g = 0 + j0.23$$

8. From the Smith chart

$$y_g = \frac{1}{z_g} = -j4.35$$

9. Add y_2 and y_g

$$y_{in} = y_2 + y_g = 1.6 - j2.75$$

which is located on the Smith chart.

10. Inverting y_{in} on the Smith chart gives

$$z_{in} = 0.16 + j0.28$$

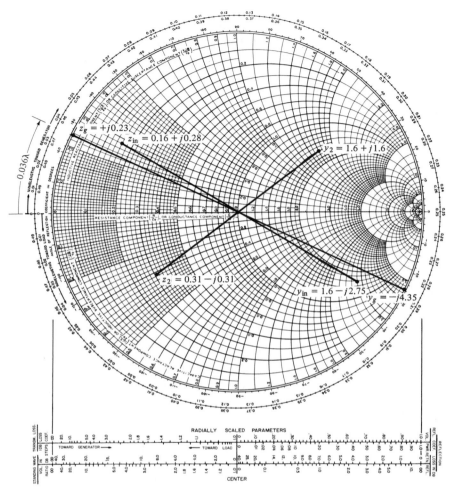

Figure 8.21 Smith chart for Example 8.2. Copyright renewal 1976 by P. H. Smith, Murray Hill, N.J.

11. Unnormalizing z_{in} by $Z_0 = 315$ reduces it to

$$Z_{in} = 50.4 + j88.2$$

12. The capacitance should be

$$C = \frac{1}{2\pi f_0(88.2)} = \frac{1}{2\pi(15 \times 10^6)(88.2)}$$

$$= 120.3 \times 10^{-12} \simeq 120 \text{ pF}$$

Since $R_{in} = 50.4$ is not exactly equal to $Z_0 = 50$, one of the physical dimensions (usually the length of the rod) can be changed slightly and then the process can be repeated. However in this case they are so close that for practical purposes this is not required.

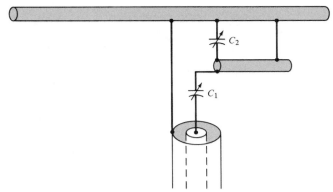

Figure 8.22   Omega match arrangement.

8.8.5   Omega Match

A slightly modified version of the gamma match is the omega match shown in Figure 8.22. The only difference between the two is that in addition to the series capacitor C_1 there is one in shunt C_2 which can aid in achieving the match. Usually the presence of C_2 makes it possible to use a shorter rod or makes it easier to match a resonant driven element. The primary function of C_2 will be to change y_{in} in step 9 of the design procedure so that when it is inverted its unnormalized real part is equal to the characteristic impedance of the input transmission line. This will possibly eliminate the need of changing the dimensions of the matching elements, if a match is not achieved.

8.8.6   Baluns and Transformers

A twin-lead transmission line (two parallel-conductor line) is a symmetrical line whereas a coaxial cable is inherently unbalanced. Because the inner and outer (inside and outside parts of it) conductors of the coax are not coupled to the antenna in the same way, they provide the unbalance. The result is a net current flow to ground on the outside part of the outer conductor. This is shown in Figure 8.23(a) where an electrical equivalent is also indicated. The amount of current flow I_3 on the outside surface of the outer conductor is determined by the impedance Z_g from the outer shield to ground. If Z_g can be made very large, I_3 can be reduced significantly. Devices that can be used to balance inherently unbalanced systems, by canceling or choking the outside current, are known as *baluns* (*bal*ance to *un*balance).

   One type of a balun is that shown in Figure 8.23(b), referred to usually as a bazooka balun. Mechanically it requires that a $\lambda/4$ in length metal sleeve, and shorted at its one end, encapsulates the coaxial line. Electrically the input impedance at the open end of this $\lambda/4$ shorted transmission line, which is equivalent to Z_g, will be very large (ideally infinity). Thus the current I_3 will be choked, if not completely eliminated, and the system will be nearly balanced.

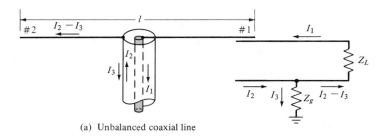

(a) Unbalanced coaxial line

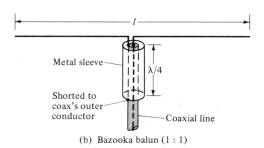

(b) Bazooka balun (1 : 1)

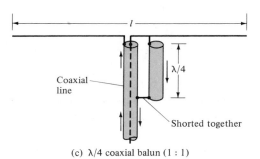

(c) λ/4 coaxial balun (1 : 1)

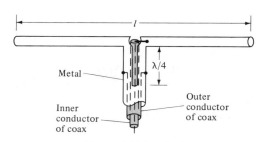

(d) Coaxial balun (1 : 1)

Figure 8.23 Balun configurations.

Another type of a balun is that shown in Figure 8.23(c). It requires that one end of a $\lambda/4$ section of a transmission line be connected to the outside shield of the main coaxial line while the other is connected to the side of the dipole which is attached to the center conductor. This balun is used to cancel the flow of I_3. The operation of it can be explained as follows: In Figure 8.23(a) the voltages between each side of the dipole and the ground are equal in magnitude but $180°$ out of phase, thus producing a current flow on the outside of the coaxial line. If the two currents I_1 and I_2 were equal in magnitude, I_3 would be zero. Since terminal #2 of the dipole is connected directly to the shield of the coax while terminal #1 is weakly coupled to it, it produces a much larger current I_2. Thus there is relatively little cancellation in the two currents.

The two currents, I_1 and I_2, can be made equal in magnitude if the center conductor of the coax is connected directly to the outer shield. If this connection was made directly at the antenna terminals, the transmission line and the antenna would be short-circuited, thus eliminating any radiation. However, the indirect parallel conductor connection of Figure 8.23(c) provides the desired current cancelation without eliminating the radiation. The current flow on the outer shield of the main line is canceled at the bottom end of the $\lambda/4$ section (where the two join together) by the equal in magnitude, but opposite in phase, current in the $\lambda/4$ section of the auxiliary line. Ideally then there is no current flow in the outer surface of the outer shield of the remaining part of the main coaxial line. It should be stated that the parallel auxiliary line need not be made $\lambda/4$ in length to achieve the balance. It is made $\lambda/4$ to prevent the upsetting of the normal operation of the antenna.

A compact construction of the balun in Figure 8.23(c) is that in Figure 8.23(d). The outside metal sleeve is split and a portion of it is removed on opposite sides. The remaining opposite parts of the outer sleeve represent electrically the two shorted $\lambda/4$ parallel transmission lines of Figure 8.23(c). All of the baluns shown in Figure 8.23 are narrowband devices.

Devices can be constructed which provide not only balancing but also step up impedance transformations. One such device is the $\lambda/4$ coaxial balun, with a $4:1$ impedance transformation, of Figure 8.24(a). The U-shaped section of the coaxial line must be $\lambda/2$ long [21].

Because all the baluns-impedance transformers that were discussed so far are narrowband devices, the bandwidth can be increased by employing ferrite cores in their construction [22]. Two such designs, one a $4:1$ or $1:4$ transformer and the other a $1:1$ balun, are shown in Figures 8.24(b) and (c). The ferrite core has a tendency to maintain high impedance levels over a wide frequency range [23]. A good design and construction can provide bandwidths of 8 or even 10 to 1. Coil coaxial baluns, constructed by coiling the coaxial line itself to form a balun [23], can provide bandwidths of 2 or 3 to 1.

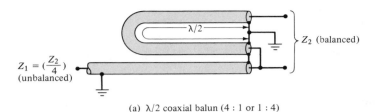

$$Z_1 = \left(\frac{Z_2}{4}\right)$$
(unbalanced)

Z_2 (balanced)

(a) $\lambda/2$ coaxial balun (4 : 1 or 1 : 4)

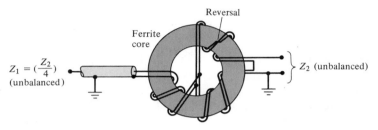

$$Z_1 = \left(\frac{Z_2}{4}\right)$$
(unbalanced)

Z_2 (unbalanced)

(b) Ferrite core transformer (4 : 1 or 1 : 4)

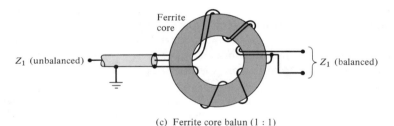

Z_1 (unbalanced)

Z_1 (balanced)

(c) Ferrite core balun (1 : 1)

Figure 8.24   Balun and ferrite core transformers.

References

1. M. Abraham, "Die electrischen Schwingungen um einen stabformingen Leiter, behandelt nach der Maxwelleschen Theorie," *Ann. Physik*, 66, pp. 435–472, 1898.
2. S. A. Schelkunoff, *Electromagnetic Waves*, Van Nostrand, New York, 1943, Chapter 11.
3. E. Hallén, "Theoretical Investigations into the Transmitting and Receiving Qualities of Antennae," *Nova Acta Regiae Soc. Sci. Upsaliensis*, Ser. IV, 11, No. 4, 1–44, 1938.
4. H. Jasik (ed.), *Antenna Engineering Handbook*, McGraw-Hill, New York, 1961, Chapter 3.
5. G. H. Brown and O. M. Woodward, Jr., "Experimentally Determined Radiation Characteristics of Conical and Triangular Antennas," *RCA Rev.*, vol. 13, No. 4, p. 425, Dec. 1952.

6. C. H. Papas and R. King, "Radiation from Wide-Angle Conical Antennas Fed by a Coaxial Line," *Proc. IRE*, vol. 39, p. 1269, November 1949.

7. C. E. Smith, C. M. Butler, and K. R. Umashankar, "Characteristics of a Wire Biconical Antenna," *Microwave Journal*, pp. 37–40, September 1979.

8. G. H. Brown and O. M. Woodward, Jr., "Experimentally Determined Impedance Characteristics of Cylindrical Antennas," *Proc. IRE*, vol. 33, pp. 257–262, 1945.

9. J. D. Kraus, *Antennas*, McGraw-Hill, New York, 1950, pp. 276–278.

10. J. H. Richmond and E. H. Newman, "Dielectric Coated Wire Antennas," *Radio Science*, vol. 11, No. 1, pp. 13–20, January 1976.

11. J. Y. P. Lee and K. G. Balmain, "Wire Antennas Coated with Magnetically and Electrically Lossy Material," *Radio Science*, vol. 14, No. 3, pp. 437–445, May-June 1979.

12. G. A. Thiele, E. P. Ekelman, Jr., and L. W. Henderson, "On the Accuracy of the Transmission Line Model for Folded Dipole," *IEEE Trans. Antennas Propag.*, vol. AP-28, No. 5, pp. 700–703, Sept. 1980.

13. A. G. Kandoian, "Three New Antenna Types and Their Applications," *Proc. IRE*, 34, pp. 70W–75W, February 1946.

14. R. W. King and T. T. Wu, "The Cylindrical Antenna with Arbitrary Driving Point," *IEEE Trans. Antennas Propag.*, AP-13, pp. 710–718, September 1965.

15. R. W. P. King, "Asymmetric Driven Antennas and the Sleeve Dipole," *Proc. IRE*, pp. 1154–1164, October 1950.

16. R. E. Collin, *Foundations for Microwave Engineering*, McGraw-Hill, New York, 1966, Chapter 5, pp. 203–258.

17. S. Y. Liao, *Microwave Devices and Circuits*, Prentice-Hall, Englewood Cliffs, New Jersey, 1980, pp. 418–422.

18. D. J. Healey, III, "An Examination of the Gamma Match," *QST*, pp. 11–15, April 1969.

19. *The ARRL Antenna Book*, American Radio Relay League, Inc., Newington, Conn., 1974, pp. 118–121.

20. H. T. Tolles, "How To Design Gamma-Matching Networks," *Ham Radio*, pp. 46–55, May 1973.

21. O. M. Woodward, Jr., "Balance Measurements on Balun Transformers," *Electronics*, vol. 26, No. 9, September 1953, pp. 188–191.

22. C. L. Ruthroff, "Some Broad-Band Transformers," *Proc. IRE*, vol. 47, August 1959, pp. 1337–1342.

23. W. L. Weeks, *Antenna Engineering*, McGraw-Hill, New York, 1968, pp. 161–180.

PROBLEMS

8.1. A 300-ohm "twin-lead" transmission line is attached to a biconical antenna.
  (a) Determine the cone angle that will match the line to an infinite length biconical antenna.
  (b) For the cone angle of part (a), determine the two smallest cone lengths that will resonate the antenna.
  (c) For the cone angle and cone lengths from part (b), what is the input VSWR?

8.2. Determine the first two resonant lengths, and the corresponding diameters and input resistances, for dipoles with $l/d = 25$, 50, and 10^4 using
   (a) the data in Figures 8.8(a) and 8.8(b)
   (b) Table 8.1

8.3. Design a resonant cylindrical stub monopole of length l, diameter d, and l/d of 50. Find the length (in λ), diameter (in λ), and the input resistance (in ohms) at the first four resonances.

8.4. A linear dipole of $l/d = 25$, 50, and 10^4 is attached to a 50-ohm line. Determine the VSWR of each l/d when
   (a) $l = \lambda/2$
   (b) $l = \lambda$
   (c) $l = 3\lambda/2$

8.5. Find the equivalent circular radius a_e for a
   (a) very thin flat plate of width $\lambda/10$
   (b) square wire with sides of $\lambda/10$
   (c) rectangular wire with sides of $\lambda/10$ and $\lambda/100$
   (d) elliptical wire with major and minor axes of $\lambda/10$ and $\lambda/20$
   (e) twin-lead transmission line with wire radii of 1.466×10^{-2} cm and separation of 0.8 cm

8.6. Compute the characteristic impedance of a two-wire transmission line with wire diameter of $d = 10^{-3}\lambda$ and center-to-center spacings of
   (a) $6.13 \times 10^{-3}\lambda$
   (b) $2.13 \times 10^{-2}\lambda$
   (c) $7.42 \times 10^{-2}\lambda$

8.7. Show that the input impedance of a two-element folded dipole of $l = \lambda/2$ is four times greater than that of an isolated element of the same length.

8.8. Design a two-element folded dipole with wire diameter of $10^{-3}\lambda$ and center-to-center spacing of $6.13 \times 10^{-3}\lambda$.
   (a) Determine its shortest length for resonance.
   (b) Compute the VSWR at the first resonance when it is attached to a 300-ohm line.

8.9. A two-element folded dipole of identical wires has an $l/d = 500$ and a center-to-center spacing of $6.13 \times 10^{-3}\lambda$ between the wires. Compute the
   (a) approximate length of a single wire at its first resonance
   (b) diameter of the wire at the first resonance
   (c) characteristic impedance of the folded dipole transmission line
   (d) input impedance of the transmission line mode model
   (e) input impedance of the folded dipole using as the radius of the antenna mode (1) the radius of the wire a, (2) the equivalent radius a_e of the wires, (3) half of the center-to-center spacing ($s/2$). Compare the results.

8.10. A $\lambda/2$ dipole is fed asymmetrically at a distance of $\lambda/8$ from one of its ends. Determine its input impedance using (8-29). Compare its value with that obtained using the impedance transfer method of Section 4.5.5.

8.11. Repeat the design of Example 8.1 using a Tschebyscheff transformer.

8.12. Repeat the design of Example 8.1 for a three-section
   (a) binomial transfer
   (b) Tschebyscheff transformer

8.13. Verify (8-44) from the expressions listed in Table 8.3.

8.14. The free-space impedance at the center point of the driven element of a 15-MHz Yagi-Uda array is $25 - j25$. Assuming the diameters of the wires of a T-match are $1.9 \times 10^{-3}\lambda(3.8$ cm) and $6.35 \times 10^{-4}\lambda(1.27$ cm), the center-to-center spacing between the wires is $7.62 \times 10^{-3}\lambda(15.24$ cm), and the length $l'/2$ of each T-match rod is $0.0285\lambda(57$ cm), find the
   (a) input impedance of the T-match
   (b) input capacitance C_{in} that will resonate the antenna
   (c) capacitance C that must be used in each leg to resonate the antenna

8.15. The input impedance of a 145.4-MHz Yagi-Uda antenna is $14 + j3$. Design a gamma match using diameters of 0.9525 cm (for the antenna) and 0.2052 cm (for the rod), and center-to-center spacing between the wires of 1.5316 cm. The match is for a 50-ohm input coaxial line. Find the shortest gamma rod length and the required capacitance. First, do the problem analytically. The design must be such that the real part of the designed input impedance is *within 1 ohm* of the required 50 ohms. Second, check your answers with the Smith chart.

8.16. Repeat Problem 8.15 for an input impedance of $14 - j3$.

8.17. A $\lambda/4$ monopole is mounted on a ground plane and has an input impedance of $34 + j17$ at $f = 145.4$ MHz. Design a gamma match to match the monopole to a 50-ohm coaxial line. The wire diameters are identical (0.9525 cm) and the center-to-center spacing is 3.1496 cm. Find the required capacitance and the shortest gamma rod length. First, do the problem analytically. The design must be such that the real part of the designed input impedance is *within 1 ohm* of the required 50 ohms. Second, check your answers with the Smith chart.

8.18. A T-match is connected to the antennas of Problems 8.15 and 8.16. Assuming that the wire diameters and lengths for each leg of the T-match are those derived for each gamma match, find the
   (a) input impedance of the T-match
   (b) capacitance C that must be connected in each leg to make the antenna system resonant

8.19. Repeat Problem 8.18 but select the lengths $l'/2$ of the T-match rods so that the input resistance is 300 ohms. Use diameters of 0.1026 cm (for the rod), 0.9525 cm (for the antenna), and center-to-center spacing of 0.7658 cm. This connection is ideal for use with a 300-ohm "twin-lead" line.

Chapter 9
Traveling Wave
and Broadband Antennas

9.1 INTRODUCTION

In the previous chapters we have presented the details of classical methods that are used to analyze the radiation characteristics of some of the simplest and most common forms of antennas (i.e., infinitely thin linear and circular wires, broadband dipoles and arrays). In practice there is a myriad of antenna configurations, and it would be almost impossible to consider all of them in this book. In addition, many of these antennas have bizzare types of geometries and it would be almost impractical, if not even impossible, to investigate each in detail. However, the general performance behavior of some of them will be presented in this chapter with a minimum of analytical formulations. Today, comprehensive analytical formulations are available for most of them, but they would require so much space that it would be impractical to include them in this book.

9.2 TRAVELING WAVE ANTENNAS

In Chapter 4, center-fed linear wire antennas were discussed whose amplitude current distribution was

1. constant for infinitesimal dipoles ($l \leq \lambda/50$)
2. linear (triangular) for short dipoles ($\lambda/50 < l \leq \lambda/10$)
3. sinusoidal for long dipoles ($l > \lambda/10$)

In all cases the phase distribution was assumed to be constant. The sinusoidal current distribution of long open-ended linear antennas is a standing wave constructed by two waves of equal amplitude and 180° phase difference at the open-end traveling in opposite directions along its length.

The voltage distribution has also a standing wave pattern except that it has maxima (loops) at the end of the line instead of nulls (nodes) as the current. In each pattern, the maxima and minima repeat every integral number of half-wavelengths. There is also a $\lambda/4$ spacing between a null and a maximum in each of the wave patterns. The current and voltage distributions on open-ended wire antennas are similar to the standing wave patterns on open-ended transmission lines. Linear antennas that exhibit current and voltage standing wave patterns formed by reflections from the open end of the wire are referred to as *standing wave* or *resonant* antennas.

Antennas can be designed which have traveling wave (uniform) patterns in current and voltage. This can be achieved by properly terminating the antenna wire so that the reflections are minimized if not completely eliminated. An example of such an antenna is a long wire that runs approximately horizontal to the earth, as shown in Figure 9.1. The input terminals consist of the ground and one end of the wire. This configuration is known as *Beverage or wave antenna*. There are many other configurations of traveling wave antennas. In general, all antennas whose current and voltage distributions can be represented by one or more traveling waves, usually in the same direction, are referred to as *traveling wave* or *nonresonant* antennas. A progressive phase pattern is usually associated with the current and voltage distributions.

Standing wave antennas, such as the dipole, can be analyzed as traveling wave antennas with waves propagating in opposite directions. Besides the long wire antenna there are many examples of traveling wave antennas such as dielectric rod (polyrod), helix, and various surface wave antennas. Aperture antennas, such as reflectors and horns, can also be treated as traveling wave antennas. In addition, arrays of closely spaced radiators (usually less than $\lambda/2$ apart) can also be analyzed as traveling wave antennas by approximating their current or field distribution by a continuous traveling wave. Yagi-Uda, log-periodic, and slots and holes in a waveguide are some examples of discrete-element traveling wave antennas. In general a traveling wave antenna is usually one that is associated with radiation from a continuous source. An excellent book on traveling wave antennas is one by C. H. Walter [1].

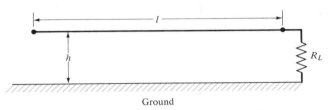

Figure 9.1 Beverage antenna configuration.

A traveling wave may be classified as a *slow* wave if its phase velocity v_p ($v_p = \omega/k$, ω =wave angular frequency, k =wave phase constant) is equal or smaller than the velocity of light c in free-space ($v_p/c \leq 1$). A fast wave is one whose phase velocity is greater than the speed of light ($v_p/c > 1$).

In general, there are two types of traveling wave antennas. One is the *surface wave* antenna defined as "an antenna which radiates power flow from discontinuities in the structure that interrupt a bound wave on the antenna surface."[*] A surface wave antenna is, in general, a slow wave structure whose phase velocity of the traveling wave is equal to or less than the speed of light in free-space ($v_p/c \leq 1$).

For slow wave structures radiation takes place only at nonuniformities, curvatures, and discontinuities. Discontinuities can be either discrete or distributed. One type of discrete discontinuity on a surface wave antenna is a transmission line terminated in an unmatched load. A distributed surface wave antenna can be analyzed in terms of the variation of the amplitude and phase of the current along its structure. In general, power flows parallel to the structure, except when losses are present, and for plane structures the fields decay exponentially away from the antenna. Most of the surface-wave antennas are endfire or near-endfire radiators. Practical configurations include line, planar surface, curved, and modulated structures.

Another traveling wave antenna is a *leaky-wave* antenna defined as "an antenna that couples power in small increments per unit length, either continuously or discretely, from a traveling wave structure to free-space."[†] Leaky-wave antennas continuously lose energy due to radiation. The fields decay along the structure in the direction of wave travel and increase in others. Most of them are fast wave structures.

9.2.1 Long Wire

An example of a slow wave traveling antenna is a long wire, as shown in Figure 9.2. An antenna is usually classified as a *long* wire antenna if it is a straight conductor with a length from one to many wavelengths. A long wire antenna has the distinction of being the first traveling wave antenna.

If the traveling wave is unattenuated along its structure, the current distribution can be represented by

$$I = \hat{a}_z I(z')e^{-jk_z z'} = \hat{a}_z I_0 e^{-jk_z z'} \tag{9-1}$$

where $I(z') = I_0$ is assumed to be constant and k_z is the phase constant of the wave traveling along the structure. Using techniques outlined and used

---

[*]"IEEE Standard Definitions of Terms for Antennas" (IEEE Std 145-1973), *IEEE Trans. Antennas and Propag.*, vol. AP-22, No. 1, January 1974.
[†] Ibid.

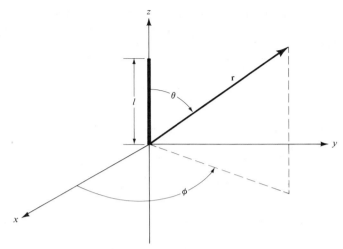

Figure 9.2 Long wire antenna.

in Chapter 4, it can be easily shown that in the far-field

$$E_r \simeq E_\phi = H_r = H_\theta = 0 \tag{9-2a}$$

$$E_\theta \simeq j\eta \frac{klI_0 e^{-jkr}}{4\pi r} e^{-j(kl/2)(K-\cos\theta)} \sin\theta \frac{\sin[(kl/2)(\cos\theta-K)]}{(kl/2)(\cos\theta-K)} \tag{9-2b}$$

$$H_\phi \simeq \frac{E_\theta}{\eta} \tag{9-2c}$$

where K is used to represent the ratio of the phase constant of the wave along the transmission line (k_z) to that of free-space (k), or

$$K = \frac{k_z}{k} = \frac{\lambda}{\lambda_g} \tag{9-3}$$

λ_g = wavelength of the wave along the transmission line

For $k_z = k$ ($K = 1$) the time-average power density can be written as

$$\mathbf{W}_{av} = \mathbf{W}_{rad} = \hat{a}_r \eta \frac{|I_0|^2}{8\pi^2 r^2} \frac{\sin^2\theta}{(\cos\theta-1)^2} \sin^2\left[\frac{kl}{2}(\cos\theta-1)\right] \tag{9-4}$$

which reduces to

$$\mathbf{W}_{av} = \mathbf{W}_{rad} = \hat{a}_r \eta \frac{|I_0|^2}{8\pi^2 r^2} \cot^2\left(\frac{\theta}{2}\right) \sin^2\left[\frac{kl}{2}(\cos\theta-1)\right] \tag{9-5}$$

From (9-5) it is evident that the power distribution of a wire antenna of length l is a multilobe pattern whose number of lobes depend upon its length. Assuming that l is very large such that the variations in the sine function of (9-5) are more rapid than those of the cotangent, the peaks of the lobes occur approximately when

$$\sin^2\left[\frac{kl}{2}(\cos\theta-1)\right]_{\theta=\theta_m}=1 \tag{9-6}$$

or

$$\frac{kl}{2}(\cos\theta_m-1)=\pm\left(\frac{2m+1}{2}\right)\pi, \qquad m=0,1,2,3,\ldots \tag{9-6a}$$

The angles where the peaks occur are given by

$$\theta_m=\cos^{-1}\left[1\pm\frac{\lambda}{2l}(2m+1)\right], \qquad m=0,1,2,3,\ldots \tag{9-7}$$

The angle where the maximum of the major lobe occurs is given by $m=0$ (or $2m+1=1$). As l becomes very large ($l\gg\lambda$) the angle of the maximum of the major lobe approaches zero degrees and the structure becomes a near endfire array.

In finding the values of the maxima, the variations of the cotangent term in (9-5) were assumed to be negligible (as compared to those of the sine term). If the effects of the cotangent term were to be included, then the values of the $2m+1$ term in (9-7) should be

$$2m+1=0.742,\ 2.93,\ 4.96,\ 6.97,\ 8.99,\ 11,\ 13,\ldots \tag{9-8}$$

(instead of $1,3,5,7,9,\ldots$) for the first, second, third, and so forth maxima. The approximate values approach those of the exact for the higher order lobes.

In a similar manner, the nulls of the pattern can be found and occur when

$$\sin^2\left[\frac{kl}{2}(\cos\theta-1)\right]_{\theta=\theta_n}=0 \tag{9-9}$$

or

$$\frac{kl}{2}(\cos\theta_n-1)=\pm n\pi, \qquad n=1,2,3,4,\ldots \tag{9-9a}$$

The angles where the nulls occur are given by

$$\theta_n=\cos^{-1}\left(1\pm n\frac{\lambda}{l}\right), \qquad n=1,2,3,4,\ldots \tag{9-10}$$

for the first, second, third, and so forth nulls.

The total radiated power can be found by integrating (9-5) over a closed sphere of radius r and reduces to

$$P_{\text{rad}}=\oiint\limits_S \mathbf{W}_{\text{rad}}\cdot d\mathbf{s}=\frac{\eta}{4\pi}|I_0|^2\left[1.415+\ln\left(\frac{kl}{\pi}\right)-C_i(2kl)+\frac{\sin(2kl)}{2kl}\right] \tag{9-11}$$

where $C_i(x)$ is the cosine integral of (4-68a). The radiation resistance is then found to be

$$R_r = \frac{2P_{rad}}{|I_0|^2} = \frac{\eta}{2\pi}\left[1.415 + \ln\left(\frac{kl}{\pi}\right) - C_i(2kl) + \frac{\sin(2kl)}{2kl}\right] \qquad (9\text{-}12)$$

Using (9-5) and (9-11) the directivity can be written as

$$D_0 = \frac{4\pi U_{max}}{P_{rad}} = \frac{2\cot^2\left[\frac{1}{2}\cos^{-1}\left(1 - \frac{0.371\lambda}{l}\right)\right]}{1.415 + \ln\left(\frac{2l}{\lambda}\right) - C_i(2kl) = \frac{\sin(2kl)}{2kl}} \qquad (9\text{-}13)$$

To verify some of the derivations, in Figure 9.3(a) we have plotted the patterns for a long wire with $l=5\lambda$ and $l=10\lambda$. The lobe near the axis of the wire in the direction of travel is the largest. The magnitudes of the other lobes decrease progressively, with an envelope proportional to $\cot^2(\theta/2)$, toward the other direction. This type of an antenna can be used when it is desired to radiate or receive predominately from one direction.

The radiation in the other direction is suppressed by reducing, if not completely eliminating, the current reflected from the end of the wire. This is accomplished by increasing the diameter of the wire or more successfully by properly terminating it to the ground, as shown in Figure 9.1. Ideally a complete elimination of the reflections (perfect match) can only be accomplished if the antenna is elevated only at small heights (compared to the wavelength) above the ground, and it is terminated by a resistive load. The value of the load resistor, to achieve the impedance match, is equal to the characteristic impedance of the wire near the ground (which is found using image theory). For a wire with diameter d and height h above the ground, an approximate value of the termination resistance can be obtained from

$$R_L = 138\log_{10}\left(4\frac{h}{d}\right) \qquad (9\text{-}14)$$

To achieve a reflection-free termination, the load resistor can be adjusted about this value until there is no standing wave on the antenna wire.

If the antenna is not properly terminated, reflected waves traveling in the opposite direction will result and form with the incident waves a standing wave pattern. Such antennas were treated in detail in Chapter 4. The radiation pattern for a $l=5\lambda$ antenna with two opposite traveling waves is shown in Figure 9.3(b) where it is compared with that of one traveling wave.

In all of the above, it was assumed that the antenna was lossless and thin enough to be represented by a current line source radiating in free-space. Wire, radiation, and ground losses will all affect the radiation characteristics

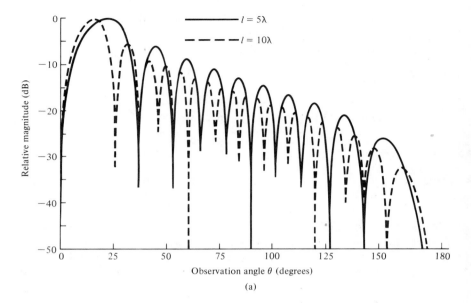

(a)

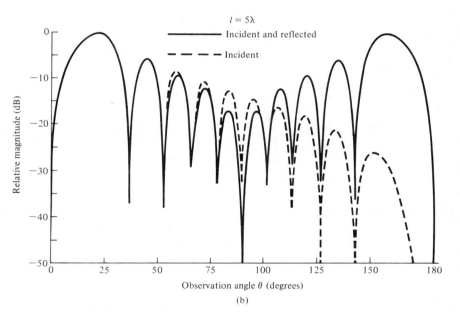

(b)

Figure 9.3   (a) Radiation amplitude patterns for matched long wire antennas.
(b) Radiation patterns for matched (incident) and unmatched (incident and reflected)
long wire antennas.

of the antenna. The contributions of the ground in the formation of the total pattern can be taken into account by introducing an image source a distance h (h=height of antenna above the ground) below the interface, as was done in Section 4.7. The height h of the antenna above the ground must be chosen so that the reflected wave (or wave from the image), which includes the phase due to reflection, is in phase with the direct wave at the angles of desired maximum radiation.

A long wire antenna is linearly polarized, and it is always parallel to the plane formed by the wire and radial vector from the center of the wire to the observation point. The direction of the linear polarization is not the same in all parts of the pattern, but it is perpendicular to the radial vector (and parallel to the vector formed by it and the wire). Thus the wire antenna of Figure 9.1, when its height above the ground is small compared to the wavelength and its main beam is near the ground, is not an effective element for horizontal polarization. Instead it is usually used to transmit or receive waves that have an appreciable vector component in the vertical plane. This is what is known as a Beverage antenna which is used more as a receiving rather than a transmitting element because of its poor radiation efficiency due to power absorbed in the load resistor.

Long wire antennas (both resonant and nonresonant) are very simple, economical, and effective directional antennas with many uses for transmitting and receiving waves in the MF (300 KHz–3 MHz) and HF (3–30 MHz) ranges.

9.2.2 V Antenna

For some applications a single long wire antenna is not very practical because (1) its directivity may be low, (2) its side lobes may be high, and (3) its main beam is inclined at an angle, which is controlled by its length. These and other drawbacks of single long wire antennas can be overcome by utilizing an array of wires.

One very practical array of long wires is the V antenna formed by using two wires each with one of its ends connected to a feed line as shown in Figure 9.4(a). In most applications, the plane formed by the legs of the V is parallel to the ground leading to a horizontal V array whose principal polarization is parallel to the ground and the plane of the V. Because of increased sidelobes, the directivity of linear dipoles begins to diminish for lengths greater than about 1.25λ, as shown in Figure 4.10. However by adjusting the included angle of a V dipole, its directivity can be made greater and its side lobes smaller than those of a corresponding linear dipole. Designs for maximum directivity usually require smaller included angles for longer V's.

Most V antennas are symmetrical ($\theta_1=\theta_2=\theta_0$ and $l_1=l_2=l$). Also V antennas can be designed to have unidirectional or bidirectional radiation patterns, as shown in Figures 9.4(b) and (c), respectively. To achieve the

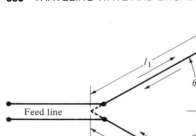

(a) V antenna

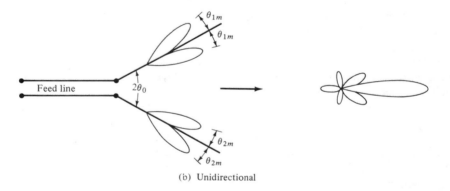

(b) Unidirectional

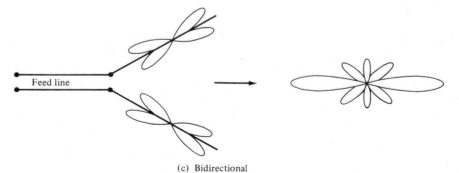

(c) Bidirectional

Figure 9.4 Unidirectional and bidirectional V antennas.

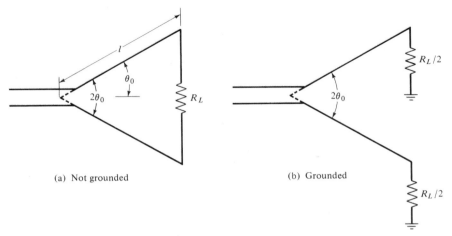

(a) Not grounded   (b) Grounded

Figure 9.5 Terminated V antennas.

unidirectional characteristics, the wires of the V antenna must by nonresonant which can be accomplished by minimizing if not completely eliminating reflections from the ends of the wire. The reflected waves can be reduced
by making the inclined wires of the V relatively thick. In theory, the
reflections can even be eliminated by properly terminating the open ends of
the V leading to a purely traveling wave antenna. One way of terminating
the V antenna will be to attach a load, usually a resistor equal in value to
the open-end characteristic impedance of the V-wire transmission line, as
shown in Figure 9.5(a). The terminating resistance can also be divided in
half and each half connected to the ground leading to the termination of
Figure 9.5(b).

The patterns of the individual wires of the V antenna are conical in
form and are inclined at an angle from their corresponding axes. The angle
of inclination is determined by the length of each wire. For the patterns of
each leg of a symmetrical V antenna to add in the direction of the line
bisecting the angle of the V and to form one major lobe, the total included
angle $2\theta_0$ of the V should be equal to $2\theta_m$, which is twice the angle that the
cone of maximum radiation of each wire makes with its axis. If the total
included angle of the V is greater than $2\theta_m$ ($2\theta_0 > 2\theta_m$) the main lobe is split
into two distinct beams. However if $2\theta_0 < 2\theta_m$, then the maximum of the
single major lobe is still along the plane that bisects the V but it is tilted
upward from the plane of the V. This may be a desired designed characteristic when the antenna is required to transmit waves upward toward the
ionosphere for optimum reflection or to receive signals reflected downward
by the ionosphere.

For a symmetrical V antenna with legs each of length l, there is an
optimum included angle which leads to the largest directivity. Design data

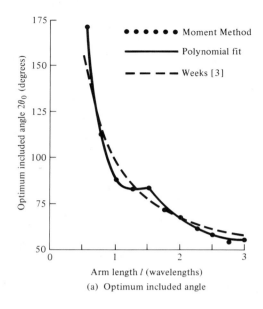

(a) Optimum included angle

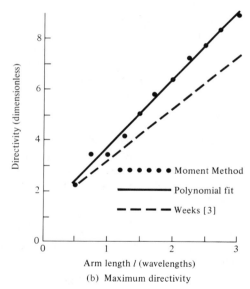

(b) Maximum directivity

Figure 9.6 Optimum included angle for maximum directivity as a function of arm length for V dipoles. (SOURCE: G. A. Thiele and E. P. Ekelman, Jr., "Design Formulas for Vee Dipoles," *IEEE Trans. Antennas Propag.*, vol. AP-28, pp. 588–590, July 1980. © (1980) IEEE)

for optimum included angles of V dipoles were computed [2] using Moment Method techniques and are shown in Figure 9.6(a). The corresponding directivities are shown in Figure 9.6(b). In each figure the dots ($\cdot$) represent values computed using the Moment Method while the solid curves represent second- or third-order polynomials fitted through the computed data. The polynomials for optimum included angles and maximum directivities are given by

$$2\theta_0 = \begin{cases} -149.3\left(\frac{l}{\lambda}\right)^3 + 603.4\left(\frac{l}{\lambda}\right)^2 - 809.5\left(\frac{l}{\lambda}\right) + 443.6 & \text{(9-15a)} \\ \quad \text{for } 0.5 \leq l/\lambda \leq 1.5 \\ 13.39\left(\frac{l}{\lambda}\right)^2 - 78.27\left(\frac{l}{\lambda}\right) + 169.77 & \text{(9-15b)} \\ \quad \text{for } 1.5 \leq l/\lambda \leq 3 \end{cases}$$

$$D_0 = 2.94\left(\frac{l}{\lambda}\right) + 1.15 \qquad \text{for } 0.5 \leq l/\lambda \leq 3 \tag{9-16}$$

The dashed curves represent data obtained from empirical formulas [3]. The corresponding input impedances of the V's are slightly smaller than those of straight dipoles.

Another form of a V antenna is shown in the insert of Figure 9.7(a). The V is formed by a monopole wire, bent at an angle over a ground plane, and by its image shown dashed. The included angle of the V as well as the length can be used to tune the antenna. For included angles greater than $120°$ ($2\theta_0 > 120°$), the antenna exhibits primarily vertical polarization with radiation patterns almost identical to those of straight dipoles. As the included angle becomes smaller than about $120°$, a horizontally polarized field component is excited which tends to fill the pattern toward the horizontal direction, making it a very attractive communication antenna for aircraft. The computed impedance of the ground plane and free-space V configurations obtained by the Moment Method [4] is shown plotted in Figure 9.7(a).

Another practical form of a dipole antenna, particularly useful for airplane or ground-plane applications, is the $90°$ bent wire configuration of Figure 9.7(b). The computed impedance of the antenna, obtained also by the Moment Method [4], is shown plotted in Figure 9.7(b). This antenna can be tuned by adjusting its perpendicular and parallel lengths h_1 and h_2. The radiation pattern in the plane of the antenna is nearly omnidirectional for $h_1 \leq 0.1\lambda$. For $h > 0.1\lambda$ the pattern approaches that of vertical $\lambda/2$ dipole.

9.2.3 Rhombic Antenna

Two V antennas can be connected at their open ends to form a diamond or rhombic antenna, as shown in Figure 9.8(a). The antenna is usually

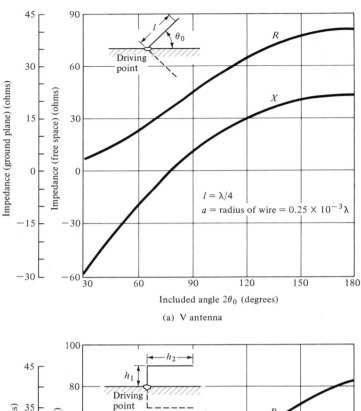

(a) V antenna

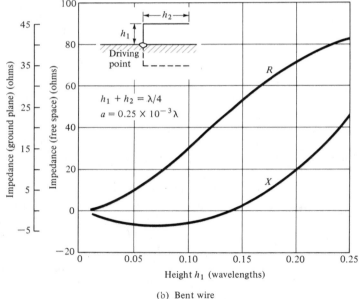

(b) Bent wire

Figure 9.7 Computed impedance ($R + jX$) of V and bent wire antennas above ground. (SOURCE: D. G. Fink (ed.), *Electronics Engineer's Handbook*, Chapter 18 (by W. F. Croswell), McGraw-Hill, New York, 1975)

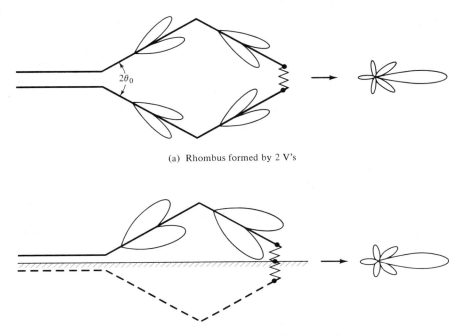

(a) Rhombus formed by 2 V's

(b) Rhombus formed by inverted V over ground

Figure 9.8 Rhombic antenna configurations.

terminated at one end in a resistor, usually about 800 ohms, in order to reduce if not eliminate reflections. The other end is used to feed the antenna. Another configuration of a rhombus is that of Figure 9.8(b) which is formed by an inverted V and its image (shown dashed). The inverted V is connected to the ground through a resistor. As with the V antennas, the pattern of rhombic antennas can be controlled by varying the element lengths, angles between elements, and the plane of the rhombus. Rhombic antennas are usually preferred over V's for nonresonant and unidirectional pattern applications because they are less difficult to terminate. Additional directivity and reduction in side lobes can be obtained by stacking, vertically or horizontally, a number of rhombic and/or V antennas to form arrays.

9.3 BROADBAND ANTENNAS

In Chapter 8 broadband dipole antennas were discussed. There are numerous other antenna designs which exhibit greater broadband characteristics than those of the dipoles. Some of these antenna can also provide circular polarization, a desired extra feature for many applications. In this section we want to discuss briefly some of the most popular broadband antennas.

9.3.1 Helical Antenna

Another basic, simple, and practical configuration of an electromagnetic radiator is that of a conducting wire wound in the form of a screw thread forming a helix as shown in Figure 9.9. In most cases the helix is used with a ground plane. In addition, the helix is usually connected to the center conductor of a coaxial transmission line at the feed point with the outer conductor of the line attached to the ground plane.

The geometrical configuration of a helix consists usually of N turns, diameter D and spacing S between each turn. The total length of the antenna is $L=NS$ while the total length of the wire is $L_n=NL_0=N\sqrt{S^2+C^2}$ where $L_0=\sqrt{S^2+C^2}$ is the length of the wire between each turn and $C=\pi D$ is the circumference of the helix. Another important parameter is the pitch angle α which is the angle formed by a line tangent to the helix wire and a plane perpendicular to the helix axis. The pitch angle is defined by

$$\alpha=\tan^{-1}\left(\frac{S}{\pi D}\right)=\tan^{-1}\left(\frac{S}{C}\right) \qquad (9\text{-}17)$$

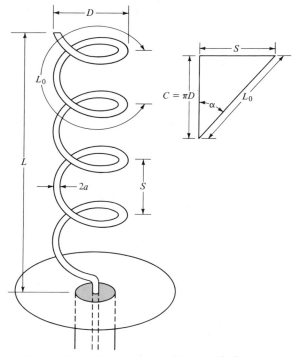

Figure 9.9 Helical antenna with ground plane.

The radiation characteristics of the antenna can be varied by controlling the size of its geometrical properties compared to the wavelength. The input impedance is critically dependent upon the pitch angle and the size of the conducting wire, especially near the feed point, and it can be adjusted by controlling their values. The general polarization of the antenna is elliptical. However circular and linear polarizations can be achieved over different frequency ranges.

The helical antenna can operate in many modes; however the two principal ones are the normal (broadside) and the axial (endfire) modes. The axial (endfire) mode is usually the most practical because it can achieve circular polarization over a wider bandwidth (usually 2:1) and it is more efficient.

Because an elliptically polarized antenna can be represented as the sum of two orthogonal linear components in time-phase quadrature, a helix can always receive a signal transmitted from a rotating linearly polarized antenna. Therefore helices are usually positioned on the ground for space telemetry applications of satellites, space probes, and ballistic missiles to transmit or receive signals that have undergone Faraday rotation by traveling through the ionosphere.

NORMAL MODE

In the normal mode of operation the field radiated by the antenna is maximum in a plane normal to the helix axis and minimum along its axis, as shown sketched in Figure 9.10(a), which is a figure-eight rotated about its axis similar to that of a linear dipole of $l < \lambda$ or a small loop ($a \ll \lambda$). To achieve the normal mode of operation, the dimensions of the helix are small compared to the wavelength (i.e., $NL_0 \ll \lambda$).

The geometry of the helix reduces to a loop of diameter D when the pitch angle approaches zero and to a linear wire of length S when it approaches 90°. Since the limiting geometries of the helix are a loop and a dipole, the far-field radiated by a small helix in the normal mode can be described in terms of the E_θ and E_ϕ components of the dipole and loop, respectively. In the normal mode, it can be thought that the helix consists of N small loops and N short dipoles connected together in series as shown in Figure 9.10(b). The fields are obtained by superposition of the fields from these elemental radiators. The planes of the loops are parallel to each other and perpendicular to the axes of the vertical dipoles. The axes of the loops and dipoles coincide with the axis of the helix.

Since in the normal mode the helix dimensions are small, the current throughout its length can be assumed to be constant and its relative far-field pattern to be independent of the number of loops and short dipoles. Thus its operation can be described accurately by the sum of the fields radiated by a small loop of radius D and a short dipole of length S, with its axis perpendicular to the plane of the loop, and each with the same constant current distribution.

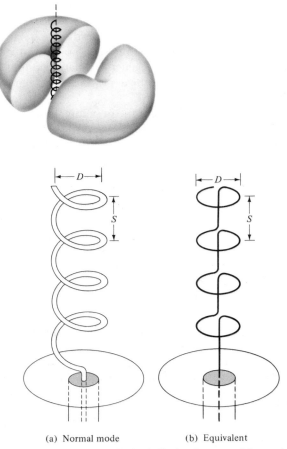

(a) Normal mode   (b) Equivalent

Figure 9.10   Normal (broadside) mode for helical antenna and its equivalent.

The far-zone electric field radiated by a short dipole of length S and constant current I_0 is E_θ, and it is given by (4-26a) as

$$E_\theta = j\eta \frac{kI_0 S e^{-jkr}}{4\pi r} \sin\theta \qquad (9\text{-}18)$$

where l is being replaced by S. In addition the electric field radiated by a loop is E_ϕ, and it is given by (5-27b) as

$$E_\phi = \eta \frac{k^2 (D/2)^2 I_0 e^{-jkr}}{4r} \sin\theta \qquad (9\text{-}19)$$

where $D/2$ is substituted for a. A comparison of (9-18) and (9-19) indicates that the two components are in time-phase quadrature, a necessary but not sufficient condition for circular or elliptical polarization.

The ratio of the magnitudes of the E_θ and E_ϕ components is defined as the axial ratio (AR), and it is given by

$$AR = \frac{|E_\theta|}{|E_\phi|} = \frac{4S}{\pi k D^2} = \frac{2\lambda S}{(\pi D)^2} \qquad (9\text{-}20)$$

By varying the D and/or S the axial ratio attains values of $0 \leq AR \leq \infty$. The value of $AR = 0$ is a special case and would occur when $E_\theta = 0$ leading to a linearly polarized wave of horizontal polarization (the helix is a loop). When $AR = \infty$, $E_\phi = 0$ and the radiated wave is linearly polarized with vertical polarization (the helix is a vertical dipole). Another special case is the one when AR is unity $(AR = 1)$ and occurs when

$$\frac{2\lambda S}{(\pi D)^2} = 1 \qquad (9\text{-}21)$$

or

$$C = \pi D = \sqrt{2S\lambda} \qquad (9\text{-}21a)$$

for which

$$\tan \alpha = \frac{S}{\pi D} = \frac{\pi D}{2\lambda} \qquad (9\text{-}22)$$

When the dimensional parameters of the helix satisfy the above relation, the radiated field is circularly polarized in *all directions* other than $\theta = 0°$ where the fields vanish.

When the dimensions of the helix do not satisfy any of the above special cases, the field radiated by the antenna is not circularly polarized. The progression of polarization change can be described geometrically by beginning with the pitch angle of zero degrees $(\alpha = 0°)$ which reduces the helix to a loop with linear horizontal polarization. As α increases, the polarization becomes elliptical with the major axis being horizontally polarized. When α, is such that $C/\lambda = \sqrt{2S/\lambda}$, $AR = 1$ and we have circular polarization. For greater values of α, the polarization again becomes elliptical but with the major axis vertically polarized. Finally when $\alpha = 90°$ the helix reduces to a linearly polarized vertical dipole.

To achieve the normal mode of operation, it has been assumed that the current throughout the length of the helix is of constant magnitude and phase. This is satisfied to a large extent provided the total length of the helix wire NL_0 is very small compared to the wavelength $(L_n \ll \lambda)$ and its end is terminated properly to reduce multiple reflections. Because of the critical dependence of its radiation characteristics on its geometrical dimensions, which must be very small compared to the wavelengths, this mode of operation is very narrow in bandwidth and its radiation efficiency is very small. Practically this mode of operation is limited, and it is seldom utilized.

AXIAL MODE

A more practical mode of operation, which can be generated with great ease, is the axial or endfire mode. In this mode of operation, there is only one major lobe and its maximum radiation intensity is along the axis of the helix, as shown in Figure 9.11. The minor lobes are at oblique angles to the axis.

To excite this mode, the diameter D and spacing S must be large fractions of the wavelength. To achieve circular polarization, primarily in the major lobe, the circumference of the helix must be in the $\frac{3}{4} < C/\lambda < \frac{4}{3}$ range (with $C/\lambda = 1$ near optimum), and the spacing about $S \simeq \lambda/4$. The pitch angle is usually $12° < \alpha < 18°$ (with $14°$ near optimum). Most often the antenna is used in conjunction with a ground plane, whose diameter is at least $\lambda/2$, and it is energized by a coaxial line. However other types of feeds (such as waveguides and dielectric rods) are possible, especially at microwave frequencies. The dimensions of the helix for this mode of operation are not as critical, thus resulting in a greater bandwidth.

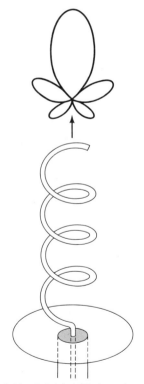

Figure 9.11   Axial (endfire) mode of helix.

The terminal impedance of a helix radiating in the axial mode is nearly resistive with values between 100 and 200 ohms. Empirical expressions, based on a large number of measurements, have been derived [5] and they are used to determine a number of parameters. The input impedance (purely resistive) is obtained by

$$R \simeq 140\left(\frac{C}{\lambda}\right) \tag{9-23}$$

which is accurate to about $\pm 20\%$, the half-power beamwidth by

$$\text{HPBW (degrees)} \simeq \frac{52\lambda^{3/2}}{C\sqrt{NS}} \tag{9-24}$$

the beamwidth between nulls by

$$\text{FNBW (degrees)} \simeq \frac{115\lambda^{3/2}}{C\sqrt{NS}} \tag{9-25}$$

the directivity by

$$D_0 \text{ (dimensionless)} \simeq 15N\frac{C^2S}{\lambda^3} \tag{9-26}$$

the axial ratio (for the condition of increased directivity) by

$$\text{AR} = \frac{2N+1}{2N} \tag{9-27}$$

and the normalized far-field pattern by

$$E = \sin\left(\frac{\pi}{2N}\right)\cos\theta\frac{\sin[(N/2)\psi]}{\sin[\psi/2]} \tag{9-28}$$

$$\text{where } \psi = 2\pi\left[\frac{S}{\lambda}(1-\cos\theta)+\frac{1}{2N}\right] \tag{9-28a}$$

All these relations are approximately valid provided $12° < \alpha < 15°$, $\frac{3}{4} < C/\lambda < \frac{4}{3}$, and $N > 3$.

The far-field pattern of the helix, as given by (9-28), has been developed by assuming that the helix consists of an array of N identical turns (each of uniform current and identical to that of the others), a uniform spacing S between them, and the elements are placed along the z-axis. The $\cos\theta$ term in (9-28) represents the field pattern of a single turn, and the last term in (9-28) is the array factor of a uniform array of N elements. The total field is obtained by multiplying the field from one turn with the array factor (pattern multiplication).

The nominal impedance of a helical antenna operating in the axial mode, computed using (9-23), is 100–200 ohms. However, many of our practical transmission lines (such as a coax) have characteristic impedance of about 50 ohms. In order to provide a better match, the impedance of the helix can be adjusted to a value of about 50 ohms by increasing the size of the helix near the feed point. This modification decreases the characteristic impedance of the conductor-ground plane effective transmission line, and it provides a lower impedance over a substantial but reduced bandwidth. For example, a 50-ohm helix has a VSWR of less than 2:1 over a 40% bandwidth compared to a 70% bandwidth for a 140-ohm helix. In addition, the 50-ohm helix has a VSWR of less than 1.2:1 over a 12% bandwidth as contrasted to a 20% bandwidth for one of 140 ohms.

A simple and effective way of increasing the thickness of the conductor near the feed point will be to bond a thin metal strip to the helix conductor [6]. For example, a metal strip 70-mm wide was used to provide a 50-ohm impedance in a helix whose conducting wire was 13-mm in diameter and it was operating at 230.77 MHz.

9.3.2 Electric-Magnetic Dipole

It has been shown in the previous section that the circular polarization of a helical antenna operating in the normal mode was achieved by assuming that the geometry of the helix is represented by a number of horizontal small loops and vertical infinitesimal dipoles. It would then seem reasonable that an antenna with only one loop and a single vertical dipole would, in theory, represent a radiator with an elliptical polarization. Ideally circular polarization, in all space, can be achieved if the current in each element can be controlled, by dividing the available power equally between the dipole and the loop, so that the magnitude of the field intensity radiated by each is equal.

Experimental models of such an antenna were designed and built [7] one operating around 350 MHz and the other near 1.2 GHz. A sketch of one of them is shown in Figure 9.12. The measured VSWR in the 1.15–1.32 GHz frequency range was less than 2:1.

This type of an antenna is very useful in UHF communication networks where considerable amounts of fading may exist. In such cases the fading of the horizontal and vertical components are affected differently and will not vary in the same manner. Hopefully, even in severe cases, there will always be one component all the time which is being affected less than the other, thus providing continuous communication. The same results would apply in VHF and/or UHF broadcasting. In addition, a transmitting antenna of this type would also provide the versatility to receive with horizontally or vertically polarized elements, providing a convenience in the architectural design of the receiving station.

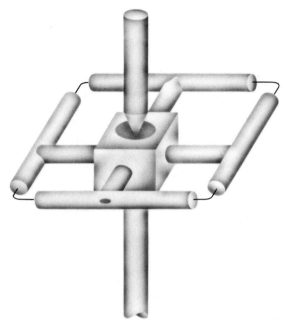

Figure 9.12 Electric-magnetic dipole configuration. (SOURCE: A. G. Kandoian, "Three New Antenna Types and Their Applications," *Proc. IRE*, vol. 34, pp. 70W–75W, February 1946. © (1946) IEEE)

9.3.3 Yagi-Uda Array of Linear Elements

Another very practical radiator in the HF (3–30 MHz), VHF (30–300 MHz), and UHF (300–3,000 MHz) ranges is the Yagi-Uda antenna. This antenna consists of a number of linear dipole elements, as shown in Figure 9.13, one of which is energized directly by a feed transmission line while the others act as parasitic radiators whose currents are induced by mutual coupling. The most common feed element for a Yagi-Uda antenna is a folded dipole. This radiator is exclusively designed to operate as an endfire array, and this is accomplished by having the parasitic elements in the forward beam act as directors while those in the rear act as reflectors. It is widely used as a home TV antenna; so it should be familiar to most of the readers, if not to the general public.

The original design and operating principles of this radiator were first described in Japanese in articles published in the Journal of I.E.E. of Japan by S. Uda of the Tohoku Imperial University in Japan [8]. In a later, but more widely circulated and read article [9], one of Professor Uda's colleagues H. Yagi described the operation of the same radiator in English. Despite the fact that Yagi in his English written paper acknowledged the work of Professor Uda on beam radiators at a wavelength of 4.4 m, it became customary throughout the world to refer to this radiator as a Yagi antenna, a generic term in the antenna dictionary. However, in order for the

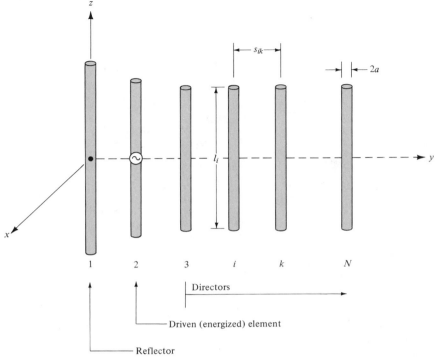

Figure 9.13   Yagi-Uda antenna configuration.

name to reflect more appropriately the contributions of both inventors, it should be called a Yagi-Uda antenna, a name that will be adopted in this book. Although the work of Uda and Yagi was done in the early 1920s and published in the middle 1920s, full acclaim in the United States was not received until 1928 when Yagi visited the United States and presented papers at meetings of the Institute of Radio Engineers (IRE) in New York, Washington, and Hartford. In addition, his work was published in the *Proceedings of IRE*, June 1928, where J. H. Dellinger, Chief of Radio Division, Bureau of Standards, Washington, D.C., and himself a pioneer of radio waves, wrote "I have never listened to a paper that I felt so sure was destined to be a classic." So true!!

The Yagi-Uda antenna has received exhaustive analytical and experimental investigations in the open literature and elsewhere. It would be impractical to list all the contributors, many of whom we may not be aware. However, we will attempt to summarize the salient points of the analyses, describe the general operation of the radiator, and present some design data.

To achieve the endfire beam formation, the parasitic elements in the direction of the beam are somewhat smaller in length than the feed element. Typically the driven element is resonant with its length slightly less than $\lambda/2$ (usually 0.45–0.49λ) whereas the lengths of the directors will be about

0.4 to 0.45λ. However, the directors are not necessarily of the same length and/or diameter. The separation between the directors is typically 0.3 to 0.4λ, and it is not necessarily uniform for optimum designs. It has been shown experimentally that for a Yagi-Uda array of 6λ total length the overall gain was independent of director spacing up to about 0.3λ. A significant drop (5–7 dB) in gain was noted for director spacings greater than 0.3λ. For that antenna, the gain was also independent of the radii of the directors up to about 0.024λ. The length of the reflector is somewhat greater than that of the feed. In addition the separation between the driven element and the reflector is somewhat smaller than the spacing between the driven element and the nearest director, and it is found to be near optimum at 0.25λ.

Since the length of each director will be smaller than its corresponding resonant length, the impedance of each will be capacitive and its current will lead the induced emf. Similarly the impedances of the reflectors will be inductive and the phases of the currents will lag those of the induced emfs. The total phase of the currents in the directors and reflectors is not determined solely by their lengths but also by their spacing to the adjacent elements. Thus properly spaced elements with lengths slightly less than their corresponding resonant lengths (less than λ/2) will act as directors because they form an array with currents approximately equal in magnitude and with equal progressive phase shifts which will reinforce the field of the energized element toward the directors. Similarly, a properly spaced element with a length of λ/2 or slightly greater will act as a reflector. Thus a Yagi-Uda array may be regarded as a structure supporting a traveling wave whose performance is determined by the current distribution in each element and the phase velocity of the traveling wave. It should be noted that the previous discussion on the lengths of the directors, reflectors, and driven elements is based on the first resonance. Higher resonances are available near lengths of λ, 3λ/2, and so forth, but are seldom used.

In practice, the major role of the reflector is played by the first element next to the one energized, and very little in the performance of a Yagi-Uda antenna is gained if more than one (at the most two) elements are used as reflectors. However, considerable improvements can be achieved if more directors are added to the array. Practically there is a limit beyond which very little is gained by the addition of more directors because of the progressive reduction in magnitude of the induced currents on the more extreme elements. Usually most antennas have about 6 to 12 directors. However, many arrays have been designed and built with 30 to 40 elements. Array lengths on the order of 6λ have been mentioned [10] as typical. A gain (relative to isotropic) of about 5 to 9 per wavelength is typical for such arrays, which would make the overall gain on the order of about 30 to 54 (14.8–17.3 dB) typical.

The radiation characteristics that are usually of interest in a Yagi-Uda antenna are the *forward and backward gains, input impedance, bandwidth, front-to-back ratio,* and *magnitude of minor lobes.* The lengths and diameters of the directors and reflectors as well as their respective spacings will determine the optimum characteristics. For a number of years optimum designs were accomplished experimentally. However with the advent of high-speed computers many different numerical techniques, based on analytical formulations, have been utilized to derive the geometrical dimensions of the array for optimum operational performance. Usually Yagi-Uda arrays have low input impedance and relatively narrow bandwidth (on the order of about 2%). Improvements in both can be achieved at the expense of others (such as gain, magnitude of minor lobes, etc.). Usually a compromise is made, and it depends on the particular design. One way to increase the input impedance without affecting the performance of other parameters is to use an impedance step up element as a feed (such as a two-element folded dipole with a step up ratio of about 4). Front-to-back ratios of about 30 ($\simeq 15$ dB) can be achieved at wider than optimum element spacings, but they usually are sacrificed somewhat to improve other desirable characteristics. For optimum designs, the minor lobes are about 30% or less (-5.23 dB or smaller) of the maximum.

The Yagi-Uda array can be summarized by saying that its performance can be considered in three parts:

1. the reflector-feeder arrangement
2. the feeder
3. the rows of directors

It has been concluded numerically and experimentally that the reflector spacing and size have (1) negligible effects on the forward gain and (2) large effects on the backward gain (front-to-back ratio) and input impedance, and they can be used to control or optimize antenna parameters without affecting the gain significantly. The feeder length and radius has a small effect on the forward gain but a large effect on the backward gain and input impedance. Its geometry is usually chosen to control the input impedance that most commonly is made real (resonant element). The size and spacing of the directors have a large effect on the forward gain, backward gain, and input impedance, and they are considered to be the most crucial elements of the array.

Yagi-Uda arrays are quite common in practice because they are lightweight, simple to build, low cost, and provide moderately desirable characteristics (including a unidirectional beam) for many applications. The design for a small number of elements (typically five or six) is simple but the design becomes quite critical if a large number of elements are used to achieve a high directivity. To increase the directivity of a Yagi-Uda array or to reduce the beamwidth in the *E*-plane, several rows of Yagi-Uda arrays can be used [11] to form a curtain antenna. To neutralize the effects of the feed transmission line, an odd number of rows is usually used.

THEORY

There have been many experimental [12], [13] investigations and analytical [14]–[19] formulations of the Yagi-Uda array. A method [16] based on rigorous integral equations for the electric field radiated by the elements in the array will be presented and it will be used to describe the complex current distributions on all the elements, the phase velocity, and the corresponding radiation patterns. Mutual interactions are also included and, in principle, there are no restrictions on the number of elements. However, for computational purposes, point-matching numerical methods, based on the techniques of Section 7.5, are used to evaluate and satisfy the integral equation at discrete points on the axis of each element rather than every-where on the surface of every element. The number of discrete points where boundary conditions are matched must be sufficient in number to allow the computed data to compare well with experimental results.

Referring to Figure 9.13, it has been shown that for small diameter wires the current on each element can be well approximated by a finite series of odd-ordered even modes. Thus the current on the nth element can be written as a Fourier series expansion of the form

$$I_n(z') = \sum_{m=1}^{M} I_{mn} \cos\left[(2m-1)\frac{\pi z'}{l_n}\right], \qquad m = 1, 2, 3, 4, \ldots \tag{9-29}$$

where I_{mn} represents the complex current coefficient of mode m on element n and l_n the corresponding length of the n element. Using the vector potential formulations of Chapter 3, it can be shown that the electric field radiated by all the elements of the array, each with a current as given by (9-29), can be written for an array with one reflector, one driven element, and D directors, as

$$E_z(x, y, z) = -j\eta\frac{\lambda}{8\pi^2} \sum_{n=1}^{N} \sum_{m=1}^{M} I_{mn} \int_{-l_n/2}^{l_n/2} G(x, y, z/x', y', z')$$

$$\times \cos\left[(2m-1)\frac{\pi}{l_n}z'\right] dz' \tag{9-30}$$

where

$$G(x, y, z/x', y', z') = \frac{e^{-jkR}}{R^5}\left[(1+jkR)(2R^2 - 3a^2) + (kaR)^2\right] \tag{9-30a}$$

$$R = \sqrt{(x-x')^2 + (y-y')^2 + a^2 + (z-z')^2} \tag{9-30b}$$

N is equal to the total number of elements (directors, feeder, and reflector). The primed coordinates (x', y', z') represent any point on each source element whereas the unprimed (x, y, z) represent the observation point. Thus for each x, y, z all source points must be included. The coefficients I_{mn} can be found by requiring the tangential E-field to vanish at M points on each director, M points on the reflector, and $M-1$ points on the driven element, and requiring a boundary condition on the current at the feed point. These boundary constraints generate a system of linear algebraic equations that allow for the solution of the complex current coefficients of the Fourier series expansion for each element.

In general, the far-zone electric field radiated by a single element is obtained by integrating (4-58) over the entire length and can be written as

$$E_\theta = j\eta \frac{ke^{-jkr}}{4\pi r} \sin\theta \int_{-l/2}^{l/2} I(z')e^{jkz'\cos\theta} dz' \qquad (9\text{-}31)$$

For the Fourier series expansion of the current as given by (9-29), the field radiated by the nth element reduces to

$$E_{\theta n} = -j\eta \frac{l_n e^{-jkr_0}}{4r_0} \sin\theta \sum_{m=1}^{M} \left[\frac{(-1)^m (2m-1) I_{mn} \cos\left(\frac{\pi l_n}{\lambda} \cos\theta \right)}{(2m-1)^2 - \left(\frac{2l_n}{\lambda} \cos\theta \right)^2} \right] \qquad (9\text{-}32)$$

where

$$r_0 \simeq r - (x\sin\theta\cos\phi + y\sin\theta\sin\phi + z\cos\theta) \qquad (9\text{-}32a)$$

Thus for N elements, *each with M modes*, the total field is given by

$$E_\theta = \sum_{n=1}^{N} E_{\theta n} = -j\eta \frac{e^{-jkr}}{4r} F_T(\theta, \phi) \qquad (9\text{-}33)$$

where

$$F_T(\theta, \phi) = \sin\theta \sum_{n=1}^{N} \left\{ l_n e^{j\psi_n} \left[\sum_{m=1}^{M} (-1)^m \frac{(2m-1) I_{mn} \cos\left(\frac{\pi l_n}{\lambda} \cos\theta \right)}{(2m-1)^2 - \left(\frac{2l_n}{\lambda} \cos\theta \right)^2} \right] \right\} \qquad (9\text{-}33a)$$

$$\psi_n = k(x_n \sin\theta\cos\phi + y_n \sin\theta\sin\phi + z_n \cos\theta) \qquad (9\text{-}33b)$$

The $F_T(\theta, \phi)$ is designated as the total pattern factor, and it would be of more complex form if the number of modes in each element is not the same.

There have been other analyses [17], [18] based on the integral equation formulation that allows the conversion to algebraic equations. In order not to belabor further the analytical formulations, which in all cases are complicated because of the antenna structure, we would like to present some numerical results and indicate design procedures.

RESULTS

Using the theory outlined in the previous pages, Thiele [16] calculated the
E- and *H*-plane patterns of a 27-element Yagi-Uda array. Because of the
storage limitations in a digital computer, the author took three modes on
each parasitic element (reflector and directors) and seven modes on the
driven element. The geometrical properties of the array were

$$N = \text{total number of elements} = 27$$
$$\text{number of directors} = 25$$
$$\text{number of reflectors} = 1$$
$$\text{number of exciters} = 1$$
$$\text{total length of reflector} = 0.5\lambda$$
$$\text{total length of feeder} = 0.47\lambda$$
$$\text{total length of each director} = 0.406\lambda$$
$$\text{spacing between reflector and feeder} = 0.125\lambda$$
$$\text{spacing between adjacent directors} = 0.34\lambda$$
$$a = \text{radius of wires} = 0.003\lambda$$

The computed *E*- and *H*-plane patterns are shown in Figures 9.14(a) and
(b), respectively. The relative current amplitude along each element is shown
in Figure 9.14(c). The current distribution along the length of the array is
not uniform. However, beyond the fifth director the amplitude seems to
level out and oscillate very slightly about the 0.2 value.

The radiation characteristics of the array can be adjusted by controlling
the geometrical parameters of the array. For example, the spacing between
the directors can be varied while holding the reflector-exciter spacing and
the lengths of all elements constant. Such a procedure was used by Cheng
and Chen [17] to optimize the directivity of a six-element (four-director,
reflector, exciter) array using a perturbational technique. The results of the
initial and the optimized (perturbed) array are shown in Table 9.1. For the
same array, they allowed all the spacings to vary while maintaining constant
all other parameters. The results are shown in Table 9.2.

Another optimization procedure is to maintain the spacings between all
the elements constant and vary the lengths so as to optimize the directivity.
The results of a six-element array [18] are shown in Table 9.3. The ultimate
optimization is to vary both the spacings and lengths. This was accomplished by Chen and Cheng [18] whereby they first optimized the array by
varying the spacing, while maintaining the lengths constant. This was
followed, on the same array, with perturbations in the lengths while maintaining the optimized spacings constant. The results of this procedure are
shown in Table 9.4 with the corresponding *H*-plane ($\theta = \pi/2, \phi$) far-field
patterns shown in Figure 9.15. In all, improvements in directivity and
front-to-back ratio are noted.

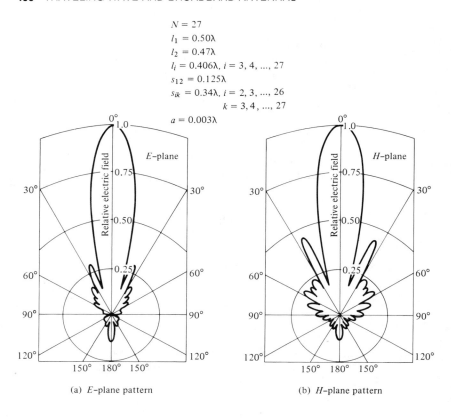

$$N = 27$$
$$l_1 = 0.50\lambda$$
$$l_2 = 0.47\lambda$$
$$l_i = 0.406\lambda, \; i = 3, 4, ..., 27$$
$$s_{12} = 0.125\lambda$$
$$s_{ik} = 0.34\lambda, \; i = 2, 3, ..., 26$$
$$k = 3, 4, ..., 27$$
$$a = 0.003\lambda$$

(a) E-plane pattern   (b) H-plane pattern

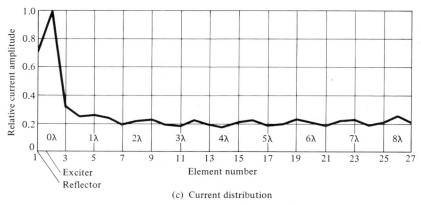

(c) Current distribution

Figure 9.14 E- and H-plane patterns and relative current amplitudes of a 27-element Yagi-Uda array. (SOURCE: G. A. Thiele, "Analysis of Yagi-Uda-Type Antennas," *IEEE Trans. Antennas Propag.*, vol. AP-17, pp. 24–31, January 1969. © (1969) IEEE)

Table 9.1 DIRECTIVITY OPTIMIZATION FOR SIX-ELEMENT YAGI-UDA ARRAY (PERTURBATION OF *DIRECTOR SPACINGS*), $l_1 = 0.51\lambda$, $l_2 = 0.50\lambda$, $l_3 = l_4 = l_5 = l_6 = 0.43\lambda$, $a = 0.003369\lambda$

	s_{21}/λ	s_{32}/λ	s_{43}/λ	s_{54}/λ	s_{65}/λ	DIRECTIVITY (dB)
INITIAL ARRAY	0.250	0.310	0.310	0.310	0.310	9.06
OPTIMIZED ARRAY	0.250	0.336	0.398	0.310	0.407	10.72

SOURCE: D. K. Cheng and C. A. Chen, "Optimum Spacings for Yagi-Uda Arrays," *IEEE Trans. Antennas Propag.*, vol. AP-21, pp. 615–623, September 1973. © (1973) IEEE.

Table 9.2 DIRECTIVITY OPTIMIZATION FOR SIX-ELEMENT YAGI-UDA ARRAY (PERTURBATION OF *ALL ELEMENT SPACINGS*), $l_1 = 0.51\lambda$, $l_2 = 0.50\lambda$, $l_3 = l_4 = l_5 = l_6 = 0.43\lambda$, $a = 0.003369\lambda$

	s_{21}/λ	s_{32}/λ	s_{43}/λ	s_{54}/λ	s_{65}/λ	DIRECTIVITY (dB)
INITIAL ARRAY	0.280	0.310	0.310	0.310	0.310	8.77
OPTIMIZED ARRAY	0.250	0.352	0.355	0.354	0.373	10.74

SOURCE: D. K. Cheng and C. A. Chen, "Optimum Spacings for Yagi-Uda Arrays," *IEEE Trans. Antennas Propag.*, vol. AP-21, pp. 615–623, September 1973. © (1973) IEEE.

Table 9.3 DIRECTIVITY OPTIMIZATION FOR SIX-ELEMENT YAGI-UDA ARRAY (PERTURBATION OF *ALL ELEMENT LENGTHS*), $s_{21} = 0.250\lambda$, $s_{32} = s_{43} = s_{54} = s_{65} = 0.310\lambda$, $a = 0.003369\lambda$

	l_1/λ	l_2/λ	l_3/λ	l_4/λ	l_5/λ	l_6/λ	DIRECTIVITY (dB)
INITIAL ARRAY	0.510	0.490	0.430	0.430	0.430	0.430	10.93
LENGTH-PERTURBED ARRAY	0.472	0.456	0.438	0.444	0.432	0.404	12.16

SOURCE: C. A. Chen and D. K. Cheng, "Optimum Element Lengths for Yagi-Uda Arrays," *IEEE Trans. Antennas Propag.*, vol. AP-23, pp. 8–15, January 1975. © (1975) IEEE.

Another parameter that was investigated for the directivity-optimized Yagi-Uda antenna was the frequency bandwidth [19]. The results of such a procedure are shown in Figure 9.16. The antenna was a six-element array optimized at a center frequency f_0. The array was designed, using space perturbations on all the elements, to yield an optimum directivity at f_0. The geometrical parameters are listed in Table 9.2. The 3-dB bandwidth seems to be almost the same for the initial and the optimized arrays. The rapid decrease in the directivity of the initial and optimized arrays at frequencies higher than f_0 and nearly constant values below f_0 may be attributed to the structure of the antenna which can support a "traveling wave" at $f < f_0$ but not at $f > f_0$. It has thus been suggested that an increase in the bandwidth can be achieved if the geometrical dimensions of the antenna are chosen slightly smaller than the optimum.

The input impedance of a Yagi-Uda array, measured at the center of the driven element, is usually small. For a 13-element array using a resonant

Table 9.4 DIRECTIVITY OPTIMIZATION FOR SIX-ELEMENT YAGI-UDA ARRAY (PERTURBATION OF *DIRECTOR SPACINGS AND ALL ELEMENT LENGTHS*), $a = 0.003369\lambda$

	l_1/λ	l_2/λ	l_3/λ	l_4/λ	l_5/λ	l_6/λ	s_{21}/λ	s_{32}/λ	s_{43}/λ	s_{54}/λ	s_{65}/λ	DIRECTIVITY (dB)
INITIAL ARRAY	0.510	0.490	0.430	0.430	0.430	0.430	0.250	0.310	0.310	0.310	0.310	10.93
ARRAY AFTER SPACING PERTURBATION	0.510	0.490	0.430	0.430	0.430	0.430	0.250	0.289	0.406	0.323	0.422	12.83
OPTIMUM ARRAY AFTER SPACING AND LENGTH PERTURBATION	0.472	0.452	0.436	0.430	0.434	0.430	0.250	0.289	0.406	0.323	0.422	13.41

SOURCE: C. A. Chen and D. K. Cheng, "Optimum Element Lengths for Yagi-Uda Arrays," *IEEE Trans. Antenna Propag.*, vol. AP-23, pp. 8–15, January 1975. © (1975) IEEE.

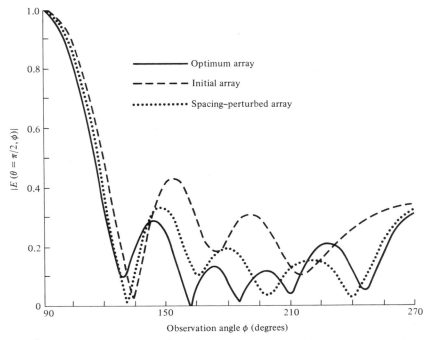

Figure 9.15 Normalized amplitude antenna patterns of initial, perturbed, and optimum six-element Yagi-Uda arrays (Table 9.4). (SOURCE: C. A. Chen and D. K. Cheng, "Optimum Element Lengths for Yagi-Uda Arrays," *IEEE Trans. Antennas Propag.*, vol. AP-23, pp. 8–15, January 1975. © (1975) IEEE)

driven element, the measured input impedances are listed in Table 9.5 [10]. Some of these values are low for matching to 50-, 75-, or 300-ohm transmission lines; however they can be increased by approximate factors of 4, 9, 16, and so forth by using a folded dipole as a feed element.

Another way to explain the endfire beam formation and whether the parameters of the Yagi-Uda array are properly adjusted for optimum directivity is by drawing a vector diagram of the progressive phase delay from element-to-element. If the current amplitudes throughout the array are equal, the total phase delay for maximum directivity should be about 180°, as is required by the Hansen-Woodyard criteria for improved endfire radiation. Since the currents in a Yagi-Uda array are not equal in all the elements, the phase velocity of the traveling wave along the antenna structure is not the same from element-to-element but it is always slower than the velocity of light and faster than the corresponding velocity for a Hansen-Woodyard design. For a Yagi-Uda array, the decrease in the phase velocity is a function of the increase in total array length.

In general then, the phase velocity, and in turn the phase shift, of a traveling wave in a Yagi-Uda array structure is controlled by the geometrical dimensions of the array and its elements, and it is not uniform from element-to-element.

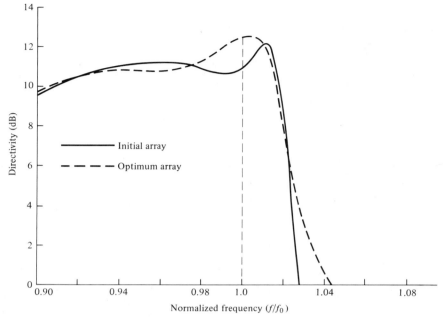

Figure 9.16 Bandwidth of initial and optimum six-element Yagi-Uda array with perturbation of all element spacings (Table 9.2). (SOURCE: N. K. Takla and L.-C. Shen, "Bandwidth of a Yagi Array with Optimum Directivity," *IEEE Trans. Antennas Propag.*, vol. AP-25, pp. 913–914, November 1977. © (1977) IEEE)

DESIGN

A government document [20] has been published which provides extensive data of experimental investigations carried out by the National Bureau of Standards to determine how parasitic element diameter, element length, spacings between elements, supporting booms of different cross-sectional areas, various reflectors, and overall length affect the measured gain. Numerous graphical data is included to facilitate the design of different length antennas to yield maximum gain. In addition design criteria are presented for stacking Yagi-Uda arrays either one above the other or

Table 9.5 INPUT IMPEDANCE OF A 15-ELEMENT YAGI-UDA ARRAY (REFLECTOR LENGTH $=0.5\lambda$; DIRECTOR SPACING $=0.34\lambda$; DIRECTOR LENGTH $=0.406\lambda$)

REFLECTOR SPACING (s_{21}/λ)	INPUT IMPEDANCE (ohms)
0.25	62
0.18	50
0.15	32
0.13	22
0.10	12

side-by-side. A step-by-step design procedure has been established in determining the geometrical parameters of a Yagi-Uda array for a desired gain (over that of a $\lambda/2$ dipole mounted at the same height above ground). The included graphs can only be used to design arrays with overall lengths (*from reflector element to last director*) of 0.4, 0.8, 1.2, 2.2, 3.2, and 4.2λ with corresponding gains of 7.1, 9.2, 10.2, 12.25, 13.4, and 14.2 dB, respectively, and with a diameter-to-wavelength ratio of $0.001 \leq d/\lambda_0 \leq 0.04$. Although the graphs do not cover all possible designs, they do accommodate most practical requests. The driven element used to derive the data was a $\lambda/2$ folded dipole, and the measurements were carried out at $f=400$ MHz. To make the reader aware of the procedure, it will be outlined by the use of an example. The procedure is identical for all other designs at frequencies where included data can accommodate the specifications.

The heart of the design is the data included in

1. Table 9.6 which represents optimized antenna parameters for six different lengths and for a $d/\lambda_0 = 0.0085$
2. Figure 9.17 which represents uncompensated director and reflector lengths for $0.001 \leq d/\lambda_0 \leq 0.04$
3. Figure 9.18 which provides compensation length increase for all the parasitic elements (directors and reflectors) as a function of boom-to-wavelength ratio $0.001 \leq D/\lambda_0 \leq 0.04$

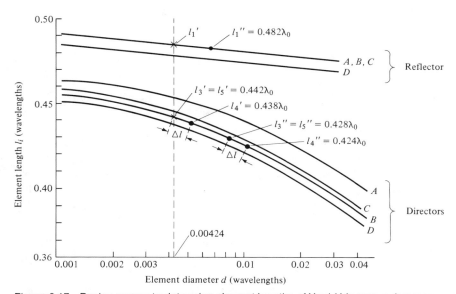

Figure 9.17   Design curves to determine element lengths of Yagi-Uda arrays. (SOURCE: P. P. Viezbicke, "Yagi Antenna Design," NBS Technical Note 688, U.S. Department of Commerce/National Bureau of Standards, December 1968)

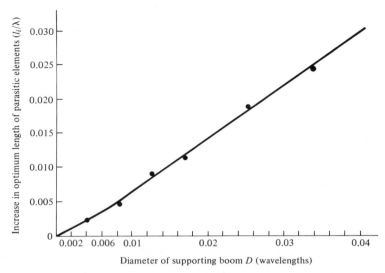

Figure 9.18 Increase in optimum length of parasitic elements as a function of metal boom diameter. (SOURCE: P. P. Viezbicke, "Yagi Antenna Design," NBS Technical Note 688, U.S. Department of Commerce/National Bureau of Standards, December 1968)

The specified information is usually the center frequency, antenna gain, d/λ_0 and D/λ_0 ratios, and it is required to find the optimum parasitic element lengths (directors and reflectors). The spacing between the directors is uniform but not the same for all designs. However, there is only one reflector and its spacing is $s = 0.2\lambda$ for all designs.

Example 9.1

Design a Yagi-Uda array with a gain (relative to a $\lambda/2$ dipole at the same height above ground) of 9.2 dB at $f_0 = 50.1$ MHz. The desired diameter of the parasitic elements is 2.54 cm and of the metal supporting boom 5.1 cm. Find the element spacings, lengths, and total array length.

SOLUTION

(a) At $f_0 = 50.1$ MHz the wavelength is $\lambda_0 = 5.988$ m $= 598.8$ cm. Thus $d/\lambda_0 = 2.54/598.8 = 4.24 \times 10^{-3}$ and $D/\lambda_0 = 5.1/598.8 = 8.52 \times 10^{-3}$.

(b) From Table 9.6, the desired array would have a total of five elements (three directors, one reflector, one feeder). For a $d/\lambda_0 = 0.0085$ ratio the optimum lengths would be those shown in the second column of Table 9.6 ($l_3 = l_5 = 0.428\lambda_0$, $\lambda_4 = 0.424\lambda_0$, and $l_1 = 0.482\lambda_0$). The overall antenna length would be $L = (0.6 + 0.2)\lambda_0 = 0.8\lambda_0$, the spacing between directors $0.2\lambda_0$, and the reflector spacing $0.2\lambda_0$. It is now desired to find the optimum lengths of the parasitic elements for a $d/\lambda_0 = 0.00424$.

Table 9.6 OPTIMIZED LENGTHS OF PARASITIC ELEMENTS FOR YAGI-UDA ANTENNAS OF SIX DIFFERENT LENGTHS

$d/\lambda = 0.0085$ $s_{12} = 0.2\lambda$		LENGTH OF YAGI-UDA (IN WAVELENGTHS)					
		0.4	0.8	1.20	2.2	3.2	4.2
LENGTH OF REFLECTOR (l_1/λ)		0.482	0.482	0.482	0.482	0.482	0.475
LENGTH OF DIRECTOR, λ	l_3	0.424	0.428	0.428	0.432	0.428	0.424
	l_4		0.424	0.420	0.415	0.420	0.424
	l_5		0.428	0.420	0.407	0.407	0.420
	l_6			0.428	0.398	0.398	0.407
	l_7				0.390	0.394	0.403
	l_8				0.390	0.390	0.398
	l_9				0.390	0.386	0.394
	l_{10}				0.390	0.386	0.390
	l_{11}				0.398	0.386	0.390
	l_{12}				0.407	0.386	0.390
	l_{13}					0.386	0.390
	l_{14}					0.386	0.390
	l_{15}					0.386	0.390
	l_{16}					0.386	
	l_{17}					0.386	
SPACING BETWEEN DIRECTORS (s_{ik}/λ)		0.20	0.20	0.25	0.20	0.20	0.308
GAIN RELATIVE TO HALF-WAVE DIPOLE (dB)		7.1	9.2	10.2	12.25	13.4	14.2
DESIGN CURVE (SEE FIGURE 9.17)		(A)	(B)	(B)	(C)	(B)	(D)

SOURCE: Peter P. Viezbicke, *Yagi Antenna Design*, NBS Technical Note 688, December 1968.

(c) Plot the optimized lengths from Table 9.6 $(l_3'' = l_5'' = 0.428\lambda_0,$ $l_4'' = 0.424\lambda_0,$ and $l_1'' = 0.482\lambda_0)$ on Figure 9.17 and mark them by a dot $(\cdot)$.

(d) In Figure 9.17 draw a vertical line through $d/\lambda_0 = 0.00424$ intersecting curves (B) at director uncompensated lengths $l_3' = l_5' = 0.442\lambda_0$ and reflector length $l_1' = 0.485\lambda_0$. Mark these points by an x.

(e) With a divider, measure the distance (Δl) along director curve (B) between points $l_3'' = l_5'' = 0.428\lambda_0$ and $l_4'' = 0.424\lambda_0$. Transpose this distance from the point $l_3' = l_5' = 0.442\lambda_0$ on curve (B), established in step (d) and marked by an x, downward along the curve and determine the uncompensated length $l_4' = 0.438\lambda_0$. Thus the boom uncompensated lengths of the array at $f_0 = 50.1$ MHz are

$$l_3' = l_5' = 0.442\lambda_0$$

$$l_4' = 0.438\lambda_0$$

$$l_1' = 0.485\lambda_0$$

(f) Correct the elements lengths to compensate for the boom diameter. From Figure 9.18, a boom diameter-to-wavelength ratio of 0.00852 requires a fractional length increase in each element of about $0.005\lambda_0$. Thus the final lengths of the elements should be

$$l_3 = l_5 = (0.442 + 0.005)\lambda_0 = 0.447\lambda_0$$

$$l_4 = (0.438 + 0.005)\lambda_0 = 0.443\lambda_0$$

$$l_1 = (0.485 + 0.005)\lambda_0 = 0.490\lambda_0$$

The design data were derived from measurements carried out on a nonconducting Plexiglas boom mounted $3\lambda_0$ above the ground. The driven element was a $\lambda/2$ folded dipole matched to a 50-ohm line by a double-stub tuner. All parasitic elements were constructed from aluminum tubing. Using Plexiglas booms, the data were repeatable and represented the same values as air-dielectric booms. However that was not the case for wooden booms because of differences in the moisture, which had a direct affect on the gain. Data on metal booms was also repeatable provided the element lengths were increased to compensate for the metal boom structure.

9.3.4 Yagi-Uda Array of Loops

Aside from the dipole, the loop antenna is one of the most basic antenna elements. The pattern of a very small loop is similar to that of a very small dipole and in the far-field region it has a null along its axis. As the circumference of the loop increases, the radiation along its axis increases and reaches near maximum at above one wavelength [21]. Thus loops can be used as the basic elements, instead of the linear dipoles, to form a Yagi-Uda array as shown in Figure 9.19. By properly choosing the dimensions of the loops and their spacing, they can form a unidirectional beam along the axis of the loops and the array.

It has been shown that the radiation characteristics of a two-element loop array, one driven element and a parasitic reflector, resulted in the elimination of corona problems at high altitudes [22]. In addition, the radiation characteristics of loop arrays mounted above ground are less affected by the electrical properties of the soil, as compared with those of dipoles [23]. A two-element loop array also resulted in a 1.8 dB higher gain than a corresponding array of two dipoles [22]. A two-element array of square loops (a feeder and a reflector) in a boxlike construction is called a "cubical quad" or simply a "quad" antenna, and it is very popular in amateur radio applications [24]. The sides of each square loop are $\lambda/4$

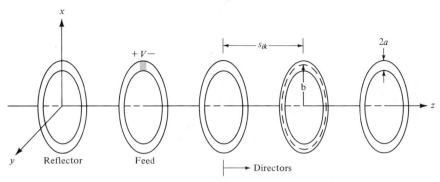

Figure 9.19   Yagi-Uda array of circular loops.

(perimeter of λ), and the loops are usually supported by a fiberglass or bamboo cross-arm assembly.

The general performance of a loop Yagi-Uda array is controlled by the same geometrical parameters (reflector, feeder, and director sizes, and spacing between elements), and it is influenced in the same manner as an array of dipoles [25].

In a numerical parametric study of coaxial Yagi-Uda arrays of circular loops [26] of 2 to 10 directors, it has been found that the optimum parameters for *maximum forward gain* were

1. circumference of feeder $2\pi b_2 \simeq 1.1\lambda$, where b_2 is its radius. This radius was chosen so that the input impedance for an isolated element is purely resistive.
2. circumference of the reflector $2\pi b_1 \simeq 1.05\lambda$, where b_1 is its radius. The size of the reflector does not strongly influence the forward gain but has a major effect on the backward gain and input impedance.
3. feeder-reflector spacing of about 0.1λ. Because it has negligible effect on the forward gain, it can be used to control the backward gain and/or the input impedance.
4. circumference of directors $2\pi b \simeq 0.7\lambda$, where b is the radius of any director and it was chosen to be the same for all. When the circumference approached a value of one wavelength, the array exhibited its cutoff properties.
5. spacing of directors of about 0.25λ, and it was uniform for all.

The radius a of all the elements was retained constant and was chosen to satisfy $\Omega = 2\ln(2\pi b_2/a) = 11$ where b_2 is the radius of the feeder.

References

1. C. H. Walter, *Traveling Wave Antennas*, McGraw-Hill, New York, 1965.
2. G. A. Thiele and E. P. Ekelman, Jr., "Design Formulas for Vee Dipoles," *IEEE Trans. Antennas Propag.*, vol. AP-28, pp. 588–590, July 1980.

3. W. L. Weeks, *Antenna Engineering*, McGraw-Hill, New York, 1968, pp. 140–142.

4. D. G. Fink (ed.), *Electronics Engineers' Handbook*, Chapter 18 (by W. F. Croswell), McGraw-Hill, New York, 1975.

5. J. Kraus, *Antennas*, McGraw-Hill, New York, 1950.

6. J. Kraus, "A 50-Ohm Input Impedance for Helical Beam Antennas," *IEEE Trans. Antennas Propag.*, vol. AP-25, p. 913, October 1977.

7. A. G. Kandoian, "Three New Antenna Types and Their Applications," *Proc. IRE*, vol. 34, pp. 70W–75W, February 1946.

8. S. Uda, "Wireless Beam of Short Electric Waves," *J. IEE.* (Japan), pp. 273–282, March 1926, and pp. 1209–1219, November 1927.

9. H. Yagi, "Beam Transmission of Ultra Short Waves," *Proc. IRE*, vol. 26, pp. 715–741, June 1928.

10. R. M. Fishender and E. R. Wiblin, "Design of Yagi Aerials," *Proc. IEE* (London), pt. 3, vol. 96, pp. 5–12, January 1949.

11. C. C. Lee and L.-C. Shen, "Coupled Yagi Arrays," *IEEE Trans. Antennas Propag.*, vol. AP-25, pp. 889–891, November 1977.

12. H. W. Ehrenspeck and H. Poehler, "A New Method for Obtaining Maximum Gain from Yagi Antennas," *IRE Trans. Antennas Propag.*, vol. AP-7, pp. 379–386, October 1959.

13. H. E. Green, "Design Data for Short and Medium Length Yagi-Uda Arrays," *Elec. Engrg. Trans. Inst. Engrgs.* (Australia), pp. 1–8, March 1966.

14. W. Wilkinshaw, "Theoretical Treatment of Short Yagi Aerials," *Proc. IEE* (London), pt. 3, vol. 93, p. 598, 1946.

15. R. J. Mailloux, "The Long Yagi-Uda Array," *IEEE Trans. Antennas Propag.*, vol. AP-14, pp. 128–137, March 1966.

16. G. A. Thiele, "Analysis of Yagi-Uda Type Antennas," *IEEE Trans. Antennas Propag.*, vol. AP-17, pp. 24–31, January 1969.

17. D. K. Cheng and C. A. Chen, "Optimum Spacings for Yagi-Uda Arrays," *IEEE Trans. Antennas Propag.*, vol. AP-21, pp. 615–623, September 1973.

18. C. A Chen and D. K. Cheng, "Optimum Element Lengths for Yagi-Uda Arrays," *IEEE Trans. Antennas Propag.*, vol. AP-23, pp. 8–15, January 1975.

19. N. K. Takla and L.-C. Shen, "Bandwidth of a Yagi Array with Optimum Directivity," *IEEE Trans. Antennas Propag.*, vol. AP-25, pp. 913–914, November 1977.

20. P. P. Viezbicke, "Yagi Antenna Design," NBS Technical Note 688, U.S. Department of Commerce/National Bureau of Standards, December 1968.

21. S. Adachi and Y. Mushiake, "Studies of Large Circular Loop Antennas," Sci. Rep. Research Institute of Tohoku University (RITU), B,9,2, pp. 79–103, 1957.

22. J. E. Lindsay, Jr., "A Parasitic End-fire Array of Circular Loop Elements," *IEEE Trans. Antennas Propag.*, vol. AP-15, pp. 697–698, September 1967.

23. E. Ledinegg, W. Paponsek, and H. L. Brueckmann, "Low-Frequency Loop Antenna Arrays: Ground Reaction and Mutual Interaction," *IEEE Trans. Antennas Propag.*, vol. AP-21, pp. 1–8, January 1973.

24. D. DeMaw (ed.), *The Radio Amateur's Handbook*, American Radio Relay League, p. 20-18, 56th ed., 1979.

25. A. Shoamanesh and L. Shafai, "Properties of Coaxial Yagi Loop Arrays," *IEEE Trans. Antennas Propag.*, vol. AP-26, pp. 547–550, July 1978.

26. A. Shoamanesh and L. Shafai, "Design Data for Coaxial Yagi Array of Circular

Loops," *IEEE Trans. Antennas Propag.*, vol. AP-27, pp. 711–713, September 1979.

PROBLEMS

9.1. Given the current distribution of (9-1), show that the
    (a) far-zone electric field intensity is given by (9-2a) and (9-2b)
    (b) average power density is given by (9-4) and (9-5)
    (c) radiated power is given by (9-11)

9.2. Determine the phase velocity (compared to free-space) of the wave on a Beverage antenna (terminated long wire) of length $l = 50\lambda$ so that the maximum occurs at angles of
    (a) $10°$
    (b) $20°$
    from the axis of the wire.

9.3. Design a Beverage antenna so that the first maximum occurs at $10°$ from its axis. Assuming the phase velocity of the wave on the line is the same as that of free-space, find the
    (a) lengths (exact and approximate) to accomplish that
    (b) angles (exact and approximate) where the next six maxima will occur
    (c) angles (exact and approximate) where the nulls, between the maxima found in parts (a) and (b), will occur
    (d) radiation resistance using the exact and approximate lengths
    (e) directivity using the exact and approximate lengths

9.4. Compute the directivity of a long wire with lengths of $l = 2\lambda$ and 3λ.

9.5. A long wire of diameter d is placed (in the air) at a height h above the ground.
    (a) Find its characteristic impedance assuming $h \gg d$.
    (b) Compare this value with (9-14).

9.6. Compute the optimum directivities of a V antenna with leg lengths of $l = 2\lambda$ and $l = 3\lambda$. Compare these values with those of Problem 9.4.

9.7. Design a symmetrical V antenna so that its optimum directivity is 8 dB. Find the lengths of each leg (in λ) and the total included angle of the V (in degrees).

9.8. Repeat the design of Problem 9.7 for an optimum directivity of 5 dB.

9.9. Design a resonant $90°$ bent, $\lambda/4$ long, $0.25 \times 10^{-3}\lambda$ radius wire antenna placed above a ground plane. Find the
    (a) height where the bent must be made
    (b) input resistance of the antenna
    (c) VSWR when the antenna is connected to a 50-ohm line

9.10. Design a five-turn helical antenna which at 400 MHz operates in the normal mode. The spacing between turns is $\lambda/50$. It is desired that the antenna possess circular polarization. Determine the
    (a) circumference of the helix (in λ and in meters)
    (b) length of a single turn (in λ and in meters)
    (c) overall length of the entire helix (in λ and in meters)
    (d) pitch angle (in degrees)

9.11. Design a five-turn helical antenna which at 300 MHz operates in the axial mode and possesses circular polarization in the major lobe. Determine the

(a) near optimum circumference (in λ and in meters)

(b) spacing (in λ and in meters) for near optimum pitch angle design

(c) input impedance

(d) half-power beamwidth (in degrees), first null beamwidth (in degrees), directivity (dimensionless and in dB), and axial ratio

(e) VSWR when the antenna is connected to 50- and 75-ohm coaxial lines

9.12. Repeat the design of Problem 9.11 at a frequency of 500 MHz.

9.13. Design a Yagi-Uda array of linear dipoles to cover all the VHF TV channels (starting with 54 MHz for channel 2 and ending with 216 MHz for channel 13. See Appendix VIII). Perform the design at $f_0 = 216$ MHz. Since the gain is not affected appreciably at $f < f_0$, as Figure 9.16 indicates, this design should accommodate all frequencies below 216 MHz. The gain of the antenna should be 14.4 dB (above isotropic). The elements and the supporting boom should be made of aluminum tubing with outside diameters of $\frac{3}{8}$ in. ($\simeq 0.95$ cm) and $\frac{3}{4}$ in. ($\simeq 1.9$ cm), respectively. Find the number of elements, their lengths and spacings, and the total length of the array (in λ, meters, and feet).

9.14. Repeat the design of Problem 9.13 for each of the following:

(a) VHF-TV channels 2–6 (54–88 MHz. See Appendix VIII)

(b) VHF-TV channels 7–13 (174–216 MHz. See Appendix VIII)

9.15. Design a Yagi-Uda antenna to cover the entire FM band of 88–108 MHz (100 channels spaced at 200 KHz apart. See Appendix VIII). The desired gain is 12.35 dB (above isotropic). Perform the design at $f_0 = 108$ MHz. The elements and the supporting boom should be made of aluminum tubing with outside diameters of $\frac{3}{8}$ in. ($\simeq 0.95$ cm) and $\frac{3}{4}$ in. ($\simeq 1.90$ cm), respectively. Find the number of elements, their lengths and spacings, and the total length of the array (in λ, meters, and feet).

9.16. Design a Yagi-Uda antenna to cover the UHF TV channels (512–806 MHz. See Appendix VIII). The desired gain is 12.35 dB (above isotropic). Perform the design at $f_0 = 806$ MHz. The elements and the supporting boom should be made of wire with outside diameters of $\frac{3}{32}$ in. ($\simeq 0.2375$ cm) and $\frac{3}{16}$ in. ($\simeq 0.475$ cm), respectively. Find the number of elements, their lengths and spacings, and the total length of the array (in λ, meters, and feet).

Chapter 10
Frequency Independent Antennas and Antenna Miniaturization

10.1 INTRODUCTION

The numerous applications of electromagnetics to the advances of technology have necessitated the exploration and utilization of most of the electromagnetic spectrum. In addition, the advent of broadband systems have demanded the design of broadband radiators. The use of simple, small, lightweight, and economical antennas, designed to operate over the entire frequency band of a given system, would be most desirable. Although in practice all the desired features and benefits cannot usually be derived from a single radiator, most can effectively be accommodated. Previous to the 1950s, antennas with broadband pattern and impedance characteristics had bandwidths not greater than 2:1. In the 1950s, a breakthrough in antenna evolution was made which extended the bandwidth to as great as 40:1 or more. The antennas introduced by the breakthrough were referred to as *frequency independent*, and they had geometries that were specified by angles. These antennas are primarily used in the 10–10,000 MHz region in a variety of practical applications such as TV, point-to-point communication, feeds for reflectors and lenses, and so forth.

In antenna scale modeling, characteristics such as impedance, pattern, polarization, and so forth, are invariant to a change of the physical size if a similar change is also made in the operating frequency or wavelength. For example, if *all* the physical dimensions are *reduced* by a factor of two, the performance of the antenna will remain unchanged if the operating frequency is *increased* by a factor of two. In other words, the performance is invariant if the electrical dimensions remain unchanged. This is the principle on which antenna scale model measurements are made. For a complete and thorough discussion of scaling, the reader is referred to Section 15.10 entitled "Scale Mode Measurements."

The scaling characteristics of antenna model measurements also indicate that if the shape of the antenna were completely specified by angles, its performance would have to be independent of frequency [1]. The infinite biconical dipole of Figure 8.1 is one such structure. To make infinite structures more practical, the designs usually require that the current on the structure decrease with distance away from the input terminals. After a certain point the current is negligible, and the structure beyond that point to infinity can be truncated and removed. Practically then the truncated antenna has a lower cutoff frequency above which its radiation characteristics are the same as those of the infinite structure. The lower cutoff frequency is that for which the current at the point of truncation becomes negligible. The upper cutoff is limited to frequencies for which the dimensions of the feed transmission line cease to look like a "point" (usually about $\lambda_2/8$ where λ_2 is the wavelength at the highest desirable frequency). Practical bandwidths are on the order of about 40 : 1. Even higher ratios (i.e., 1000 : 1) can be achieved in antenna design but they are not necessary, since they would far exceed the bandwidths of receivers and transmitters.

Even though the shape of the biconical antenna can be completely specified by angles, the current on its structure does not diminish with distance away from the input terminals, and its pattern does not have a limiting form with frequency. This can be seen by examining the current distribution as given by (8-11). It is evident that there are phase but no amplitude variations with the radial distance r. Thus the biconical structure cannot be truncated to form a frequency independent antenna. In practice, however, antenna shapes exist which satisfy the general shape equation, as proposed by Rumsey [1], to have frequency independent characteristics in pattern, impedance, polarization, and so forth, and with current distribution which diminishes rapidly.

Rumsey's general equation will first be developed, and it will be used as the unifying concept to link the major forms of frequency independent antennas. Classical shapes of such antennas include the equiangular geometries of planar and conical spiral structures investigated thoroughly by Dyson [2], [3], and the logarithmically periodic structures proposed and developed by DuHamel and Isbell [4], [5].

Fundamental limitations in electrically small antennas will be discussed in Section 10.5. These will be derived using spherical mode theory, with the antenna enclosed in a virtual sphere. Minimum Q curves, which place limits on the achievable bandwidth, will be included.

10.2 THEORY

The analytical treatment of frequency independent antennas presented here parallels that introduced by Rumsey [1] and simplified by Elliott [6] for three-dimensional configurations.

We begin by assuming that an antenna, whose geometry is best described by the spherical coordinates (r, θ, ϕ), has both terminals infinitely close to the origin and each is symmetrically disposed along the $\theta = 0, \pi$-axes. It is assumed that the antenna is perfectly conducting, it is surrounded by an infinite homogeneous and isotropic medium, and its surface or an edge on its surface is described by a curve

$$r = F(\theta, \phi) \qquad (10\text{-}1)$$

where r represents the distance along the surface or edge. If the antenna is to be scaled to a frequency that is K times lower than the original frequency, the antenna's physical surface must be made K times greater to maintain the same electrical dimensions. Thus the new surface is described by

$$r' = KF(\theta, \phi) \qquad (10\text{-}2)$$

The new and old surfaces are identical; that is, not only are they similar but they are also congruent (if both surfaces are infinite). Congruence can be established only by rotation in ϕ. Translation is not allowed because the terminals of both surfaces are at the origin. Rotation in θ is prohibited because both terminals are symmetrically disposed along the $\theta = 0, \pi$-axes.

For the second antenna to achieve congruence with the first, it must be rotated by an angle C so that

$$KF(\theta, \phi) = F(\theta, \phi + C) \qquad (10\text{-}3)$$

The angle of rotation C depends on K but neither depends on θ nor ϕ. Physical congruence implies that the original antenna would electrically behave the same at both frequencies. However the radiation pattern will be rotated azimuthally through an angle C. For unrestricted values of K $(0 \leq K \leq \infty)$, the pattern will rotate by C in ϕ with frequency, because C depends on K, but its shape will be unaltered. Thus the impedance and pattern will be frequency independent.

To obtain the functional representation of $F(\theta, \phi)$, both sides of (10-3) are differentiated with respect to C to yield

$$\frac{d}{dC}[KF(\theta, \phi)] = \frac{dK}{dC}F(\theta, \phi) = \frac{\partial}{\partial C}[F(\theta, \phi + C)]$$

$$= \frac{\partial}{\partial(\phi + C)}[F(\theta, \phi + C)] \qquad (10\text{-}4)$$

and with respect to ϕ to give

$$\frac{\partial}{\partial \phi}[KF(\theta, \phi)] = K\frac{\partial F(\theta, \phi)}{\partial \phi} = \frac{\partial}{\partial \phi}[F(\theta, \phi + C)]$$

$$= \frac{\partial}{\partial(\phi + C)}[F(\theta, \phi + C)] \qquad (10\text{-}5)$$

Equating (10-5) to (10-4) yields

$$\frac{dK}{dC}F(\theta,\phi)=K\frac{\partial F(\theta,\phi)}{\partial\phi} \tag{10-6}$$

Using (10-1) we can write (10-6) as

$$\frac{1}{K}\frac{dK}{dC}=\frac{1}{r}\frac{\partial r}{\partial\phi} \tag{10-7}$$

Since the left side of (10-7) is independent of θ and ϕ, a general solution for the surface $r=F(\theta,\phi)$ of the antenna is

$$r=F(\theta,\phi)=e^{a\phi}f(\theta) \tag{10-8}$$

$$\text{where } a=\frac{1}{K}\frac{dK}{dC} \tag{10-8a}$$

and $f(\theta)$ is a completely arbitrary function.

Thus for any antenna to have frequency independent characteristics, its surface must be described by (10-8). This can be accomplished by specifying the function $f(\theta)$ or its derivatives. Subsequently, interesting, practical, and extremely useful antenna configurations will be introduced whose surfaces are described by (10-8).

10.3 EQUIANGULAR SPIRAL ANTENNAS

The equiangular spiral is one geometrical configuration whose surface can be described by angles. It thus fulfills all the requirements for shapes that can be used to design frequency independent antennas. Since a curve along its surface extends to infinity, it is necessary to designate the length of the arm to specify a finite size antenna. The lowest frequency of operation occurs when the total arm length is comparable to the wavelength [2]. For all frequencies above this, the pattern and impedance characteristics are frequency independent.

10.3.1 Planar Spiral

The shape of an equiangular plane spiral curve can be derived by letting the derivative of $f(\theta)$ in (10-8) be

$$\frac{df}{d\theta}=f'(\theta)=A\delta\left(\frac{\pi}{2}-\theta\right) \tag{10-9}$$

where A is a constant and δ is the Dirac delta function. Using (10-9) reduces (10-8) to

$$r|_{\theta=\pi/2}=\rho=\begin{cases} Ae^{a\phi}=\rho_0e^{a(\phi-\phi_0)}, & \theta=\pi/2 \\ 0 & \text{elsewhere} \end{cases} \tag{10-10}$$

where

$$A = \rho_0 e^{-a\phi_0} \tag{10-10a}$$

In wavelengths, (10-10) can be written as

$$\rho_\lambda = \frac{\rho}{\lambda} = \frac{A}{\lambda} e^{a\phi} = A e^{a[\phi + \ln(\lambda)/a]} = e^{a(\phi + \phi_1)} \tag{10-11}$$

where

$$\phi_1 = \frac{1}{a} \ln(\lambda) \tag{10-11a}$$

Another form of (10-10) is

$$\phi = \frac{1}{a} \ln\left(\frac{\rho}{A}\right) = \tan\psi \ln\left(\frac{\rho}{A}\right) = \tan\psi(\ln\rho - \ln A) \tag{10-12}$$

where $1/a$ is the rate of expansion of the spiral and ψ is the angle between the radial distance ρ and the tangent to the spiral, as shown in Figure 10.1(a).

It is evident from (10-11) that changing the wavelength is equivalent to varying ϕ_0 which results in nothing more than a pure rotation of the infinite structure pattern. Within limitations imposed by the arm length, similar characteristics have been observed for finite structures. The same result can be concluded by examining (10-12). Increasing the logarithm of the frequency ($\ln f$) by C_0 is equivalent to rotating the structure by $C_0 \tan\psi$. As a result, the pattern is merely rotated but otherwise unaltered. Thus we have frequency independent antennas.

The total length L of the spiral can be calculated by

$$L = \int_{\rho_0}^{\rho_1} \left[\rho^2 \left(\frac{d\phi}{d\rho}\right)^2 + 1\right]^{1/2} d\rho \tag{10-13}$$

which reduces, using (10-10), to

$$\boxed{L = (\rho_1 - \rho_0)\sqrt{1 + \frac{1}{a^2}}} \tag{10-14}$$

where ρ_0 and ρ_1 represent the inner and outer radii of the spiral.

Various geometrical arrangements of the spiral have been used to form different antenna systems. If ϕ_0 in (10-10) is 0 and π the spiral wire antenna takes the form of Figure 10.1(b). The arrangements of Figures 10.1(c) and 10.1(d) are each obtained when $\phi_0 = 0$, $\pi/2$, π, and $3\pi/2$. Numerous other combinations are possible.

An equiangular metallic solid surface, designated as P, can be created by defining the curves of its edges, using (10-10), as

$$\rho_2 = \rho_2' e^{a\phi} \tag{10-15a}$$

$$\rho_3 = \rho_3' e^{a\phi} = \rho_2' e^{a(\phi - \delta)} \tag{10-15b}$$

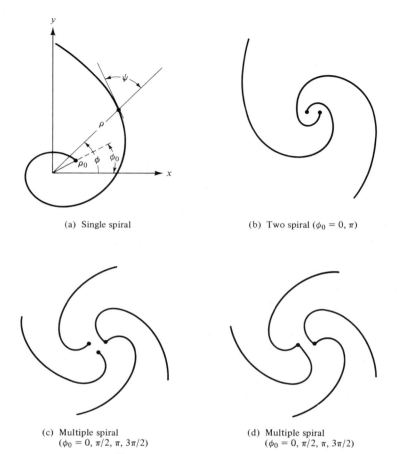

(a) Single spiral

(b) Two spiral ($\phi_0 = 0$, π)

(c) Multiple spiral
($\phi_0 = 0$, $\pi/2$, π, $3\pi/2$)

(d) Multiple spiral
($\phi_0 = 0$, $\pi/2$, π, $3\pi/2$)

Figure 10.1   Spiral wire antennas.

where

$$\rho_3' = \rho_2' e^{-a\delta} \tag{10-15c}$$

such that

$$K = \frac{\rho_3}{\rho_2} = e^{-a\delta} < 1 \tag{10-16}$$

The two curves, which specify the edges of the conducting surface, are of identical relative shape with one magnified relative to the other or rotated by an angle δ with respect to the other. The magnification or rotation allows the arm of conductor P to have a finite width, as shown in Figure 10.2(a).

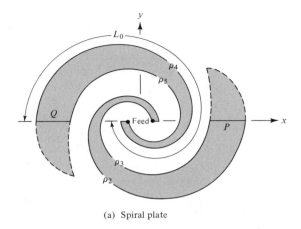

(a) Spiral plate

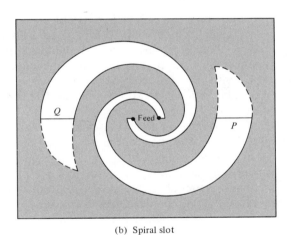

(b) Spiral slot

Figure 10.2   Spiral plate and slot antennas.

The metallic arm of a second conductor, designated as Q, can be defined by

$$\rho_4 = \rho_4' e^{a\phi} = \rho_2' e^{a(\phi-\pi)} \tag{10-17}$$

where

$$\rho_4' = \rho_2' e^{-a\pi} \tag{10-17a}$$

$$\rho_5 = \rho_5' e^{a\phi} = \rho_4' e^{a(\phi-\delta)} = \rho_2' e^{a(\phi-\pi-\delta)} \tag{10-18}$$

where

$$\rho_5' = \rho_4' e^{-a\delta} = \rho_2' e^{-a(\pi+\delta)} \tag{10-18a}$$

The system composed of the two conducting arms, P and Q, constitutes a balanced system, and it is shown in Figure 10.2(a). The finite size of the structure is specified by the fixed spiraling length L_0 along the centerline of the arm. The entire structure can be completely specified by the rotation angle δ, the arm length L_0, the rate of spiral $1/a$, and the terminal size ρ_2'. However, it has been found that most characteristics can be described adequately by only three; that is, L_0, ρ_2', and $K = e^{-a\delta}$ as given by (10-16). In addition each arm is usually tapered at its end, shown by dashed lines in Figure 10.2(a), to provide a better matching termination.

The previous analytical formulations can be used to describe two different antennas. One antenna would consist of two metallic arms suspended in free-space, as shown in Figure 10.2(a), and the other of a spiraling slot on a large conducting plane, as shown in Figure 10.2(b). The second is also usually tapered to provide better matching termination. The slot antenna is the most practical, because it can be conveniently fed by a balanced coaxial arrangement [2] to maintain its overall balancing. The antenna in Figure 10.2(a) with $\delta = \pi/2$ is self-complementary, as defined by Babinet's principle [7], and its input impedance for an infinite structure should be $188.5 \simeq 60\pi$ ohms (for discussion of Babinet's Principle see Section 11.8). Experimentally, measured mean input impedances were found to be only about 164 ohms. The difference between theory and experiment is attributed to the finite arm length, finite thickness of the plate, and nonideal feeding conditions.

Spiral slot antennas, with good radiation characteristics, can be built with one-half to three turns. The most optimum design seems to be that with 1.25 to 1.5 turns with an overall length equal to or greater than one wavelength. The rate of expansion should not exceed about 10 per turn. The patterns are bidirectional, single-lobed, broadside (maximum normal to the plane), and must vanish along the directions occupied by the infinite structure. The wave is circularly polarized near the axis of the main lobe over the usable part of the bandwidth. For a fixed cut, the beamwidth will vary with frequency since the pattern rotates. Typical variations are on the order of $10°$. In general, however, slot antennas with more broad arms and/or more tightly wound spirals exhibit smoother and more uniform patterns with smaller variations in beamwidth with frequency. For symmetrical structures, the pattern is also symmetrical with no tilt to the lobe structure.

To maintain the symmetrical characteristics, the antenna must be fed by an electrically and geometrically balanced line. One method that achieves geometrical balancing requires that the coax is embedded into one of the arms of the spiral. To maintain symmetry, a dummy cable is usually placed into the other arm. No appreciable currents flow on the feed cables because of the rapid attenuation of the fields along the spiral. If the feed line is electrically unbalanced, a balun must be used. This will limit the bandwidth of the system.

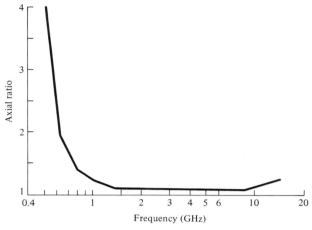

Figure 10.3   On-axis polarization as a function of frequency for one-turn spiral slot.
(SOURCE: J. D. Dyson, "The Equiangular Spiral Antenna," *IRE Trans. Antennas Propag.*, vol. AP-7, pp. 181–187, April 1959. © (1959) IEEE)

The polarization of the radiated wave is controlled by the length of the arms. For very low frequencies, such that the total arm length is small compared to the wavelength, the radiated field is linearly polarized. As the frequency increases, the wave becomes elliptically polarized and eventually it achieves circular polarization. Since the pattern is essentially unaltered through this frequency range, the polarization change with frequency can be used as a convenient criterion to select the lower cutoff frequency of the usable bandwidth. In many practical cases, this is chosen to be the point where the axial ratio is equal or less than 2 to 1, and it occurs typically when the overall armlength is about one wavelength. A typical variation in axial ratio of the on-axis field as a function of frequency for a one-turn slot antenna is shown in Figure 10.3. The off-axis radiated field has nearly circular polarization over a smaller part of the bandwidth. In addition to the limitation imposed on the bandwidth by the overall length of the arms, another critical factor that can extend or reduce the bandwidth is the construction precision of the feed.

The input impedance of a balanced equiangular slot antenna converges rapidly as the frequency is increased, and it remains reasonably constant for frequencies for which the arm length is greater than about one wavelength. Measured values for a 700–2500 MHz antenna [2] were about 75–100 ohms with VSWR's of less than 2 to 1 for 50-ohm lines.

For slot antennas radiating in free-space, without dielectric material or cavity backing, typical measured efficiencies are about 98% for arm lengths equal to or greater than one wavelength. Rapid decreases are observed for shorter arms.

10.3.2 Conical Spiral

The shape of a nonplanar spiral can be described by defining the derivative of $f(\theta)$ to be

$$\frac{df}{d\theta} = f'(\theta) = A\delta(\beta - \theta) \tag{10-19}$$

in which β is allowed to take any value in the range $0 \le \beta \le \pi$. For a given value of β, (10-19) in conjunction with (10-8) describes a spiral wrapped on a conical surface. The edges of one conical spiral surface are defined by

$$r_2 = r_2' e^{(a\sin\theta_0)\phi} = r_2' e^{b\phi} \tag{10-20a}$$

$$r_3 = r_3' e^{a\sin\theta_0\phi} = r_2' e^{a\sin\theta_0(\phi-\delta)} \tag{10-20b}$$

where

$$r_3' = r_2' e^{-(a\sin\theta_0)\delta} \tag{10-20c}$$

Figure 10.4 Conical spiral metal strip antenna. (SOURCE: *Antennas, Antenna Masts and Mounting Adaptors*, American Electronic Laboratories, Inc., Lansdale, Pa., Catalog 7.5M-7-79. Courtesy of American Electronic Laboratories, Inc., Montgomeryville, PA 18936 USA)

and θ_0 is half of the total included cone angle. Larger values of θ_0 in $0 \leq \theta \leq \pi/2$ represent less tightly wound spirals. These equations correspond to (10-15a)–(10-15c) for the planar surface. The second arm of a balanced system can be defined by shifting each of (10-20a)–(10-20c) by 180°, as was done for the planar surface by (10-17)–(10-18a). A conical spiral metal strip antenna of elliptical polarization is shown in Figure 10.4 [8].

The conducting conical spiral surface can be constructed conveniently by forming, using printed circuit techniques, the conical arms on the dielectric cone which is also used as a support. The feed cable can be bonded to the metal arms which are wrapped around the cone. Symmetry can be preserved by observing the same precautions, like the use of a dummy cable, as was done for the planar surface.

A distinct difference between the planar and conical spirals is that the latter provides unidirectional radiation (single lobe) toward the apex of the cone with the maximum along the axis. Circular polarization and relatively constant impedances are preserved over large bandwidths. Smoother patterns have been observed for unidirectional designs. Conical spirals can be used in conjunction with a ground plane, with a reduction in bandwidth when they are flush-mounted on the plane.

10.4 LOG-PERIODIC ANTENNAS

Another type of an antenna configuration, which closely parallels the frequency independent concept, is the log-periodic structure introduced by DuHamel and Isbell [4]. Because the entire shape of it cannot be solely specified by angles, it is not truly frequency independent.

10.4.1 Planar and Wire Surfaces

A planar log-periodic structure is shown in Figure 10.5(a). It consists of a metal strip whose edges are specified by the angle $\alpha/2$. However, in order to specify the length from the origin to any point on the structure, a distance characteristic must be included.

In spherical coordinates (r, θ, ϕ) the shape of the structure can be written as

$$\theta = \text{periodic function of } \left[b\ln(r) \right] \tag{10-21}$$

An example of it would be

$$\theta = \theta_0 \sin\left[b\ln\left(\frac{r}{r_0}\right) \right] \tag{10-22}$$

It is evident from (10-22) that the values of θ are repeated whenever the logarithm of the radial frequency $\ln(\omega) = \ln(2\pi f)$ differs by $2\pi/b$. The performance of the system is then periodic as a function of the logarithm of the frequency; thus the name *logarithmic-periodic or log-periodic*.

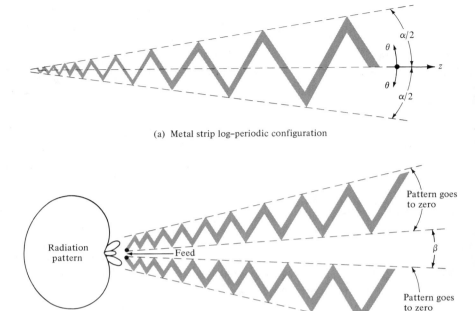

(a) Metal strip log–periodic configuration

(b) Log–periodic metal strip antenna

Figure 10.5   Typical metal strip log-periodic configuration and antenna structure.

A typical log-periodic antenna configuration is shown in Figure 10.5(b). It consists of two coplanar arms of the Figure 10.5(a) geometry. The pattern is unidirectional toward the apex of the cone formed by the two arms, and it is linearly polarized. Although the patterns of this and other log-periodic structures are not completely frequency independent, the amplitude variations of certain designs are very slight. Thus practically they are frequency independent.

Log-periodic wire antennas were introduced by DuHamel [4]. While investigating the current distribution on log-periodic surface structures of the form shown in Figure 10.6(a), he discovered that the fields on the conductors attenuated very sharply with distance. This suggested that perhaps there was a strong current concentration at or near the edges of the conductors. Thus removing part of the inner surface to form a wire antenna as shown in Figure 10.6(b) should not seriously degrade the performance of the antenna. To verify this, a wire antenna, with geometrical shape identical to the pattern formed by the edges of the conducting surface, was built and it was investigated experimentally. As predicted, it was found that the performance of this antenna was almost identical to that of Figure 10.6(a); thus the discovery of a much simpler, lighter in weight, cheaper, and less wind resistant antenna. Nonplanar geometries in the form of a V, formed by bending one arm relative to the other, are also widely used.

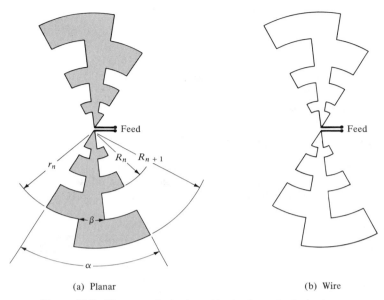

(a) Planar   (b) Wire

Figure 10.6   Planar and wire logarithmically periodic antennas.

If the wires or the edges of the plates are linear (instead of curved), the geometries of Figure 10.6 reduce, respectively, to the trapezoidal tooth log-periodic structures of Figure 10.7. These simplifications result in more convenient fabrication geometries with no loss in operational performance. There are numerous other bizarre but practical configurations of log-periodic structures, including log-periodic arrays.

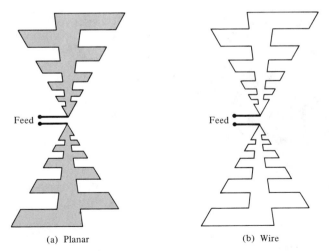

(a) Planar   (b) Wire

Figure 10.7   Planar and wire trapezoidal toothed log-periodic antennas.

If the geometries of Figure 10.6 use uniform periodic teeth, we define the geometric ratio of the log-periodic structure by

$$\tau = \frac{R_n}{R_{n+1}} \tag{10-23}$$

and the width of the antenna slot by

$$\chi = \frac{r_n}{R_{n+1}} \tag{10-24}$$

The geometric ratio τ of (10-23) defines the period of operation. For example, if two frequencies f_1 and f_2 are one period apart, they are related to the geometric ratio τ by

$$\tau = \frac{f_1}{f_2}, \qquad f_2 > f_1 \tag{10-25}$$

Extensive studies on the performance of the antenna of Figure 10.6(b) as a function of α, β, τ, and χ, have been performed [9]. In general, these structures performed almost as well as the planar and conical structures. The only major difference is that the log-periodic configurations are linearly polarized instead of circular.

A commercial lightweight, cavity-backed, linearly polarized, flush-mounted log-periodic slot antenna and its associated gain characteristics are shown in Figures 10.8(a) and (b) [8]. Typical electrical characteristics are: VSWR—2:1; E-plane beamwidth—70°; H-plane beamwidth—70°. The

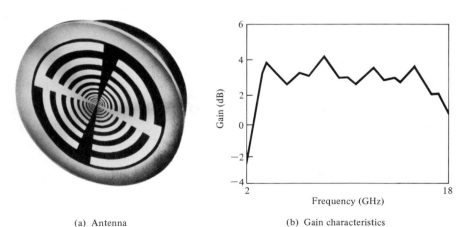

(a) Antenna   (b) Gain characteristics

Figure 10.8 Linearly polarized flush-mounted cavity-backed log-periodic slot antenna and typical gain characteristics. (SOURCE: *Antennas, Antenna Masts and Mounting Adaptors*, American Electronic Laboratories, Inc., Landsdale, Pa., Catalog 7.5M-7-79. Courtesy of American Electronic Laboratories, Inc., Montgomeryville, PA 18936 USA)

maximum diameter of the cavity is about 2.4 in. (6.1 cm), the depth is 1.75 in. (4.445 cm), and the weight is near 5 oz (0.14 kg).

10.4.2 Dipole Array

To the layman, the most recognized log-periodic antenna structure is the configuration introduced by Isbell [5] which is shown in Figure 10.9(a). It consists of a sequence of side-by-side parallel linear dipoles forming a coplanar array. Although this antenna has similar directivities as the Yagi-Uda array (7–12 dB), they are achievable and maintained over much wider bandwidths. There are, however, major differences between them.

While the geometrical dimensions of the Yagi-Uda array elements do not follow any set pattern, the lengths (l_n's), spacings (R_n's), diameters (d_n's), and even gap spacings at dipole centers (s_n's) of the log-periodic array increase logarithmically as defined by the inverse of the geometric ratio τ. That is,

$$\frac{1}{\tau} = \frac{l_2}{l_1} = \frac{l_{n+1}}{l_n} = \frac{R_2}{R_1} = \frac{R_{n+1}}{R_n} = \frac{d_2}{d_1} = \frac{d_{n+1}}{d_n} = \frac{s_2}{s_1} = \frac{s_{n+1}}{s_n} \qquad (10\text{-}26)$$

Another parameter that is usually associated with a dipole array is σ defined by

$$\sigma = \frac{d_n}{2l_n} \qquad (10\text{-}26a)$$

Straight lines through the dipole ends meet to form an angle α which is a characteristic of frequency independent structures.

Because it is usually very difficult to obtain wires or tubing of many different diameters and to maintain tolerances of very small gap spacings, constant dimensions in these can be used. These relatively minor factors will not sufficiently degrade the overall performance.

While only one element of the Yagi-Uda array is directly energized by the feed line, while the others operate in a parasitic mode, all the elements of the log-periodic array are connected. There are two basic methods, as shown in Figures 10.9(b) and 10.9(c), which could be used to connect and feed the elements of a log-periodic dipole array. In both cases the antenna is fed at the small end of the structure.

The currents in the elements of Figure 10.9(b) have the same phase relationship as the terminal phases. If in addition the elements are closely spaced, the phase progression of the currents is to the right. This produces an endfire beam in the direction of the longer elements and interference effects to the pattern result.

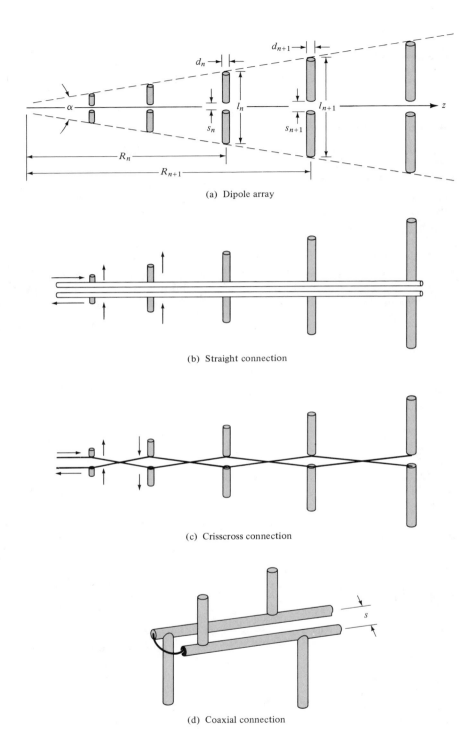

(a) Dipole array

(b) Straight connection

(c) Crisscross connection

(d) Coaxial connection

Figure 10.9 Log-periodic dipole array and associated connections.

It was recognized that by mechanically crisscrossing or transposing the feed between adjacent elements, as shown in Figure 10.9(c), a 180° phase is added to the terminal of each element. Since the phase between the adjacent closely spaced short elements is almost in opposition, very little energy is radiated by them and their interference effects are negligible. However, at the same time, the longer and larger spaced elements will radiate. The mechanical phase reversal between these elements produces a phase progression so that the energy is beamed endfire in the direction of the shorter elements. The most active elements for this feed arrangement are those that are near resonant with a combined radiation pattern toward the vertex of the array.

The feed arrangement of Figure 10.9(c) is convenient provided the input feed line is a balanced line like the two-conductor transmission line. Using a coaxial cable as a feed line, a practical method to achieve the 180° phase reversal between adjacent elements is shown in Figure 10.9(d). This feed arrangement provides a built-in broadband balun resulting in a balanced overall system. The elements and the feeder line of this array are usually made of piping. The coaxial cable is brought to the feed through the hollow part of one of the feeder line pipes. While the outside conductor of the coax is connected to that conductor at the feed, its inner conductor is extended and it is connected to the other pipe of the feeder line.

If the geometrical pattern of the log-periodic array, as defined by (10-26), is to be maintained to achieve a truly log-periodic configuration, an infinite structure would result. However, to be useful as a practical broadband radiator, the structure is truncated at both ends. This limits the frequency of operation to a given bandwidth.

The cutoff frequencies of the truncated structure are determined by the electrical lengths of the longest and shortest elements of the structure. The lower cutoff frequency occurs approximately when the longest element is $\lambda/2$ while the high cutoff frequency occurs when the shortest element is nearly $\lambda/2$. At a given frequency within the bandwidth, the active region of a log-periodic dipole array is near the element whose length is nearly or slightly smaller than $\lambda/2$. The role of active elements is passed from the longer to the shorter elements as the frequency increases. Also the energy from the shorter active elements traveling toward the longer inactive elements decreases very rapidly so that a negligible amount is reflected from the truncated end. The movement of the active region of the antenna, and its associated phase center, is an undesirable characteristic in the design of feeds for reflector and lens antennas.

The decrease of energy toward the longer inactive elements is demonstrated in Figure 10.10(a). The curves represent typical computed and measured transmission line voltages (amplitude and phase) on a log-periodic dipole array [10] as a function of distance from its apex. These are feeder-line voltages at the base of the elements of an array with $\tau=0.95$, $\sigma=0.0564$, $N=13$, and $l_n/d_n=177$. The frequency of operation is such that

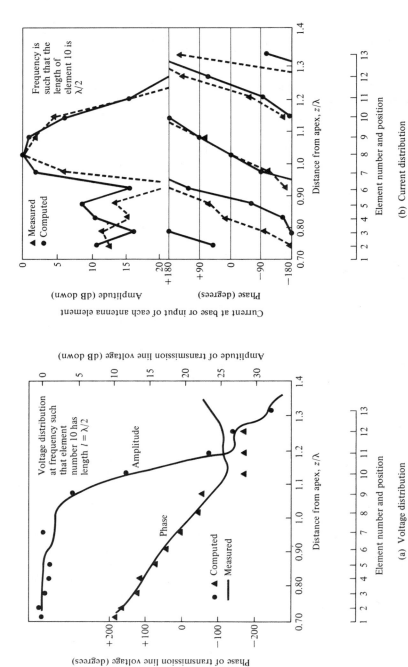

Figure 10.10 Measured and computed voltage and current distributions on a log-periodic dipole array of 13 elements with frequency such that $l_{10} = \lambda/2$. (SOURCE: R. L. Carrel, "Analysis and Design of the Log-Periodic Dipole Antenna," Ph.D. Dissertation, Elec. Eng. Dept., University of Illinois, 1961, University Microfilms, Inc., Ann Arbor, Michigan)

element No. 10 is $\lambda/2$. The amplitude voltage is nearly constant from the first (the feed) to the eighth element while the corresponding phase is uniformly progressive. Very rapid decreases in amplitude and nonlinear phase variations are noted beyond the eighth element.

The region of constant voltage along the structure is referred to as the transmission region, because it resembles that of a matched transmission line. Along the structure, there is about 150° phase change for every $\lambda/4$ free-space length of transmission line. This indicates that the phase velocity of the wave traveling along the structure is $v_p = 0.6v_0$, where v_0 is the free-space velocity of a plane wave. The smaller velocity results from the shunt capacitive loading of the line by the smaller elements. The loading is almost constant per unit length because there are larger spacings between the longer elements.

The corresponding current distribution is shown in Figure 10.10(b). It is noted that the rapid decrease in voltage is associated with strong current excitation of elements 7–10 followed by a rapid decline. The region of high current excitation is designated as the active region, and it encompasses 4 to 5 elements for this design. The voltage and current excitations of the longer elements (beyond the ninth) are relatively small, reassuring that the truncated larger end of the structure is not affecting the performance. The smaller elements, because of their length, are not excited effectively. As the frequency changes, the relative voltage and current patterns remain essentially the same, but they move toward the direction of the active region.

There is a linear increase in current phase, especially in the active region, from the shorter to the longer elements. This phase shift progression is opposite in direction to that of an unloaded line. It suggests that on the log-periodic antenna structure there is a wave that travels toward the feed forming a unidirectional endfire pattern toward the vertex.

The radiated wave of a single log-periodic dipole array is linearly polarized, and it has horizontal polarization when the plane of the antenna is parallel to the ground. Bidirectional patterns and circular polarization can be obtained by phasing multiple log-periodic dipole arrays. For these, the overall effective phase center can be maintained at the feed.

If the input impedance of a log-periodic antenna is plotted as a function of frequency, it will be repetitive. However, if it is plotted as a function of the *logarithm* of the frequency, it will be *periodic* (not necessarily sinusoidal) with each cycle being exactly identical to the preceding one. Hence the name *log-periodic*, because the variations are *periodic* with respect to the *logarithm* of the frequency. A typical variation of the impedance as a function of frequency is shown in Figure 10.11. Other parameters that undergo similar variations are the pattern, directivity, beamwidth, and side lobe level.

The periodicity of the structure does not ensure broadband operation. However, if the variations of the impedance, pattern, directivity, and so forth within one cycle are made sufficiently small and acceptable for the

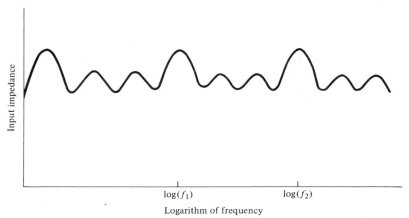

Figure 10.11 Typical input impedance variation of a log-periodic antenna as a function of the logarithm of the frequency.

corresponding bandwidth of the cycle, broadband characteristics are ensured within acceptable limits of variation. The total bandwidth is determined by the number of repetitive cycles for the given truncated structure.

The frequency span Δf of each cycle is determined by the geometric ratio as defined by (10-25) and (10-26).* Taking the logarithm of both sides in (10-25) reduces to

$$\Delta f = \ln(f_2) - \ln(f_1) = \ln\left(\frac{1}{\tau}\right) \tag{10-27}$$

The variations that occur within a given cycle ($f_1 \leq f \leq f_2 = f_1/\tau$) will repeat identically at other cycles of the bandwidth defined by $f_n/\tau^{n-1} \leq f \leq f_n/\tau^n$, $n = 1, 2, 3, \ldots$.

Typical designs of log-periodic dipole arrays have apex angles of $10° \leq \alpha \leq 45°$ and $0.95 \leq \tau \leq 0.7$. There is a relation between the values of α and τ. As α increases, the corresponding τ values decrease, and vice versa. Larger values of α or smaller values of τ result in more compact designs which require smaller number of elements separated by larger distances. In contrast, smaller values of α or larger values of τ require a larger number of elements that are closer together. For this type of a design, there are more elements in the active region which are nearly $\lambda/2$. Therefore the variations of the impedance and other characteristics as a function of frequency are smaller, because of the smoother transition between elements, and the gains are larger.

Experimental models of log-periodic dipole arrays have been built and measurements were made [5]. The input impedances (purely resistive) and

---

*In some cases, the impedance (but not the pattern) may vary with a period which is one-half of (10-27). That is, $\Delta f = \frac{1}{2}\ln(1/\tau)$.

Table 10.1 INPUT RESISTANCES (R_{in} IN OHMS) AND DIRECTIVITIES (dB ABOVE ISOTROPIC) FOR LOG-PERIODIC DIPOLE ARRAYS

α	$\tau = 0.81$		$\tau = 0.89$		$\tau = 0.95$	
	R_{in} (ohms)	D_0 (dB)	R_{in} (ohms)	D_0 (dB)	R_{in} (ohms)	D_0 (dB)
10	98	—	82	9.8	77.5	10.7
12.5	—	—	77	—	—	—
15	—	7.2	—	—	—	—
17.5	—	—	76	7.7	62	8.8
20	—	—	74	—	—	—
25	—	—	63	7.2	—	8.0
30	80	—	64	—	54	—
35	—	—	56	6.5	—	—
45	65	5.2	59	6.2	—	—

SOURCE: D. E. Isbell, "Log Periodic Dipole Arrays," *IRE Trans. Antennas Propag.*, vol. AP-8, pp. 260–267, May 1960. © (1960) IEEE.

corresponding directivities (*above isotropic*) for three different designs are listed in Table 10.1. Larger directivities can be achieved by arraying multiple log-periodic dipole arrays. There are other configurations of log-periodic dipole array designs, including those with V instead of linear elements [11]. This array provides moderate bandwidths with good directivities at the higher frequencies, and it is widely used as a single TV antenna covering the entire frequency spectrum from the lowest VHF channel (54 MHz) to the highest UHF (806 MHz). Typical gain, VSWR, and E- and H-plane half-power beamwidths of commercial log-periodic dipole arrays are shown in Figures 10.12(a),(b),(c), respectively [8]. The overall length of each of these antennas is about 105 in. (41.4 cm) while the largest element in each has an overall length of about 122 in. (48 cm). The weight of each antenna is about 31 lb ($\simeq$ 14 kg).

The ultimate goal of any antenna configuration is the design that meets certain specifications. Probably the most introductory, complete, and practical design procedure for a log-periodic dipole array is that by Carrel [10]. To aid in the design, he has a set of curves and nomographs. The general configuration of a log-periodic array is described in terms of the design parameters τ, α, and σ related by

$$\alpha = \tan^{-1} \left[\frac{1 - \tau}{4\sigma} \right]$$

(10-28)

Once two of them are specified, the other can be found. Directivity (in dB) contour curves as a function of τ for various values of σ are shown in Figure 10.13.

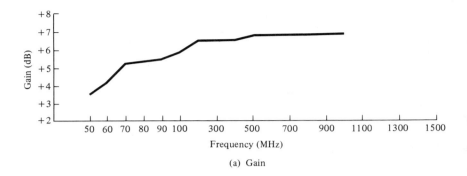

(a) Gain

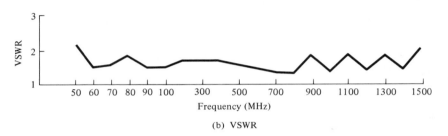

(b) VSWR

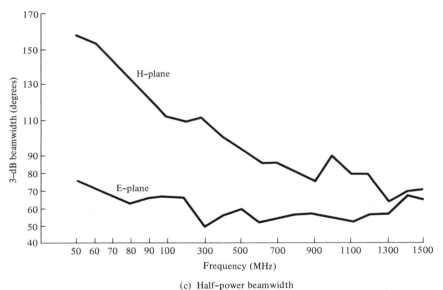

(c) Half–power beamwidth

Figure 10.12 Typical gain, VSWR, and half-power beamwidth of commercial log-periodic dipole arrays. (SOURCE: *Antennas, Antenna Masts and Mounting Adaptors*, American Electronic Laboratories, Inc., Lansdale, Pa., Catalog 7.5M-7-79. Courtesy of American Electronic Laboratories, Inc., Montgomeryville, PA 18936 USA)

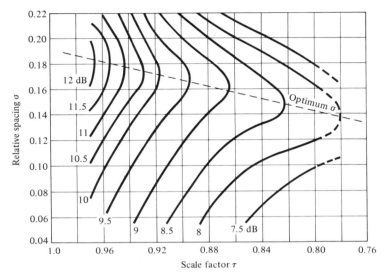

Figure 10.13 Computed contours of constant directivity versus σ and τ for log-periodic dipole arrays. (SOURCE: R. L. Carrel, "Analysis and Design of the Log-Periodic Dipole Antenna," Ph.D. Dissertation, Elec. Eng. Dept., University of Illinois, 1961, University Microfilms, Inc., Ann Arbor Michigan)

While the bandwidth of the system determines the lengths of the shortest and longest elements of the structure, the width of the active region depends on the specific design. Carrel [10] has introduced a semiempirical equation to calculate the bandwidth of the active region B_{ar} related to α and τ by

$$B_{ar} = 1.1 + 7.7(1-\tau)^2 \cot \alpha \tag{10-29}$$

In practice a slightly larger bandwidth (B_s) is usually designed than that which is required (B). The two are related by

$$B_s = BB_{ar} = B\left[1.1 + 7.7(1-\tau)^2 \cot \alpha\right] \tag{10-30}$$

where

B_s = designed bandwidth

B = desired bandwidth

B_{ar} = active region bandwidth

The total length of the structure L, from the shortest (l_{min}) to the longest (l_{max}) element, is given by

$$L = \frac{\lambda_{max}}{4} \left(1 - \frac{1}{B_s}\right) \cot \alpha \qquad (10\text{-}31)$$

where

$$\lambda_{max} = 2 l_{max} = \frac{v}{f_{min}} \qquad (10\text{-}31a)$$

From the geometry of the system, the number of elements are determined by

$$N = 1 + \frac{\ln(B_s)}{\ln(1/\tau)} \qquad (10\text{-}32)$$

The center-to-center spacing s of the feeder line conductors can be determined by specifying the required input impedance (assumed to be real), and the diameter of the dipole elements and the feeder line conductors. To accomplish this, we first define an average characteristic impedance of the elements given by

$$Z_a = 120 \left[\ln\left(\frac{l_n}{d_n}\right) - 2.25 \right] \qquad (10\text{-}33)$$

where l_n/d_n is the length-to-diameter ratio of the nth element of the array. For an ideal log-periodic design, this ratio should be the same for all the elements of the array. Practically, however, the elements are usually divided into one, two, three or more groups with all the elements in each group having the same diameter but not the same length. The number of groups is determined by the total number of elements of the array. Usually three groups (for the small, middle, and large elements) should be sufficient.

The effective loading of the dipole elements on the input line is characterized by the graphs shown in Figure 10.14 where

$\sigma' = \sigma/\sqrt{\tau}$ = relative mean spacing

Z_a = average characteristic impedance of the elements

R_{in} = input impedance (real)

Z_0 = characteristic impedance of the feeder line

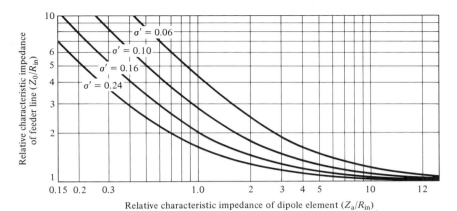

Figure 10.14 Relative characteristic impedance of a feeder line as a function of relative characteristic impedance of dipole element. (SOURCE: R. L. Carrel, "Analysis and Design of the Log-Periodic Dipole Antenna," Ph.D. Dissertation, Elec. Eng. Dept., University of Illinois, 1961, University Microfilms, Inc., Ann Arbor, Michigan)

The center-to-center spacing s between the two rods of the feeder line, each of identical diameter d, is determined by

$$s = d \cosh\left(\frac{Z_0}{120}\right) \qquad (10\text{-}34)$$

10.4.3 Design of Dipole Array

The design procedure assumes that the directivity (in dB), input impedance R_{in} (real), diameter of elements of feeder line (d), and the lower and upper frequencies ($B = f_{max}/f_{min}$) of the bandwidth are specified. It then proceeds as follows:

1. Given D_0 (dB), determine σ and τ from Figure 10.13.
2. Determine α using (10-28).
3. Determine B_{ar} using (10-29) and B_s using (10-30).
4. Find L using (10-31) and N using (10-32).
5. Determine Z_a using (10-33) and $\sigma' = \sigma/\sqrt{\tau}$.
6. Determine Z_0/R_{in} using Figure 10.14.
7. Find s using (10-34).

Example 10.1

Design a log-periodic dipole antenna, of the form shown in Figure 10.9(d), to cover all the VHF TV channels (starting with 54 MHz for channel 2 and ending with 216 MHz for channel 13. See Appendix VIII.) The desired directivity is 9 dB and the input impedance is 50 ohms (ideal for a match to 50-ohm coaxial cable). The elements should be made of aluminum tubing with $\frac{3}{4}$ in. (1.9 cm) outside diameter for the largest element and the feeder line and $\frac{3}{16}$ in. (0.48 cm) for the smallest element. These diameters yield identical l/d ratios for the smallest and largest elements.

SOLUTION

1. From Figure 10.13, for $D_0 = 9$ dB the optimum σ is $\sigma = 0.157$ and the corresponding τ is $\tau = 0.865$.

2. Using (10-28)

$$\alpha = \tan^{-1} \left[\frac{1-0.865}{4(0.157)} \right] = 12.13° \simeq 12°$$

3. Using (10-29)

$$B_{ar} = 1.1 + 7.7(1-0.865)^2 \cot(12.13°) = 1.753$$

and from (10-30)

$$B_s = BB_{ar} = \frac{226}{54}(1.753) = 4(1.753) = 7.01$$

4. Using (10-31a)

$$\lambda_{max} = \frac{v}{f_{min}} = \frac{3 \times 10^8}{54 \times 10^6} = 5.556 \text{ m } (18.227 \text{ ft})$$

From (10-31)

$$L = \frac{5.556}{4}\left(1 - \frac{1}{7.01}\right)\cot(12.13°) = 5.541 \text{ m } (18.178 \text{ ft})$$

and from (10-32)

$$N = 1 + \frac{\ln(7.01)}{\ln(1/0.865)} = 14.43 \text{ (14 or 15 elements)}$$

5. $\sigma' = \dfrac{\sigma}{\sqrt{\tau}} = \dfrac{0.157}{\sqrt{0.865}} = 0.169$

At the lowest frequency

$$l_{max} = \frac{\lambda_{max}}{2} = \frac{18.227}{2} = 9.1135 \text{ ft}$$

$$\frac{l_{max}}{d_{max}} = \frac{9.1135(12)}{0.75} = 145.816$$

Using (10-33)

$$Z_a = 120[\ln(145.816) - 2.25] = 327.88 \text{ ohms}$$

Thus

$$\frac{Z_a}{R_{in}} = \frac{327.88}{50} = 6.558$$

6. From Figure 10.14

$$Z_0 \simeq 1.2 R_{in} = 1.2(50) = 60 \text{ ohms}$$

7. Using (10-34), assuming the feeder line conductor is made of the same size tubing as the largest element of the array, the center-to-center spacing of the feeder conductors is

$$s = \frac{3}{4} \cosh\left(\frac{60}{120}\right) = 0.846 \simeq 0.85 \text{ in.}$$

which allows for a 0.1-in. separation between their conducting surfaces.

For such a high-gain antenna, this is obviously a good practical design. If a lower gain is specified and designed for, a smaller length will result.

10.5 FUNDAMENTAL LIMITS OF ELECTRICALLY SMALL ANTENNAS

In all areas of electrical engineering, especially in electronic devices and computers, the attention has been shifted toward miniaturization. Electromagnetics, and antennas in particular, are of no exception. A large emphasis in the last few years has been placed toward electrically small antennas, including printed board designs. However, there are fundamental limits as to how small the antenna elements can be made. The basic limitations are imposed by the free-space wavelength to which the antenna element must couple to, which has not been or is expected to be miniaturized [12].

An excellent paper on the fundamental limits in antennas has been published [12], and most of the material in this section is drawn from it. It reviews the limits of electrically small, superdirective, super-resolution, and high-gain antennas. The limits on electrically small antennas are derived by assuming that the entire antenna structure (with a largest linear dimension of $2r$), and its transmission line and oscillator are all enclosed within a sphere of radius r as shown in Figure 10.15(a). Because of the arbitrary current or source distribution of the antenna inside the sphere, its radiated field outside the sphere is expressed as a complete set of orthogonal spherical vector waves or modes. For vertically polarized omnidirectional antennas, only TM_{m0} circularly symmetric (no azimuthal variations) modes are required. Each mode is used to represent a spherical wave which propagates in the outward radial direction. This approach was introduced first by Chu [13], and it was followed by Harrington [14]. Earlier papers on

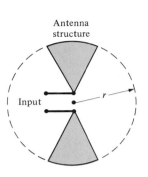

Antenna structure

Input

(a) Biconical antenna within a sphere (after C. J. Chu [13])

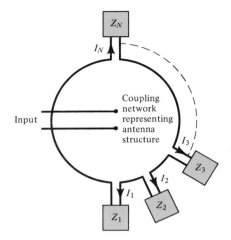

Input

Coupling network representing antenna structure

(b) Equivalent network of a vertically–polarized omnidirectional antenna (after C. J. Chu [13])

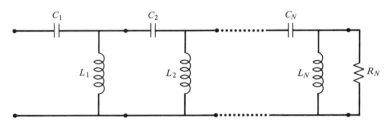

(c) Equivalent circuit for N spherical modes

Figure 10.15 Antenna within a sphere of radius r, and its equivalent circuit modeling. (SOURCE: C. J. Chu, "Physical Limitations of Omnidirectional Antennas," *J. Appl. Phys.*, vol. 19, pp. 1163–1175, December 1948)

the fundamental limitations and performance of small antennas were published by Wheeler [15]–[17]. He derived the limits of a small dipole and a small loop (used as a magnetic dipole) from the limitations of a capacitor and an inductor, respectively. The capacitor and inductor were chosen to occupy, respectively, volumes equal to those of the dipole and the loop.

Using the mathematical formulation introduced by Chu [13], the source or current distribution of the antenna system inside the sphere is not uniquely determined by the field distribution outside the sphere. Since it is possible to determine an infinite number of different source or current distributions inside the sphere, for a given field configuration outside the sphere, Chu [13] confined his interest to the most favorable source distribution and its corresponding antenna structure that could exist within the sphere. This approach was taken to minimize the details and to simplify the task of identifying the antenna structure. It was also assumed that the desired current or source distribution minimizes the amount of energy stored inside the sphere so that the input impedance at a given frequency is resistive.

Because the spherical wave modes outside the sphere are orthogonal, the total energy (electric or magnetic) outside the sphere and the complex power transmitted across the closed spherical surface are equal, respectively, to the sum of the energies and complex powers associated with each corresponding spherical mode. Therefore there is no coupling, in energy or power, between any two modes outside the sphere. As a result, the space outside the sphere can be replaced by a number of independent equivalent circuits as shown in Figure 10.15(b). The number of equivalent circuits is equal to the number of spherical wave modes outside the sphere, plus one. The terminals of each equivalent circuit are connected to a box which represents the inside of the sphere, and from inside the box a pair of terminals are drawn to represent the input terminals. Using this procedure, the antenna space problem has been reduced to one of equivalent circuits.

The radiated power of the antenna is calculated from the propagating modes while all modes contribute to the reactive power. When the sphere (which encloses the antenna element) becomes very small, there exist no propagating modes. Therefore the Q of the system becomes very large since all modes are evanescent (below cutoff) and contribute very little power. However, unlike closed waveguides, each evanescent mode here has a real part (even though it is very small).

For a lossless antenna (radiation efficiency $e_{cd} = 100\%$), the equivalent circuit of each spherical mode is a single network section with a series C and a shunt L. The total circuit is a ladder network of $L-C$ sections (one for each mode) with a final shunt resistive load, as shown in Figure 10.15(c). The resistive load is used to represent the normalized antenna radiation resistance.

From this circuit structure, the input impedance is found. The Q of each mode is formed by the ratio of its stored to its radiated energy. When several modes are supported, the Q is formed from the contributions of all the modes.

It has been shown that the higher order modes within a sphere of radius r become evanescent when $kr < 1$. Therefore the Q of the system, for the lowest order TM mode, reduces to [12]

$$Q = \frac{1 + 3(kr)^2}{(kr)^3 \left[1 + (kr)^2\right]} \overset{kr \ll 1}{\simeq} \frac{1}{(kr)^3} \tag{10-35}$$

When two modes are excited, one TE and the other TM, the values of Q are halved. Equation (10-35), which relates the lowest achievable Q to the largest linear dimension of an electrically small antenna, is independent of the geometrical configuration of the antenna within the sphere of radius r. The shape of the radiating element within the bounds of the sphere only determines whether TE, TM, or TE and TM modes are excited. *Therefore*

(10-35) represents the fundamental limit on the electrical size of an antenna. In practice, this limit is only approached but is never exceeded or even equaled.

The losses of an antenna can be taken into account by including a loss resistance in series with the radiation resistance, as shown by the equivalent circuits of Figures 2.18(b) and 2.19(b). This influences the Q of the system and the antenna radiation efficiency as given by (2-86).

Computed values of Q versus kr for idealized antennas enclosed within a sphere of radius r, and with radiation efficiencies of $e_{cd} = 100$, 50, 10, and 5, are shown plotted in Figure 10.16. These curves represent the minimum values of Q that can be obtained from an antenna whose structure can be enclosed within a sphere of radius r and whose radiated field, outside the sphere, can be represented by a single spherical wave mode.

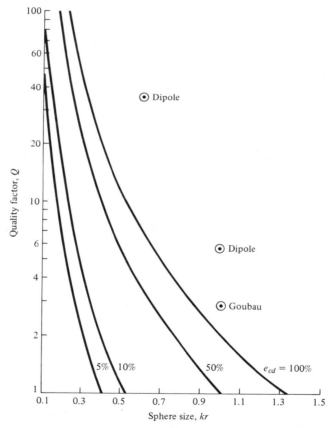

Figure 10.16 Fundamental limits of Q versus antenna size (enclosed within a sphere of radius r) for single-mode antennas of various radiation efficiencies. (SOURCE: R. C. Hansen, "Fundamental Limitations in Antennas," *Proc. IEEE*, vol. 69, No. 2, February 1981. © (1981) IEEE)

For antennas with equivalent circuits of fixed values, the fractional bandwidth is related to the Q of the system by

$$\text{fractional bandwidth} = \text{FBW} = \frac{\Delta f}{f_0} = \frac{1}{Q} \tag{10-36}$$

where

f_0 = center frequency

Δf = bandwidth

The relationship of (10-36) is valid for $Q \gg 1$ since the equivalent resonant circuit with fixed values is a good approximation for an antenna. For values of $Q < 2$, (10-36) is not accurate.

To compare the results of the minimum Q curves of Figure 10.16 with values of practical antenna structures, data points for a small linear dipole and a Goubau [18] antenna are included in the same figure. For a small linear dipole of length l and wire radius a, its impedance is given by [12]

$$Z_{\text{in}} \simeq 20 \pi^2 \left(\frac{l}{\lambda} \right)^2 - j120 \frac{\left[\ln \left(\frac{l}{2a} \right) - 1 \right]}{\tan \left(\pi \frac{l}{\lambda} \right)} \tag{10-37}$$

and its corresponding Q by

$$Q \simeq \frac{\left[\ln \left(\frac{l}{2a} \right) - 1 \right]}{\left(\pi \frac{l}{\lambda} \right)^2 \tan \left(\pi \frac{l}{\lambda} \right)} \tag{10-38}$$

The real part in (10-37) is identical to (4-37). The computed Q values of the small dipole were for $kl/2 = kr \simeq 0.62$ and 1.04 with $l/2a = l/d = 50$, and of the Goubau antenna were for $kr \simeq 1.04$.

It is apparent that the Q's of the dipole are much higher than the corresponding values of the minimum Q curves even for the 100% efficient antennas. However the Goubau antenna, of the same radius sphere, demonstrates a lower value of Q and approaches the values of the 100% minimum Q curve. This indicates that the fractional bandwidth of the Goubau antenna, which is inversely proportional to its Q as defined by (10-36), is higher than that of a dipole enclosed within the same radius sphere. In turn, the bandwidth of an idealized antenna, enclosed within the same sphere, is even larger.

From the above, it is concluded that *the bandwidth of an antenna (which can be closed within a sphere of radius r) can be improved only if the antenna utilizes efficiently, with its geometrical configuration, the available volume within the sphere.* The dipole, being a one-dimensional structure, is a poor utilizer of the available volume within the sphere. However a Goubau antenna, being a clover leaf dipole with coupling loops over a ground plane (or a double clover leaf dipole without a ground plane), is a more effective design for utilizing the available three-dimensional space within the sphere. A design that utilizes the space even more efficiently than the Goubau antenna would possess a lower Q and a higher fractional bandwidth. Ultimately, the values would approach the minimum Q curves. In practice, these curves are only approached but are never exceeded or even equaled.

References

1. V. H. Rumsey, "Frequency Independent Antennas," *1957 IRE National Convention Record*, pt. 1, pp. 114–118.
2. J. D. Dyson, "The Equiangular Spiral Antenna," *IRE Trans. Antennas Propag.*, vol. AP-7, pp. 181–187, April 1959.
3. J. D. Dyson, "The Unidirectional Equiangular Spiral Antenna," *IRE Trans. Antennas Propag.*, vol. AP-7, pp. 329–334, October 1959.
4. R. H. DuHamel and D. E. Isbell, "Broadband Logarithmically Periodic Antenna Structures," *1957 IRE National Convention Record*, pt. 1, pp. 119–128.
5. D. E. Isbell, "Log Periodic Dipole Arrays," *IRE Trans. Antennas Propag.*, vol. AP-8, pp. 260–267, May 1960.
6. R. S. Elliott, "A View of Frequency Independent Antennas," *The Microwave Journal*, pp. 61–68, December 1962.
7. H. G. Booker, "Slot Aerials and Their Relation to Complementary Wire Aerials," *Journal of IEE* (London), vol. 93, pt. IIIA, April 1946.
8. *Antennas, Antenna Masts and Mounting Adaptors*, American Electronic Laboratories, Inc., Lansdale, Pa., Catalog 7.5M-7-79.
9. R. H. DuHamel and F. R. Ore, "Logarithmically Periodic Antenna Designs," *IRE National Convention Record*, pt. 1, pp. 139–152, 1958.
10. R. L. Carrel, "Analysis and Design of the Log-Periodic Dipole Antenna," Ph.D. Dissertation, Elec. Eng. Dept., University of Illinois, 1961, University Microfilms, Inc., Ann Arbor, Michigan.
11. P. E. Mays and R. L. Carrel, "Log-Periodic Resonant-V Arrays," presented at WESCON, San Francisco, California, Aug. 22–25, 1961.
12. R. C. Hansen, "Fundamental Limitations in Antennas," *Proc. IEEE*, vol. 69, No. 2, February 1981.
13. L. J. Chu, "Physical Limitations of Omnidirectional Antennas," *J. Appl. Phys.*, vol. 19, pp. 1163–1175, December 1948.
14. R. F. Harrington, "Effect of Antenna Size on Gain, Bandwidth, and Efficiency," *J. Res. Nat. Bur. Stand.-D, Radio Propagation*, vol. 64D, pp. 1–12, Jan.–Feb. 1960.
15. H. A. Wheeler, "Fundamental Limitations of Small Antennas," *Proc. IRE*, pp. 1479–1488, December 1947.
16. H. A. Wheeler, "The Radiansphere Around a Small Antenna," *Proc. IRE*, pp. 1325–1331, August 1959.
17. H. A. Wheeler, "Small Antennas," *IEEE Trans. Antennas Propag.*, vol. AP-23, No. 4, pp. 462–469, July 1975.
18. G. Goubau, "Multi-element Monopole Antennas," *Proc. Workshop on Electrically Small Antennas ECOM*, Ft. Monmouth, N. J., pp. 63–67, May 1976.

PROBLEMS

10.1. Design a symmetrical two-wire plane spiral ($\phi_0 = 0, \pi$) at $f = 10$ MHz with total feed terminal separation of $10^{-3}\lambda$. The total length of each spiral should be one wavelength and each wire should be of one turn.
   (a) Determine the rate of spiral of each wire.
   (b) Find the radius (in λ and in meters) of each spiral at its terminal point.
   (c) Plot the geometric shape of one wire. Use meters for its length.

10.2. Verify (10-28).

10.3. Design log-periodic dipole arrays, of the form shown in Figure 10.9(d), each with directivities of 9 dB, input impedance of 75 ohms, and each with the following additional specifications: Cover the (see Appendix VIII)
   (a) VHF TV channels 2–13 (54–216 MHz). Use aluminum tubing with outside diameters of $\frac{3}{4}$ in. (1.905 cm) and $\frac{3}{16}$ in. (0.476 cm) for the largest and smallest elements, respectively.
   (b) VHF TV channels 2–6 (54–88 MHz). Use diameters of 1.905 and 1.1169 cm for the largest and smallest elements, respectively.
   (c) VHF TV channels 7–13 (174–216 MHz). Use diameters of 0.6 and 0.476 cm for the largest and smallest elements, respectively.
   (d) UHF TV channels (512–806 MHz). The largest and smallest elements should have diameters of 0.2 and 0.128 cm, respectively.
   (e) FM band of 88–108 MHz (100 channels at 200 KHz apart). The largest and smallest elements should have diameters of 1.169 and 0.9525 cm, respectively.
   In each design, the feeder line should have the same diameter as the largest element.

10.4. For each design in Problem 10.3, determine the
   (a) span of each period (cycle) over which the radiation characteristics will vary only slightly
   (b) number of periods (cycles) within the desired bandwidth

Chapter 11
Aperture Antennas, and
Ground Plane Edge Effects

(GEOMETRICAL THEORY OF DIFFRACTION)

11.1 INTRODUCTION

Aperture antennas are most common at microwave frequencies. There are many different geometrical configurations of an aperture antenna with some of the most popular shown in Figure 1.3. They may take the form of a waveguide or a horn whose aperture may be square, rectangular, circular, elliptical, or any other configuration. Aperture antennas are very practical for space applications, because they can be flush-mounted to the surface of the spacecraft or aircraft. Their opening can be covered with a dielectric material to protect them from environmental conditions. This type of mounting does not disturb the aerodynamic profile of the craft, which in high-speed applications is critical.

In this chapter, the mathematical tools will be developed to analyze the radiation characteristics of aperture antennas. The concepts will be demonstrated by examples and illustrations. Because they are the most practical, emphasis will be given to the rectangular and circular configurations. Due to mathematical complexities, the observations will be restricted to the far-field region. The edge effects, due to the finite size of the ground plane to which the aperture is mounted, will be taken into account by using diffraction methods such as the Geometrical Theory of Diffraction, better known as GTD.

The radiation characteristics of wire antennas can be determined once the current distribution on the wire is known. For many configurations, however, the current distribution is not known exactly and only physical intuition or experimental measurements can provide a reasonable approximation to it. This is even more evident in aperture antennas (slits, slots, waveguides, horns, reflectors, lenses). It is therefore expedient to have alternate methods to compute the radiation characteristics of antennas. Emphasis will be placed on techniques that for their solution rely primarily not on the current distribution but on reasonable approximations of the fields on or in the vicinity of the antenna structure. One such technique is the *Field Equivalence Principle*.

11.2 FIELD EQUIVALENCE PRINCIPLE: HUYGENS' PRINCIPLE

The *field equivalence* is a principle by which actual sources, such as an antenna and transmitter, are replaced by equivalent sources. The fictitious sources are said to be *equivalent within a region* because *they produce the same fields within that region*. The formulations of scattering and diffraction problems by the equivalence principle are more suggestive to approximations.

The field equivalence was introduced in 1936 by S. A. Schelkunoff [1], and it is a more rigorous formulation of Huygens' principle [2] which states that "*each point on a primary wavefront can be considered to be a new source of a secondary spherical wave and that a secondary wavefront can be constructed as the envelope of these secondary spherical waves* [3]." The equivalence principle is based on the *uniqueness theorem* which states that "*a field in a lossy region is uniquely specified by the sources within the region plus the tangential components of the electric field over the boundary, or the tangential components of the magnetic field over the boundary, or the former over part of the boundary and the latter over the rest of the boundary* [4]." The field in a lossless medium is considered to be the limit, as the losses go to zero, of the corresponding field in a lossy medium. Thus if the tangential electric and magnetic fields are completely known over a closed surface, the fields in the source-free region can be determined.

By the equivalence principle, the fields outside an imaginary closed surface are obtained by placing over the closed surface suitable electric- and magnetic-current densities which satisfy the boundary conditions. The current densities are selected so that the fields inside the closed surface are zero and outside they are equal to the radiation produced by the actual sources. Thus the technique can be used to obtain the fields radiated outside a closed surface by sources enclosed within it. The formulation is exact but requires integration over the closed surface. The degree of accuracy depends on the knowledge of the tangential components of the fields over the closed surface.

In most applications, the closed surface is selected so that most of it coincides with the conducting parts of the physical structure. This is preferred because the vanishing of the tangential electric components over the conducting parts of the surface reduces the physical limits of integration.

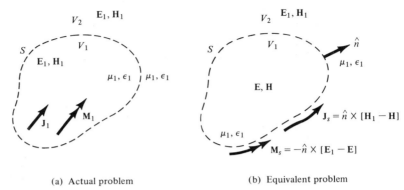

(a) Actual problem   (b) Equivalent problem

Figure 11.1   Actual and equivalent problem models.

The equivalence principle is developed by considering an actual radiating source, which electrically is represented by current densities $\mathbf{J}_1$ and $\mathbf{M}_1$, as shown in Figure 11.1(a). The source radiates fields $\mathbf{E}_1$ and $\mathbf{H}_1$ everywhere. However, it is desired to develop a method that will yield the fields outside a closed surface. To accomplish this, a closed surface S is chosen, shown dashed in Figure 11.1(a), which encloses the current densities $\mathbf{J}_1$ and $\mathbf{M}_1$. The volume within S is denoted by V_1 and outside S by V_2. *The primary task will be to replace the original problem, shown in Figure 11.1(a), by an equivalent one which will yield the same fields E_1 and H_1 outside S (within V_2).* The formulation of the problem can be aided eminently if the closed surface is judiciously chosen so that fields over most, if not the entire surface, are known a priori.

An equivalent problem of Figure 11.1(a) is shown in Figure 11.1(b). The original sources $\mathbf{J}_1$ and $\mathbf{M}_1$ are removed, and we assume that there exists a field $\mathbf{E}$ and $\mathbf{H}$ inside S and a field $\mathbf{E}_1$ and $\mathbf{H}_1$ outside of S. For these fields to exist within and outside S, they must satisfy the boundary conditions on the tangential electric and magnetic field components. Thus on the imaginary surface S there must exist the *equivalent sources*

$$\mathbf{J}_s = \hat{n} \times [\mathbf{H}_1 - \mathbf{H}] \tag{11-1}$$

$$\mathbf{M}_s = -\hat{n} \times [\mathbf{E}_1 - \mathbf{E}] \tag{11-2}$$

and they radiate into an *unbounded space* (same medium everywhere). *The current densities of (11-1) and (11-2) are said to be equivalent only within V_2, because they will produce the original field (E_1, H_1) only outside S. A field $\mathbf{E}, \mathbf{H}$, different from the original (E_1, H_1), will result within V_1.* Since the currents of (11-1) and (11-2) radiate in an unbounded space, the fields can be determined using (3-27)–(3-30a) and the geometry of Figure 11.2(a). In Figure 11.2(a), R is the distance from any point on the surface S, where $\mathbf{J}_s$ and $\mathbf{M}_s$ exist, to the observation point.

So far, the tangential components of *both* $\mathbf{E}$ and $\mathbf{H}$ have been used in setting up the equivalent problem. From electromagnetic uniqueness con-

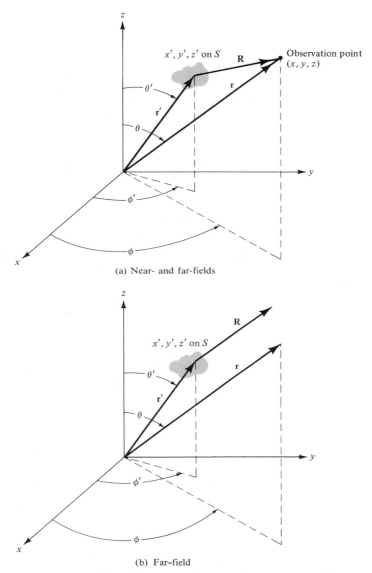

(a) Near- and far-fields

(b) Far–field

Figure 11.2   Coordinate system for aperture antenna analysis.

cepts, it is known that the tangential components of only **E** or **H** are needed to determine the field. It will be demonstrated that equivalent problems can be found which require only the magnetic currents (tangential **E**) or only electric currents (tangential **H**). This will require modifications to the equivalent problem of Figure 11.1(b).

Since the fields **E, H** within S can be anything (this is not the region of interest), it can be assumed that they are zero. In that case the equivalent problem of Figure 11.1(b) reduces to that of Figure 11.3(a) with the equivalent current densities being equal to

$$\mathbf{J}_s = \hat{n} \times (\mathbf{H}_1 - \mathbf{H})\big|_{\mathbf{H}=0} = \hat{n} \times \mathbf{H}_1 \tag{11-3}$$

$$\mathbf{M}_s = -\hat{n} \times (\mathbf{E}_1 - \mathbf{E})\big|_{\mathbf{E}=0} = -\hat{n} \times \mathbf{E}_1 \tag{11-4}$$

This form of the field equivalence principle is known as *Love's Equivalence Principle* [5]. Since the current densities of (11-3) and (11-4) radiate in an unbounded medium (same μ, ε everywhere), they can be used in conjunction with (3-27)–(3-30a) to find the fields everywhere.

The Love's Equivalence Principle of Figure 11.3(a) produces a null field within the imaginary surface S. Since the value of the $\mathbf{E} = \mathbf{H} = 0$ within S cannot be disturbed if the properties of the medium within it are changed, let us assume that it is replaced by a perfect electric conductor ($\sigma = \infty$). The introduction of the perfect conductor will have an effect on the equivalent source $\mathbf{J}_s$, and it will prohibit the use of (3-27)–(3-30a) since the current densities no longer radiate into an unbounded medium. Imagine that the geometrical configuration of the electric conductor is identical to the profile of the imaginary surface S, over which $\mathbf{J}_s$ and $\mathbf{M}_s$ exist. As the electric conductor takes its place, as shown in Figure 11.3(b), the electric current

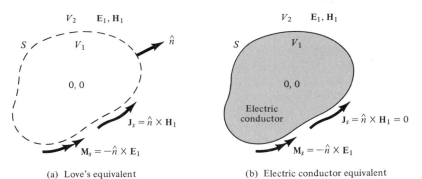

(a) Love's equivalent   (b) Electric conductor equivalent

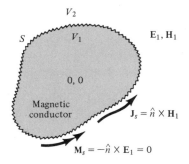

(c) Magnetic conductor equivalent

Figure 11.3 Equivalence principle models.

density $\mathbf{J}_s$, which is tangent to the surface S, is short-circuited by the electric conductor. Thus the equivalent problem of Figure 11.3(a) reduces to that of Figure 11.3(b). There exists only a magnetic current density $\mathbf{M}_s$ over S, and it radiates in the presence of the electric conductor producing outside S the original fields $\mathbf{E}_1, \mathbf{H}_1$. Within S the fields are zero but, as before, that is not a region of interest. The difficulty in trying to use the equivalent problem of Figure 11.3(b) is that (3-27)–(3-30a) cannot be used, because the current densities do not radiate into an unbounded medium. The problem of a magnetic current radiating in the presence of an electric conducting surface must be solved. So it seems that the equivalent problem is just as difficult as the original problem itself.

Before some special simple geometries are considered and some suggestions are made for approximating complex geometries, let us introduce another equivalent problem. Referring to Figure 11.3(a), let us assume that instead of placing a perfect electric conductor within S we introduce a perfect magnetic conductor which will short out the magnetic current and reduce the equivalent problem to that shown in Figure 11.3(c). As was with the equivalent problem of Figure 11.3(b), (3-27)–(3-30a) cannot be used with Figure 11.3(c) and the problem is just as difficult as that of Figure 11.3(b) or the original of Figure 11.1(a).

To begin to see the utility of the field equivalence principle, especially that of Figure 11.3(b), let us assume that the surface of the electric conductor is flat and extends to infinity as shown in Figure 11.4(a). For this geometry, the problem is to determine how a magnetic source radiates in the presence of a flat electric conductor. From image theory, this problem reduces to that of Figure 11.4(b) where an imaginary magnetic source is introduced on the side of the conductor and takes its place (remove

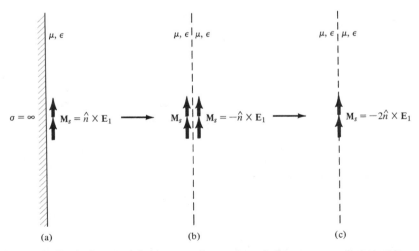

(a)   (b)   (c)

Figure 11.4   Equivalent models for magnetic source radiation near a perfect electric conductor.

conductor). Since the imaginary source is in the same direction as the equivalent source, the equivalent problem of Figure 11.4(b) reduces to that of Figure 11.4(c). The magnetic current is doubled, it radiates in an unbounded medium, and (3-27)–(3-30a) can be used. The equivalent problem of Figure 11.4(c) will yield the correct $\mathbf{E}, \mathbf{H}$ fields to the right side of the interface. If the surface of the obstacle is not flat and infinite, but its curvature is large compared to the wavelength, a good approximation will be the equivalent problem of Figure 11.3(c).

SUMMARY

In the analysis of electromagnetic problems, many times it is easier to form equivalent problems that will yield the same solution within a region of interest. This is the case for scattering, diffraction, and aperture antenna problems. In this chapter, the main interest is in aperture antennas. The concepts will be demonstrated with examples.

The steps that must be used to form an equivalent and solve an aperture problem are as follows:

1. Select an imaginary surface that encloses the actual sources (the aperture). The surface must be judiciously chosen so that the tangential components of the electric and/or the magnetic field are known, exactly or approximately, over its entire span. In many cases this surface is a flat plane extending to infinity.

2. Over the imaginary surface form equivalent current densities $\mathbf{J}_s, \mathbf{M}_s$ which take one of the following forms:
   a. $\mathbf{J}_s$ and $\mathbf{M}_s$ over S assuming that the **E**- and **H**-fields within S are not zero
   b. or $\mathbf{J}_s$ and $\mathbf{M}_s$ over S assuming that the **E**- and **H**-fields within S are zero (Love's theorem)
   c. or $\mathbf{M}_s$ over S ($\mathbf{J}_s = 0$) assuming that within S the medium is a perfect electric conductor
   d. or $\mathbf{J}_s$ over S ($\mathbf{M}_s = 0$) assuming that within S the medium is a perfect magnetic conductor

3. Solve the equivalent problem. For forms (a) and (b), (3-27)–(3-30a) can be used. For form (c), the problem of a magnetic current source next to a perfect electric conductor must be solved [(3-27)–(3-30a) cannot be used directly, because the current density does not radiate into an unbounded medium]. If the electric conductor is an infinite flat plane, the problem can be solved exactly by image theory. For form (d), the problem of an electric current source next to a perfect magnetic conductor must be solved. Again (3-27)–(3-30a) cannot be used directly. If the magnetic conductor is an infinite flat plane, the problem can be solved exactly by image theory.

To demonstrate the usefulness and application of the field equivalence theorem to aperture antenna theory, an example will be considered.

Example 11.1

A waveguide aperture is mounted on an infinite ground plane, as shown in Figure 11.5(a). Assuming that the tangential components of the electric field over the aperture are known, and are given by $\mathbf{E}_a$, find an equivalent problem that will yield the same fields $\mathbf{E}, \mathbf{H}$ radiated by the aperture to the right side of the interface.

SOLUTION
First an imaginary closed surface is chosen. For this problem it is appropriate to select a flat plane extending from minus infinity to plus infinity, as shown in Figure 11.5(b). Over the infinite plane, the equivalent current densities $\mathbf{J}_s$ and $\mathbf{M}_s$ are formed. Since the tangential components of $\mathbf{E}$ do not exist outside the aperture, because of vanishing boundary conditions, the magnetic current density $\mathbf{M}_s$ is only nonzero over the aperture. The electric current density $\mathbf{J}_s$ is nonzero everywhere and is yet unknown. Now let us assume that an imaginary flat electric conductor approaches the surface S, and it shorts out the current density $\mathbf{J}_s$ everywhere. $\mathbf{M}_s$ exists only

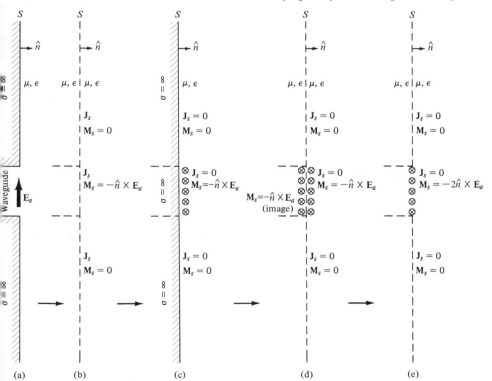

Figure 11.5 Equivalent models for waveguide aperture mounted on an infinite flat electric ground plane.

over the space occupied originally by the aperture, and it radiates in the presence of the conductor [see Figure 11.5(c)]. By image theory, the conductor can be removed and replaced by an imaginary (equivalent) source $\mathbf{M}_s$ as shown in Figure 11.5(d), which is analogous to Figure 11.4(b). Finally, the equivalent problem of Figure 11.5(d) reduces to that of Figure 11.5(e), which is analogous to that of Figure 11.4(c). The original problem has been reduced to a very simple equivalent, and (3-27)–(3-30a) can be utilized for its solution.

In this chapter the theory will be developed to compute the field radiated by an aperture, like that shown in Figure 11.5(a), making use of its equivalent of Figure 11.5(e). For other problems, their equivalent forms will not necessarily be the same as that shown in Figure 11.5(e).

11.3 RADIATION EQUATIONS

In Chapter 3 and in the previous section it was stated that the fields radiated by sources $\mathbf{J}_s$ and $\mathbf{M}_s$ in an unbounded medium can be computed by using (3-27)–(3-30a) where the integration must be performed over the entire surface occupied by $\mathbf{J}_s$ and $\mathbf{M}_s$. These equations yield valid solutions for all observation points [6]. For most problems, the main difficulty is the inability to perform the integrations in (3-27) and (3-28). However for far-field observations, the complexity of the formulation can be reduced.

As was shown in Section 4.3, for far-field observations R can most commonly be approximated by

$$R \simeq r - r' \cos\psi \qquad \text{for phase variations} \qquad \text{(11-5a)}$$

$$R \simeq r \qquad \text{for amplitude variations} \qquad \text{(11-5b)}$$

where ψ is the angle between the vectors $\mathbf{r}$ and $\mathbf{r}'$, as shown in Figure 11.2(b). The primed coordinates $(x', y', z'$ or $r', \theta', \phi')$ indicate the space occupied by the sources $\mathbf{J}_s$ and $\mathbf{M}_s$, over which integration must be performed. The unprimed coordinates $(x, y, z$ or $r, \theta, \phi)$ represent the observation point. Geometrically the approximation of (11-5a) assumes that the vectors $\mathbf{R}$ and $\mathbf{r}$ are parallel, as shown in Figure 11.2(b).

Using (11-5a) and (11-5b), (3-27) and (3-28) can be written as

$$\mathbf{A} = \frac{\mu}{4\pi} \iint_S \mathbf{J}_s \frac{e^{-jkR}}{R} \, ds' \simeq \frac{\mu e^{-jkr}}{4\pi r} \mathbf{N} \qquad \text{(11-6)}$$

$$\mathbf{N} = \iint_S \mathbf{J}_s e^{jkr'\cos\psi} \, ds' \qquad \text{(11-6a)}$$

$$\mathbf{F} = \frac{\varepsilon}{4\pi} \iint_S \mathbf{M}_s \frac{e^{-jkR}}{R} \, ds' \simeq \frac{\varepsilon e^{-jkr}}{4\pi r} \mathbf{L} \qquad \text{(11-7)}$$

$$\mathbf{L} = \iint_S \mathbf{M}_s e^{jkr'\cos\psi} \, ds' \qquad \text{(11-7a)}$$

In Section 3.6 it was shown that in the far-field only the θ and ϕ components of the **E**- and **H**-fields are dominant. Although the radial components are not necessarily zero, they are negligible compared to the θ and ϕ components. Using (3-58a)–(3-59b), the $\mathbf{E}_A$ of (3-29) and $\mathbf{H}_F$ of (3-30) can be written as

$$(E_A)_\theta \simeq -j\omega A_\theta \qquad (11\text{-}8a)$$

$$(E_A)_\phi \simeq -j\omega A_\phi \qquad (11\text{-}8b)$$

$$(H_F)_\theta \simeq -j\omega F_\theta \qquad (11\text{-}8c)$$

$$(H_F)_\phi \simeq -j\omega F_\phi \qquad (11\text{-}8d)$$

and the $\mathbf{E}_F$ of (3-29) and $\mathbf{H}_A$ of (3-30), with the aid of (11-8a)–(11-8d), as

$$(E_F)_\theta \simeq +\eta(H_F)_\phi = -j\omega\eta F_\phi \qquad (11\text{-}9a)$$

$$(E_F)_\phi \simeq -\eta(H_F)_\theta = +j\omega\eta F_\theta \qquad (11\text{-}9b)$$

$$(H_A)_\theta \simeq -\frac{(E_A)_\phi}{\eta} = +j\omega\frac{A_\phi}{\eta} \qquad (11\text{-}9c)$$

$$(H_A)_\phi \simeq +\frac{(E_A)_\theta}{\eta} = -j\omega\frac{A_\theta}{\eta} \qquad (11\text{-}9d)$$

Combining (11-8a)–(11-8d) with (11-9a)–(11-9d), and making use of (11-6)–(11-7a) the total **E**- and **H**-fields can be written as

$$E_r \simeq 0 \qquad (11\text{-}10a)$$

$$E_\theta \simeq -\frac{jke^{-jkr}}{4\pi r}(L_\phi + \eta N_\theta) \qquad (11\text{-}10b)$$

$$E_\phi \simeq +\frac{jke^{-jkr}}{4\pi r}(L_\theta - \eta N_\phi) \qquad (11\text{-}10c)$$

$$H_r \simeq 0 \qquad (11\text{-}10d)$$

$$H_\theta \simeq \frac{jke^{-jkr}}{4\pi r}\left(N_\phi - \frac{L_\theta}{\eta}\right) \qquad (11\text{-}10e)$$

$$H_\phi \simeq -\frac{jke^{-jkr}}{4\pi r}\left(N_\theta + \frac{L_\phi}{\eta}\right) \qquad (11\text{-}10f)$$

The N_θ, N_ϕ, L_θ, and L_ϕ can be obtained from (11-6a) and (11-7a). That is,

$$\mathbf{N} = \iint_S \mathbf{J}_s e^{+jkr'\cos\psi}\,ds' = \iint_S (\hat{a}_x J_x + \hat{a}_y J_y + \hat{a}_z J_z)e^{+jkr'\cos\psi}\,ds' \quad (11\text{-}11a)$$

$$\mathbf{L} = \iint_S \mathbf{M}_s e^{+jkr'\cos\psi}\,ds' = \iint_S (\hat{a}_x M_x + \hat{a}_y M_y + \hat{a}_z M_z)e^{+jkr'\cos\psi}\,ds'$$

$$(11\text{-}11b)$$

Using the rectangular-to-spherical component transformation, obtained by taking the inverse (in this case also the transpose) of (4-5), (11-11a) and (11-11b) reduce for the θ and ϕ components to

$$N_\theta = \iint_S \left[J_x \cos\theta\cos\phi + J_y\cos\theta\sin\phi - J_z\sin\theta \right] e^{+jkr'\cos\psi}\,ds' \qquad \text{(11-12a)}$$

$$N_\phi = \iint_S \left[-J_x\sin\phi + J_y\cos\phi \right] e^{+jkr'\cos\psi}\,ds' \qquad \text{(11-12b)}$$

$$L_\theta = \iint_S \left[M_x\cos\theta\cos\phi + M_y\cos\theta\sin\phi - M_z\sin\theta \right] e^{+jkr'\cos\psi}\,ds' \qquad \text{(11-12c)}$$

$$L_\phi = \iint_S \left[-M_x\sin\phi + M_y\cos\phi \right] e^{+jkr'\cos\psi}\,ds' \qquad \text{(11-12d)}$$

SUMMARY

To summarize the results, the procedure that must be followed to solve a problem using the radiation integrals will be outlined. Figures 11.2(a) and 11.2(b) are used to indicate the geometry.

1. Select a closed surface over which the total electric and magnetic fields $\mathbf{E}_a$ and $\mathbf{H}_a$ are known.
2. Form the equivalent current densities $\mathbf{J}_s$ and $\mathbf{M}_s$ over S using (11-3) and (11-4) with $\mathbf{H}_1 = \mathbf{H}_a$ and $\mathbf{E}_1 = \mathbf{E}_a$.
3. Determine the $\mathbf{A}$ and $\mathbf{F}$ potentials using (11-6)–(11-7a) where the integration is over the closed surface S.
4. Determine the radiated $\mathbf{E}$- and $\mathbf{H}$-fields using (3-29) and (3-30).

The above steps are valid for all regions (near-field and far-field) outside the surface S. If, however, the observation point is in the far-field, steps 3 and 4 can be replaced by 3' and 4'. That is,

3'. Determine N_θ, N_ϕ, L_θ, and L_ϕ using (11-12a)–(11-12d).
4'. Determine the radiated $\mathbf{E}$- and $\mathbf{H}$-fields using (11-10a)–(11-10f).

Some of the steps outlined above can be reduced by the judicious choice of the equivalent model. In the remaining sections of this chapter, the techniques will be applied and demonstrated with examples of rectangular and circular apertures.

11.4 DIRECTIVITY

The directivity of an aperture can be found in a manner similar to that of other antennas. The primary task is to formulate the radiation intensity $U(\theta, \phi)$, using the far-zone electric and magnetic field components. That is,

$$U(\theta, \phi) = \frac{1}{2}\text{Re}\left[(\hat{a}_\theta E_\theta + \hat{a}_\phi E_\phi) \times (\hat{a}_\theta H_\theta + \hat{a}_\phi H_\phi)^* \right] = \frac{1}{2\eta}\left(|E_\theta|^2 + |E_\phi|^2 \right)$$

$$\text{(11-13)}$$

which in normalized form reduces to

$$U_n(\theta,\phi) = \left(|E_\theta(\theta,\phi)|^2 + |E_\phi(\theta,\phi)|^2\right) = B_0 F(\theta,\phi) i \qquad (11\text{-}13a)$$

The directive properties can then be found using (2-18)–(2-22).

Because the radiation intensity $U(\theta,\phi)$ for each aperture antenna will be of a different form, a general equation for the directivity cannot be formed. However, a general FORTRAN computer program has been written to compute the directivity of any antenna, including an aperture, once the radiation intensity is specified. The program is based on the formulations of (11-13a), (2-18)–(2-20), and (2-22), and it is shown at the end of Chapter 2. In the main program, it requires the lower and upper bounds on θ and ϕ. The radiation intensity for the antenna in question must be specified in the subroutine $U(\theta,\phi,F)$ of the program.

Expressions for the directivity of some simple aperture antennas, rectangular and circular, will be derived in later sections of this chapter.

11.5 RECTANGULAR APERTURES

In practice, the rectangular aperture is probably the most common microwave antenna. Because of its configuration, the rectangular coordinate system is the most convenient system to express the fields at the aperture and to perform the integration. Shown in Figure 11.6 are the three most common and convenient coordinate positions used for the solution of an aperture antenna. In Figure 11.6(a) the aperture lies in the y-z plane, in Figure 11.6(b) in the x-z plane, and in Figure 11.6(c) in the x-y plane. For a given field distribution, the analytical forms for the fields for each of the arrangements would not be the same. However the computed values will be the same, since the physical problem is identical in all cases.

For each of the geometries shown in Figure 11.6, the only difference in the analysis will be in the formulation of

1. the components of the equivalent currents ($J_x, J_y, J_z, M_x, M_y, M_z$)
2. the difference in paths from the source to the observation point ($r' \cos\psi$)
3. the differential area ds'

In general, the nonzero components of $\mathbf{J}_s$ and $\mathbf{M}_s$ are

$$J_y, J_z, M_y, M_z \qquad \left[\text{Figure } 11.6(a)\right] \qquad\qquad (11\text{-}14a)$$

$$J_x, J_z, M_x, M_z \qquad \left[\text{Figure } 11.6(b)\right] \qquad\qquad (11\text{-}14b)$$

$$J_x, J_y, M_x, M_y \qquad \left[\text{Figure } 11.6(c)\right] \qquad\qquad (11\text{-}14c)$$

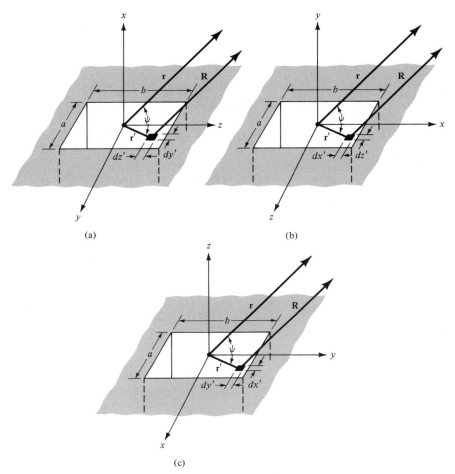

Figure 11.6   Rectangular aperture positions for antenna system analysis.

The differential paths take the form of

$$r'\cos\psi=\mathbf{r'}\cdot\hat{a}_r=\left(\hat{a}_y\,y'+\hat{a}_z\,z'\right)\cdot\left(\hat{a}_x\sin\theta\cos\phi+\hat{a}_y\sin\theta\sin\phi+\hat{a}_z\cos\theta\right)$$

$$=y'\sin\theta\sin\phi+z'\cos\theta\quad\left[\text{Figure 11.6(a)}\right]\tag{11-15a}$$

$$r'\cos\psi=\mathbf{r'}\cdot\hat{a}_r=\left(\hat{a}_x\,x'+\hat{a}_z\,z'\right)\cdot\left(\hat{a}_x\sin\theta\cos\phi+\hat{a}_y\sin\theta\sin\phi+\hat{a}_z\cos\theta\right)$$

$$=x'\sin\theta\cos\phi+z'\cos\theta\quad\left[\text{Figure 11.6(b)}\right]\tag{11-15b}$$

$$r'\cos\psi=\mathbf{r'}\cdot\hat{a}_r=\left(\hat{a}_x\,x'+\hat{a}_y\,y'\right)\cdot\left(\hat{a}_x\sin\theta\cos\phi+\hat{a}_y\sin\theta\sin\phi+\hat{a}_z\cos\theta\right)$$

$$=x'\sin\theta\cos\phi+y'\sin\theta\sin\phi\quad\left[\text{Figure 11.6(c)}\right]\tag{11-15c}$$

and the differential areas are represented by

$$ds' = dy'\,dz' \qquad [\text{Figure } 11.6(a)] \qquad\qquad (11\text{-}16a)$$

$$ds' = dx'\,dz' \qquad [\text{Figure } 11.6(b)] \qquad\qquad (11\text{-}16b)$$

$$ds' = dx'\,dy' \qquad [\text{Figure } 11.6(c)] \qquad\qquad (11\text{-}16c)$$

11.5.1 Uniform Distribution on an Infinite Ground Plane

The first aperture to be examined is a rectangular aperture mounted on an infinite ground plane, as shown in Figure 11.7. To reduce the mathematical complexities, initially the field over the opening will be assumed to be constant and given by

$$\mathbf{E}_a = \hat{a}_y E_0 \qquad -a/2 \le x' \le a/2, \quad -b/2 \le y' \le b/2 \qquad (11\text{-}17)$$

where E_0 is a constant. The task will be to find the fields radiated by it, the pattern beamwidths, the side lobe levels of the pattern, and the directivity. To accomplish these, the equivalent will be formed first.

EQUIVALENT
To form the equivalent, a closed surface is chosen which extends from $-\infty$ to $+\infty$ on the x-y plane. Since the physical problem of Figure 11.7 is identical to that of Figure 11.5(a), its equivalents are those of Figures

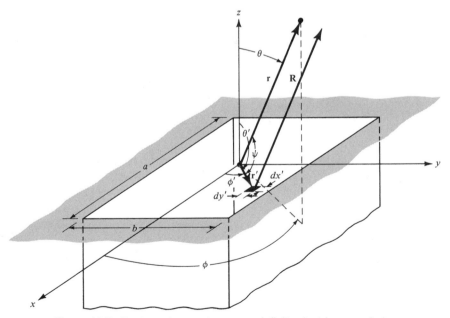

Figure 11.7   Rectangular aperture on an infinite electric ground plane.

11.5(a)–(e). Using the equivalent of Figure 11.5(e)

$$\mathbf{M}_s = \begin{cases} -2\hat{n}\times\mathbf{E}_a = -2\hat{a}_z\times\hat{a}_y E_0 = +\hat{a}_x 2E_0 & \begin{array}{l} -a/2\leq x'\leq a/2 \\ -b/2\leq y'\leq b/2 \end{array} \\ 0 \quad \text{elsewhere} \end{cases}$$

$$\mathbf{J}_s = 0 \quad \text{everywhere} \tag{11-18}$$

RADIATION FIELDS: ELEMENT AND SPACE FACTORS

The far-zone fields radiated by the aperture of Figure 11.7 can be found by using (11-10a)–(11-10f), (11-12a)–(11-12d), (11-14c), (11-15c), (11-16c), and (11-18). Thus,

$$N_\theta = N_\phi = 0 \tag{11-19}$$

$$L_\theta = \int_{-b/2}^{+b/2}\int_{-a/2}^{+a/2}[M_x\cos\theta\cos\phi]e^{jk(x'\sin\theta\cos\phi+y'\sin\theta\sin\phi)}\,dx'\,dy'$$

$$\boxed{L_\theta = \cos\theta\cos\phi\left[\int_{-b/2}^{+b/2}\int_{-a/2}^{+a/2}M_x e^{jk(x'\sin\theta\cos\phi+y'\sin\theta\sin\phi)}\,dx'\,dy'\right]}$$

$$\tag{11-19a}$$

In (11-19a), the integral within the brackets represents the *space factor* for a two-dimensional distribution. It is analogous to the space factor of (4-58a) for a line source (one-dimensional distribution). For the L_θ components of the vector potential $\mathbf{F}$, the *element factor* is equal to the product of the factor outside the brackets in (11-19a) and the factor outside the brackets in (11-10c). The total field is equal to the product of the element and space factors, as defined by (4-59), and expressed in (11-10b) and (11-10c).

Using the integral

$$\int_{-c/2}^{+c/2}e^{j\alpha z}\,dz = c\left[\frac{\sin\left(\frac{\alpha}{2}c\right)}{\frac{\alpha}{2}c}\right] \tag{11-20}$$

(11-19a) reduces to

$$L_\theta = 2abE_0\left[\cos\theta\cos\phi\left(\frac{\sin X}{X}\right)\left(\frac{\sin Y}{Y}\right)\right] \tag{11-21}$$

where

$$X = \frac{ka}{2}\sin\theta\cos\phi \tag{11-21a}$$

$$Y = \frac{kb}{2}\sin\theta\sin\phi \tag{11-21b}$$

Similarly it can be shown that

$$L_\phi = -2abE_0\left[\sin\phi\left(\frac{\sin X}{X}\right)\left(\frac{\sin Y}{Y}\right)\right] \tag{11-22}$$

Substituting (11-19), (11-21), and (11-22) into (11-10a)–(11-10f), the fields radiated by the aperture can be written as

$$E_r = 0 \tag{11-23a}$$

$$E_\theta = j\frac{abkE_0e^{-jkr}}{2\pi r}\left[\sin\phi\left(\frac{\sin X}{X}\right)\left(\frac{\sin Y}{Y}\right)\right] \tag{11-23b}$$

$$E_\phi = j\frac{abkE_0e^{-jkr}}{2\pi r}\left[\cos\theta\cos\phi\left(\frac{\sin X}{X}\right)\left(\frac{\sin Y}{Y}\right)\right] \tag{11-23c}$$

$$H_r = 0 \tag{11-23d}$$

$$H_\theta = -\frac{E_\phi}{\eta} \tag{11-23e}$$

$$H_\phi = +\frac{E_\theta}{\eta} \tag{11-23f}$$

Equations (11-23a)–(11-23f) represent the three-dimensional distributions of the far-zone fields radiated by the aperture. In the laboratory, only a two-dimensional plots can be measured. To reconstruct experimentally a three-dimensional plot, a series of two-dimensional plots must be made. In many applications, however, only a pair of two-dimensional plots are usually sufficient. These are the principal E- and H-plane patterns whose definition was stated in Section 2.2.2 and illustrated with Figure 2.3.

For the problem in Figure 11.7, the E-plane pattern is in the y-z plane ($\phi = \pi/2$) and the H-plane is in the x-z plane ($\phi = 0$). Thus

E-Plane ($\phi = \pi/2$)

$$E_r = E_\phi = 0 \tag{11-24a}$$

$$E_\theta = j\frac{abkE_0e^{-jkr}}{2\pi r}\left[\frac{\sin\left(\frac{kb}{2}\sin\theta\right)}{\frac{kb}{2}\sin\theta}\right] \tag{11-24b}$$

H-Plane ($\phi = 0$)

$$E_r = E_\theta = 0 \tag{11-25a}$$

$$E_\phi = j\frac{abkE_0e^{-jkr}}{2\pi r}\left\{\cos\theta\left[\frac{\sin\left(\frac{ka}{2}\sin\theta\right)}{\frac{ka}{2}\sin\theta}\right]\right\} \tag{11-25b}$$

To demonstrate the techniques, three-dimensional patterns have been plotted in Figures 11.8 and 11.9. The dimensions of the aperture are indicated in each figure. Multiple lobes appear, because the dimensions of the aperture are greater than one wavelength. The number of lobes increases

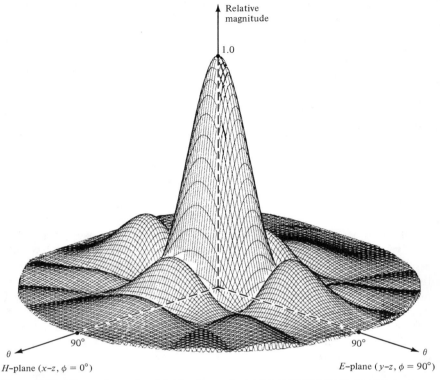

Figure 11.8 Three-dimensional field pattern of a constant field rectangular aperture mounted on an infinite ground plane ($a=3\lambda, b=2\lambda$).

as the dimensions increase. For the aperture whose dimensions are $a=3\lambda$ and $b=2\lambda$ (Figure 11.8), there are a total of five lobes in the principal H-plane and three lobes in the principal E-plane. The pattern in the H-plane is only a function of the dimension a whereas that in the E-plane is only influenced by b. In the E-plane, the side lobe formed on each side of the major lobe is a result of $\lambda < b \leq 2\lambda$. In the H-plane, the first minor lobe on each side of the major lobe is formed when $\lambda < a \leq 2\lambda$ and the second side lobe when $2\lambda < a \leq 3\lambda$. Additional lobes are formed when one or both of the aperture dimensions increase. This is illustrated in Figure 11.9 for an aperture with $a = b = 3\lambda$.

The two-dimensional principal plane patterns for the aperture with $a=3\lambda, b=2\lambda$ are shown in Figure 11.10. For this and for all other size apertures mounted on an infinite ground plane, the H-plane patterns along the ground plane vanish. This is dictated by the boundary conditions. The E-plane patterns, in general, do not have to vanish along the ground plane, unless the dimension of the aperture in that plane (in this case b) is a multiple of a wavelength.

The patterns computed above assume that the aperture is mounted on an infinite ground plane. In practice, infinite ground planes are not realiz-

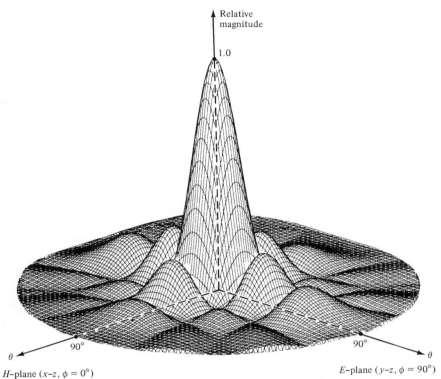

H–plane (*x*-*z*, $\phi = 0°$)   *E*–plane (*y*-*z*, $\phi = 90°$)

Figure 11.9 Three-dimensional field pattern of a constant field square aperture mounted on an infinite ground plane ($a=b=3\lambda$).

able, but they can be approximated by large structures. Edge effects, on the patterns of apertures mounted on finite size ground planes, can be accounted for by diffraction techniques. They will be introduced and illustrated in Section 11.9. Computed results, which include diffractions, agree extremely well with measurements [7]–[9].

BEAMWIDTHS

For the *E*-plane pattern given by (11-24b), the maximum radiation is directed along the *z*-axis ($\theta=0$). The nulls (zeroes) will occur when

$$\frac{kb}{2} \sin \theta \Big|_{\theta=\theta_n} = n\pi, \qquad n=1,2,3,\ldots \tag{11-26}$$

or at the angles of

$$\theta_n = \sin^{-1}\left(\frac{2n\pi}{kb}\right) = \sin^{-1}\left(\frac{n\lambda}{b}\right) \text{ rad}$$

$$= 57.3 \sin^{-1}\left(\frac{n\lambda}{b}\right) \text{ degrees}, \qquad n=1,2,3,\ldots \tag{11-26a}$$

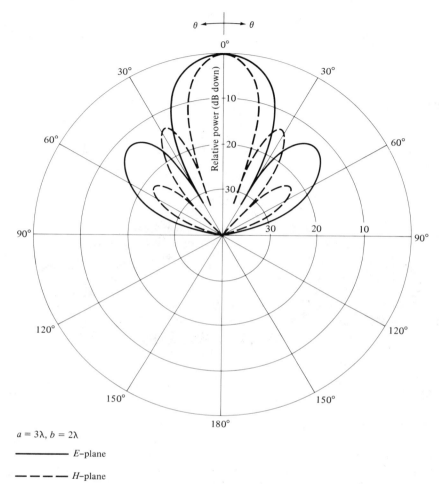

$a = 3\lambda, b = 2\lambda$

——————— *E*-plane

— — — — *H*-plane

Figure 11.10 *E*- and *H*-plane amplitude patterns for uniform distribution aperture mounted on an infinite ground plane ($a=3\lambda, b=2\lambda$).

If $b \gg n\lambda$, (11-26a) reduces approximately to

$$\theta_n \simeq \frac{n\lambda}{b} \text{ rad} = 57.3\left(\frac{n\lambda}{b}\right) \text{ degrees}, \qquad n=1,2,3,\ldots \qquad (11\text{-}26b)$$

The total *beamwidth between nulls* is given by

$$\Theta_n = 2\theta_n = 2\sin^{-1}\left(\frac{n\lambda}{b}\right) \text{ rad}$$

$$= 114.6\sin^{-1}\left(\frac{n\lambda}{b}\right) \text{ degrees}, \qquad n=1,2,3,\ldots \qquad (11\text{-}27)$$

or approximately (for large apertures, $b \gg n\lambda$) by

$$\Theta_n \simeq \frac{2n\lambda}{b} \text{ rad} = 114.6\left(\frac{n\lambda}{b}\right) \text{ degrees}, \qquad n=1,2,3,\ldots \tag{11-27a}$$

The *first null beamwidth* (FNBW) is obtained by letting $n=1$.
The half-power point occurs when (see Appendix I)

$$\frac{kb}{2}\sin\theta\Big|_{\theta=\theta_h} = 1.391 \tag{11-28}$$

or at an angle of

$$\theta_h = \sin^{-1}\left(\frac{2.782}{kb}\right) = \sin^{-1}\left(\frac{0.443\lambda}{b}\right) \text{ rad}$$

$$= 57.3\sin^{-1}\left(\frac{0.443\lambda}{b}\right) \text{ degrees} \tag{11-28a}$$

If $b \gg 0.443\lambda$, (11-28a) reduces approximately to

$$\theta_h \simeq \left(0.443\frac{\lambda}{b}\right) \text{ rad} = 25.38\left(\frac{\lambda}{b}\right) \text{ degrees} \tag{11-28b}$$

Thus the total *half-power beamwidth* (HPBW) is given by

$$\Theta_h = 2\theta_h = 2\sin^{-1}\left(\frac{0.443\lambda}{b}\right) \text{ rad} = 114.6\sin^{-1}\left(\frac{0.443\lambda}{b}\right) \text{ degrees}$$

$$\tag{11-29}$$

or approximately (when $b \gg 0.443\lambda$) by

$$\Theta_h \simeq \left(0.883\frac{\lambda}{b}\right) \text{ rad} = 50.6\left(\frac{\lambda}{b}\right) \text{ degrees} \tag{11-29a}$$

The maximum of the first side lobe will occur when (see Appendix I)

$$\frac{kb}{2}\sin\theta\Big|_{\theta=\theta_s} = 4.494 \tag{11-30}$$

or at an angle of

$$\theta_s = \sin^{-1}\left(\frac{8.988}{kb}\right) = \sin^{-1}\left(\frac{1.43\lambda}{b}\right) \text{ rad} = 57.3\sin^{-1}\left(\frac{1.43\lambda}{b}\right) \text{ degrees}$$

$$\tag{11-30a}$$

If $b \gg 1.43\lambda$, (11-30a) reduces to

$$\theta_s \simeq 1.43\left(\frac{\lambda}{b}\right) \text{ rad} = 81.9\left(\frac{\lambda}{b}\right) \text{ degrees} \tag{11-30b}$$

The total beamwidth between first side lobes (FSLBW) is given by

$$\Theta_s = 2\theta_s = 2\sin^{-1}\left(\frac{1.43\lambda}{b}\right) \text{ rad} = 114.6\sin^{-1}\left(\frac{1.43\lambda}{b}\right) \text{ degrees}$$

$$\tag{11-30c}$$

or approximately ($b \gg 1.43\lambda$) by

$$\Theta_s \simeq 2.86\left(\frac{\lambda}{b}\right) \text{ rad} = 163.8\left(\frac{\lambda}{b}\right) \text{ degrees} \qquad (11\text{-}30d)$$

SIDE LOBE LEVEL
The maximum of (11-24b) at the first side lobes is given by (see Appendix I)

$$|E_\theta(\theta = \theta_s)| = \left|\frac{\sin(4.494)}{4.494}\right| = 0.217 = -13.26 \text{ dB} \qquad (11\text{-}31)$$

which is 13.26 dB down from the maximum of the main lobe.

An approximate value of the maximum of the first side lobe can be obtained by assuming that the maximum of (11-24b) occurs when its numerator is maximum. That is, when

$$\frac{kb}{2}\sin\theta\Big|_{\theta=\theta_s} \simeq \frac{3\pi}{2} \qquad (11\text{-}32)$$

Thus,

$$|E_\theta(\theta = \theta_s)| \simeq \frac{1}{3\pi/2} = 0.212 = -13.47 \text{ dB} \qquad (11\text{-}33)$$

These values are very close to the exact ones given by (11-31).

A similar procedure can be followed to find the nulls, 3-dB points, beamwidth between nulls and 3-dB points, angle where maximum of first side lobe occurs, and its magnitude at that point for the H-plane pattern of (11-25b). A comparison between the E- and H-plane patterns of (11-24b) and (11-25b) shows that they are similar in form except for the additional $\cos\theta$ term that appears in (11-25b). An examination of the terms in (11-25b) will reveal that the $\cos\theta$ term is a much slower varying function than the $\sin(ka\sin\theta/2)/(ka\sin\theta/2)$ term, especially when a is large.

As a first approximation, (11-26)–(11-33), with b replaced by a, can also be used for the H-plane. More accurate expressions can be obtained by also including the $\cos\theta$ term. In regions well removed from the major lobe, the inclusion of the $\cos\theta$ term becomes more essential for accurate results.

DIRECTIVITY
The directivity for the aperture can be found using (11-23a)–(11-23c), (11-13)–(11-13a), and (2-18)–(2-22). The analytical details using this procedure, especially the integration to compute the radiated power (P_{rad}), are more cumbersome.

Because the aperture is mounted on an infinite ground plane, an alternate and much simpler method can be used to compute the radiated power. The average power density is first formed using the fields at the aperture, and it is then integrated over the physical bounds of the opening. The integration is confined to the physical bounds of the opening. Using

Figure 11.7 and assuming that the magnetic field at the aperture is given by

$$\mathbf{H}_a = -\hat{a}_x \frac{E_0}{\eta} \tag{11-34}$$

where η is the intrinsic impedance, the radiated power reduces to

$$P_{rad} = \oint\!\!\!\oint_S \mathbf{W}_{av} \cdot d\mathbf{s} = \frac{|E_0|^2}{2\eta} \int\!\!\!\int_{S_a} ds = ab\frac{|E_0|^2}{2\eta} \tag{11-35}$$

The maximum radiation intensity (U_{max}), using the fields of (11-23a)–(11-23b), occurs toward $\theta=0°$ and it is equal to

$$U_{max} = \left(\frac{ab}{\lambda}\right)^2 \frac{|E_0|^2}{2\eta} \tag{11-36}$$

Thus the directivity is equal to

$$\boxed{D_0 = \frac{4\pi U_{max}}{P_{rad}} = \frac{4\pi}{\lambda^2}ab = \frac{4\pi}{\lambda^2}A_p = \frac{4\pi}{\lambda^2}A_{em}} \tag{11-37}$$

where

A_p =physical area of the aperture

A_{em} =maximum effective area of the aperture

Using the definition of (2-99), it is shown that *the physical and maximum effective areas of a constant distribution aperture are equal.*

The beamwidths, side lobe levels, and directivity of this and other apertures are summarized in Table 11.1.

Example 11.2

A rectangular aperture with a constant field distribution, with $a=3\lambda$ and $b=2\lambda$, is mounted on an infinite ground plane. Compute the

(a) FNBW in the E-plane
(b) HPBW in the E-plane
(c) FSLBW in the E-plane
(d) FSLMM in the E-plane
(e) directivity using (11-37)
(f) directivity using the computer program at the end of Chapter 2, the fields of (11-23a)–(11-23f), and the formulation of Section 11.4

SOLUTION

(a) Using (11-27)

$$\Theta_1 = 114.6\sin^{-1}\left(\tfrac{1}{2}\right) = 114.6(0.524) = 60°$$

Table 11.1 EQUIVALENTS, FIELDS, BEAMWIDTHS, SIDE LOBE LEVELS, AND DIRECTIVITIES OF RECTANGULAR APERTURES

	UNIFORM DISTRIBUTION APERTURE ON GROUND PLANE	UNIFORM DISTRIBUTION APERTURE IN FREE-SPACE	TE$_{10}$-MODE DISTRIBUTION APERTURE ON GROUND PLANE
Aperture distribution of tangential components (analytical)	$\mathbf{E}_a = \hat{a}_y E_0 \begin{cases} -a/2 \leq x' \leq a/2 \\ -b/2 \leq y' \leq b/2 \end{cases}$	$\mathbf{E}_a = \hat{a}_y E_0$ $\mathbf{H}_a = -\hat{a}_x \dfrac{E_0}{\eta}$ $\begin{cases} -a/2 \leq x' \leq a/2 \\ -b/2 \leq y' \leq b/2 \end{cases}$	$\mathbf{E}_a = \hat{a}_y E_0 \cos\left(\dfrac{\pi}{a} x'\right)$ $= -a/2 \leq x' \leq a/2$ $= -b/2 \leq y' \leq b/2$
Aperture distribution of tangential components (graphical)			
Equivalent	$\mathbf{M}_s = \begin{cases} -2\hat{n} \times \mathbf{E}_a & -a/2 \leq x' \leq a/2 \\ & -b/2 \leq y' \leq b/2 \\ 0 & \text{elsewhere} \end{cases}$ $\mathbf{J}_s = 0 \quad \text{everywhere}$	$\mathbf{M}_s = -\hat{n} \times \mathbf{E}_a \begin{cases} -a/2 \leq x' \leq a/2 \\ -b/2 \leq y' \leq b/2 \end{cases}$ $\mathbf{J}_s = \hat{n} \times \mathbf{H}_a$ $\mathbf{M}_s \simeq \mathbf{J}_s \simeq 0 \quad \text{elsewhere}$	$\mathbf{M}_s = \begin{cases} -2\hat{n} \times \mathbf{E}_a & -a/2 \leq x' \leq a/2 \\ & -b/2 \leq y' \leq b/2 \\ 0 & \text{elsewhere} \end{cases}$ $\mathbf{J}_s = 0$
Far-zone fields $X = \dfrac{ka}{2}\sin\theta\cos\phi$ $Y = \dfrac{kb}{2}\sin\theta\sin\phi$ $C = j\dfrac{abkE_0 e^{-jkr}}{2\pi r}$	$E_r = H_r = 0$ $E_\theta = C\sin\phi \dfrac{\sin X}{X}\dfrac{\sin Y}{Y}$ $E_\phi = C\cos\theta\cos\phi \dfrac{\sin X}{X}\dfrac{\sin Y}{Y}$ $H_\theta = -E_\phi/\eta$ $H_\phi = E_\theta/\eta$	$E_r = H_r = 0$ $E_\theta = \dfrac{C}{2}\sin\phi(1+\cos\theta)\dfrac{\sin X}{X}\dfrac{\sin Y}{Y}$ $E_\phi = \dfrac{C}{2}\cos\phi(1+\cos\theta)\dfrac{\sin X}{X}\dfrac{\sin Y}{Y}$ $H_\theta = -E_\phi/\eta$ $H_\phi = E_\theta/\eta$	$E_r = H_r = 0$ $E_\theta = -\dfrac{\pi}{2}C\sin\phi \dfrac{\cos X}{(X)^2 - \left(\frac{\pi}{2}\right)^2}\dfrac{\sin Y}{Y}$ $E_\phi = -\dfrac{\pi}{2}C\cos\theta\cos\phi \dfrac{\cos X}{(X)^2 - \left(\frac{\pi}{2}\right)^2}\dfrac{\sin Y}{Y}$ $H_\theta = -E_\phi/\eta$ $H_\phi = E_\theta/\eta$

Half-power beamwidth (degrees)	E-plane $b \gg \lambda$	$\dfrac{50.6}{b/\lambda}$	$\dfrac{50.6}{b/\lambda}$	$\dfrac{50.6}{b/\lambda}$
	H-plane $a \gg \lambda$	$\dfrac{50.6}{a/\lambda}$	$\dfrac{50.6}{a/\lambda}$	$\dfrac{68.8}{a/\lambda}$
First null beamwidth (degrees)	E-plane $b \gg \lambda$	$\dfrac{114.6}{b/\lambda}$	$\dfrac{114.6}{b/\lambda}$	$\dfrac{114.6}{b/\lambda}$
	H-plane $a \gg \lambda$	$\dfrac{114.6}{a/\lambda}$	$\dfrac{114.6}{a/\lambda}$	$\dfrac{171.9}{a/\lambda}$
First side lobe max. (to main max.) (dB)	E-plane	-13.26	-13.26	-13.26
	H-plane	$\begin{array}{c}-13.26\\ a \gg \lambda\end{array}$	$\begin{array}{c}-13.26\\ a \gg \lambda\end{array}$	$\begin{array}{c}-23\\ a \gg \lambda\end{array}$
Directivity D_0 (dimensionless)		$\dfrac{4\pi}{\lambda^2}(\text{area}) = 4\pi\left(\dfrac{ab}{\lambda^2}\right)$	$\dfrac{4\pi}{\lambda^2}(\text{area}) = 4\pi\left(\dfrac{ab}{\lambda^2}\right)$	$\dfrac{8}{\pi^2}\left[4\pi\left(\dfrac{ab}{\lambda^2}\right)\right] = 0.81\left[4\pi\left(\dfrac{ab}{\lambda^2}\right)\right]$

(b) Using (11-29)

$$\Theta_h = 114.6 \sin^{-1}\left(\frac{0.443}{2}\right) = 114.6(0.223) = 25.6°$$

(c) Using (11-30c)

$$\Theta_s = 2\theta_s = 114.6 \sin^{-1}\left(\frac{1.43}{2}\right) = 114.6(0.796) = 91.3°$$

(d) Using (11-31)

$$|E_\theta|_{\theta=\theta_s} = 0.217 \simeq -13.26 \text{ dB}$$

(e) Using (11-37)

$$D_0 = 4\pi(3)(2) = 75.4 = 18.77 \text{ dB}$$

(f) Using the computer program at the end of Chapter 2

$$D_0 \simeq 80.4 = 19.05 \text{ dB}$$

The difference in directivity values using (11-37) and the computer program is not attributed on the accuracy of the numerical method. The main contributor is the aperture tangential magnetic field of (11-34), which was assumed to be related to the aperture tangential electric field by the intrinsic impedance. Although this is a good assumption for large size apertures, it is not exact. Therefore the directivity value computed using the computer should be considered to be the more accurate.

11.5.2 Uniform Distribution in Space

The second aperture to be examined is that of Figure 11.7 when it is *not* mounted on an infinite ground plane. The field distribution is given by

$$\left.\begin{array}{l} \mathbf{E}_a = \hat{a}_y E_0 \\ \\ \mathbf{H}_a = -\hat{a}_x \dfrac{E_0}{\eta} \end{array}\right\} \quad \begin{array}{l} -a/2 \le x' \le a/2 \\ \\ -b/2 \le y' \le b/2 \end{array} \qquad (11\text{-}38)$$

where E_0 is a constant. The geometry of the opening for this problem is identical to the previous one. However the equivalents and radiated fields are different, because this time the aperture is not mounted on an infinite ground plane.

EQUIVALENT
To form the equivalent, a closed surface is chosen which again extends from $-\infty$ to $+\infty$ on the x-y plane. Over the entire surface $\mathbf{J}_s$ and $\mathbf{M}_s$ are formed. The difficulty encountered in this problem is that both $\mathbf{J}_s$ and $\mathbf{M}_s$ are not zero outside the opening, and expressions for them are not known there. The replacement of the semi-infinite medium to the left of the boundary

(negative z) by an imaginary electric or magnetic conductor will only eliminate one or the other current densities ($\mathbf{J}_s$ or $\mathbf{M}_s$) but not both. Thus, even though an exact equivalent for this problem exists in principle, it cannot be used practically because the fields outside the opening are not known a priori. We are therefore forced to adopt an approximate equivalent.

The usual and most accurate relaxation will be to assume that both $\mathbf{E}_a$ and $\mathbf{H}_a$ (and in turn $\mathbf{M}_s$ and $\mathbf{J}_s$) exist over the opening but are zero outside it. It has been shown, by comparison with measurements and other available data, that this approximate equivalent yields the best results.

RADIATED FIELDS

Using a procedure similar to that of the previous section, the radiation characteristics of this aperture can be derived. A summary of them is shown in Table 11.1.

The field components of this aperture are identical in form to those of the aperture when it is mounted on an infinite ground plane if the $(1 + \cos\theta)$ term in each component is replaced by 2. Thus for small values of θ (in the main lobe and especially near its maximum), the patterns of the two apertures are almost identical. This procedure can be used, in general, to relate the fields of an aperture when it is and it is not mounted on an infinite ground plane. However, the coordinate system chosen must have the z-axis perpendicular to the aperture.

A three-dimensional pattern for an aperture with $a = 3\lambda$, $b = 2\lambda$ was computed, and it is shown in Figure 11.11. The dimensions of this aperture are the same as those of Figure 11.8. However the angular limits over which the radiated fields now exist have been extended to $0° \leq \theta \leq 180°$. Although the general structures of the two patterns are similar, they are not identical. Because of the enlarged space over which fields now exist, additional minor lobes are formed.

BEAMWIDTHS AND SIDE LOBE LEVELS

To find the beamwidths and the angle at which the maximum of the side lobe occurs, it is usually assumed that the $(1 + \cos\theta)$ term is a much slower varying function than the $\sin(ka\sin\theta/2)/(ka\sin\theta/2)$ or the $\sin(kb\sin\theta/2)/(kb\sin\theta/2)$ terms. This is an approximation, and it is more valid for large apertures (large a and/or b) and for angles near the main maximum. More accurate results can be obtained by considering the $(1 + \cos\theta)$ term. Thus (11-26)–(11-33) can be used, to a good approximation, to compute the beamwidths and side lobe level. A summary is included in Table 11.1.

DIRECTIVITY

Although the physical geometry of the opening of this problem is identical to that of Section 11.5.1, their directivities are not identical. This is evident

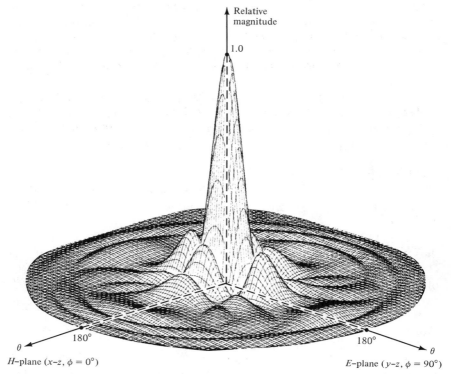

Figure 11.11 Three-dimensional field pattern of a constant field rectangular aperture ($a=3\lambda$, $b=2\lambda$).

by examining their far-zone field expressions or by realizing that the fields outside the aperture along the x-y plane are not exactly the same.

To derive an exact expression for the directivity of this aperture would be a very difficult task. Since the patterns of the apertures are nearly the same, especially at the main lobe, their directivities are almost the same. To verify this, an example is taken.

Example 11.3

Repeat the problem of Example 11.2 for an aperture that is not mounted on an infinite ground plane.

SOLUTION
Since the E-plane patterns of the two apertures are identical, the FNBW, HPBW, FSLBW, and FSLMM will be the same. The directivities as computed by (11-37), will also be the same. Since the fields radiated by the two apertures are not identical, their directivities computed using the

far-zone fields will not be exactly the same. Therefore for this problem

$$D_0 \simeq 81.16 = 19.09 \text{ dB}$$

As with Example 11.2, the directivities computed using (11-37) and the computer program do not agree exactly. For this problem, however, neither one is exact. For (11-37), it has been assumed that the aperture tangential magnetic field is related to the aperture tangential electric field by the intrinsic impedance η. This relationship is good but not exact. For the computer program, the formulation is based on the equivalent of this section where the fields outside the aperture were assumed to be negligible. Again this is a good assumption for some problems, but it is not exact.

A summary of the radiation characteristics of this aperture is included in Table 11.1 where it is compared with that of other apertures.

11.5.3 TE$_{10}$-Mode Distribution on an Infinite Ground Plane

In practice, a commonly used aperture antenna is that of a rectangular waveguide mounted on an infinite ground plane. At the opening, the field is usually approximated by the dominant TE$_{10}$-mode. Thus

$$\mathbf{E}_a = \hat{a}_y E_0 \cos\left(\frac{\pi}{a}x'\right) \qquad \begin{cases} -a/2 \le x' \le +a/2 \\ -b/2 \le y' \le +b/2 \end{cases} \qquad (11\text{-}39)$$

EQUIVALENT, RADIATED FIELDS, BEAMWIDTHS, AND SIDE LOBE LEVELS
Because the physical geometry of this antenna is identical to that of Figure 11.7, their equivalents and the procedure to analyze each one are identical. They differ only in the field distribution over the aperture.

The details of the analytical formulation are not included. However, a summary of its radiation characteristics is included in Table 11.1. The E-plane pattern of this aperture is identical in form (with the exception of a normalization factor) to the E-plane of the aperture of Section 11.5.1. This is expected, since the TE$_{10}$-mode field distribution along the E-plane (y-z plane) is also a constant. That is not the case for the H-plane or at all other points removed from the principal planes. To demonstrate that, a three-dimensional pattern for the TE$_{10}$-mode aperture with $a = 3\lambda, b = 2\lambda$ was computed and it is shown in Figure 11.12. This pattern should be compared with that of Figure 11.8.

The expressions for the beamwidths and side lobe levels in the E-plane are identical to those given by (11-26)–(11-33). However those for the H-plane are more complex, and a simple procedure is not available. Computations for the HPBW, FNBW, FSLBW, FSLMM in the E- and H-planes were made, and they are shown graphically in Figures 11.13 and 11.14.

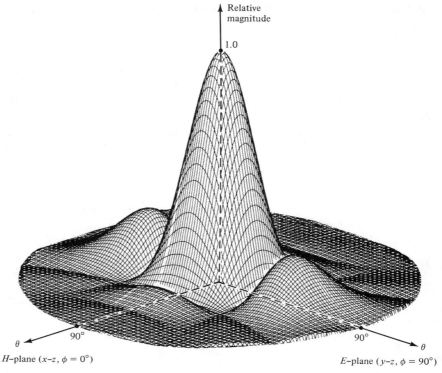

Figure 11.12   Three-dimensional field pattern of a TE$_{10}$-mode rectangular waveguide mounted on an infinite ground plane ($a=3\lambda$, $b=2\lambda$).

DIRECTIVITY AND APERTURE EFFICIENCY

The directivity of this aperture is found in the same manner as that of the uniform distribution aperture of Section 11.5.1. Using the aperture electric field of (11-39), and assuming that the aperture magnetic field is related to the electric field by the intrinsic impedance η, the radiated power can be written as

$$P_{\text{rad}}= \oiint_S \mathbf{W}_{\text{av}} \cdot d\mathbf{s}=ab\frac{|E_0|^2}{4\eta} \tag{11-39a}$$

The maximum radiation intensity occurs at $\theta=0°$, and it is given by

$$U_{\text{max}}=\frac{8}{\pi^2}\left(\frac{ab}{\lambda}\right)^2\frac{|E_0|^2}{4\eta} \tag{11-39b}$$

Thus the directivity is equal to

$$D_0=\frac{8}{\pi^2}\left[ab\left(\frac{4\pi}{\lambda^2}\right)\right]=0.81\left[ab\left(\frac{4\pi}{\lambda^2}\right)\right]=0.81A_p\left(\frac{4\pi}{\lambda^2}\right)=A_{\text{em}}\left(\frac{4\pi}{\lambda^2}\right) \tag{11-39c}$$

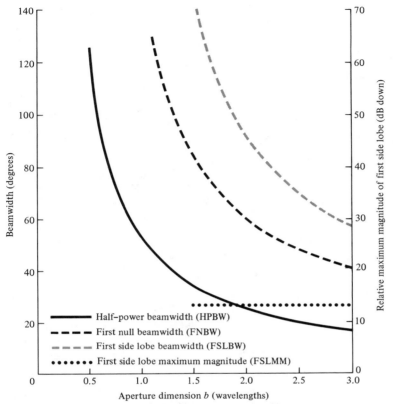

Figure 11.13   *E*-plane beamwidths and first side lobe relative maximum magnitude for TE$_{10}$-mode rectangular waveguide mounted on an infinite ground plane.

In general, the maximum effective area A_{em} is related to the physical area A_p by

$$A_{em} = \varepsilon_{ap} A_p, \qquad 0 \le \varepsilon_{ap} \le 1 \tag{11-40}$$

where ε_{ap} is the aperture efficiency. For this problem $\varepsilon_{ap} = 8/\pi^2 \simeq 0.81$. The aperture efficiency is a figure-of-merit which indicates how efficiently the physical area of the antenna is utilized. Typically, aperture antennas have aperture efficiencies from about 30% to 90%, horns from 35% to 80% (optimum gain horns have $\varepsilon_{ap} \simeq 50\%$), and circular reflectors from 50% to 80%.

For reflectors, the aperture efficiency is a function of many factors. The most prominent are the spillover, amplitude taper, phase distribution, polarization uniformity, blockage, and surface random errors. These are discussed in detail in Section 13.4.1 of Chapter 13.

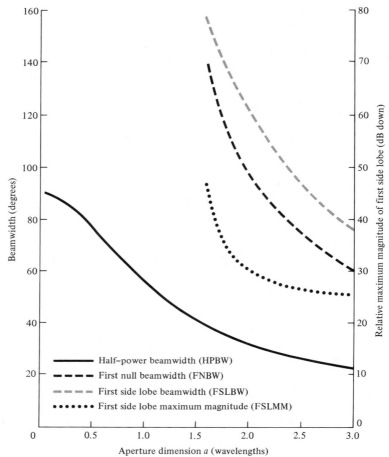

Figure 11.14 *H*-plane beamwidths and first side lobe relative maximum magnitude for TE$_{10}$-mode rectangular waveguide mounted on an infinite ground plane.

11.5.4 Beam Efficiency

The beam efficiency for an antenna was introduced in Section 2.10 and was defined by (2-53). When the aperture is mounted on the *x-y* plane, the beam efficiency can be calculated using (2-54). The beam efficiency can be used to judge the ability of the antenna to discriminate between signals received through its main lobe and those through the minor lobes. Beam efficiencies for rectangular apertures with different aperture field distributions are plotted, versus the half-cone angle θ_1, in Figure 11.15. The uniform field distribution aperture has the least ability to discriminate between main lobe and minor lobe signals. The aperture radiates in an unbounded medium, and it is not mounted on an infinite ground plane. The lower abscissa scale is in terms of θ_1 (in degrees), and it should be used only when $a = b = 20\lambda$.

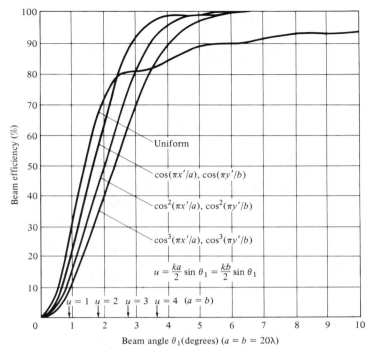

Figure 11.15   Beam efficiency versus half-cone angle θ_1, for a square aperture with different field distributions. The aperture is not mounted on an infinite ground plane. (SOURCE: D. G. Fink (ed.), *Electronics Engineers' Handbook*, Section 18 (by W. F. Croswell), McGraw-Hill, New York, 1975)

The upper abscissa scale is in terms of $u[u = (ka/2)\sin\theta_1 = (kb/2)\sin\theta_1]$, and it should be used for any square aperture.

Example 11.4

Determine the beam efficiency, within a cone of half-angle $\theta_1 = 10°$, for a square aperture with uniform field distribution and with

(a) $a = b = 20\lambda$
(b) $a = b = 3\lambda$

SOLUTION
The solution is carried out using the curves of Figure 11.15.

(a) When $a = b = 20\lambda$, the lower abscissa scale can be used. For $\theta_1 = 10°$, the efficiency for the uniform aperture is about 94%.
(b) For $a = b = 3\lambda$ and $\theta_1 = 10°$

$$u = \frac{ka}{2}\sin\theta_1 = 3\pi\sin(10°) = 1.64$$

Using the upper abscissa scale, the efficiency for the uniform aperture at $u = 1.64$ is about 58%.

11.6 CIRCULAR APERTURES

A widely used microwave antenna is the circular aperture. One of the attractive features of this configuration is its simplicity in construction. In addition, closed form expressions for the fields of all the modes that can exist over the aperture can be obtained.

The procedure followed to determine the fields radiated by a circular aperture is identical to that of the rectangular, as summarized in Section 11.3. The primary differences lie in the formulation of the equivalent currents (J_x, J_y, J_z, M_x, M_y, M_z), the differential paths from the source to the observation point ($r' \cos \psi$), and the differential area (ds'). Before an example is considered, these differences will be reformulated for the circular aperture.

Because of the circular profile of the aperture, it is often convenient and desirable to adopt cylindrical coordinates for the solution of the fields. In most cases, therefore, the electric and magnetic field components over the circular opening will be known in cylindrical form; that is, E_ρ, E_ϕ, E_z, H_ρ,

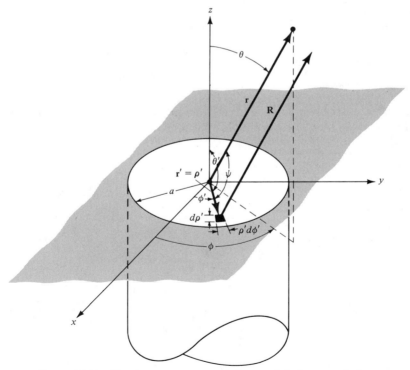

Figure 11.16 Circular aperture mounted on an infinite ground plane.

H_ϕ, and H_z. Thus the components of the equivalent currents $\mathbf{M}_s$ and $\mathbf{J}_s$ would also be conveniently expressed in cylindrical form (M_ρ, M_ϕ, M_z, J_ρ, J_ϕ, J_z). In addition, the required integration over the aperture to find N_θ, N_ϕ, L_θ, and L_ϕ of (11-12a)–(11-12d) should also be done in cylindrical coordinates. It is then desirable to reformulate $r' \cos \psi$ and ds', as given by (11-15a)–(11-16c).

The most convenient position for placing the aperture is that shown in Figure 11.16 (aperture on x-y plane). The transformation between the rectangular and cylindrical components of J_s is given by (see Appendix VII)

$$
\begin{bmatrix} J_x \\ J_y \\ J_z \end{bmatrix} = \begin{bmatrix} \cos \phi' & -\sin \phi' & 0 \\ \sin \phi' & \cos \phi' & 0 \\ 0 & 0 & 1 \end{bmatrix} \begin{bmatrix} J_\rho \\ J_\phi \\ J_z \end{bmatrix}
\tag{11-41a}
$$

A similar transformation exists for the components of $\mathbf{M}_s$. The rectangular and cylindrical coordinates are related by (see Appendix VII)

$$
\begin{aligned}
x' &= \rho' \cos \phi' \\
y' &= \rho' \sin \phi' \\
z' &= z'
\end{aligned}
\tag{11-41b}
$$

Using (11-41a), (11-12a)–(11-12d) can be written as

$$
N_\theta = \iint_S \left[J_\rho \cos \theta \cos(\phi - \phi') + J_\phi \cos \theta \sin(\phi - \phi') - J_z \sin \theta \right]
$$
$$
\times e^{+jkr'\cos\psi} \, ds'
\tag{11-42a}
$$

$$
N_\phi = \iint_S \left[-J_\rho \sin(\phi - \phi') + J_\phi \cos(\phi - \phi') \right] e^{+jkr'\cos\psi} \, ds'
\tag{11-42b}
$$

$$
L_\theta = \iint_S \left[M_\rho \cos \theta \cos(\phi - \phi') + M_\phi \cos \theta \sin(\phi - \phi') - M_z \sin \theta \right]
$$
$$
\times e^{+jkr'\cos\psi} \, ds'
\tag{11-42c}
$$

$$
L_\phi = \iint_S \left[-M_\rho \sin(\phi - \phi') + M_\phi \cos(\phi - \phi') \right] e^{+jkr'\cos\psi} \, ds'
\tag{11-42d}
$$

where $r' \cos \psi$ and ds' can be written, using (11-15c) and (11-41b), as

$$
r' \cos \psi = x' \sin \theta \cos \phi + y' \sin \theta \sin \phi = \rho' \sin \theta \cos(\phi - \phi')
\tag{11-43a}
$$
$$
ds' = dx' \, dy' = \rho' \, d\rho' \, d\phi'
\tag{11-43b}
$$

In summary, for a circular aperture antenna the fields radiated can be obtained by *either* of the following:

1. If the fields over the aperture are known in *rectangular components*, use the same procedure as for the rectangular aperture with (11-43a) and (11-43b) substituted in (11-12a)–(11-12d).
2. If the fields over the aperture are known in *cylindrical components*, use the same procedure as for the rectangular aperture with

(11-42a)–(11-42d), along with (11-43a) and (11-43b), taking the place of (11-12a)–(11-12d).

11.6.1 Uniform Distribution on an Infinite Ground Plane

To demonstrate the methods, the field radiated by a circular aperture mounted on an infinite ground plane will be formulated. To simplify the mathematical details, the field over the aperture will be assumed to be constant and given by

$$\mathbf{E}_a = \hat{a}_y E_0 \qquad \rho' \le a \tag{11-44}$$

where E_0 is a constant.

EQUIVALENT AND RADIATION FIELDS
The equivalent problem of this is identical to that of Figure 11.7. That is,

$$\mathbf{M}_s = \begin{cases} -2\hat{n} \times \mathbf{E}_a = \hat{a}_x 2E_0 & \rho' \le a \\ 0 & \text{elsewhere} \end{cases} \\ \mathbf{J}_s = 0 \qquad\qquad \text{everywhere} \tag{11-45}$$

Thus,

$$N_\theta = N_\phi = 0 \tag{11-46}$$

$$L_\theta = 2E_0 \cos\theta \cos\phi \int_0^a \rho' \left[\int_0^{2\pi} e^{+jk\rho' \sin\theta \cos(\phi - \phi')} d\phi' \right] d\rho' \tag{11-47}$$

Because

$$\int_0^{2\pi} e^{+jk\rho' \sin\theta \cos(\phi - \phi')} d\phi' = 2\pi J_0(k\rho' \sin\theta) \tag{11-48}$$

(11-47) can be written as

$$L_\theta = 4\pi E_0 \cos\theta \cos\phi \int_0^a J_0(k\rho' \sin\theta) \rho' d\rho' \tag{11-49}$$

where $J_0(t)$ is the Bessel function of the first kind of order zero. Making the substitution

$$t = k\rho' \sin\theta$$
$$dt = k \sin\theta \, d\rho' \tag{11-49a}$$

reduces (11-49) to

$$L_\theta = \frac{4\pi E_0 \cos\theta \cos\phi}{(k \sin\theta)^2} \int_0^{ka\sin\theta} t J_0(t) \, dt \tag{11-49b}$$

Since

$$\int_0^\beta z J_0(z) \, dz = z J_1(z) \Big|_0^\beta = \beta J_1(\beta) \tag{11-50}$$

where $J_1(\beta)$ is the Bessel function of order one, (11-49b) takes the form of

$$L_\theta = 4\pi a^2 E_0 \left\{ \cos\theta \cos\phi \left[\frac{J_1(ka\sin\theta)}{ka\sin\theta} \right] \right\} \tag{11-51}$$

Similarly

$$L_\phi = -4\pi a^2 E_0 \sin\phi \left[\frac{J_1(ka\sin\theta)}{ka\sin\theta} \right] \tag{11-52}$$

Using (11-46), (11-51), and (11-52), the electric field components of (11-10a)–(11-10c) can be written as

$$E_r = 0 \tag{11-53a}$$

$$E_\theta = j\frac{ka^2 E_0 e^{-jkr}}{r} \left\{ \sin\phi \left[\frac{J_1(ka\sin\theta)}{ka\sin\theta} \right] \right\} \tag{11-53b}$$

$$E_\phi = j\frac{ka^2 E_0 e^{-jkr}}{r} \left\{ \cos\theta \cos\phi \left[\frac{J_1(ka\sin\theta)}{ka\sin\theta} \right] \right\} \tag{11-53c}$$

In the principal E- and H-planes, the electric field components simplify to

E-Plane ($\phi = \pi/2$)

$$E_r = E_\phi = 0 \tag{11-54a}$$

$$E_\theta = j\frac{ka^2 E_0 e^{-jkr}}{r} \left[\frac{J_1(ka\sin\theta)}{ka\sin\theta} \right] \tag{11-54b}$$

H-Plane ($\phi = 0$)

$$E_r = E_\theta = 0 \tag{11-55a}$$

$$E_\phi = j\frac{ka^2 E_0 e^{-jkr}}{r} \left\{ \cos\theta \left[\frac{J_1(ka\sin\theta)}{ka\sin\theta} \right] \right\} \tag{11-55b}$$

A three-dimensional pattern has been computed for the constant field circular aperture of $a = 1.5\lambda$, and it is shown in Figure 11.17. The pattern in Figure 11.17 seems to be symmetrical. However closer observation, especially through the two-dimensional E- and H-plane patterns, will reveal that not to be the case. It does, however, possess characteristics that are almost symmetrical.

Table 11.2 EQUIVALENTS, FIELDS, BEAMWIDTHS, SIDE LOBE LEVELS, AND DIRECTIVITIES OF CIRCULAR APERTURES

ON GROUND PLANE	UNIFORM DISTRIBUTION APERTURE ON GROUND PLANE	TE_{11}-MODE DISTRIBUTION APERTURE ON GROUND PLANE
Aperture distribution of tangential components (analytical)	$\mathbf{E}_a = \hat{a}_y E_0 \quad \rho' \leq a$	$\mathbf{E}_a = \hat{a}_\rho E_\rho + \hat{a}_\phi E_\phi \quad \left. \begin{array}{l} \\ \\ \end{array} \right\} \begin{array}{l} \rho' \leq a \\ \chi_{11}' = 1.841 \end{array}$ $E_\rho = E_0 J_1(\chi_{11}'\rho'/a)\sin\phi'/\rho'$ $E_\phi = E_0 J_1'(\chi_{11}'\rho'/a)\cos\phi' \quad ' = \dfrac{\partial}{\partial\rho'}$
Aperture distribution of tangential components (graphical)		
Equivalent	$\mathbf{M}_s = \begin{cases} -2\hat{n}\times\mathbf{E}_a & \rho'\leq a \text{ elsewhere} \\ 0 & \text{everywhere} \end{cases}$ $\mathbf{J}_s = 0$	$\mathbf{M}_s = \begin{cases} -2\hat{n}\times\mathbf{E}_a & \rho'\leq a \\ 0 & \text{elsewhere everywhere} \end{cases}$ $\mathbf{J}_s = 0$
Far-zone fields $Z = ka\sin\theta$ $C_1 = j\dfrac{ka^2 E_0 e^{-jkr}}{r}$ $C_2 = j\dfrac{kaE_0 J_1(\chi_{11}') e^{-jkr}}{r}$ $\chi_{11}' = 1.841$	$E_r = H_r = 0$ $E_\theta = jC_1\sin\phi\dfrac{J_1(Z)}{Z}$ $E_\phi = jC_1\cos\theta\cos\phi\dfrac{J_1(Z)}{Z}$ $H_\theta = -E_\phi/\eta$ $H_\phi = E_\theta/\eta$	$E_r = H_r = 0$ $E_\theta = C_2\sin\phi\dfrac{J_1(Z)}{Z}$ $E_\phi = C_2\cos\theta\cos\phi\dfrac{J_1'(Z)}{1-(Z/\chi_{11})^2}$ $H_\theta = -E_\phi/\eta$ $H_\phi = E_\theta/\eta$ $J_1'(Z) = J_0(Z) - J_1(Z)/Z$

482

Half-power beamwidth (degrees)	E-plane $a \gg \lambda$	$\dfrac{29.2}{a/\lambda}$	$\dfrac{29.2}{a/\lambda}$
	H-plane $a \gg \lambda$	$\dfrac{29.2}{a/\lambda}$	$\dfrac{37.0}{a/\lambda}$
First null beamwidth (degrees)	E-plane $a \gg \lambda$	$\dfrac{69.9}{a/\lambda}$	$\dfrac{69.9}{a/\lambda}$
	H-plane $a \gg \lambda$	$\dfrac{69.9}{a/\lambda}$	$\dfrac{98.0}{a/\lambda}$
First side lobe max. (to main max.) (dB)	E-plane	-17.6	-17.6
	H-plane	-17.6	-26.2
Directivity D_0 (dimensionless)		$\dfrac{4\pi}{\lambda^2}\,(\text{area}) = \dfrac{4\pi}{\lambda^2}(\pi a^2) = \left(\dfrac{2\pi a}{\lambda}\right)^2$	$0.836\left(\dfrac{2\pi a}{\lambda}\right)^2 = 10.5\pi\left(\dfrac{a}{\lambda}\right)^2$

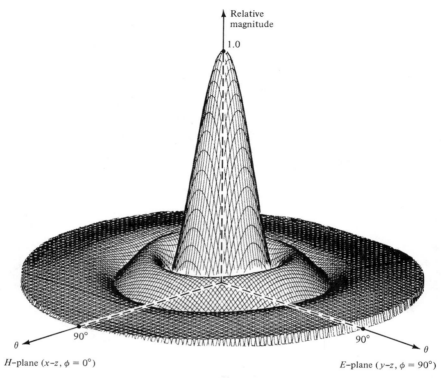

Figure 11.17 Three-dimensional field pattern of a constant field circular aperture mounted on an infinite ground plane ($a = 1.5\lambda$).

BEAMWIDTH, SIDE LOBE LEVEL, AND DIRECTIVITY

Exact expressions for the beamwidths and side lobe levels cannot be obtained easily. However approximate expressions are available, and they are shown tabulated in Table 11.2. More exact data can be obtained by numerical methods.

Since the field distribution over the aperture is constant, the directivity is given by

$$D_0 = \frac{4\pi}{\lambda^2} A_{\text{em}} = \frac{4\pi}{\lambda^2} A_p = \frac{4\pi}{\lambda^2} (\pi a^2) = \left(\frac{2\pi a}{\lambda}\right)^2 = \left(\frac{C}{\lambda}\right)^2 \qquad (11\text{-}56)$$

since the maximum effective area A_{em} is equal to the physical area A_p of the aperture [as shown for the rectangular aperture in (11-37)].

A summary of the radiation parameters of this aperture is included in Table 11.2 on preceding pages 482–483.

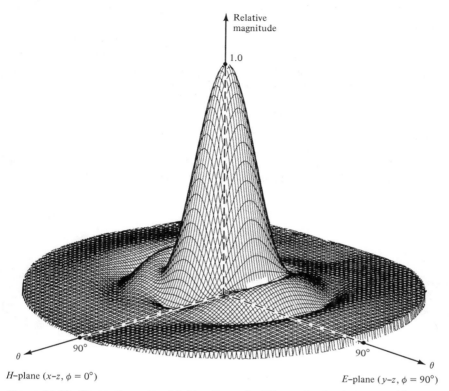

Relative
magnitude

1.0

90°

90°

θ

θ

H-plane $(x\text{-}z, \phi = 0°)$

E-plane $(y\text{-}z, \phi = 90°)$

Figure 11.18   Three-dimensional field pattern of a TE$_{11}$-mode circular waveguide mounted on an infinite ground plane ($a = 1.5\lambda$).

11.6.2   TE$_{11}$-Mode Distribution on an Infinite Ground Plane

A very practical antenna is a circular waveguide of radius a mounted on an infinite ground plane, as shown in Figure 11.16. However, the field distribution over the aperture is usually that of the dominant TE$_{11}$-mode for a circular waveguide given by

$$E_\rho = \frac{E_0}{\rho'} J_1\left(\frac{\chi_{11}'}{a}\rho'\right)\sin\phi'$$

$$E_\phi = E_0 \frac{\partial}{\partial\rho'}\left[J_1\left(\frac{\chi_{11}'}{a}\rho'\right)\right]\cos\phi'$$

$$E_z = 0$$

$$\chi_{11}' = 1.841$$

(11-57)

The analysis of this problem is assigned, at the end of this chapter, as an exercise to the reader (Problem 11.19). However, a three-dimensional pattern for $a = 1.5\lambda$ was calculated, and it is shown in Figure 11.18. This pattern should be compared with that of Figure 11.17 for the constant aperture field distribution.

The beamwidths and the side lobe levels in the *E*- and *H*-planes are different, and exact closed form expressions cannot be obtained. However, they can be calculated using iterative methods, and the data are shown in Figures 11.19 and 11.20 for the *E*- and *H*-planes, respectively.

A summary of all the radiation characteristics is included in Table 11.2.

11.6.3 Beam Efficiency

Beam efficiency, as defined by (2-53) and calculated by (2-54), for circular apertures not mounted on infinite ground planes is shown in Figure 11.21.

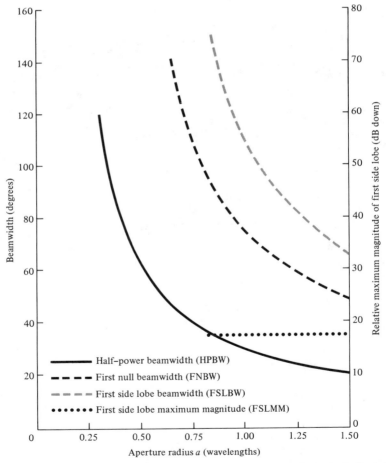

Figure 11.19 *E*-plane beamwidths and first side lobe relative maximum magnitude for TE$_{11}$-mode circular aperture mounted on an infinite ground plane.

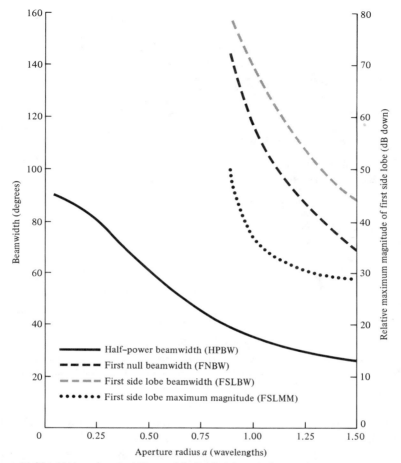

Figure 11.20 *H*-plane beamwidths and first side lobe relative maximum magnitude for TE$_{11}$-mode circular waveguide mounted on an infinite ground plane.

The lower abscissa scale (in degrees) is in terms of the half-cone angle θ_1 (in degrees), and it should be used only when the radius of the aperture is 20λ ($a = 20λ$). The upper abscissa scale is in terms of u ($u = ka\sin\theta_1$), and it should be used for any radius circular aperture.

The procedure for finding the beam efficiency of a circular aperture is similar to that of a rectangular aperture as discussed in Section 11.5.4, illustrated in Figure 11.15, and demonstrated by Example 11.4.

11.7 MICROSTRIP ANTENNAS

In aircraft and spacecraft applications, where size, weight, cost, perfor-mance, ease of installation, and aerodynamic profile are constraints, low profile antennas may be required. To meet these specifications, microstrip

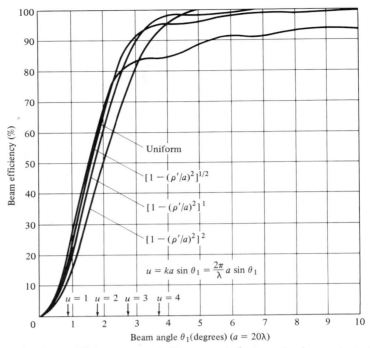

Figure 11.21 Beam efficiency versus half-cone angle θ_1, for a circular aperture with different field distributions. The aperture is not mounted on an infinite ground plane. (SOURCE: D. G. Fink (ed.), *Electronics Engineers' Handbook*, Section 18 (by W. F. Croswell), McGraw-Hill, New York, 1975)

antennas [11]–[17] can be used. These antennas can be flush-mounted to metal or other existing surfaces, and they only require space for the feed line which is usually placed behind the ground plane. Major operational disadvantages of microstrip antennas are their inefficiency and their very narrow frequency bandwidth which is typically only a fraction of a percent or at most a few percent.

Microstrip antennas consist of a very thin ($t \ll \lambda$) metallic strip (patch) placed a small fraction of a wavelength ($h \ll \lambda$) above a ground plane. The strip (patch) and the ground plane are separated by a dielectric sheet (referred to as the substrate), as shown in Figure 11.22(a). The radiating elements and the feed lines are usually photoetched on the dielectric substrate. The radiating patch may be square, rectangular, circular, elliptical, or any other configuration. Square, rectangular, and circular are the most common because of ease of analysis and fabrication. The feed line is often also a conducting strip, usually of smaller width. Coaxial-line feeds, where the inner conductor of the coax is attached to the radiating patch, are also widely used. Linear and circular polarizations can be achieved with microstrip antennas. Arrays of microstrip elements, with single or multiple feeds, may also be used to obtain greater directivities.

Because the thickness of the microstrip is usually very small, the waves generated within the dielectric substrate (between the patch and the ground plane) undergo considerable reflections when they arrive at the edge of the strip. Therefore only a small fraction of the incident energy is radiated; thus the antenna is considered to be very inefficient, and it behaves more like a cavity instead of a radiator.

11.7.1 Radiated Fields

The field structure within the substrate and between the radiating element and the ground plane is sketched in Figures 11.22(a) and 11.22(b). It undergoes a phase reversal along the length, as indicated in the side view of Figure 11.22(b), but it is approximately uniform along its width.

The antenna consists of two slots, each of width w and height h, and placed perpendicular to the feed line. The slots are separated by a very low impedance parallel-plate transmission line of length l which acts as a transformer. The length of the transmission line is approximately $\lambda_g/2$, where λ_g is the guide wavelength, in order for the fields at the aperture of the two slots to have opposite polarization. The two slots form a two-element array with a spacing of $\lambda_g/2$ between the elements. Parallel to the ground plane, the components of the field add in phase and give a maximum radiation normal to the element.

The electric field at the aperture of each slot can be decomposed into x- and y-components. The y-components are out of phase and their contributions cancel out. The radiated fields can be found by treating the antenna as an aperture, as shown in Figure 11.22(c). Since the feed lines are chosen so as to excite only a TEM-mode, the x-component of the electric field at the aperture can be assumed to be constant and equal to

$$\mathbf{E}_a = \hat{a}_x E_0 \begin{cases} -h/2 \le x' \le h/2 \\ -w/2 \le z' \le w/2 \end{cases} \tag{11-58}$$

Using the equivalence principle of Section 11.3, it can be shown that each slot will radiate the same fields as a magnetic dipole with magnetic current density $\mathbf{M}_s$ equal to

$$\mathbf{M}_s = \begin{cases} -2\hat{n} \times \mathbf{E}_a = -2\hat{a}_y \times \hat{a}_x E_0 = \hat{a}_z 2E_0 & \begin{cases} -h/2 \le x' \le h/2 \\ -w/2 \le z' \le w/2 \end{cases} \\ 0 & \text{elsewhere} \end{cases}$$

$$\tag{11-59a}$$

and

$$\mathbf{J}_s = 0 \qquad \text{everywhere} \qquad (11\text{-}59b)$$

The total field will be the sum of the two-element array with each element representing one of the slots.

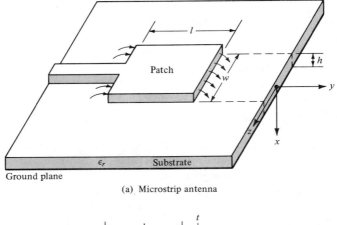

(a) Microstrip antenna

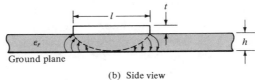

(b) Side view

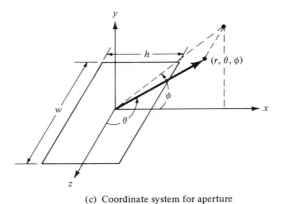

(c) Coordinate system for aperture

Figure 11.22   Microstrip antenna and coordinate system.

Following a procedure similar to that used to analyze the aperture in Section 11.5.1, the far-zone electric fields can be written as

$$E_r \simeq E_\theta \simeq 0 \tag{11-60a}$$

$$E_\phi \simeq -j\frac{hwkE_0 e^{-jkr}}{2\pi r}\left\{\sin\theta\left[\frac{\sin(X)}{X}\right]\left[\frac{\sin(Z)}{Z}\right]\right\} \tag{11-60b}$$

where

$$X = \frac{kh}{2} \sin\theta \cos\phi \qquad (11\text{-}60c)$$

$$Z = \frac{kw}{2} \cos\theta \qquad (11\text{-}60d)$$

For small values of h ($h \ll \lambda$), (11-60b) reduces to

$$E_\phi \simeq -j\frac{V_0 e^{-jkr}}{\pi r}\sin\theta \frac{\sin\left(\frac{kw}{2}\cos\theta\right)}{\cos\theta} \qquad (11\text{-}60e)$$

where $V_0 = hE_0$ is the voltage across the slot.

Microstrip antennas resemble dielectric loaded cavities, and they exhibit higher order resonances. The fields within the dielectric substrate (between the patch and the ground plane) can be found more accurately by treating that region as a cavity bounded by electric conductors (above and below it) and by a magnetic wall (to simulate an open circuit) along the perimeter of the patch. This is an approximate model, which in principle leads to a reactive input impedance (of zero or infinite value of resonance), and it does not radiate any power. However, assuming that the actual fields are approximately those generated by such a model, the computed pattern, input admittance, and resonant frequencies compare well with measurements [17]. This is an accepted approach, and it is similar to the perturbation methods that have been very successful in the analysis of waveguides, cavities, and radiators [4].

The fields within the dielectric substrate can be found by assuming that only an E_x-component, whose functional variations are independent of x, exists between the patch and the ground plane. In addition, E_x must satisfy the scalar Helmholtz wave equation. For a rectangular patch of dimensions l and w, it is most convenient to use rectangular coordinates. Thus,

$$(\nabla^2 + k_d^2)E_x(y,z) = \left(\frac{\partial^2}{\partial y^2} + \frac{\partial^2}{\partial z^2}\right)E_x(y,z)$$

$$= \begin{cases} 0 & \text{(away from the feed)} \qquad (11\text{-}61a) \\ j\omega\mu_0 J_x & \text{(at the feed)} \qquad (11\text{-}61b) \end{cases}$$

where $k_d = \omega\sqrt{\mu_0\varepsilon}$, $\varepsilon = \varepsilon_r\varepsilon_0$.

If the origin is taken at one of the patch corners of Figure 11.22(a) ($0 \le x \le h, 0 \le y \le l, 0 \le z \le w$), the solution of the homogeneous wave equation of (11-61a) can be written, subject to the boundary conditions of

$$\left.\frac{\partial E_x}{\partial z}\right|_{z=0} = \left.\frac{\partial E_x}{\partial z}\right|_{z=w} = 0 \quad \text{or} \quad H_y(z=0) = H_y(z=w) = 0 \qquad (11\text{-}61c)$$

and

$$\left.\frac{\partial E_x}{\partial y}\right|_{y=0} = \left.\frac{\partial E_x}{\partial y}\right|_{y=l} = 0 \quad \text{or} \quad H_z(y=0) = H_y(y=l) = 0 \qquad \text{(11-61d)}$$

as

$$E_x = A_{mn}\cos(k_y y)\cos(k_z z) = A_{mn}\cos\left(\frac{m\pi}{l}y\right)\cos\left(\frac{n\pi}{w}z\right) \qquad \text{(11-61e)}$$

where

$$k_y^2 + k_z^2 = \left(\frac{m\pi}{l}\right)^2 + \left(\frac{n\pi}{w}\right)^2 = k_r^2 = \omega_r^2\mu_0\varepsilon = (2\pi f_r)^2\mu_0\varepsilon \qquad \text{(11-61f)}$$

or

$$(f_r)_{mn} = \frac{1}{2\pi\sqrt{\mu_0\varepsilon}}\sqrt{\left(\frac{m\pi}{l}\right)^2 + \left(\frac{n\pi}{w}\right)^2} \qquad \begin{matrix} m = 0,1,2,3,\ldots \\ n = 0,1,2,3,\ldots \end{matrix} \qquad \text{(11-61g)}$$

The $m = n = 0$ mode reduces to the electrostatic field configuration. A_{mn} represents the amplitude constant and $(f_r)_{mn}$ the resonant frequency of the mnth mode. The resonant frequencies occur when the front-back or the left-right slots are separated by an integral number of half-wavelengths (in the substrate). For $l > w$, the lowest order resonant frequency (other than $m = n = 0 \Rightarrow f_r = 0$) occurs when $m = 1$, $n = 0$ or

$$(f_r)_{10} = \frac{1}{2l\sqrt{\mu_0\varepsilon}} \qquad \text{(11-61h)}$$

Each term of (11-61e) satisfies the boundary conditions, and all the terms (as a group) form a set of orthogonal functions. The corresponding magnetic field components are obtained using (11-61e) and Maxwell's curl equation of (3-21) with $\mathbf{M} = 0$, and they are given by

$$H_x = 0 \qquad \text{(11-61i)}$$

$$H_y = -j\frac{1}{\omega\mu}\frac{\partial E_x}{\partial z} = j\frac{n\pi}{w\mu\omega}A_{mn}\cos\left(\frac{m\pi}{l}y\right)\sin\left(\frac{n\pi}{w}z\right) \qquad \text{(11-61j)}$$

$$H_z = j\frac{1}{\omega\mu}\frac{\partial E_x}{\partial y} = -j\frac{m\pi}{l\mu\omega}A_{mn}\sin\left(\frac{m\pi}{l}y\right)\cos\left(\frac{n\pi}{w}z\right) \qquad \text{(11-61k)}$$

In the presence of an x-directed source at the feed, the total E_x must satisfy the wave equation of (11-61b). The general solution is comprised of an arbitrary linear sum of a complete set of orthogonal functions each of the form of (11-61e), and it can be written as

$$E_x = \sum_n \sum_m A_{mn}\cos\left(\frac{m\pi}{l}y\right)\cos\left(\frac{n\pi}{w}z\right) \qquad \text{(11-61l)}$$

The constants A_{mn} can be found by employing orthogonality conditions. The final form of (11-61*l*) is included in [17].

The field components derived above can be used to form equivalent magnetic current densities along the perimeter of the patch (equivalent electric current densities do not exist along the perimeter because $\mathbf{H}_{\text{tan}}=0$ there). These currents can then be used to find more accurate expressions for the radiated fields which compare well with measurements [17]. To account for fringing and to attain better accuracies, effective dimensions can be introduced [17].

Similar procedures can be employed for circular patches, and for some other useful configurations, whose primary radiation characteristics are tabulated in [17]. The approximate resonant frequencies for a circular patch of radius a are given by

$$(f_r)_{mn} = \frac{\chi_{mn}'}{2\pi a\sqrt{\mu\varepsilon}} \qquad \begin{matrix} m=0,1,2,3,\ldots \\ n=1,2,3,4,\ldots \end{matrix} \qquad \text{(11-62)}$$

where χ_{mn}' represents the zeros $(n=1,2,3,\ldots)$ of the derivative of the Bessel function $J_m(x)$ of the first kind of order m [i.e., $J_m'(\chi_{mn}')=0$], which are tabulated in [4]. The lowest order resonant frequency occurs when $m=1$, $n=1$ $(\chi_{11}'=1.841)$.

Other methods of analysis are available [15], [16]. Microstrip antenna patterns have been computed and agree well with measurements [11]–[13], [15], [17].

11.7.2 Radiation Conductance

The radiation conductance G can be obtained using a procedure similar to the radiation resistance of a wire element. The power density is first formed, and it is integrated over a closed sphere (in this case over a hemisphere) to find the radiated power P_{rad}. Then the conductance is related to P_{rad}. Using (11-60e), it reduces to

$$G = \frac{2P_{\text{rad}}}{|V_0|^2} = \frac{1}{120\pi^2}I \qquad \text{(11-63)}$$

where

$$I = \int_0^\pi \left[\frac{\sin\left(\dfrac{kw}{2}\cos\theta \right)}{\cos\theta} \right]^2 \sin^3\theta \, d\theta \qquad \text{(11-63a)}$$

Since (11-63a) cannot be integrated in closed form, numerical techniques have been used to evaluate it [13]. A plot of the conductance as a function of w (in λ) is shown in Figure 11.23.

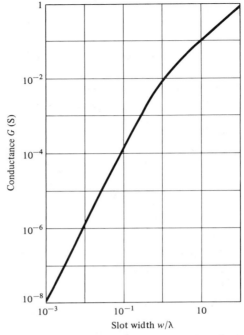

Figure 11.23 Slot conductance as a function of slot width w/λ. (SOURCE: A. G. Derneryd, "Linearly Polarized Microstrip Antennas," *IEEE Trans. Antennas Propag.*, vol. AP-24, No. 6, pp. 846–851, Nov. 1976. © (1976) IEEE)

For small and large values of w, (11-63) reduces to

$$G \simeq \frac{1}{90}\left(\frac{w}{\lambda}\right)^2, \qquad \text{for } w \ll \lambda \tag{11-64a}$$

$$G \simeq \frac{1}{120}\left(\frac{w}{\lambda}\right)^2, \qquad \text{for } w \gg \lambda \tag{11-64b}$$

Complex input impedances have also been computed using more advanced techniques [16].

11.7.3 Directivity

It can also be shown, using procedures outlined previously, that the directivity of the microstrip is equal to

$$D_0 = \frac{4\pi U_{\max}}{P_{\text{rad}}} = \left(\frac{2\pi w}{\lambda}\right)^2 \frac{1}{I} \tag{11-65}$$

where I is defined by (11-63a). For small and large values of w, (11-65) reduces to

$$
\begin{array}{lll}
D_0 \simeq 3 = 4.77 \text{ dB} & \text{for } w \ll \lambda & \text{(11-65a)} \\
1 D_0 \simeq 4 = 6.02 \text{ dB} & \text{for } w \gg \lambda & \text{(11-65b)}
\end{array}
$$

The value of $D_0 = 3(4.77 \text{ dB})$, is equivalent to the directivity of a small slot radiating into a half-space.

11.7.4 Bandwidth

A major limitation of a microstrip antenna is its narrow frequency bandwidth. The bandwidth is primarily controlled by the characteristics of the parallel plate transmission line. Usually it ranges from a fraction of a percent to a few percent. There are basically four methods that can be used to increase the bandwidth [11]. These are:

1. Increase the thickness (h) of the parallel plate transmission line which in turn increases its characteristic impedance. However, if the antenna is to retain its low profile and conformal characteristics, the increase in thickness is undesirable. For most applications, the low profile advantages outweigh the limitations of the bandwidth. For bandwidths of less than 1%, both requirements are usually satisfied.
2. Use a high dielectric constant (ε_r) substrate to decrease the physical dimensions of the parallel plate line.
3. Increase the inductance of the microstrip by cutting holes or slots into it.
4. Add reactive components to reduce the VSWR.

11.7.5 Arrays

To increase the directivity of the antenna, multiple microstrip radiators may be cascaded to form an array. The elements may be fed by a single line or multiple lines as shown in Figures 11.24(a) and (b). The use of multiple

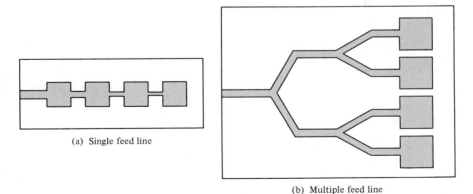

(a) Single feed line

(b) Multiple feed line

Figure 11.24   Single and multiple feed microstrip arrays.

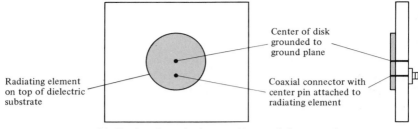

Center of disk
grounded to
ground plane

Radiating element
on top of dielectric
substrate

Coaxial connector with
center pin attached to
radiating element

(a) Circular microstrip element with grounded center and
fed from the back (after J. Q. Howell [12])

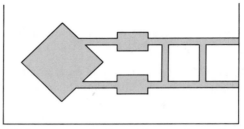

(b) Square microstrip element driven at adjacent sides
through a 90° hybrid (after R. E. Munson [11])

Figure 11.25   Circularly polarized microstrip antennas. (SOURCES: J. Q. Howell, "Microstrip Antennas," *IEEE Trans. Antennas Propag.*, vol. AP-23, No. 1, pp. 90–93, Jan. 1975. © (1975) IEEE; R. E. Munson, "Conformal Microstrip Antennas and Microstrip Phased Arrays," *IEEE Trans. Antennas Propag.*, vol. AP-22, No. 1, pp. 74–78, Jan. 1974. © (1974) IEEE)

elements also provides a mechanism to electronically scan the antenna. This is accomplished by the use of phase shifters which control the phase excitation of each element radiator.

11.7.6   Circular Polarization

Microstrip antennas are primarily linear radiators. Circular polarization can be obtained by exciting two orthogonal antenna modes with a 90° time-phase difference. Two ways of accomplishing this are shown in Figures 11.25(a) and (b). In Figure 11.25(a), a center-grounded circular disk radiator is driven from the back by two probes located 90° apart. The square radiator of Figure 11.25(b) is driven at two adjacent sides, and it uses a 90° hybrid.

11.8   BABINET'S PRINCIPLE

Now that wire and aperture antennas have been analyzed, one may inquire as to whether there is any relation between them. This can be answered better by first introducing *Babinet's principle* which in optics states that *when the field behind a screen with an opening is added to the field of a complementary structure, the sum is equal to the field when there is no screen.*

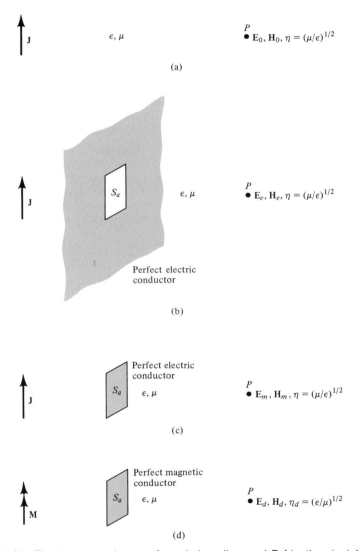

Figure 11.26 Electric source in an unbounded medium and Babinet's principle equivalents.

Babinet's principle in optics does not consider polarization, which is so vital in antenna theory; it deals primarily with absorbing screens. An extension of Babinet's principle, which includes polarization and the more practical conducting screens, was introduced by Booker [18]. Referring to Figure 11.26(a), let us assume that an electric source $\mathbf{J}$ radiates into an unbounded medium of intrinsic impedance $\eta = (\mu/\varepsilon)^{1/2}$ and produces at point P the field $\mathbf{E}_0, \mathbf{H}_0$. The same field can be obtained by combining the fields when the electric source radiates in a medium with intrinsic impedance $\eta = (\mu/\varepsilon)^{1/2}$ in the presence of

1. an infinite, planar, very thin, perfect electric conductor with an opening S_a, which produces at P the field $\mathbf{E}_e, \mathbf{H}_e$ [Figure 11.26(b)]
2. a flat, very thin, perfect magnetic conductor S_a, which produces at P the field $\mathbf{E}_m, \mathbf{H}_m$ [Figure 11.26(c)].

That is,

$$\mathbf{E}_0 = \mathbf{E}_e + \mathbf{E}_m$$
$$\mathbf{H}_0 = \mathbf{H}_e + \mathbf{H}_m \tag{11-66}$$

The field produced by the source in Figure 11.26(a) can also be obtained by combining the fields of

1. an electric source $\mathbf{J}$ radiating in a medium with intrinsic impedance $\eta = (\mu/\varepsilon)^{1/2}$ in the presence of an infinite, planar, very thin, perfect electric conductor S_a, which produces at P the fields $\mathbf{E}_e, \mathbf{H}_e$ [Figure 11.26(b)]
2. a magnetic source $\mathbf{M}$ radiating in a medium with intrinsic impedance $\eta_d = (\varepsilon/\mu)^{1/2}$ in the presence of a flat, very thin, perfect electric conductor S_a, which produces at P the fields $\mathbf{E}_d, \mathbf{H}_d$ [Figure 11.26(d)]

That is,

$$\mathbf{E}_0 = \mathbf{E}_e + \mathbf{H}_d$$
$$\mathbf{H}_0 = \mathbf{H}_e - \mathbf{E}_d \tag{11-67}$$

The dual of Figure 11.26(d) is more easily realized in practice than that of Figure 11.26(c).

To obtain Figure 11.26(d) from Figure 11.26(c), $\mathbf{J}$ is replaced by $\mathbf{M}$, $\mathbf{E}_m$ by $\mathbf{H}_d$, $\mathbf{H}_m$ by $-\mathbf{E}_d$, ε by μ, and μ by ε. This is a form of duality so often used in electromagnetics (see Section 3.7, Table 3.2). The electric screen with the opening in Figure 11.26(b) and the electric conductor of Figure 11.26(d) are also dual. They are usually referred to as complementary structures, because when combined they form a single solid screen with no overlaps. A proof of Babinet's principle and its extension can be found in the literature [4].

Using Booker's extension it can be shown [18], by referring to Figure 11.27, that if a screen and its complement are immersed in a medium with an intrinsic impedance η and have terminal impedances of Z_s and Z_c, respectively, the impedances are related by

$$\boxed{Z_s Z_c = \frac{\eta^2}{4}} \tag{11-68}$$

To obtain the impedance Z_c of the complement (dipole) in a practical arrangement, a gap must be introduced to represent the feed points. In addition, the far-zone fields radiated by the opening on the screen

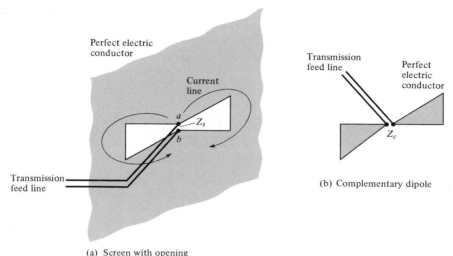

(a) Screen with opening

(b) Complementary dipole

Figure 11.27   Opening on a screen and its complementary dipole.

$(E_{\theta s}, E_{\phi s}, H_{\theta s}, H_{\phi s})$ are related to the far-zone fields of the complement $(E_{\theta c}, E_{\phi c}, H_{\theta c}, H_{\phi c})$ by

$$E_{\theta s} = H_{\theta c}, \qquad E_{\phi s} = H_{\phi c}, \qquad H_{\theta s} = -\frac{E_{\theta c}}{\eta_0^2}, \qquad H_{\phi s} = -\frac{E_{\phi c}}{\eta_0^2} \qquad \text{(11-69)}$$

Infinite, flat, very thin conductors are not realizable in practice but can be closely approximated. If a slot is cut into a plane conductor that is large compared to the wavelength and the dimensions of the slot, the behavior predicted by Babinet's principle can be realized to a high degree. The impedance properties of the slot may not be affected as much by the finite dimensions of the plane as would be its pattern. The slot of Figure 11.27(a) will also radiate on both sides of the screen. Unidirectional radiation can be obtained by placing a backing (box or cavity) behind the slot, forming a so-called cavity-backed slot whose radiation properties (impedance and pattern) are determined by the dimensions of the cavity.

To demonstrate the application of Babinet's principle, an example is considered.

Example 11.5

A very thin half-wavelength slot is cut on an infinite, planar, very thin, perfectly conducting electric screen as shown in Figure 11.28(a). Find its input impedance. Assume it is radiating into free-space.

SOLUTION

From Babinet's principle and its extension we know that a very thin half-wavelength dipole, shown in Figure 11.28(b), is the complementary

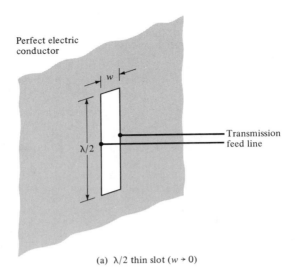

(a) $\lambda/2$ thin slot ($w \to 0$)

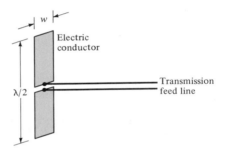

(b) $\lambda/2$ flat thin dipole ($w \to 0$)

Figure 11.28 Half-wavelength thin slot on an electric screen and its complement.

structure to the slot. From Chapter 4, the terminal (input) impedance of the dipole is $Z_c = 73 + j42.5$. Thus the terminal (input) impedance of the slot, using (11-68), is given by

$$Z_s = \frac{\eta_0^2}{4Z_c} \simeq \frac{(376.7)^2}{4(73 + j42.5)} \simeq \frac{35{,}475.72}{73 + j42.5}$$

$$Z_s \simeq 362.95 - j211.31$$

The slot of Figure 11.28(a) can be made to resonate by choosing the dimensions of its complement (dipole) so that it is also resonant. The pattern of the slot will be identical in shape to that of the dipole except that the **E**- and **H**-fields will be interchanged. When a vertical slot is mounted on a vertical screen, as shown in Figure 11.29(a), its electric field is horizontally polarized while that of the dipole is vertically polarized [Fig.

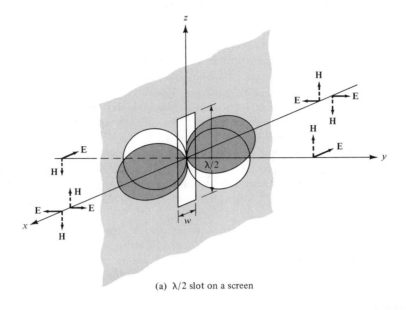

(a) λ/2 slot on a screen

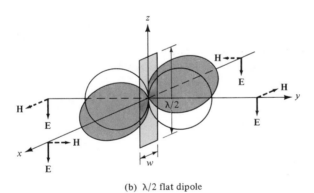

(b) λ/2 flat dipole

Figure 11.29   Radiation fields of a λ/2 slot on a screen and of a λ/2 flat dipole. (SOURCE: J. D. Kraus, *Antennas*, McGraw-Hill, New York, 1950, chapter 13)

11.29(b)]. Changing the position of the slot or the screen will change the polarization.

The slot antenna, as a cavity-backed design, has been utilized in a variety of law enforcement applications. Its main advantage is that it can be fabricated and concealed within metallic objects, and with a small transmitter it can provide covert communications. There are various methods of feeding a slot antenna [19]. For proper operation, the cavity depth must be equal to odd multiples of $\lambda_g/4$, where λ_g is the guide wavelength.

11.9   GROUND PLANE EDGE EFFECTS: THE GEOMETRICAL THEORY OF DIFFRACTION

Infinite size (physically and/or electrically) ground planes are not realizable in practice, but they can be approximated closely by very large structures. The radiation characteristics of antennas (current distribution, pattern, impedance, etc.) mounted on finite size ground planes can be modified considerably, especially in regions of very low intensity, by the effects of the edges. The ground plane edge diffractions for an aperture antenna are illustrated graphically in Figure 11.30. For these problems, rigorous solutions do not exist unless the object's surface can be described by curvilinear coordinates. Presently there are two methods that can be used conveniently to account for the edge effects. One technique is the *Moment Method* (MM) [20] discussed in Section 7.5 and the other is the *Geometrical Theory of Diffraction* (GTD) [21].

The Moment Method describes the solution in the form of an integral, and it can be used to handle arbitrary shapes. It mostly requires the use of a digital computer for numerical computations and, because of capacity limitations of present-day computers, it is most convenient for objects small in terms of a wavelength. Therefore, it is usually referred to as a low-frequency asymptotic method.

When the dimensions of the radiating object are large compared to the wavelength, high-frequency asymptotic techniques can be used to analyze many otherwise not mathematically tractable problems. One such technique, which has received considerable attention in the past few years, is the Geometrical Theory of Diffraction (GTD) which was originally developed

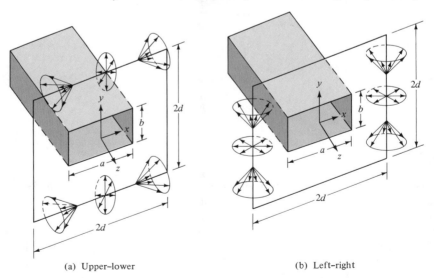

(a) Upper–lower   (b) Left–right

Figure 11.30   Diffraction mechanisms for an aperture mounted on a finite size ground plane (diffractions at upper-lower and left-right edges of the ground plane).

by Keller [21]. The GTD is an extension of the classical $Geometrical\ Optics$ (GO; direct, reflected, and refracted rays), and it overcomes some of the limitations of GO by introducing a diffraction mechanism.

The diffracted field, which is determined by a generalization of Fermat's principle [22], is initiated at points on the surface of the object where there is a discontinuity in the incident GO field (incident and reflected shadow boundaries). The phase of the field on a diffracted ray is assumed to be equal to the product of the optical length of the ray (from some reference point) and the phase constant of the medium. Appropriate phase jumps must be added as a ray passes through a caustic.* The amplitude is assumed to vary in accordance with the principle of conservation of energy in a narrow tube of rays. The initial value of the field on a diffracted ray is determined from the incident field with the aid of an appropriate diffraction coefficient (which, in general, is a dyadic for electromagnetic fields).

When the source is located a distance s' from the point of diffraction and the observations are made at a distance s from it, as shown in Figure 4.28, the diffracted field can be written, in general, as

$$E^d(s) = E^i(Q) \cdot \underset{\sim}{D} \sqrt{\frac{s'}{s(s'+s)}}\, e^{-jks} = E^i(Q) \cdot \underset{\sim}{D} A(s',s) e^{-jks} \quad \text{(11-70)}$$

where

$$A(s',s) = \begin{cases} \dfrac{1}{\sqrt{s}} & \begin{array}{l}\text{for plane,}\\ \text{cylindrical,}\\ \text{and conical}\\ \text{wave incidence}\end{array} & \text{(11-70a)} \\[2em] \sqrt{\dfrac{s'}{s(s+s')}} \underset{\sim}{\overset{s \gg s'}{\approx}} \dfrac{\sqrt{s'}}{s} & \begin{array}{l}\text{for spherical}\\ \text{wave incidence}\end{array} & \text{(11-70b)} \end{cases}$$

$E^i(Q)$ = incident field at the point of diffraction

$\underset{\sim}{D}$ = diffraction coefficient (usually a dyadic)

$A(s',s)$ = spatial attenuation (spreading) factor

A modified spreading factor is needed for diffraction from a curved-edge wedge (see Section 11.9.3). The diffraction coefficient is usually determined from the asymptotic solutions of the simplest boundary-value problems which have the same local geometry at the points of diffraction as the

---

*A caustic is a point or a line through which all the rays of a wave pass. Examples of it are the focal point of a paraboloid (parabola of revolution) and the focal line of a parabolic cylinder. The field at the caustic is infinite because, in principle, an infinite number of rays pass through it.

object(s) of investigation. Geometries of this type are referred to as *canonical* problems. One of the simplest geometries, which will be discussed in this chapter, is a conducting wedge. Another is that of a conducting, smooth and convex, surface [23]–[25].

The primary objective in using the GTD to solve complicated geometries is to resolve each such problem in smaller components [7]–[9], [25]. The partitioning is made so that each smaller component represents a canonical geometry of a known solution. These techniques have also been applied for the modeling and analysis of antennas on airplanes [26], and they have combined both wedge and smooth conducting surface diffractions [23], [25]. The ultimate solution is a superposition of the contributions from each canonical problem.

Some of the advantages of GTD are:

1. It is simple to use.
2. It can be used to solve complicated problems that do not have exact solutions.
3. It provides physical insight into the radiation and scattering mechanisms from the various parts of the structure.
4. It yields accurate results which compare extremely well with experiments and other methods.
5. It can be combined with other techniques such as the Moment Method [27].

11.9.1   Edge Diffraction Coefficient

In order to examine the manner in which fields are diffracted by edges, it is necessary to have available an edge diffraction coefficient. To derive a diffraction coefficient for an edge, we consider a canonical problem (one that has the same local geometry near the edge), like that shown in Figure 11.31.

The system consists of an infinite line source (either electric or magnetic) placed near a two-dimensional electric conducting wedge of included angle $(2 - n)\pi$ rad. If observations are made on a circle of constant radius from the edge of the wedge, it is apparent that in addition to the direct ray (OP) there are rays that are reflected from the side of the wedge (ORP) which contribute to the intensity at point P. These rays obey Fermat's principle (minimize the path between points O and P by including points on the side of the wedge) and deduce Snell's law of reflection. It would then seem appropriate to extend the class of such points to include in the trajectory rays that pass through the edge of the wedge (OQP), leading to the generalized Fermat's principle [21]. This class of rays are designated as diffracted rays and they lead to the *law of diffraction*.

By considering rays that obey only geometrical optics radiation mechanisms (direct and reflected), we can separate the space surrounding the wedge into three different field regions. Using the geometrical coordinates of Figure 11.31, the following geometrical optics fields will contribute to the

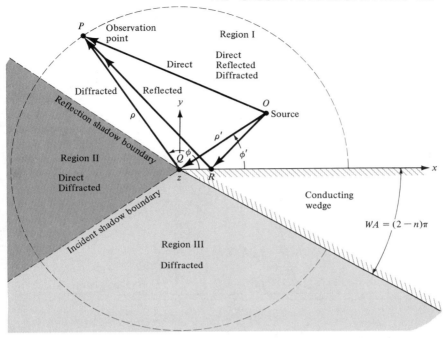

Figure 11.31 Two-dimensional electric conducting wedge and field regions.

corresponding regions:

REGION I	REGION II	REGION III
$(0 < \phi < \pi - \phi')$	$(\pi - \phi' < \phi < \pi + \phi')$	$(\pi + \phi' < \phi < n\pi)$
Direct and reflected	Direct	None

With the above fields, it is evident that

1. discontinuities in the field will be formed along the boundary separating regions I and II (*R*eflected *S*hadow *B*oundary) and the boundary separating regions II and III (*I*ncident *S*hadow *B*oundary)
2. no field will be present in region III (shadow region)

This is demonstrated in Figure 11.32 by the dashed (----) curve. It represents the normalized angular distribution of the geometrical optics field of a horizontally polarized unit amplitude cylindrical wave incident upon a half-plane ($n = 2$). The observations are made in the far-field region. Similar results occur for a vertically polarized wave. Since neither of the above phenomena are present in a physically realizable field, modifications and/or additions must be made.

To *remove* the discontinuities along the boundaries and to *modify* the fields in *all* three regions, diffracted fields must be included. To obtain expressions for the diffracted field distribution, we consider a two-dimensional wedge and a line source (either electric or magnetic) as shown

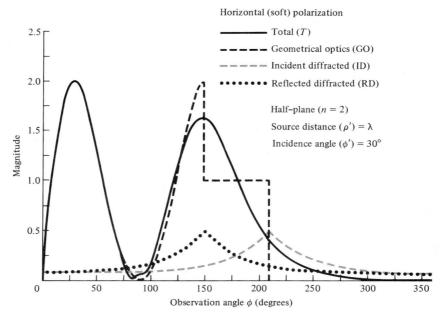

Figure 11.32 Normalized far-zone field distribution of a horizontally (soft) polarized cylindrical wave incident upon a conducting half-plane ($n=2$).

in Figure 11.31. The fields of an electric line source satisfy the homogeneous Dirichlet boundary conditions ($E_z = 0$ on both faces of the wedge) while the fields of the magnetic line source satisfy the homogeneous Neumann boundary condition ($\partial E_z / \partial\phi = 0$ or $H_z = 0$ on both faces of the wedge). The faces of the wedge are formed by two semi-infinite intersecting planes. The infinitely long line source is parallel to the edge of the wedge, and its position is described by the coordinate (ρ', ϕ'). The typical field point is denoted by (ρ, ϕ). The line source is assumed to have unit strength.

Initially only normal incidence diffraction by a straight edge [as shown in Figure 11.33(a)] will be considered. Curved-edge and oblique incidence diffractions [28], as shown in Figures 11.37 and 11.33(b), respectively, will be discussed in Sections 11.9.3 and 11.9.5.

The diffraction coefficient for the geometry of Figure 11.31 is obtained by [29]

1. finding the Green's function solution in the form of an infinite series using modal techniques, and then approximating it for large values of $k\rho$ (far-field observations)
2. converting the infinite series Green's function solution into the form of an integral
3. performing, on the integral form of the Green's function, a high-frequency asymptotic expansion (in inverse powers of $k\rho'$) using standard techniques, such as the method of steepest descents

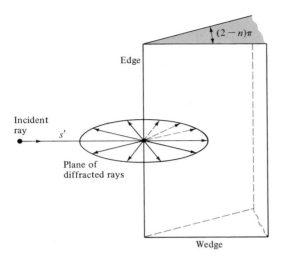

(a) Normal incidence

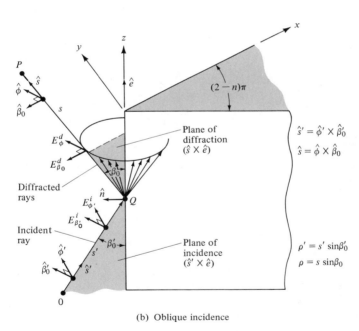

(b) Oblique incidence

Figure 11.33 Diffraction mechanism by a conducting wedge for normal and oblique incidences.

It can be shown that the diffraction coefficient D_s for the electric line source (referred to as *soft* or *horizontal polarization*) is given by [28], [29]

Soft (Horizontal) Polarization: Dirichlet Boundary Condition ($E_z=0$ on the Faces of the Wedge)

$$D_s(\rho',\beta^-,\beta^+,n)=D^i(\rho',\beta^-,n)-D^r(\rho',\beta^+,n)$$

(11-71)

where

$$D^i(\rho',\beta^-,n)=-\frac{e^{-j\pi/4}}{2n\sqrt{2\pi k}}$$
$$\{C^+(\beta^-,n)F[k\rho'g^+(\beta^-)]+C^-(\beta^-,n)F[k\rho'g^-(\beta^-)]\}$$

(11-71a)

$$D^r(\rho',\beta^+,n)=-\frac{e^{-j\pi/4}}{2n\sqrt{2\pi k}}$$
$$\{C^+(\beta^+,n)F[k\rho'g^+(\beta^+)]+C^-(\beta^+,n)F[k\rho'g^-(\beta^+)]\}$$

(11-71b)

D^i and D^r are referred to, respectively, as the incident and reflected diffraction coefficients.

The other functions and parameters in (11-71)–(11-71b) are defined by

$$C^+(\beta,n)=\cot\left(\frac{\pi+\beta}{2n}\right),\qquad C^-(\beta,n)=\cot\left(\frac{\pi-\beta}{2n}\right)$$

(11-72a)

$$F[k\rho'g(\beta)]=2j\sqrt{k\rho'g(\beta)}\,e^{+jk\rho'g(\beta)}\int_{\sqrt{k\rho'g(\beta)}}^{\infty}e^{-j\tau^2}\,d\tau$$

(11-72b)

$$\beta^+=\phi+\phi',\qquad \beta^-=\phi-\phi'$$

(11-72c)

$$g^+=1+\left[\cos(\phi\pm\phi')-2n\pi N^+\right]$$

(11-72d)

$$g^-=1+\left[\cos(\phi\pm\phi')=2n\pi N^-\right]$$

(11-72e)

with N^+ or N^- being a positive or negative integer or zero, whichever most closely satisfies the equation

$$2n\pi N^+-(\phi\pm\phi')=+\pi\qquad (\text{for } I_{+\pi})$$

(11-72f)

$$2n\pi N^--(\phi\pm\phi')=-\pi\qquad (\text{for } I_{-\pi})$$

(11-72g)

For a magnetic line source (referred to as *hard* or *vertical polarization*), its diffraction coefficient D_h can be written as

Hard (Vertical) Polarization: Neumann Boundary Condition ($\partial E_z/\partial\phi=0$ or $H_z=0$ on the Faces of the Wedge)

$$D_h(\rho',\beta,n)=D^i(\rho',\beta^-,n)+D^r(\rho',\beta^+,n)$$

(11-73)

where D^i and D^r are defined, respectively, by (11-71a) and (11-71b). It is apparent that the diffraction coefficients for soft and hard polarizations are functions of the source and observation angles ϕ' and ϕ, respectively.

The function $F(x)$ of (11-72b) is known as the transition function, and it involves a Fresnel integral. If the observations are made away from the incident $(\phi = \pi + \phi')$ and reflection $(\phi = \pi - \phi')$ shadow boundaries, the transition function $F(x)$ of (11-72b) is nearly unity [28] and the diffraction coefficients of (11-71) and (11-73) reduce, respectively, to

$$
D_s = \frac{e^{-j\pi/4}\sin\left(\dfrac{\pi}{n}\right)}{n\sqrt{2\pi k}}\left[\frac{1}{\cos\left(\dfrac{\pi}{n}\right)-\cos\left(\dfrac{\beta^-}{n}\right)} - \frac{1}{\cos\left(\dfrac{\pi}{n}\right)-\cos\left(\dfrac{\beta^+}{n}\right)}\right]
$$

(11-74a)

$$
D_h = \frac{e^{-j\pi/4}\sin\left(\dfrac{\pi}{n}\right)}{n\sqrt{2\pi k}}\left[\frac{1}{\cos\left(\dfrac{\pi}{n}\right)-\cos\left(\dfrac{\beta^-}{n}\right)} + \frac{1}{\cos\left(\dfrac{\pi}{n}\right)-\cos\left(\dfrac{\beta^+}{n}\right)}\right]
$$

(11-74b)

The diffraction coefficients of (11-74a) and (11-74b) have much simpler mathematical form, but are less accurate, than those of (11-71) and (11-73). In fact, their values along the incident and reflected shadow boundaries are infinite. The diffraction coefficients of (11-71) and (11-73) are valid everywhere, and they can be computed very efficiently using the computer subroutine at the end of this chapter, for the product of the $C(\beta, n)F[k\rho g(\beta)]$ functions. The program is based on a numerical algorithm reported in [30] for the Fresnel integral. The author recommends the subroutine for all computer modeled problems.

Associated with the incident and reflected diffraction coefficients are incident and reflected diffracted fields. These are obtained by multiplying the amplitude of the incident wave by the corresponding diffraction coefficients. The total diffracted field is usually designated as V_B, and it is written as

$$
V_B(\rho', \beta^\pm, n) = V_B^i(\rho', \beta^-, n) \mp V_B^r(\rho', \beta^+, n) \tag{11-75}
$$

where

$$
V_B^i = \text{incident diffracted field} = D^i(\rho', \beta^-, n)\frac{e^{-jk\rho'}}{\sqrt{\rho'}} \tag{11-75a}
$$

$$
V_B^r = \text{reflected diffracted field} = D^r(\rho', \beta^+, n)\frac{e^{-jk\rho'}}{\sqrt{\rho'}} \tag{11-75b}
$$

The minus sign between the two terms in (11-75) is used for horizontally polarized (soft) fields and the plus for vertically polarized (hard) fields.

For a unit amplitude, horizontally polarized wave incident at an angle $\phi' = 30°$ on a conducting half-plane, the normalized far-zone incident and reflected diffracted fields are plotted in Figure 11.32. The incident diffracted field is more dominant near the incident shadow boundary ($\phi = 180° + \phi' = 210°$) while the reflected diffracted field is more dominant near the reflected shadow boundary ($\phi = 180° - \phi' = 150°$). The amplitude of the field at each boundary is equal to 0.5; however, its phase undergoes a 180° phase reversal as each of the boundaries (incident and/or reflected) is crossed. The discontinuities of the diffracted fields at these two shadow boundaries are used to compensate for the discontinuities created at the same boundaries by the geometrical optics fields (incident and reflected). The result is a smooth transition in the total field as the shadow boundaries are crossed. This is demonstrated by the solid curve in Figure 11.32. The incident and reflected diffracted fields not only remove the discontinuities, respectively, at the incident and reflected shadow boundaries, but modify the total field in all other space to more appropriate and correct values. All these principles are well demonstrated in Figure 11.32 for the horizontally polarized wave. Similar results occur for vertically polarized waves.

11.9.2   Aperture on a Finite-Size Ground Plane

To demonstrate the versatility of the GTD technique, it has been applied to analyze the principal elevation pattern of an axial-TEM slot (with dimension a very large) mounted above a finite-size square ground plane, as shown in Figure 11.30. This geometry represents a radiating system which has many practical microwave applications.

In addition to the direct and reflected field contributions (referred to as Geometrical Optics, GO), there are diffracted fields from the edges of the ground plane. The radiation mechanisms are illustrated graphically in Figure 11.30.

The incident and reflected field are obtained by assuming the ground plane is infinite in extent. Using the coordinate system of Figure 11.7 and the results of Section 11.5.1, the normalized geometrical optics field can be written as

$$E_{go}(r,\theta) = E_0 \left[\frac{\sin\left(\dfrac{ka}{2}\sin\theta\right)}{\dfrac{ka}{2}\sin\theta} \right] \frac{e^{-jkr}}{r} \qquad 0 \le \theta \le \pi/2 \qquad (11\text{-}76)$$

The field diffracted from wedge #1 can be obtained using the formulation of (11-70). Referring to the geometry of Figure 11.34, the field diffracted from wedge #1 can be written as

$$E_1^{\,d}(\theta) = E^i(Q_1) D_h(\rho' = d, \beta, n = 2) A(d, r_1) e^{-jkr_1} \qquad (11\text{-}77)$$

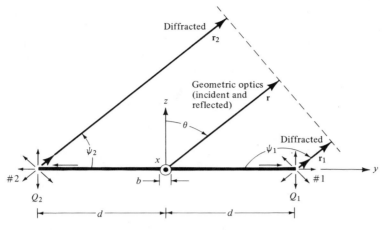

Figure 11.34 Aperture geometry in principal E-plane ($\phi = \pi/2$).

where

$$E^i(Q_1) = \frac{1}{2} E_{go}\left(r = d, \theta = \frac{\pi}{2}\right) = \frac{E_0}{2} \frac{\sin\left(\frac{ka}{2}\right)}{\frac{ka}{2}} \frac{e^{-jkd}}{d}$$

(11-77a)

$$D_h(\rho' = d, \beta^{\pm}, n = 2) = D^i(\rho' = d, \beta^-, n = 2) + D^r(\rho' = d, \beta^+, n = 2)$$

(11-77b)

$$A(d, r_1) = \frac{\sqrt{d}}{r_1}$$

(11-77c)

Since the angle of incidence from the main source toward the point of diffraction Q_1 is zero degrees,

$$\beta^- = \beta^+ = \psi_1 \pm 0 = \psi_1 = \theta + \frac{\pi}{2} = \beta$$

(11-78a)

and

$$D_h(\rho' = d, \beta^{\pm}, n = 2) = 2D^i(\rho' = d, \beta, n = 2) = 2D^r(\rho' = d, \beta, n = 2)$$

(11-78b)

For far-field observations

$$r_1 \simeq r - d\cos\left(\frac{\pi}{2} - \theta\right) = r - d\sin\theta \qquad \text{for phase terms} \qquad (11\text{-}79a)$$

$$r_1 \simeq r \qquad\qquad\qquad\qquad\qquad \text{for amplitude terms} \qquad (11\text{-}79b)$$

Thus (11-77) reduces to

$$E_1^d(\theta) = E_0 \frac{\sin\left(\frac{ka}{2}\right)}{\frac{ka}{2}} \left[\frac{e^{-jkd}}{d} D^{i,r}(\rho' = d, \beta = \theta + \pi/2, n = 2) \right]$$

$$\times e^{jkd\sin\theta} \frac{e^{-jkr}}{r}$$

$$E_1^d(\theta) = E_0 \frac{\sin\left(\frac{ka}{2}\right)}{\frac{ka}{2}} V_B^{i,r}(\rho' = d, \beta = \theta + \pi/2, n = 2) e^{+jkd\sin\theta} \frac{e^{-jkr}}{r}$$

(11-80)

$D^{i,r}$ in (11-80) represents either D^i of (11-71a) or D^r of (11-71b). The same holds for $V_B^{i,r}$.

In computing D^i or D^r, it is recommended that the very efficient computer subroutine at the end of this chapter be utilized to calculate the product of the $CF = C(\beta, n)F[k\rho g(\beta)]$ functions. In calling the subroutine, the user must specify only

$R =$ distance ρ' from the source to the point of diffraction (*in wavelengths*)

$\text{ANG} = \beta^- = \phi - \phi'$ (*in degrees*) *or* $\text{ANG} = \beta^+ = \phi + \phi'$ (*in degrees*)

$\text{FN} = n = 2 - (\text{WA})/\pi$ where $\text{WA} =$ wedge angle (*in radians*)

The subroutine computes

$\text{RCF} =$ real part of CF product

$\text{UCF} =$ imaginary part of CF product

If (11-74a) or (11-74b) is used in the calculations, the pattern will not be very accurate near the incident and reflected shadow boundaries (for this problem near $\theta = \pi/2$). In fact, the pattern will be infinity at the corresponding shadow boundaries and not very accurate in the neighborhood of each.

In a similar manner, the diffractions from wedge #2 can be written as

$$E_2^d = -E_0 \frac{\sin\left(\frac{ka}{2}\right)}{\frac{ka}{2}} V_B^{i,r}(\rho' = d, \beta, n = 2) e^{-jkd\sin\theta} \frac{e^{-jkr}}{r} \qquad (11\text{-}81)$$

where

$$\beta = \psi_2 = \begin{cases} \dfrac{\pi}{2} - \theta, & 0 \le \theta \le \dfrac{\pi}{2} \\[2mm] \dfrac{5\pi}{2} - \theta, & \dfrac{\pi}{2} < \theta \le \pi \end{cases} \qquad (11\text{-}81a)$$

To verify the techniques, computations were made for the far-field amplitude pattern using the geometrical optics formulation of (11-76), and the combination of (11-76), (11-80), and (11-81). The results are shown in Figure 11.35. There is obviously an excellent agreement between theory and experiment when diffractions from the edges are included. Even the very fine ripple structure in the forward region and the back lobes in the rear region are predicted with an extremely good accuracy, both in position and in amplitude. The ripple structure in the forward region represents the interference pattern formed by the contributions from the geometrical

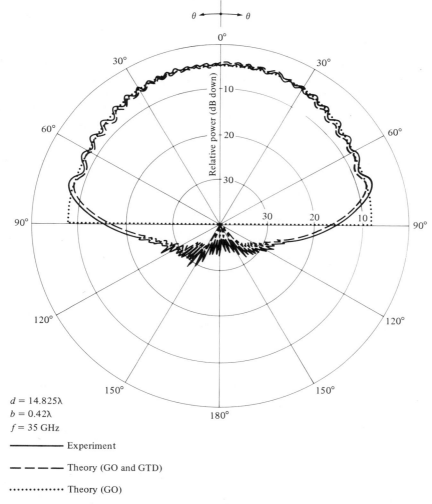

$d = 14.825\lambda$
$b = 0.42\lambda$
$f = 35$ GHz

——————— Experiment

— — — — Theory (GO and GTD)

•••••••••••• Theory (GO)

Figure 11.35 Principal *E*-plane amplitude patterns of an aperture antenna mounted on a finite size ground plane.

optics and diffracted fields. The radiation intensity in the rear region is solely due to the diffractions from the edges of the ground plane.

The techniques, utilizing the same diffraction coefficients, have been applied with similar success to many problems [7]–[9], [23]–[28]. These include linear elements, loops, apertures, horns, arrays, and so forth, mounted near or on geometrically complex structures of finite dimensions. The patterns of a $\lambda/4$ monopole (operating at $f = 1$ GHz) mounted on an infinite ground plane (GO) and a finite ground plane (GO and GTD) of 4×4 ft ($2w = 1.22$ m) computed using similar techniques (see Problem 11.38) are shown in Figure 11.36. The agreement between theory and experiment for the finite ground plane is extremely good.

11.9.3 Curved-Edge Diffraction

If the wave is obliquely incident (at an angle β_0') upon a curved wedge, as shown in Figure 11.37, the diffracted fields can be found using (11-70) except that the spatial attenuation factor $A(s', s)$ must take the form of

$$A(s', s) = \sqrt{\frac{\rho_c}{s(\rho_c + s)}} \tag{11-82}$$

$$\frac{1}{\rho_c} = \frac{1}{\rho_e} - \frac{\hat{n} \cdot (\hat{s}' - \hat{s})}{\rho_g \sin^2 \beta_0'} \tag{11-82a}$$

where

ρ_c = distance between caustic at edge and second caustic of diffracted ray

ρ_e = radius of curvature of incidence wavefront in the edge-fixed plane of incidence which contains unit vectors $\hat{s}'$ and $\hat{e}$ (infinite for plane, cylindrical, and conical waves; $\rho_e = s'$ for spherical waves)

ρ_g = radius of curvature of edge at diffraction point

$\hat{n}$ = unit vector normal to edge at Q and directed away from the center of curvature

$\hat{s}'$ = unit vector in direction of incidence

$\hat{s}$ = unit vector in direction of diffraction

β_0' = angle between $\hat{s}'$ and tangent to the edge at point of diffraction

$\hat{e}$ = unit vector tangent to the edge at the point of diffraction

For normal incidence $\beta_0' = 0$.

The spatial attenuation factor of (11-82) creates additional caustics, other than the ones that occur at the points of diffraction. Each caustic occurs at a distance ρ_c from the one at the diffraction point. Diffracted fields in the regions of the caustics must be corrected to remove the discontinuities and inaccuracies from them.

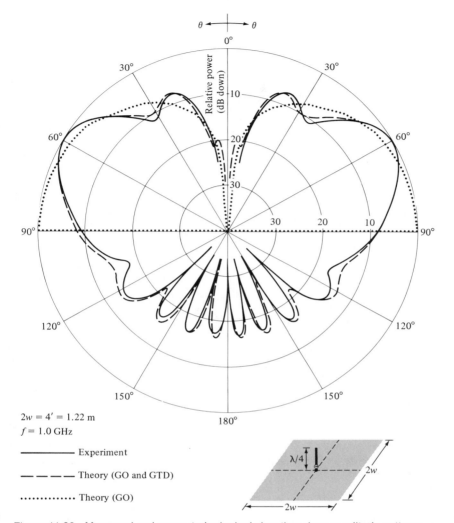

Figure 11.36   Measured and computed principal elevation plane amplitude patterns of a $\lambda/4$ monopole above infinite and finite square ground planes.

11.9.4   Equivalent Currents in Diffraction

In contrast to diffraction by straight edges, diffraction by curved edges creates caustics. If observations are not made at or near caustics, ordinary diffraction techniques can be applied; otherwise, corrections must be made.

One technique that can be used to correct for caustic discontinuities and inaccuracies is the concept of the equivalent currents [31]. To apply this principle, the two-dimensional wedge of Figure 11.33 is replaced by an

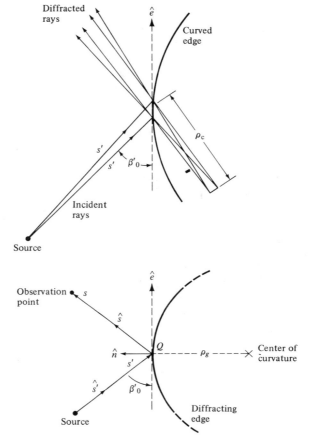

Figure 11.37 Geometry of oblique incidence diffraction by a curved-edge two-dimensional wedge.

equivalent two-dimensional

1. electric line source of equivalent electric current I^e, for soft polarization diffraction, or by a
2. magnetic line source of equivalent magnetic current I^m, for hard polarization diffraction

The equivalent currents I^e and I^m are adjusted so that the field radiated by each of the line sources is equal to the diffracted field of the corresponding polarization.

The electric field radiated by a two-dimensional electric line source placed along the z-axis with a constant current I_z^e is given by [4] (also

Problem 4.9 of this book)

$$E_z = -\frac{k^2 I_z^e}{4\omega\varepsilon} H_0^{(2)}(k\rho) \overset{k\rho \to \text{large}}{\simeq} I_z^e \frac{\eta k}{2} \sqrt{\frac{j}{2\pi k}} \frac{e^{-jk\rho}}{\sqrt{\rho}}$$ (11-83a)

where $H_0^{(2)}(k\rho)$ is the Hankel function of the second kind of zero order. The approximate form of (11-83a) is valid for large distances of observation (far-field), and it is obtained by replacing the Hankel function by its asymptotic formula for large argument [see Appendix V, Equation (V-17)].

The magnetic field radiated by a two-dimensional magnetic line source placed along the z-axis with a constant current I_z^m, can be obtained using the duality theorem (Section 3.7, Table 3.2) and (11-83a). Thus

$$H_z = -\frac{k^2 I_z^m}{4\omega\mu} H_0^{(2)}(k\rho) \overset{k\rho \to \text{large}}{\simeq} I_z^m \frac{k}{2\eta} \sqrt{\frac{j}{2\pi k}} \frac{e^{-jk\rho}}{\sqrt{\rho}}$$ (11-83b)

To determine the equivalent electric current I_z^e, (11-38a) is equated to the field diffracted by a wedge when the incident field is of soft polarization. A similar procedure is used for the equivalent magnetic I_z^m of (11-38b). Using (11-70), (11-70a), (11-83a), (11-83b), and assuming normal incidence, we can write that

$$E_z^i(Q) D_s(\beta^-, \beta^+, n) \frac{e^{-jk\rho}}{\sqrt{\rho}} = I_z^e \frac{\eta k}{2} \sqrt{\frac{j}{2\pi k}} \frac{e^{-jk\rho}}{\sqrt{\rho}}$$ (11-84a)

$$H_z^i(Q) D_h(\beta^-, \beta^+, n) \frac{e^{-jk\rho}}{\sqrt{\rho}} = I_z^m \frac{k}{2\eta} \sqrt{\frac{j}{2\pi k}} \frac{e^{-jk\rho}}{\sqrt{\rho}}$$ (11-84b)

where

$E_z^i(Q) =$ incident electric field at the diffraction point Q

$H_z^i(Q) =$ incident magnetic field at the diffraction point Q

$D_s =$ diffraction coefficient for soft polarization [(11-71) or (11-74a)]

$D_h =$ diffraction coefficient for hard polarization [(11-73) or (11-74b)]

Solving (11-84a) and (11-84b) for I_z^e and I_z^m, respectively, leads to

$$I_z^e = \frac{\sqrt{8\pi k}}{\eta k} e^{-j\pi/4} E_z^i(Q) D_s(\beta^-, \beta^+, n)$$ (11-85a)

$$I_z^m = \frac{\eta\sqrt{8\pi k}}{k} e^{-j\pi/4} H_z^i(Q) D_h(\beta^-, \beta^+, n)$$ (11-85b)

If the wedge of Figure 11.33 is of finite length l, its equivalent current will also be of finite length. The far-zone field radiated by each can be obtained by using techniques similar to those of Chapter 4. Assuming the edge is along the z-axis, the far-zone electric field radiated by an electric line-source of length l can be written using (4-58a) as

$$E_\theta^e = j\eta \frac{ke^{-jkr}}{4\pi r} \sin\theta \int_{-l/2}^{l/2} I_z^e(z') e^{jkz'\cos\theta}\, dz' \qquad (11\text{-}86a)$$

Using duality, the magnetic field of a magnetic line source can be written as

$$H_\theta^m = j\frac{ke^{-jkr}}{4\pi\eta r} \sin\theta \int_{-l/2}^{l/2} I_z^m(z') e^{-jkz'\cos\theta}\, dz' \qquad (11\text{-}86b)$$

For a constant equivalent current, the integrals in (11-86a) and (11-86b) reduce to a $\sin(\xi)/\xi$ form.

If the equivalent current is distributed along a circular loop of radius a and it is parallel to the xy-plane, the field radiated by each of the equivalent currents can be obtained using the techniques of Chapter 5, Section 5.3. Thus

$$E_\phi^e = \frac{-j\omega\mu a e^{-jkr}}{4\pi r} \int_0^{2\pi} I_\phi^e(\phi') \cos(\phi - \phi') e^{jka\sin\theta\cos(\phi-\phi')}\, d\phi' \qquad (11\text{-}87a)$$

$$H_\phi^m = \frac{-j\omega\varepsilon a e^{-jkr}}{4\pi r} \int_0^{2\pi} I_\phi^m(\phi') \cos(\phi - \phi') e^{jka\sin\theta\cos(\phi-\phi')}\, d\phi' \qquad (11\text{-}87b)$$

If the equivalent currents are constant, the field is not a function of the azimuthal observation angle ϕ and (11-87a) and (11-87b) reduce, using (5-39), to

$$E_\phi^e = \frac{a\omega\mu e^{-jkr}}{2r} I_\phi^e J_1(ka\sin\theta) \qquad (11\text{-}88a)$$

$$H_\phi^m = \frac{a\omega\varepsilon e^{-jkr}}{2r} I_\phi^m J_1(ka\sin\theta) \qquad (11\text{-}88b)$$

where $J_1(x)$ is the Bessel function of the first kind of order one.

For diffraction by an edge of finite length, the equivalent-current concept for diffraction assumes that each incremental segment of the edge radiates as would a corresponding segment of an infinite-length two-dimensional edge. Similar assumptions are used for diffraction from finite-length curved edges. The concepts, although approximate, have been shown to yield very good results.

To demonstrate the technique of curved-edge diffraction and the equivalent-current concept, the radiation of a $\lambda/4$ monopole (blade) mounted on a circular ground plane was modeled. The analytical formulation is assigned as a problem at the end of the chapter (Problem 11.41). The computed pattern is shown in Figure 11.38 where it is compared with measurements.

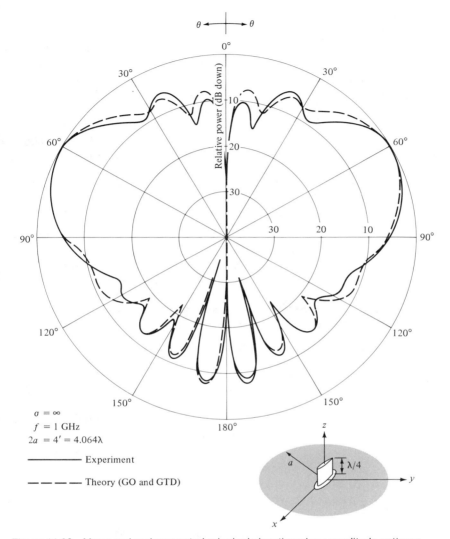

Figure 11.38   Measured and computed principal elevation plane amplitude patterns of a $\lambda/4$ monopole (blade) above a circular ground plane.

To make corrections for the diffracted field discontinuity and inaccuracy at and near the symmetry axis ($\theta = 0°$ and $180°$), due to axial caustics, the rim of the ground plane was modeled as a ring radiator [32]. Equivalent currents were used to compute the pattern in the region of $0° \leq \theta \leq \theta_0$ and $180° - \theta_0 \leq \theta \leq 180°$. In the other space, a two-point diffraction was used. The two points were taken diametrically opposite of each other, and they were contained in the plane of observation. The value of θ_0 depends upon the curvature of the ground plane. For most moderate size ground planes, θ_0 is in the range of $15° < \theta_0 < 30°$.

A very good agreement between theory and experiment is exhibited in Figure 11.38. For this size ground plane, the blending of the two-point diffraction pattern and the pattern from the ring-source radiator was performed for $\theta_0 \simeq 30°$. It should be noted that the minor lobes near the symmetry axis ($\theta \simeq 0°$ and $\theta \simeq 180°$) for the circular ground plane are more intense than the corresponding ones for the square plane of Figure 11.36. In addition, the back lobe nearest $\theta = 180°$ is of greater magnitude than the one next to it. These effects are due to the ring-source radiation by the rim [32] of the circular ground plane toward the symmetry axis.

11.9.5 Oblique Incidence Edge Diffraction

The formulations derived previously were for a normal incidence diffraction and led to scalar diffraction coefficients. If a plane wave is obliquely incident upon a two-dimensional wedge, as shown in Figure 11.33(b), it can be shown that by defining ray-fixed coordinate systems [28] [(s', β_0', ϕ') for the source and (s, β_0, ϕ) for the observation point], in contrast to the edge-fixed coordinate system ($\rho', \phi', z'; \rho, \phi, z$), the diffracted field of (11-70) can be written in a general form as

$$\mathbf{E}^d(s) = \mathbf{E}^i(Q) \cdot \underset{\sim}{\mathbf{D}}(\phi, \phi', n; \beta_0') \sqrt{\frac{s'}{s(s'+s)}} e^{-jks} \tag{11-89}$$

where $\underset{\sim}{\mathbf{D}}(\phi, \phi', n; \beta_0')$ is the dyadic edge-diffraction for illumination of the wedge by plane, cylindrical, conical, or spherical waves.

Introducing an edge-fixed plane of incidence with the unit vectors $\hat{\beta}_0'$ and $\hat{\phi}'$ parallel and perpendicular to it, and a plane of diffraction with the unit vectors $\hat{\beta}_0$ and $\hat{\phi}$ parallel and perpendicular to it, we can write the radial unit vectors of incidence and diffraction, respectively, as

$$\hat{s}' = \hat{\phi}' \times \hat{\beta}'_0$$
$$\hat{s} = \hat{\phi} \times \hat{\beta}_0 \tag{11-90}$$

where $\hat{s}'$ points toward the point of diffraction. With the adoption of the ray-fixed coordinate systems, the dyadic diffraction coefficient can be represented by the

$$\boxed{\underset{\sim}{\mathbf{D}}(\phi, \phi', n; \beta_0') = -\hat{\beta}_0' \hat{\beta}_0 D_s(\phi, \phi', n; \beta_0') - \hat{\phi}' \hat{\phi} D_h(\phi, \phi', n; \beta_0')}$$

$$\tag{11-91}$$

where D_s and D_h are the scalar diffraction coefficients for soft and hard polarizations. If an edge-fixed coordinate system was adopted, the dyadic coefficient would be the sum of seven dyads which in matrix notation would be represented by a 3×3 matrix with seven nonvanishing elements instead of the 2×2 matrix with two nonvanishing elements.

For the diffraction shown in Figure 11.33(b), we can write in matrix form the diffracted E-field components which are parallel ($E_{\beta_0}{}^d$) and perpendicular ($E_\phi{}^d$) to the plane of diffraction as

$$\begin{bmatrix} E_{\beta_0}{}^d(s) \\ E_\phi{}^d(s) \end{bmatrix} = -\begin{bmatrix} D_s & 0 \\ 0 & D_h \end{bmatrix} \begin{bmatrix} E_{\beta_0}{}^i(Q) \\ E_\phi{}^i(Q) \end{bmatrix} A(s',s)e^{-jks} \qquad (11\text{-}92)$$

where

$$E_{\beta_0}{}^i(Q) = \hat{\beta}_0' \cdot \mathbf{E}_i = \text{component of incident E-field parallel to the plane of incidence}$$

$$(11\text{-}92a)$$

$$E_\phi{}^i(Q) = \hat{\phi}' \cdot \mathbf{E}_i = \text{component of incident E-field perpendicular to the plane of incidence}$$

$$(11\text{-}92b)$$

D_s and D_h are the diffraction coefficients for soft and hard polarizations, and they are related to the diffraction function of (11-75) by

$$D_s(\phi, \phi', n; \beta_0') = \left[V_B(L, \phi - \phi', n) - V_B(L, \phi + \phi', n) \right] \frac{\sqrt{L}\, e^{jkL}}{\sin \beta_0'}$$

$$(11\text{-}93a)$$

$$D_h(\phi, \phi', n; \beta_0') = \left[V_B(L, \phi - \phi', n) + V_B(L, \phi + \phi', n) \right] \frac{\sqrt{L}\, e^{jkL}}{\sin \beta_0'}$$

$$(11\text{-}93b)$$

L is a distance parameter, and it is defined by [refer to Figure 11.33(b)]

$$L = \begin{cases} s\sin^2\beta_0' & \text{plane wave incidence} \\[2mm] \dfrac{\rho\rho'}{\rho+\rho'} & \begin{array}{l}\text{cylindrical wave incidence}\\ (\rho = s\sin\beta_0,\ \rho' = s'\sin\beta_0')\end{array} \\[3mm] \dfrac{ss'\sin^2\beta_0'}{s+s'} & \text{conical and spherical wave incidence} \end{cases} \qquad (11\text{-}94)$$

The spatial attenuation factor $A(s',s)$, which describes how the field intensity varies along the diffracted ray, is given by

$$A(s) = \begin{cases} \dfrac{1}{\sqrt{s}} & \begin{array}{l}\text{plane, cylindrical, and conical}\\ \text{wave incidence}\end{array} \\[4mm] \sqrt{\dfrac{s'}{s(s'+s)}} & \text{spherical wave incidence} \end{cases} \qquad (11\text{-}95)$$

If the observations are made in the far-field ($s \gg s'$ or $\rho \gg \rho'$), the distance parameter L and spatial attenuation factor $A(s', s)$ reduce, respectively, to

$$L = \begin{cases} s\sin^2\beta_0' & \text{plane wave incidence} \\ \rho' & \text{cylindrical wave incidence} \\ s'\sin^2\beta_0' & \text{conical and spherical wave incidence} \end{cases} \qquad (11\text{-}96)$$

$$A(s) = \begin{cases} \dfrac{1}{\sqrt{s}} & \begin{array}{l}\text{plane, cylindrical, and conical} \\ \text{wave incidence}\end{array} \\[2ex] \dfrac{\sqrt{s'}}{s} & \text{spherical wave incidence} \end{cases} \qquad (11\text{-}97)$$

For normal incidence, $\beta_0 = \beta_0' = \pi/2$.

For oblique incidence curved-edge diffraction, the spatial attenuation factor is given by (11-82)–(11-82a) and the equivalent currents of (11-85a) and (11-85b) take the form

$$I_z^e = \frac{\sqrt{8\pi k}}{\eta k} e^{-j\pi/4} E_z^i(Q) D_s(\beta^-, \beta^+, n; \beta_0') e^{jkl\cos\beta_0'} \qquad (11\text{-}98a)$$

$$I_z^m = \frac{\eta\sqrt{8\pi k}}{k} e^{-j\pi/4} H_z^i(Q) D_h(\beta^-, \beta^+, n; \beta_0') e^{jkl\cos\beta_0'} \qquad (11\text{-}98b)$$

where l is the length of the finite wedge and D_s and D_h are given by (11-93a) and (11-93b), respectively.

References

1. S. A. Schelkunoff, "Some Equivalence Theorems of Electromagnetics and Their Application to Radiation Problems," *Bell System Tech. J.* vol. 15, pp. 92–112, 1936.
2. C. Huygens, *Traite de la Lumiere*, Leyeden, 1690. Translated into English by S. P. Thompson, London, 1912, reprinted by The University of Chicago Press.
3. J. D. Kraus and K. R. Carver, *Electromagnetics* (second edition), McGraw-Hill, New York, 1973, pp. 464–467.
4. R. F. Harrington, *Time-Harmonic Electromagnetic Fields*, McGraw-Hill, New York, 1961, pp. 100–103, 143–263.
5. A. E. H. Love, "The integration of the equations of propagation of electric waves," *Phil. Trans. Roy. Soc. London, Ser. A*, vol. 197, 1901, pp. 1–45.
6. R. Mittra (ed.), *Computer Techniques for Electromagnetics*, Pergamon Press, New York, 1973, pp. 9–13.
7. C. A. Balanis and L. Peters, Jr., "Equatorial Plane Pattern of an Axial-TEM Slot on a Finite Size Ground Plane," *IEEE Trans. Antennas Propag.*, vol. AP-17, pp. 351–353, May 1969.
8. C. A. Balanis, "Pattern Distortion Due to Edge Diffractions," *IEEE Trans. Antennas Propag.*, vol. AP-18, pp. 551–563, July 1970.
9. C. R. Cockrell and P. H. Pathak, "Diffraction Theory Techniques Applied to Aperture Antennas on Finite Circular and Square Ground Planes," *IEEE Trans. Antennas Propag.*, vol. AP-22, No. 3, pp. 443–448, May 1975.

10. D. G. Fink (ed.), *Electronics Engineers' Handbook*, Section 18 (Antennas by W. F. Croswell), McGraw-Hill, New York, 1975.

11. R. E. Munson, "Conformal Microstrip Antennas and Microstrip Phased Arrays," *IEEE Trans. Antennas Propag.*, vol. AP-22, No. 1, pp. 74–78, Jan. 1974.

12. J. Q. Howell, "Microstrip Antennas," *IEEE Trans. Antennas Propag.*, vol. AP-23, No. 1, pp. 90–93, Jan. 1975.

13. A. G. Derneryd, "Linearly Polarized Microstrip Antennas," *IEEE Trans. Antennas Propag.*, vol. AP-24, No. 6, pp. 846–851, Nov. 1976.

14. L. C. Shen, S. A. Long, M. R. Allerding, and M. D. Walton, "Resonant Frequency of a Circular Disc, Printed-Circuit Antenna," *IEEE Trans. Antennas Propag.*, vol. AP-25, No. 4, pp. 595–596, July 1977.

15. P. K. Agrawal and M. C. Bailey, "An Analysis Technique for Microstrip Antennas," *IEEE Trans. Antennas Propag.*, vol. AP-25, No. 6, pp. 756–759, Nov. 1977.

16. N. K. Uzunoglu, N. G. Alexopoulos, and F. G. Fikioris, "Radiation Properties of Microstrip Dipoles," *IEEE Trans. Antennas Propag.*, vol. AP-27, No. 6, pp. 853–858, Nov. 1979.

17. Y. T. Lo, D. Solomon, and W. F. Richards, "Theory and Experiment on Microstrip Antennas," *IEEE Trans. Antennas Propag.*, vol. AP-27, No. 2, pp. 137–145, March 1979.

18. H. G. Booker, "Slot Aerials and Their Relation to Complementary Wire Aerials," *J. Inst. Elec. Engrs.*, pt III A, 1946, pp. 620–626.

19. J. D. Kraus, *Antennas*, McGraw-Hill, New York, 1950, Chapter 13.

20. R. F. Harrington, *Field Computation by Moment Methods*, Macmillan Co., New York, 1968.

21. J. B. Keller, "Geometrical Theory of Diffraction," *Journal Optical Society of America*, vol. 52, No. 2, pp. 116–130, February 1952.

22. R. G. Kouyoumjian, "The Geometrical Theory of Diffraction and Its Applications," in *Numerical and Asymptotic Techniques in Electromagnetics* (R. Mittra, ed.), Springer-Verlag, New York, 1975.

23. P. H. Pathak and R. G. Kouyoumjian, "An Analysis of the Radiation from Apertures on Curved Surfaces by the Geometrical Theory of Diffraction," *Proc. IEEE*, vol. 62, No. 11, pp. 1438–1447, Nov. 1974.

24. G. L. James, *Geometrical Theory of Diffraction for Electromagnetic Waves*, Peter Peregrinus, Ltd., Stevenage, Herts., England, 1976.

25. C. A. Balanis and L. Peters, Jr., "Analysis of Aperture Radiation from an Axially Slotted Circular Conducting Cylinder Using GTD," *IEEE Trans. Antennas Propag.*, vol. AP-17, No. 1, pp. 93–97, Jan. 1969.

26. C. A. Balanis and Y. -B. Cheng, "Antenna Radiation and Modeling for Microwave Landing System," *IEEE Trans. Antennas Propag.*, vol. AP-24, No. 4, pp. 490–497, July 1976.

27. W. D. Burnside, C. L. Yu, and R. J. Marhefka, "A Technique to Combine the Geometrical Theory of Diffraction and the Moment Method," *IEEE Trans. Antennas Propag.*, vol. AP-23, No. 4, pp. 551–558, July 1975.

28. R. G. Kouyoumjian and P. H. Pathak, "A Uniform Geometrical Theory of Diffraction for an Edge in a Perfectly Conducting Surface," *Proc. IEEE*, vol. 62, No. 11, pp. 1448–1461, Nov. 1974.

29. D. L. Hutchins, "Asymptotic Series Describing the Diffraction of a Plane Wave by a Two-Dimensional Wedge of Arbitrary Angle," Ph.D. Dissertation, The Ohio State University, Dept. of Electrical Engineering, 1967.

30. J. Boersma, "Computation of Fresnel Integrals," *J. Math. Comp.*, vol. 14, p. 380, 1960.
31. C. E. Ryan, Jr., and L. Peters, Jr., "Evaluation of Edge-Diffracted Fields Including Equivalent Currents for the Caustic Regions," *IEEE Trans. Antennas Propag.*, vol. AP-17, pp. 292–299, May 1969, (Also corrections to this paper on p. 275, March 1970).
32. C. A. Balanis, "Radiation from Conical Surfaces Used for High-Speed Spacecraft," *Radio Science*, vol. 7, pp. 339–343, February 1972.

PROBLEMS

11.1. A rectangular aperture, of dimensions a and b, is mounted on an infinite ground plane, as shown in Figure 11.6(a). Assuming the tangential field over the aperture is given by

$$\mathbf{E}_a = \hat{a}_z E_0 \qquad -a/2 \le y' \le a/2, \qquad -b/2 \le z' \le b/2$$

find the far-zone spherical electric and magnetic field components radiated by the aperture.

11.2. Repeat Problem 11.1 when the same aperture is analyzed using the coordinate system of Figure 11.6(b). The tangential aperture field distribution is given by

$$\mathbf{E}_a = \hat{a}_x E_0 \qquad -b/2 \le x' \le b/2, \qquad -a/2 \le z' \le a/2$$

11.3. Repeat Problem 11.1 when the aperture field is given by

$$\mathbf{E}_a = \hat{a}_z E_0 \cos\left(\frac{\pi}{a} y'\right), \qquad -a/2 \le y' \le a/2, \qquad -b/2 \le z' \le b/2$$

11.4. Repeat Problem 11.2 when the aperture field distribution is given by

$$\mathbf{E}_a = \hat{a}_x E_0 \cos\left(\frac{\pi}{a} z'\right) \qquad -b/2 \le x' \le b/2, \qquad -a/2 \le z' \le a/2$$

11.5. Find the fields radiated by the apertures of Problems
   (a) 11.1 (b) 11.2
   (c) 11.3 (d) 11.4
   when each of the apertures with their associated field distributions are *not* mounted on a ground plane. Assume the tangential **H**-field at the aperture is related to the **E**-field by the intrinsic impedance.

11.6. Find the fields radiated by the rectangular aperture of Section 11.5.3 when it is not mounted on an infinite ground plane.

11.7. For the rectangular aperture of Section 11.5.3 (with $a = 4\lambda, b = 3\lambda$), compute the
   (a) E-plane beamwidth (*in degrees*) between the maxima of the *second* minor lobe
   (b) E-plane amplitude (*in dB*) of the maximum of the second minor lobe (relative to the maximum of the major lobe)
   (c) approximate directivity of the antenna using Kraus' formula. Compare it with the value obtained using the expression in Table 11.1.

11.8. For the rectangular aperture of Section 11.5.1 with $a = b = 3\lambda$, compute the directivity using (11-37) and the computer program at the end of Chapter 2.

11.9. For the rectangular aperture of Section 11.5.2 with $a = b = 3\lambda$, compute the directivity using (11-37) and the computer program at the end of Chapter 2.

11.10. Compute the directivity of the aperture of Section 11.5.3, using the computer program at the end of Chapter 2, when
(a) $a=3\lambda, b=2\lambda$
(b) $a=b=3\lambda$

11.11. Repeat Problem 11.10 when the aperture is not mounted on an infinite ground plane.

11.12. For the rectangular aperture of Section 11.5.3 with $a=3\lambda, b=2\lambda$, compute the
(a) E-plane half-power beamwidth
(b) H-plane half-power beamwidth
(c) E-plane first-null beamwidth
(d) H-plane first-null beamwidth
(e) E-plane first side lobe maximum (relative to main maximum)
(f) H-plane first side lobe maximum (relative to main maximum)
using the formulas of Table 11.1. Compare the results with the data from Figures 11.13 and 11.14.

11.13. A square waveguide aperture, of dimensions $a = b$ and lying on the x-y-plane, is radiating into free-space. Assuming a $\cos(\pi x'/a)$ by $\cos(\pi y'/b)$ distribution over the aperture, find the dimensions of the aperture (in wavelengths) so that the beam efficiency within a 37° total included angle cone is 90%.

11.14. Verify (11-39a), (11-39b), (11-39c), and (11-40).

11.15. Compute the aperture efficiency of a rectangular aperture, mounted on an infinite ground plane as shown in Figure 11.7, with an **E**-field aperture distribution directed toward y but with variations
(a) triangular in the x and uniform in the y
(b) cosine-squared in the x and uniform in the y
(c) cosine in the x and cosine in the y
How do they compare with those of a cosine distribution?

11.16. An X-band (8.2–12.4 GHz) WR 90 rectangular waveguide, with inner dimensions of 0.9 in. (2.29 cm) and 0.4 in. (1.02 cm), is mounted on an infinite ground plane. Assuming the waveguide is operating in the dominant TE_{10}-mode, find its directivity at $f=10$ GHz using the
(a) computer program at the end of Chapter 2
(b) formula in Table 11.1
Compare the answers.

11.17. Repeat Problem 11.16 at $f=20$ GHz for a K-band (18–26.5 GHz) WR 42 rectangular waveguide with inner dimensions of 0.42 in. (1.067 cm) and 0.17 in. (0.432 cm).

11.18. Find the far-zone fields radiated when the circular aperture of Section 11.6.1 is not mounted on an infinite ground plane.

11.19. Derive the far-zone fields when the circular aperture of Section 11.6.2
(a) is
(b) is not
mounted on an infinite ground plane.

11.20. For the circular aperture of Section 11.6.1, compute its directivity, using the computer program at the end of Chapter 2, when its radius is
(a) $a=0.5\lambda$
(b) $a=1.5\lambda$
(c) $a=3.0\lambda$
Compare the results with data from Table 11.2.

11.21. Repeat Problem 11.20 when the circular aperture of Section 11.6.1 is not mounted on an infinite ground plane. Compare the results with those of Problem 11.20.

11.22. For the circular aperture of Problem 11.19, compute the directivity, using the computer program at the end of Chapter 2, when its radius is
(a) $a = 0.5\lambda$
(b) $a = 1.5\lambda$
(c) $a = 3.0\lambda$
Compare the results with data from Table 11.2.

11.23. For the circular aperture of Section 11.6.2 with $a = 1.5\lambda$, compute the
(a) E-plane half-power beamwidth
(b) H-plane half-power beamwidth
(c) E-plane first-null beamwidth
(d) H-plane first-null beamwidth
(e) E-plane first side lobe maximum (relative to main maximum)
(f) H-plane first side lobe maximum (relative to main maximum)
using the formulas of Table 11.2. Compare the results with the data from Figures 11.19 and 11.20.

11.24. A circular aperture of radius a is mounted on an infinite electric ground plane. Assuming the opening is on the x-y plane and its field distribution is given by
(a) $\mathbf{E}_a = \hat{a}_y E_0 \left[1 - \left(\dfrac{\rho'}{a} \right)^2 \right] \qquad \rho' \leq a$

(b) $\mathbf{E}_a = \hat{a}_y E_0 \left[1 - \left(\dfrac{\rho'}{a} \right)^2 \right]^2 \qquad \rho' \leq a$
find the far-zone electric and magnetic field components radiated by the antenna.

11.25. A coaxial line of inner and outer radius a and b, respectively, is mounted on an infinite electric ground plane. Assuming that the electric field over the aperture of the coax is

$$\mathbf{E}_a = -\hat{a}_\rho \frac{V}{\varepsilon \ln(b/a)} \frac{1}{\rho'}, \qquad a \leq \rho' \leq b$$

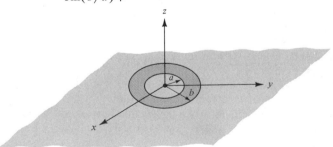

where V is the applied voltage and ε is the permittivity of the coax medium, find the far-zone spherical electric and magnetic field components radiated by the antenna.

11.26. It is desired to design a circular aperture antenna with a field distribution over its opening of

$$E = C \left[1 - (\rho'/a)^2 \right]$$

where C is a constant, a its radius, and ρ' any point on the aperture, such that its beam efficiency within a 60° total included angle cone is 90%. Find its radius in wavelengths.

11.27. For the antenna of Problem 11.26, find its efficiency within a 40° total included angle cone when its radius is 2λ.

11.28. For the microstrip antenna of Figure 11.22, derive the
   (a) fields of (11-60a)–(11-60d)
   (b) conductance of (11-63), (11-63a)
   (c) directivity of (11-64)–(11-65b)

11.29. For a microstrip antenna with dimensions of $h = 0.005\lambda$, $w = 0.25\lambda$,
   (a) find the direction (θ, ϕ) of maximum radiation
   (b) identify the E-plane and compute the half-power beamwidth and side lobe level
   (c) identify the H-plane and compute the half-power beamwidth and side lobe level

11.30. A vertical dipole is radiating into a free-space medium and produces fields E_0 and H_0. Illustrate alternate methods for obtaining the same fields using Babinet's principle and extensions of it.

11.31. Numerically, using the computer program at the end of this chapter, show that the incident diffracted field of Figure 11.32 is equal to 0.5 at its shadow boundary but its phase undergoes a 180° phase jump as the boundary is crossed.

11.32. Repeat Problem 11.31 for the reflected diffracted field at the reflection shadow boundary of Figure 11.32.

11.33. Repeat the calculations of Figure 11.32 for the vertical (hard) polarization.

11.34. Compute at $\phi = 270°$ the far-zone
   (a) incident diffracted
   (b) reflected diffracted
   (c) total diffracted
   (d) total (GO and diffracted)
   fields when a unity amplitude horizontally polarized (soft) cylindrical wave at $\rho' = \lambda$ is incident at an angle of $\phi' = 30°$ upon a half-plane $(n = 2)$.

11.35. Repeat Problem 11.34 for a vertically polarized (hard) cylindrical wave.

11.36. Repeat Problems 11.34 and 11.35 when a unit amplitude plane wave is incident at $\phi' = 30°$ upon a half-plane $(n = 2)$. The observations are made at a distance of λ from the edge of the wedge and at an observation angle of $\phi = 270°$. *Hint*: Use the principle of reciprocity.

11.37. Verify (11-81) for the field diffracted from wedge #2.

11.38. Derive the far-zone fields, GO and diffracted, of the $\lambda/4$ monopole of Figure 11.36 using the radiation mechanism shown in the adjoining figure.
   Show that the fields can be written as

$$E_{GO}(\theta) = E_0 \left[\frac{\cos\left(\frac{\pi}{2}\cos\theta\right)}{\sin\theta} \right] \frac{e^{-jkr}}{r}, \quad 0 < \theta < \pi/2$$

$$E_1^d(\theta) = E_0 V_B(w, \psi_1, 2) e^{+jkw\sin\theta} \frac{e^{-jkr}}{r}$$

$$\psi_1 = \frac{\pi}{2} + \theta, \quad 0 < \theta < \pi$$

$$E_2^d(\theta) = -E_0 V_B(w, \psi_2, 2) e^{-jkw\sin\theta} \frac{e^{-jkr}}{r}$$

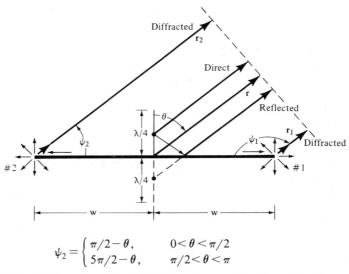

$$\psi_2 = \begin{cases} \pi/2 - \theta, & 0 < \theta < \pi/2 \\ 5\pi/2 - \theta, & \pi/2 < \theta < \pi \end{cases}$$

11.39. Using duality, show that (11-83b) can be obtained from (11-83a).

11.40. Derive (11-87a) and (11-87b).

11.41. Repeat Problem 11.38 for a $\lambda/4$ monopole mounted on a circular ground plane. For radiation near the symmetry axis ($\theta = 0°$ and $180°$), model the rim of the ground plane as a ring-source radiator using equivalent current concepts of Section 11.9.4 Compute the pattern for a ground plane with diameter of $d = 4.064\lambda$ and compare it with those shown in Figure 11.38.

COMPUTER PROGRAM—DIFFRACTION COEFFICIENT

```
C  ****************************************************************
C       THIS COMPUTER PROGRAM COMPUTES THE PRODUCT CF OF THE
C       C AND F FUNCTION AS GIVEN BY EQUATIONS (11-72A) AND
C       (11-72B),RESPECTIVELY.IN CALLING THE SUBROUTINE THE
C       USER MUST SPECIFY:
C          R = DISTANCE FROM THE SOURCE TO THE POINT OF DIFFRACT-
C              ION (IN WAVELENGTHS)
C        ANG = ANGLE OF (PHI-PHI') (IN DEGREES);EQU.(11-72C)
C              OR
C        ANG = ANGLE OF (PHI+PHI') (IN DEGREES);EQU.(11-72C)
C         FN = N;INDICATES ANGULAR SIZE OF WEDGE;N=2-WA/PI
C
C       THE OUTPUT IS:
C       RCF = REAL PART OF THE CF PRODUCT
C       UCF = IMAGINARY PART OF THE CF PRODUCT
C  ****************************************************************
        SUBROUTINE CF(RCF,UCF,R,ANG,FN)
        REAL*8 RAG,DP,TSIN,DCOS,DSIN
        COMPLEX*8 CMPLEX,CEXP
        COMPLEX TOP,EXP,UPPI,UNPI
        PI=3.1415927
        TPI=2.0*PI
        ANG=ANG*PI/180.000
        TOP=CMPLX(0.0,2.0*SQRT(TPI*R))
        N=IFIX((PI+ANG)/(2.0*FN*PI)+0.5)
        DN=FLOAT (N)
        A=1.0+COS(ANG-2.0*FN*PI*DN)
        BOTL=SQRT (TPI*R*A)
        EXP=CEXP(CMPLX(0.0,TPI*R*A))
        CALL FRNELS (C,S,BOTL)
        C=SQRT(PI/2.0)*(0.5-C)
        S=SQRT(PI/2.0)*(S-0.5)
        RAG=(PI+ANG)/(2.0*FN)
        TSIN=DSIN(RAG)
        TS=ABS(SNGL(TSIN))
        X=10.0
        Y=1.0/**5
        IF(TS.GT.Y) GO TO 442
        COMP=-SQRT(2.0)*FN*SIN(ANG/2.0-FN*PI*DN)
        IF(COS(ANG/2.0-FN*PI*DN).LT.0.0) COMP=-COMP
        GO TO 443
442     DP=SQRT(A)*DCOS(RAG)/TSIN
        COMP=SNGL(DP)
443     UPPI=TOP*EXP*COMP*CMPLX(C,S)
        N=IFIX((-PI+ANG)/(2.0*FN*PI)+0.5
        DN=FLOAT(N)
        A=1.0+COS(ANG-2.0*FN*PI*DN)
        BOTL=SQRT(TPI*R*A)
        EXP=CEXP(CMPLX(0.0,TPI*R*A))
        CALL FRNELS (C,S,BOTL)
        C=SQRT(PI/2.0)*(0.5-C)
        S=SQRT(PI/2.0)*(S-0.5)
        RAG=(PI-ANG)/(2.0*FN)
        TSIN=DSIN(RAG)
        TS=ABS(SNGL(TSIN))
        IF(TS.GT.Y) GO TO 542
        COMP=SQRT(2.0)*FN*SIN(ANG/2.0-FN*PI*DN)
        IF(COS(ANG/2.0-FN*PI*DN).LE.0.0) COMP=-COMP
        GO TO 123
542     DP=SQRT(A)*DCOS(RAG)/TSIN
        COMP=SNGL(DP)
123     UNPI=TOP*EXP*COMP*CMPLX(C,S)
        ANG=ANG*180.0/PI
        RCF=REAL(UPPI+UNPI)
```

```
          UCF=AIMAG(UPPI+UNPI)
          RETURN
          END

C    COMPUTER SUBROUTINE FOR FRESNEL FUNCTION

          SUBROUTINE FRNELS (C,S,XS)
          DIMENSION A(12),B(12),CC(12),D(12)
          A(1)=1.595769140
          A(2)=-0.000001702
          A(3)=-6.808568854
          A(4)=-0.000576361
          A(5)=6.920691902
          A(6)=-0.016898657
          A(7)=-3.050485660
          A(8)=-0.075752419
          A(9)=0.850663781
          A(10)=-0.025639041
          A(11)=-0.150230960
          A(12)=0.034404779
          B(1)=-0.000000033
          B(2)=4.255387524
          B(3)=-0.000092810
          B(4)=-7.780020400
          B(5)=-0.009520895
          B(6)=5.075161298
          B(7)=-0.138341947
          B(8)=-1.363729124
          B(9)=-0.403349276
          B(10)=0.702222016
          B(11)=-0.216195929
          B(12)=0.019547031
          CC(1)=0.0
          CC(2)=-0.024933975
          CC(3)=0.000003936
          CC(4)=0.005770956
          CC(5)=0.000689892
          CC(6)=-0.009497136
          CC(7)=0.011948809
          CC(8)=-0.006748873
          CC(9)=0.000246420
          CC(10)=0.002102967
          CC(11)=-0.001217930
          CC(12)=0.000233939
          D(1)=0.199471140
          D(2)=0.000000023
          D(3)=-0.009351341
          D(4)=0.000023006
          D(5)=0.004851466
          D(6)=0.001903218
          D(7)=-0.017122914
          D(8)=0.029064067
          D(9)=-0.027928955
          D(10)=0.016497308
          D(11)=-0.005598515
          D(12)=0.000838386
          IF(XS.LE.0.0) GO TO 414
          X=XS
          X=X*X
          FR=0.0
          FI=0.0
          K=13
          IF(X-4.0) 10,40,40
   10     Y=X/4.0
```

```
20   K=K-1
     FR=(FR+A(K))*Y
     FI=(FI+B(K))*Y
     IF(K-2) 30,30,20
30   FR=FR+A(1))
     FI=FI+B(1)
     C=(FR*COS(X)+FI*SIN(X))*SQRT(Y)
     S=(FR*SIN(X)-FI*COS(X))*SQRT(Y)
     RETURN
40   Y=4.0/X
50   K=K-1
     FR=(FR+CC(K))*Y
     FI=(FI+D(K))*Y
     IF(K-2) 60,60,50
60   FR=FR+CC(1)
     FI=FI+D(1)
     C=0.5+(FR*COS(X)+FI*SIN(X))*SQRT(Y)
     S=0.5+(FR*SIN(X)-FI*COS(X))*SQRT(Y)
     RETURN
414  C=-0.0
     S=-0.0
     RETURN
     END
```

Chapter 12
Horns

12.1 INTRODUCTION

One of the simplest and probably the most widely used microwave antenna is the horn. Its existence and early use dates back to the late 1800s. Although neglected somewhat in the early 1900s, its revival began in the late 1930s from the interest in microwaves and waveguide transmission lines during the period of World War II. Since that time a number of articles have been written describing its radiation mechanism, optimization design methods, and applications. Many of the articles published since 1939 which deal with the fundamental theory, operating principles, and designs of a horn as a radiator can be found in a book of reprinted papers [1].

The horn is widely used as a feed element for large radio astronomy, satellite tracking, and communication dishes found installed throughout the world. In addition to its utility as a feed for reflectors and lenses, it is a common element of phased arrays and serves as a universal standard for calibration and gain measurements of other high-gain antennas. Its widespread applicability stems from its simplicity in construction, ease of excitation, versatility, large gain, and preferred overall performance.

An electromagnetic horn can take many different forms, four of which are shown in Figure 12.1. The horn is nothing more than a hollow pipe of different cross sections which has been tapered to a larger opening. The type, direction, and amount of taper can have a profound effect on the overall performance of the element as a radiator. In this chapter, the fundamental theory of horn antennas will be examined. In addition, data will be presented that can be used to understand better the operation of a horn and its design as an efficient radiator.

12.2 *E*-PLANE SECTORAL HORN

The E-plane sectoral horn is one whose opening is flared in the direction of the E-field, and it is shown in Figure 12.2(a).* A more detailed geometry is shown in Figure 12.2(b).

*Although the coordinates x, y, z form (in the conventional way) a left-hand coordinate system, the coordinates ρ, ψ, x are used as a cylindrical system which is analogous to the conventional ρ, ϕ, z cylindrical system. This notation is being adopted because it is most convenient to find the fields within the horn (see Prob. 12.1).

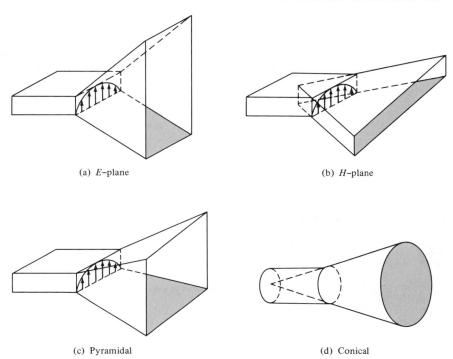

(a) *E*-plane

(b) *H*-plane

(c) Pyramidal

(d) Conical

Figure 12.1   Typical electromagnetic horn antenna configurations.

12.2.1   Aperture Fields

The horn can be treated as an aperture antenna. To find its radiation characteristics, the equivalent principle techniques developed in Chapter 11 can be utilized. To develop an exact equivalent of it, it is necessary that the tangential electric and magnetic field components over a closed surface are known. The closed surface that is usually selected is an infinite plane that coincides with the aperture of the horn. When the horn is not mounted on an infinite ground plane, the fields outside the aperture are not known and an exact equivalent cannot be formed. However the usual approximation is to assume that the fields outside the aperture are zero, as was done for the aperture of Section 11.5.2.

   The fields at the aperture of the horn can be found by treating the horn as a radial waveguide [2], [3]. The fields within the horn can be expressed in terms of cylindrical TE and TM wave functions which include Hankel functions. This method finds the fields not only at the aperture of the horn but also within the horn. The process is straightforward but laborious, and it will not be included here. However, it is assigned as an exercise at the end of the chapter (Problem 12.1).

   It can be shown that if the (1) fields of the feed waveguide are those of its dominant TE_{10} mode and (2) horn length is large compared to the aperture dimensions, the lowest order mode fields at the aperture of the horn are given by

$$E_z' = E_x' = H_y' = 0 \tag{12-1a}$$

$$E_y'(x', y') \simeq E_1 \cos\left(\frac{\pi}{a}x'\right) e^{-j[ky'^2/(2\rho_1)]} \tag{12-1b}$$

$$H_z'(x', y') \simeq jE_1\left(\frac{\pi\eta}{ka}\right) \sin\left(\frac{\pi}{a}x'\right) e^{-j[ky'^2/(2\rho_1)]} \tag{12-1c}$$

$$H_x'(x', y') \simeq -\frac{E_1}{\eta} \cos\left(\frac{\pi}{a}x'\right) e^{-j[ky'^2/(2\rho_1)]} \tag{12-1d}$$

$$\rho_1 = \rho_e \cos\psi_e \tag{12-1e}$$

where E_1 is a constant. The primes are used to indicate the fields at the aperture of the horn. The expressions are similar to the fields of a TE_{10}-mode for a rectangular waveguide with aperture dimensions of a and $b_1(b_1 > a)$. The only difference is the complex exponential term which is used here to represent the quadratic phase variations of the fields over the aperture of the horn.

The necessity of the quadratic phase term in (12-1b)–(12-1d) can be illustrated geometrically. Referring to Figure 12.2(b), let us assume that at the imaginary apex of the horn (shown dashed) there exists a line source radiating cylindrical waves. As the waves travel in the outward radial direction, the constant phase fronts are cylindrical. At any point y' at the aperture of the horn, the phase of the field will not be the same as that at the origin ($y'=0$). The phase is different because the wave has traveled different distances from the apex to the aperture. The difference in path of travel, designated as $\delta(y')$, can be obtained by referring to Figure 12.2(b). For any point y'

$$[\rho_1 + \delta(y')]^2 = \rho_1^2 + (y')^2 \tag{12-2}$$

or

$$\delta(y') = -\rho_1 + [\rho_1^2 + (y')^2]^{1/2} = -\rho_1 + \rho_1\left[1 + \left(\frac{y'}{\rho_1}\right)^2\right]^{1/2} \tag{12-2a}$$

Using the binomial expansion and retaining only the first two terms of it, (12-2a) reduces to

$$\boxed{\delta(y') \simeq -\rho_1 + \rho_1\left[1 + \frac{1}{2}\left(\frac{y'}{\rho_1}\right)^2\right] = \frac{1}{2}\left(\frac{y'^2}{\rho_1}\right)} \tag{12-2b}$$

When (12-2b) is multiplied by the phase factor k, the result is identical to the quadratic phase term in (12-1b)–(12-1d).

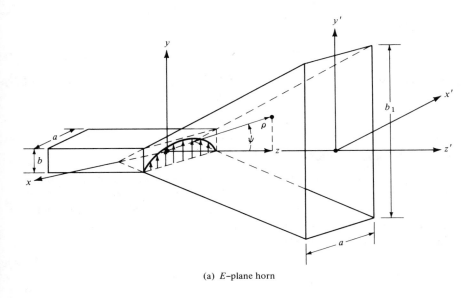

(a) *E*-plane horn

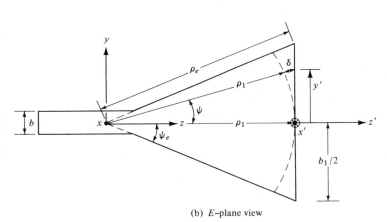

(b) *E*-plane view

Figure 12.2   *E*-plane horn and coordinate system.

Example 12.1

Design an *E*-plane sectoral horn so that the maximum phase deviation at the aperture of the horn is 56.72°. The dimensions of the horn are $a = 0.5\lambda$, $b = 0.25\lambda$, $b_1 = 2.75\lambda$.

SOLUTION
Using (12-2b)

$$\Delta\phi\Big|_{\max} = k\delta(y')\Big|_{y'=b_1/2} = \frac{k}{2}\frac{(b_1/2)^2}{\rho_1} = 56.72\left(\frac{\pi}{180}\right)$$

or

$$\rho_1 = \left(\frac{2.75}{2}\right)^2 \frac{180}{56.72}\lambda = 6\lambda$$

The total flare angle of the horn should be equal to

$$2\psi_e = 2\tan^{-1}\left(\frac{b_1/2}{\rho_1}\right) = 2\tan^{-1}\left(\frac{2.75/2}{6}\right) = 25.81°$$

12.2.2 Radiated Fields

To find the fields radiated by the horn, only the tangential components of the **E**- and/or **H**-fields over a closed surface must by known. The closed surface is chosen to coincide with an infinite plane passing through the mouth of the horn. To solve for the fields, the approximate equivalent of Section 11.5.2 is used. That is,

$$\left.\begin{aligned} J_y &= -\frac{E_1}{\eta}\cos\left(\frac{\pi}{a}x'\right)e^{-jk\delta(y')} \\ M_x &= E_1\cos\left(\frac{\pi}{a}x'\right)e^{-jk\delta(y')} \end{aligned}\right\} \begin{aligned} &-a/2 \le x' \le a/2 \\ &-b_1/2 \le y' \le b_1/2 \end{aligned} \tag{12-3}$$

and

$$\mathbf{J}_s = \mathbf{M}_s = 0 \qquad \text{elsewhere} \tag{12-3a}$$

Using (11-12a)

$$N_\theta = -\frac{E_1}{\eta}\cos\theta\sin\phi I_1 I_2 \tag{12-4}$$

where

$$I_1 = \int_{-a/2}^{+a/2}\cos\left(\frac{\pi}{a}x'\right)e^{jkx'\sin\theta\cos\phi}\,dx'$$

$$= -\left(\frac{\pi a}{2}\right)\left[\frac{\cos\left(\frac{ka}{2}\sin\theta\cos\phi\right)}{\left(\frac{ka}{2}\sin\theta\cos\phi\right)^2 - \left(\frac{\pi}{2}\right)^2}\right] \tag{12-4a}$$

$$I_2 = \int_{-b_1/2}^{+b_1/2}e^{-jk[\delta(y')-y'\sin\theta\sin\phi]}\,dy' \tag{12-4b}$$

The integral of (12-4b) can also be evaluated in terms of cosine and sine Fresnel integrals. To do this, I_2 can be written, by completing the square, as

$$I_2 = \int_{-b_1/2}^{+b_1/2}e^{-j[ky'^2/(2\rho_1)-k_y y']}\,dy'$$

$$= e^{j(k_y^2\rho_1/2k)}\int_{-b_1/2}^{+b_1/2}e^{-j[(ky'-k_y\rho_1)^2/2k\rho_1]}\,dy' \tag{12-5}$$

where

$$k_y = k \sin\theta \sin\phi \tag{12-5a}$$

Making a change of variable

$$\sqrt{\frac{\pi}{2}}\, t = \sqrt{\frac{1}{2k\rho_1}}\, (ky' - k_y\rho_1) \tag{12-6a}$$

$$t = \sqrt{\frac{1}{\pi k\rho_1}}\, (ky' - k_y\rho_1) \tag{12-6b}$$

$$dt = \sqrt{\frac{k}{\pi\rho_1}}\, dy' \tag{12-6c}$$

reduces (12-5) to

$$I_2 = \sqrt{\frac{\pi\rho_1}{k}}\, e^{j(k_y{}^2\rho_1/2k)} \int_{t_1}^{t_2} e^{-j(\pi/2)t^2}\, dt$$

$$= \sqrt{\frac{\pi\rho_1}{k}}\, e^{j(k_y{}^2\rho_1/2k)} \int_{t_1}^{t_2} \left[\cos\left(\frac{\pi}{2}t^2\right) - j\sin\left(\frac{\pi}{2}t^2\right)\right] dt \tag{12-7}$$

and takes the form of

$$I_2 = \sqrt{\frac{\pi\rho_1}{k}}\, e^{j(k_y{}^2\rho_1/2k)}\{[C(t_2) - C(t_1)] - j[S(t_2) - S(t_1)]\} \tag{12-8}$$

where

$$\boxed{t_1 = \sqrt{\frac{1}{\pi k\rho_1}}\left(-\frac{kb_1}{2} - k_y\rho_1\right)} \tag{12-8a}$$

$$\boxed{t_2 = \sqrt{\frac{1}{\pi k\rho_1}}\left(\frac{kb_1}{2} - k_y\rho_1\right)} \tag{12-8b}$$

$$C(x) = \int_0^x \cos\left(\frac{\pi}{2}t^2\right) dt \tag{12-8c}$$

$$S(x) = \int_0^x \sin\left(\frac{\pi}{2}t^2\right) dt \tag{12-8d}$$

$C(x)$ and $S(x)$ are known as the cosine and sine Fresnel integrals and are well tabulated [4] (see Appendix IV). Computer subroutines are also available for efficient numerical evaluation of each [5], [6].

Using (12-4a) and (12-8), (12-4) can be written as

$$N_\theta = E_1 \frac{\pi a}{2} \sqrt{\frac{\pi\rho_1}{k}}\, e^{j(k_y{}^2\rho_1/2k)}$$

$$\times \left\{ \frac{\cos\theta\sin\phi}{\eta} \left[\frac{\cos\left(\dfrac{k_x a}{2}\right)}{\left(\dfrac{k_x a}{2}\right)^2 - \left(\dfrac{\pi}{2}\right)^2} \right] F(t_1, t_2) \right\} \tag{12-9}$$

where

$$k_x = k \sin \theta \cos \phi \qquad (12\text{-}9a)$$

$$k_y = k \sin \theta \sin \phi \qquad (12\text{-}9b)$$

$$F(t_1, t_2) = [C(t_2) - C(t_1)] - j[S(t_2) - S(t_1)] \qquad (12\text{-}9c)$$

In a similar manner, N_ϕ, L_θ, L_ϕ of (11-12b)–(11-12d) reduce to

$$N_\phi = E_1 \frac{\pi a}{2} \sqrt{\frac{\pi \rho_1}{k}} \, e^{j(k_y{}^2 \rho_1/2k)} \left\{ \frac{\cos \phi}{\eta} \left[\frac{\cos\left(\dfrac{k_x a}{2}\right)}{\left(\dfrac{k_x a}{2}\right)^2 - \left(\dfrac{\pi}{2}\right)^2} \right] F(t_1, t_2) \right\}$$

$$(12\text{-}10a)$$

$$L_\theta = E_1 \frac{\pi a}{2} \sqrt{\frac{\pi \rho_1}{k}} \, e^{j(k_y{}^2 \rho_1/2k)}$$

$$\times \left\{ -\cos \theta \cos \phi \left[\frac{\cos\left(\dfrac{k_x a}{2}\right)}{\left(\dfrac{k_x a}{2}\right)^2 - \left(\dfrac{\pi}{2}\right)^2} \right] F(t_1, t_2) \right\} \qquad (12\text{-}10b)$$

$$L_\phi = E_1 \frac{\pi a}{2} \sqrt{\frac{\pi \rho_1}{2}} \, e^{j(k_y{}^2 \rho_1/2k)} \left\{ \sin \phi \left[\frac{\cos\left(\dfrac{k_x a}{2}\right)}{\left(\dfrac{k_x a}{2}\right)^2 - \left(\dfrac{\pi}{2}\right)^2} \right] F(t_1, t_2) \right\}$$

$$(12\text{-}10c)$$

The electric field components radiated by the horn can be obtained by using (11-10a)–(11-10c), and (12-9)–(12-10c). Thus

$$E_r = 0 \qquad (12\text{-}11a)$$

$$E_\theta = -j \frac{a\sqrt{\pi k \rho_1} \, E_1 e^{-jkr}}{8r}$$

$$\times \left\{ e^{j(k_y{}^2 \rho_1/2k)} \sin \phi (1 + \cos \theta) \left[\frac{\cos\left(\dfrac{k_x a}{2}\right)}{\left(\dfrac{k_x a}{2}\right)^2 - \left(\dfrac{\pi}{2}\right)^2} \right] F(t_1, t_2) \right\}$$

$$(12\text{-}11b)$$

$$
E_\phi = -j\frac{a\sqrt{\pi k\rho_1}\,E_1 e^{-jkr}}{8r}
$$

$$
\times \left\{ e^{j(k_y{}^2\rho_1/2k)}\cos\phi(\cos\theta+1)\left[\frac{\cos\left(\dfrac{k_x a}{2}\right)}{\left(\dfrac{k_x a}{2}\right)^2 - \left(\dfrac{\pi}{2}\right)^2}\right]F(t_1,t_2)\right\}
$$

(12-11c)

where t_1, t_2, k_x, k_y, and $F(t_1,t_2)$ are given, respectively, by (12-8a), (12-8b), (12-9a), (12-9b), and (12-9c). The corresponding **H**-field components are obtained using (11-10d)–(11-10f).

In the principal *E*- and *H*-planes, the electric field reduces to

E-Plane ($\phi = \pi/2$)

$$E_r = E_\phi = 0 \tag{12-12a}$$

$$E_\theta = -j\frac{a\sqrt{\pi k\rho_1}\,E_1 e^{-jkr}}{8r}\left\{ -e^{j(k\rho_1\sin^2\theta/2)}\left(\frac{2}{\pi}\right)^2(1+\cos\theta)F(t_1',t_2')\right\} \tag{12-12b}$$

$$t_1' = \sqrt{\frac{k}{\pi\rho_1}}\left(-\frac{b_1}{2} - \rho_1\sin\theta\right) \tag{12-12c}$$

$$t_2' = \sqrt{\frac{k}{\pi\rho_1}}\left(+\frac{b_1}{2} - \rho_1\sin\theta\right) \tag{12-12d}$$

H-Plane ($\phi = 0$)

$$E_r = E_\theta = 0 \tag{12-13a}$$

$$E_\phi = -j\frac{a\sqrt{\pi k\rho_1}\,E_1 e^{-jkr}}{8r}\left\{(1+\cos\theta)\left[\frac{\cos\left(\dfrac{ka}{2}\sin\theta\right)}{\left(\dfrac{ka}{2}\sin\theta\right)^2 - \left(\dfrac{\pi}{2}\right)^2}\right]F(t_1'',t_2'')\right\} \tag{12-13b}$$

$$t_1'' = -\frac{b_1}{2}\sqrt{\frac{k}{\pi\rho_1}} \tag{12-13c}$$

$$t_2'' = +\frac{b_1}{2}\sqrt{\frac{k}{\pi\rho_1}} \tag{12-13d}$$

To better understand the performance of an *E*-plane sectoral horn and gain some insight into its performance as an efficient radiator, a three-dimensional normalized field pattern has been plotted in Figure 12.3

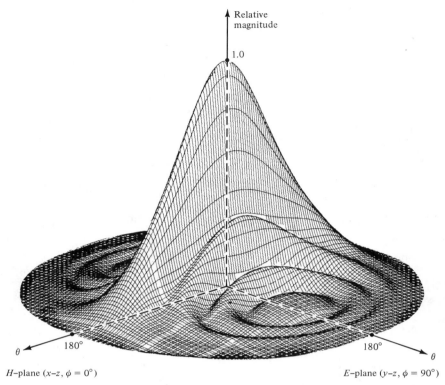

Figure 12.3 Three-dimensional field pattern of E-plane sectoral horn ($\rho_1 = 6\lambda$, $b_1 = 2.75\lambda$, $a = 0.5\lambda$).

utilizing (12-11a)–(12-11c). As expected, the E-plane pattern is much narrower than the H-plane because of the flaring and larger dimensions of the horn in that direction. Figure 12.3 provides an excellent visual view of the overall radiation performance of the horn. To display additional details, the corresponding normalized E- and H-plane patterns (in dB) are illustrated in Figure 12.4. These patterns also illustrate the narrowness of the E-plane and provide information on the relative levels of the pattern in those two planes.

To examine the behavior of the pattern as a function of flaring, the E-plane patterns for a horn antenna with $\rho_1 = 15\lambda$ and with flare angles of $20° \leq 2\psi_e \leq 35°$ are plotted in Figure 12.5. A total of four patterns is illustrated. Since each pattern is symmetrical, only half of each pattern is displayed. For small included angles, the pattern becomes narrower as the flare increases. Eventually the pattern begins to widen, becomes flatter around the main lobe, and the phase tapering at the aperture is such that even the main maximum does not occur on axis. This is illustrated in Figure

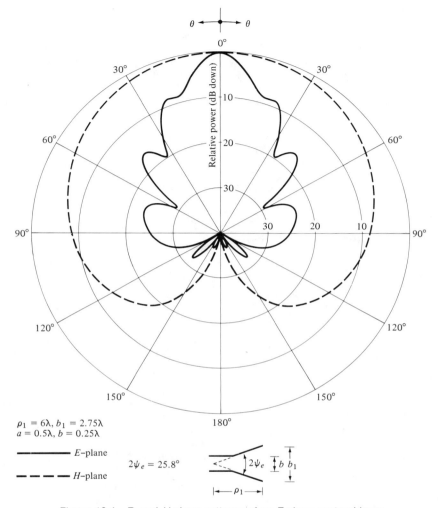

Figure 12.4   *E*- and *H*-plane patterns of an *E*-plane sectoral horn.

12.5 by the pattern with $2\psi_e = 35°$. As the flaring is extended beyond that point, the flatness (with certain allowable ripple) increases and eventually the main maximum returns again on axis. It is also observed that as the flaring increases, the pattern exhibits much sharper cutoff characteristics. In practice, to compensate for the phase taper at the opening, a lens is usually placed at the aperture making the pattern of the horn always narrower as its flare increases.

Similar pattern variations occur as the length of the horn is varied while the flare angle is held constant. As the length decreases the pattern begins to

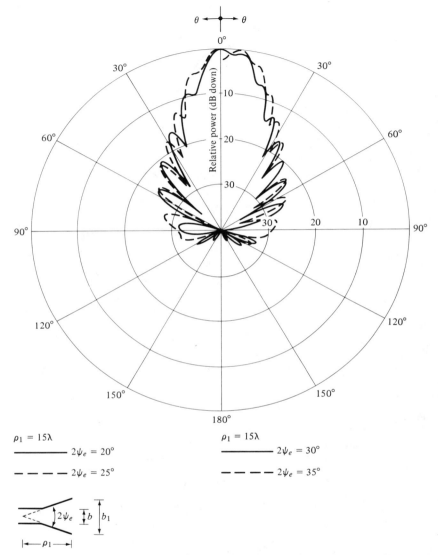

Figure 12.5 *E*-plane patterns of *E*-plane sectoral horn for constant length and different included angles.

broaden and eventually becomes flatter (with a ripple). Below a certain length, the main maximum does not even occur on axis, and the pattern continues to broaden and to become flatter (within an allowable ripple) until the maximum returns on axis. The process continues indefinitely.

An observation of the *E*-plane pattern, as given by (12-12a)–(12-12d), indicates that the *magnitude of the normalized pattern, excluding the factor*

$(1+\cos\theta)$, can be written as

$$E_{\theta n}=F(t_1',t_2')=[C(t_2')-C(t_1')]-j[S(t_2')-S(t_1')] \tag{12-14a}$$

$$t_1'=\sqrt{\frac{k}{\pi\rho_1}}\left(-\frac{b_1}{2}-\rho_1\sin\theta\right)$$

$$=2\sqrt{\frac{b_1^2}{8\lambda\rho_1}}\left[-1-\frac{1}{4}\left(\frac{8\rho_1\lambda}{b_1^2}\right)\left(\frac{b_1}{\lambda}\sin\theta\right)\right]$$

$$=2\sqrt{s}\left[-1-\frac{1}{4}\left(\frac{1}{s}\right)\left(\frac{b_1}{\lambda}\sin\theta\right)\right] \tag{12-14b}$$

$$t_2'=\sqrt{\frac{k}{\pi\rho_1}}\left(\frac{b_1}{2}-\rho_1\sin\theta\right)$$

$$=2\sqrt{\frac{b_1^2}{8\lambda\rho_1}}\left[1-\frac{1}{4}\left(\frac{8\rho_1\lambda}{b_1^2}\right)\left(\frac{b_1}{\lambda}\sin\theta\right)\right]$$

$$=2\sqrt{s}\left[1-\frac{1}{4}\left(\frac{1}{s}\right)\left(\frac{b_1}{\lambda}\sin\theta\right)\right] \tag{12-14c}$$

$$s=\frac{b_1^2}{8\lambda\rho_1} \tag{12-14d}$$

For a given value of s, the field of (12-14a) can be plotted as a function of $b_1/\lambda\sin\theta$, as shown in Figure 12.6 for $s=\frac{1}{64}, \frac{1}{8}, \frac{1}{4}, \frac{1}{2}, \frac{3}{4}$, and 1. These plots are usually referred to as *universal curves*, because from them the normalized E-plane pattern of any E-plane sectoral horn can be obtained. This is accomplished by first determining the value of s from a given b_1 and ρ_1 by using (12-14d). For that value of s, the field strength (in dB) as a function of $(b_1/\lambda)\sin\theta$ (or as a function of θ for a given b_1) is obtained from Figure 12.6. Finally the value of $(1+\cos\theta)$, normalized to 0 dB and written as $20\log_{10}[(1+\cos\theta)/2]$, is added to that number to arrive at the required field strength.

Example 12.2

An E-plane horn has dimensions of $a=0.5\lambda$, $b=0.25\lambda$, $b_1=2.75\lambda$, and $\rho_1=6\lambda$. Find its E-plane normalized field intensity (in dB *and* as a voltage ratio) at an angle of $\theta=90°$ using the universal curves of Figure 12.6.

SOLUTION
Using (12-14d)

$$s=\frac{b_1^2}{8\lambda\rho_1}=\frac{(2.75)^2}{8(6)}=0.1575\simeq\frac{1}{6.3}$$

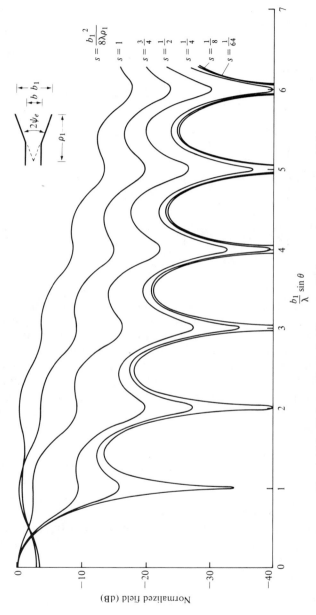

Figure 12.6 *E-plane universal patterns for E-plane sectoral and pyramidal horns.*

None of the curves in Figure 12.6 represents $s = \frac{1}{64}$. Therefore interpolation will be used between the $s = \frac{1}{4}$ and $s = \frac{1}{8}$ curves.

At $\theta = 90°$

$$\frac{b_1}{\lambda} \sin(\theta) = 2.75 \sin(90°) = 2.75$$

and at that point the field intensity between the $s = \frac{1}{4}$ and $s = \frac{1}{8}$ curves is about -20 dB. Therefore the total field intensity at $\theta = 90°$ is equal to

$$E_\theta = -20 + 20 \log_{10}\left(\frac{1 + \cos 90°}{2}\right) = -20 - 6 = -26 \text{ dB}$$

or as a normalized voltage ratio of

$$E_\theta = 0.05$$

which closely agrees with the results of Figure 12.4.

12.2.3 Directivity

The directivity is one of the parameters that is often used as a figure-of-merit to describe the performance of an antenna. To find the directivity, the maximum radiation is formed. That is,

$$U_{max} = U(\theta, \phi)|_{max} = \frac{r^2}{2\eta} |E|^2_{max} \tag{12-15}$$

For most horn antennas, $|E|_{max}$ is directed nearly along the z-axis ($\theta = 0$). Thus

$$|E|_{max} = \sqrt{|E_\theta|^2_{max} + |E_\phi|^2_{max}} = \frac{2a\sqrt{\pi k \rho_1}}{\pi^2 r} |E_1||F(t)| \tag{12-16}$$

Using (12-11b), (12-11c), and (12-9c)

$$|E_\theta|_{max} = \frac{2a\sqrt{\pi k \rho_1}}{\pi^2 r} |E_1 \sin \phi F(t)| \tag{12-16a}$$

$$|E_\phi|_{max} = \frac{2a\sqrt{\pi k \rho_1}}{\pi^2 r} |E_1 \cos \phi F(t)| \tag{12-16b}$$

$$F(t) = [C(t) - jS(t)] \tag{12-16c}$$

$$t = \frac{b_1}{2}\sqrt{\frac{k}{\pi \rho_1}} = \frac{b_1}{\sqrt{2\lambda \rho_1}} \tag{12-16d}$$

since

$$k_x = k_y = 0 \tag{12-16e}$$

$$t_1 = -t = -\frac{b_1}{2}\sqrt{\frac{k}{\pi\rho_1}} = -\frac{b_1}{\sqrt{2\lambda\rho_1}} \tag{12-16f}$$

$$t_2 = +t = +\frac{b_1}{2}\sqrt{\frac{k}{\pi\rho_1}} = \frac{b_1}{\sqrt{2\lambda\rho_1}} \tag{12-16g}$$

$$C(-t) = -C(t) \tag{12-16h}$$

$$S(-t) = -S(t) \tag{12-16i}$$

Thus

$$U_{max} = \frac{r^2}{2\eta}|\mathbf{E}|^2_{max} = \frac{2a^2 k\rho_1}{\eta\pi^3}|E_1|^2|F(t)|^2$$

$$= \frac{4a^2\rho_1|E_1|^2}{\eta\lambda\pi^2}|F(t)|^2 \tag{12-17}$$

where

$$|F(t)|^2 = \left[C^2\left(\frac{b_1}{\sqrt{2\lambda\rho_1}}\right) + S^2\left(\frac{b_1}{\sqrt{2\lambda\rho_1}}\right)\right] \tag{12-17a}$$

The total power radiated can be found by simply integrating the average power density over the aperture of the horn. Using (12-1a)–(12-1d)

$$P_{rad} = \frac{1}{2}\iint_{S_0} \mathrm{Re}(\mathbf{E}'\times\mathbf{H}'^*)\cdot d\mathbf{s} = \frac{1}{2\eta}\int_{-b_1/2}^{+b_1/2}\int_{-a/2}^{+a/2}|E_1|^2\cos^2\left(\frac{\pi}{a}x'\right)dx'\,dy' \tag{12-18}$$

which reduces to

$$P_{rad} = |E_1|^2\frac{b_1 a}{4\eta} \tag{12-18a}$$

Using (12-17) and (12-18a), the directivity for the E-plane horn can be written as

$$\boxed{\begin{aligned} D_E &= \frac{4\pi U_{max}}{P_{rad}} = \frac{64a\rho_1}{\pi\lambda b_1}|F(t)|^2 \\ &= \frac{64a\rho_1}{\pi\lambda b_1}\left[C^2\left(\frac{b_1}{\sqrt{2\lambda\rho_1}}\right) + S^2\left(\frac{b_1}{\sqrt{2\lambda\rho_1}}\right)\right] \end{aligned}} \tag{12-19}$$

The overall performance of an antenna system can often be judged by its beamwidth and/or its directivity. The half-power beamwidth (HPBW),

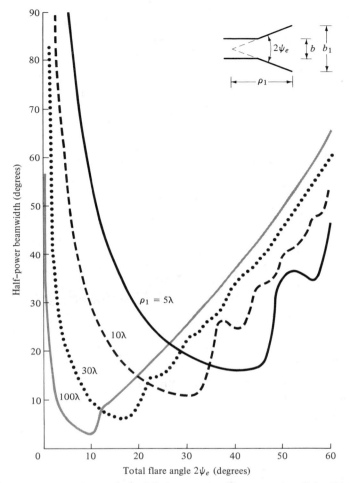

Figure 12.7 Half-power beamwidth of *E*-plane sectoral horn as a function of included angle and for different lengths.

as a function of flare angle, for different horn lengths is shown in Figure 12.7. In addition, the directivity (normalized with respect to the constant aperture dimension a) is displayed in Figure 12.8. For a given length, the horn exhibits a monotonic decrease in half-power beamwidth and an increase in directivity up to a certain flare. Beyond that point a monotonic increase in beamwidth and decrease in directivity is indicated followed by rises and falls. The increase in beamwidth and decrease in directivity beyond a certain flare indicate the broadening of the main beam.

If the values of b_1 (in λ), which correspond to the maximum directivities in Figure 12.8, are plotted versus their corresponding values of ρ_1 (in λ),

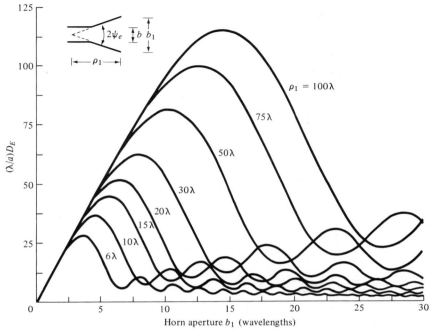

Figure 12.8   Normalized directivity of *E*-plane sectoral horn as a function of aperture size and for different lengths.

it can be shown that each optimum directivity occurs when

$$b_1 \simeq \sqrt{2\lambda\rho_1}$$ (12-19a)

with a corresponding value of *s* equal to

$$s\Big|_{b_1=\sqrt{2\lambda\rho_1}} = s_{op} = \frac{b_1}{8\lambda\rho_1}\Big|_{b_1=\sqrt{2\lambda\rho_1}} = \frac{1}{4}$$ (12-19b)

The directivity of an *E*-plane sectoral horn can also be computed by using the following procedure [7].

1. Calculate *B* by

$$B = \frac{b_1}{\lambda}\sqrt{\frac{50}{\rho_e/\lambda}}$$ (12-20a)

2. Using this value of *B*, find the corresponding value of G_E from Figure 12.9. If, however, the value of *B* is smaller than 2, compute G_E using

$$G_E = \frac{32}{\pi}B$$ (12-20b)

3. Calculate D_E by using the value of G_E from Figure 12.9 or from (12-20b). Thus

$$\boxed{D_E = \frac{a}{\lambda} \frac{G_E}{\sqrt{\dfrac{50}{\rho_e/\lambda}}}}$$

(12-20c)

Example 12.3

An *E*-plane sectoral horn has dimensions of $a=0.5\lambda$, $b=0.25\lambda$, $b_1=2.75\lambda$, and $\rho_1=6\lambda$. Compute the directivity using (12-19) and (12-20c). Compare the answers.

SOLUTION
For this horn

$$\frac{b_1}{\sqrt{2\lambda\rho_1}} = \frac{2.75}{\sqrt{2(6)}} = 0.794$$

Therefore (from Appendix IV)

$$[C(0.794)]^2 = (0.72)^2 = 0.518$$
$$[S(0.794)]^2 = (0.24)^2 = 0.0576$$

Using (12-19)

$$D_E = \frac{64(0.5)6}{2.75\pi}(0.518 + 0.0576) = 12.79 = 11.07 \text{ dB}$$

To compute the directivity using (12-20c), the following parameters are evaluated:

$$\rho_e = \lambda\sqrt{(6)^2 + \left(\frac{2.75}{2}\right)^2} = 6.1555\lambda$$

$$\sqrt{\frac{50}{\rho_e/\lambda}} = \sqrt{\frac{50}{6.1555}} = 2.85$$

$$B = 2.75(2.85) = 7.84$$

For $B=7.84$, $G_E=73.5$ from Figure 12.9. Thus, using (12-20c)

$$D_E = \frac{0.5(73.5)}{2.85} = 12.89 = 11.10 \text{ dB}$$

Obviously an excellent agreement between the results of (12-19) and (12-20c).

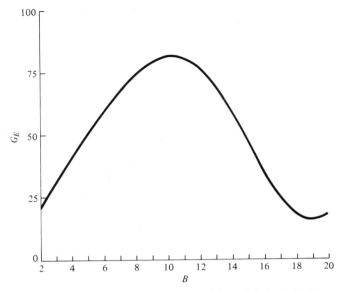

Figure 12.9 G_E as a function of B. (SOURCE: Adopted from data by E. H. Braun, "Some Data for the Design of Electromagnetic Horns," *IRE Trans. Antennas Propag.*, vol. AP-4, No. 1, January 1956. © (1956) IEEE)

12.3 *H*-PLANE SECTORAL HORN

Flaring the dimensions of a rectangular waveguide in the direction of the **H**-field while keeping the other constant, forms an *H*-plane sectoral horn shown in Figure 12.1(b). A more detailed geometry is shown in Figure 12.10.

The analysis procedure for this horn is similar to that for the *E*-plane horn, which was outlined in the previous section. Instead of including all the details of the formulation, a summary of each radiation characteristic will be given.

12.3.1 Aperture Fields

The fields at the aperture of the horn can be found by treating the horn as a radial waveguide forming an imaginary apex shown dashed in Figure 12.10. Using this method, it can be shown that at the aperture of the horn

$$E_x' = H_y' = 0 \tag{12-21a}$$

$$E_y'(x') = E_2 \cos\left(\frac{\pi}{a_1} x'\right) e^{-jk\delta(x')} \tag{12-21b}$$

$$H_x'(x') = -\frac{E_2}{\eta} \cos\left(\frac{\pi}{a_1} x'\right) e^{-jk\delta(x')} \tag{12-21c}$$

$$\delta(x') = \frac{1}{2}\left(\frac{x'^2}{\rho_2}\right) \tag{12-21d}$$

$$\rho_2 = \rho_h \cos\psi_h \tag{12-21e}$$

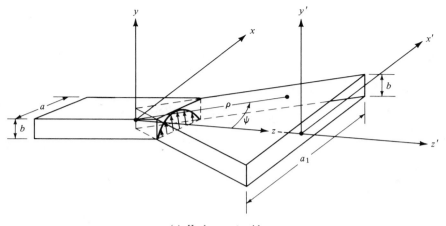

(a) H-plane sectoral horn

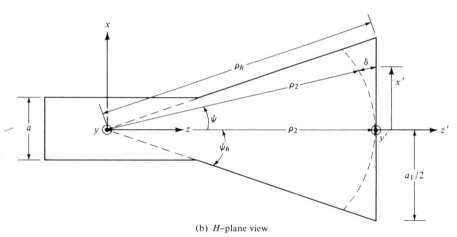

(b) H-plane view

Figure 12.10 H-plane sectoral horn and coordinate system.

12.3.2 Radiated Fields

The fields radiated by the horn can be found by first formulating the equivalent current densities $\mathbf{J}_s$ and $\mathbf{M}_s$. Using (12-21a)–(12-21c), it can be shown that over the aperture of the horn

$$J_x = J_z = M_y = M_z = 0 \tag{12-22a}$$

$$J_y = -\frac{E_2}{\eta}\cos\left(\frac{\pi}{a_1}x'\right)e^{-jk\delta(x')} \tag{12-22b}$$

$$M_x = E_2\cos\left(\frac{\pi}{a_1}x'\right)e^{-jk\delta(x')} \tag{12-22c}$$

and they are assumed to be zero elsewhere. Thus (11-12a) can be expressed as

$$N_\theta = \iint_S J_y \cos\theta \cos\phi e^{+jkr'\cos\psi} \, ds' = -\frac{E_2}{\eta} \cos\theta \sin\phi I_1 I_2 \qquad (12\text{-}23)$$

where

$$I_1 = \int_{-b/2}^{+b/2} e^{+jky'\sin\theta\sin\phi} \, dy' = b\left[\frac{\sin\left(\dfrac{kb}{2}\sin\theta\sin\phi\right)}{\dfrac{kb}{2}\sin\theta\sin\phi}\right] \qquad (12\text{-}23a)$$

$$I_2 = \int_{-a_1/2}^{+a_1/2} \cos\left(\frac{\pi}{a_1}x'\right) e^{-jk[\delta(x')-x'\sin\theta\cos\phi]} \, dx' \qquad (12\text{-}23b)$$

By rewriting $\cos[(\pi/a_1)x']$ as

$$\cos\left(\frac{\pi}{a_1}x'\right) = \left[\frac{e^{j(\pi/a_1)x'} + e^{-j(\pi/a_1)x'}}{2}\right] \qquad (12\text{-}24)$$

(12-23b) can be expressed as

$$I_2 = I_2' + I_2'' \qquad (12\text{-}25)$$

where

$$I_2' = \frac{1}{2}\sqrt{\frac{\pi\rho_2}{k}} \, e^{j(k_x'^2\rho_2/2k)}\{[C(t_2')-C(t_1')]-j[S(t_2')-S(t_1')]\} \qquad (12\text{-}26)$$

$$\boxed{t_1' = \sqrt{\frac{1}{\pi k\rho_2}}\left(-\frac{ka_1}{2}-k_x'\rho_2\right)} \qquad (12\text{-}26a)$$

$$\boxed{t_2' = \sqrt{\frac{1}{\pi k\rho_2}}\left(+\frac{ka_1}{2}-k_x'\rho_2\right)} \qquad (12\text{-}26b)$$

$$\boxed{k_x' = k\sin\theta\cos\phi + \frac{\pi}{a_1}} \qquad (12\text{-}26c)$$

$$I_2'' = \frac{1}{2}\sqrt{\frac{\pi\rho_2}{k}} \, e^{j(k_x''^2\rho_2/2k)}\{[C(t_2'')-C(t_1'')]-j[S(t_2'')-S(t_1'')]\}$$

$$(12\text{-}27)$$

$$\boxed{t_1'' = \sqrt{\frac{1}{\pi k\rho_2}}\left(-\frac{ka_1}{2}-k_x''\rho_2\right)} \qquad (12\text{-}27a)$$

$$\boxed{t_2'' = \sqrt{\frac{1}{\pi k\rho_2}}\left(+\frac{ka_1}{2}-k_x''\rho_2\right)} \qquad (12\text{-}27b)$$

$$\boxed{k_x'' = k\sin\theta\cos\phi - \frac{\pi}{a_1}} \qquad (12\text{-}27c)$$

$C(x)$ and $S(x)$ are the cosine and sine Fresnel integrals of (12-8c) and (12-8d), and they are well tabulated (see Appendix IV).

With the aid of (12-23a), (12-25), (12-26), and (12-27), Equation (12-23) reduces to

$$N_\theta = -E_2 \frac{b}{2}\sqrt{\frac{\pi\rho_2}{k}}$$

$$\times \left\{ \frac{\cos\theta\sin\phi}{\eta} \frac{\sin Y}{Y}\left[e^{jf_1}F(t_1', t_2') + e^{jf_2}F(t_1'', t_2'')\right] \right\} \tag{12-28}$$

$$\boxed{F(t_1, t_2) = \left[C(t_2) - C(t_1)\right] - j\left[S(t_2) - S(t_1)\right]} \tag{12-28a}$$

$$\boxed{f_1 = \frac{k_x'^2 \rho_2}{2k}} \tag{12-28b}$$

$$\boxed{f_2 = \frac{k_x''^2 \rho_2}{2k}} \tag{12-28c}$$

$$\boxed{Y = \frac{kb}{2}\sin\theta\sin\phi} \tag{12-28d}$$

In a similar manner, N_ϕ, L_θ, and L_ϕ of (11-12b)–(11-12d) can be written as

$$N_\phi = -E_2 \frac{b}{2}\sqrt{\frac{\pi\rho_2}{k}}$$

$$\times \left\{ \frac{\cos\phi}{\eta} \frac{\sin Y}{Y}\left[e^{jf_1}F(t_1', t_2') + e^{jf_2}F(t_1'', t_2'')\right] \right\} \tag{12-29a}$$

$$L_\theta = E_2 \frac{b}{2}\sqrt{\frac{\pi\rho_2}{k}}$$

$$\times \left\{ \cos\theta\cos\phi \frac{\sin Y}{Y}\left[e^{jf_1}F(t_1', t_2') + e^{jf_2}F(t_1'', t_2'')\right] \right\} \tag{12-29b}$$

$$L_\phi = -E_2 \frac{b}{2}\sqrt{\frac{\pi\rho_2}{k}}$$

$$\times \left\{ \sin\phi \frac{\sin Y}{Y}\left[e^{jf_1}F(t_1', t_2') + e^{jf_2}F(t_1'', t_2'')\right] \right\} \tag{12-29c}$$

The far-zone electric field components of (11-10a)–(11-10c) can then be expressed as

$$\boxed{E_r = 0} \tag{12-30a}$$

$$E_\theta = jE_2 \frac{b}{8} \sqrt{\frac{k\rho_2}{\pi}} \frac{e^{-jkr}}{r}$$
$$\times \left\{ \sin\phi (1+\cos\theta) \frac{\sin Y}{Y} \left[e^{jf_1} F(t_1', t_2') + e^{jf_2} F(t_1'', t_2'') \right] \right\}$$

(12-30b)

$$E_\phi = jE_2 \frac{b}{8} \sqrt{\frac{k\rho_2}{\pi}} \frac{e^{-jkr}}{r}$$
$$\times \left\{ \cos\phi (\cos\theta + 1) \frac{\sin Y}{Y} \left[e^{jf_1} F(t_1', t_2') + e^{jf_2} F(t_1'', t_2'') \right] \right\}$$

(12-30c)

The electric field in the principal E- and H-planes reduces to

E-Plane ($\phi = \pi/2$)

$$E_r = E_\phi = 0 \tag{12-31a}$$

$$E_\theta = jE_2 \frac{b}{8} \sqrt{\frac{k\rho_2}{\pi}} \frac{e^{-jkr}}{r}$$
$$\times \left\{ (1+\cos\theta) \frac{\sin Y}{Y} \left[e^{jf_1} F(t_1', t_2') + e^{jf_2} F(t_1'', t_2'') \right] \right\} \tag{12-31b}$$

$$Y = \frac{kb}{2} \sin\theta \tag{12-31c}$$

$$k_x' = \frac{\pi}{a_1} \tag{12-31d}$$

$$k_x'' = -\frac{\pi}{a_1} \tag{12-31e}$$

H-Plane ($\phi = 0$)

$$E_r = E_\theta = 0 \tag{12-32a}$$

$$E_\phi = jE_2 \frac{b}{8} \sqrt{\frac{k\rho_2}{\pi}} \frac{e^{-jkr}}{r}$$
$$\times \left\{ (\cos\theta + 1) \left[e^{jf_1} F(t_1', t_2') + e^{jf_2} F(t_1'', t_2'') \right] \right\} \tag{12-32b}$$

$$k_x' = k\sin\theta + \frac{\pi}{a_1} \tag{12-32c}$$

$$k_x'' = k\sin\theta - \frac{\pi}{a_1} \tag{12-32d}$$

with f_1, f_2, $F(t_1', t_2')$, $F(t_1'', t_2'')$, t_1', t_2', t_1'', and t_2'' as defined above.

Computations similar to those for the *E*-plane sectoral horn were also performed for the *H*-plane sectoral horn. A three-dimensional field pattern of an *H*-plane sectoral horn is shown in Figure 12.11. Its corresponding *E*- and *H*-plane patterns are displayed in Figure 12.12. This horn exhibits narrow pattern characteristics in the flared *H*-plane.

Normalized *H*-plane patterns for a given length horn ($\rho_2 = 12\lambda$) and different flare angles are shown in Figure 12.13. A total of four patterns is illustrated. Since each pattern is symmetrical, only half of each pattern is displayed. As the included angle is increased, the pattern begins to become narrower up to a given flare. Beyond that point the pattern begins to broaden, attributed primarily to the phase taper (phase error) across the aperture of the horn. To correct this, a lens is usually placed at the horn aperture which would yield narrower patterns as the flare angle is increased. Similar pattern variations are evident when the flare angle of the horn is maintained fixed while its length is varied.

The *universal curves* for the *H*-plane sectoral horn are based on (12-32b), in the absence of the factor $(1 + \cos\theta)$. Neglecting the $(1 + \cos\theta)$

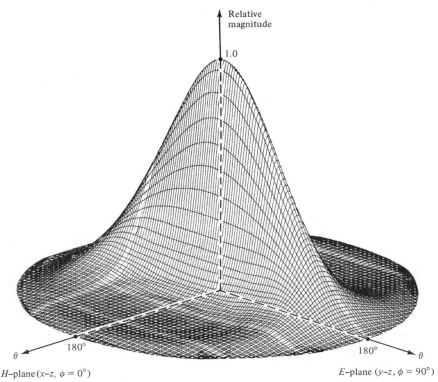

H–plane (x–z, $\phi = 0°$)   *E*–plane (y–z, $\phi = 90°$)

Figure 12.11 Three-dimensional field pattern of an *H*-plane sectoral horn ($\rho_2 = 6\lambda$, $a_1 = 5.5\lambda$, $b = 0.25\lambda$).

factor, the normalized H-plane electric field of the H-plane sectoral horn can be written as

$$E_{\phi n}=\left[e^{jf_1}F(t_1{}',t_2{}')+e^{jf_2}F(t_1{}'',t_2{}'')\right] \tag{12-33}$$

$$F(t_1{}',t_2{}')=\left[C(t_2)-C(t_1)\right]-j\left[S(t_2)-S(t_1)\right] \tag{12-33a}$$

$$f_1=\frac{k_x{}'^2\rho_2}{2k}=\frac{\rho_2}{2k}\left(k\sin\theta+\frac{\pi}{a_1}\right)^2$$

$$=\frac{\pi}{8}\left(\frac{1}{t}\right)\left(\frac{a_1}{\lambda}\sin\theta\right)^2\left[1+\frac{1}{2}\left(\frac{\lambda}{a_1\sin\theta}\right)\right]^2 \tag{12-33b}$$

$$f_2=\frac{k_x{}''^2\rho_2}{2k}=\frac{\rho_2}{2k}\left(k\sin\theta-\frac{\pi}{a_1}\right)^2$$

$$=\frac{\pi}{8}\left(\frac{1}{t}\right)\left(\frac{a_1}{\lambda}\sin\theta\right)^2\left[1-\frac{1}{2}\left(\frac{\lambda}{a_1\sin\theta}\right)\right]^2 \tag{12-33c}$$

$$t_1{}'=\sqrt{\frac{1}{\pi k\rho_2}}\left(-\frac{ka_1}{2}-k_x{}'\rho_2\right)$$

$$=2\sqrt{t}\left[-1-\frac{1}{4}\left(\frac{1}{t}\right)\left(\frac{a_1}{\lambda}\sin\theta\right)-\frac{1}{8}\left(\frac{1}{t}\right)\right] \tag{12-33d}$$

$$t_2{}'=\sqrt{\frac{1}{\pi k\rho_2}}\left(+\frac{ka_1}{2}+k_x{}'\rho_2\right)$$

$$=2\sqrt{t}\left[+1-\frac{1}{4}\left(\frac{1}{t}\right)\left(\frac{a_1}{\lambda}\sin\theta\right)-\frac{1}{8}\left(\frac{1}{t}\right)\right] \tag{12-33e}$$

$$t_1{}''=\sqrt{\frac{1}{\pi k\rho_2}}\left(-\frac{ka_1}{2}+k_x{}''\rho_2\right)$$

$$=2\sqrt{t}\left[-1-\frac{1}{4}\left(\frac{1}{t}\right)\left(\frac{a_1}{\lambda}\sin\theta\right)+\frac{1}{8}\left(\frac{1}{t}\right)\right] \tag{12-33f}$$

$$t_2{}''=\sqrt{\frac{1}{\pi k\rho_2}}\left(\quad\frac{ka_1}{2}\quad k_x{}''\rho_2\right)$$

$$=2\sqrt{t}\left[+1-\frac{1}{4}\left(\frac{1}{t}\right)\left(\frac{a_1}{\lambda}\sin\theta\right)+\frac{1}{8}\left(\frac{1}{t}\right)\right] \tag{12-33g}$$

$$t=\frac{a_1{}^2}{8\lambda\rho_2} \tag{12-33h}$$

For a given value of t, as given by (12-33h), the normalized field of (12-33) is plotted in Figure 12.14 as a function of $(a_1/\lambda)\sin\theta$ for $t=\frac{1}{64},\frac{1}{8},\frac{1}{4},\frac{1}{2},\frac{3}{4}$ and 1. Following a procedure identical to that for the E-plane sectoral horn, the H-plane pattern of any H-plane sectoral horn can be obtained from these curves. The normalized value of the $(1+\cos\theta)$ factor in dB, written as $20\log_{10}[(1+\cos\theta)/2]$, must also be included.

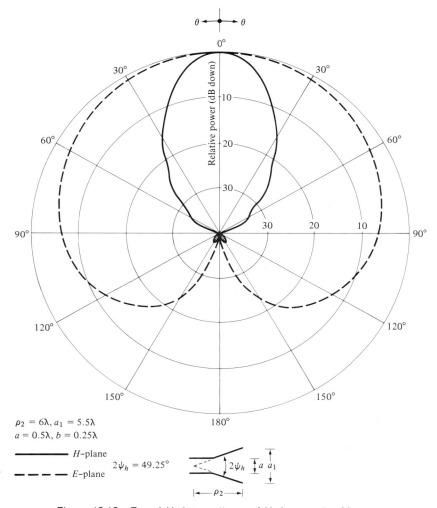

Figure 12.12   *E*- and *H*-plane patterns of *H*-plane sectoral horn.

12.3.3   Directivity

To find the directivity of the *H*-plane sectoral horn, a procedure similar to that for the *E*-plane is used. As for the *E*-plane sectoral horn, the maximum radiation is directed nearly along the *z*-axis ($\theta = 0$). Thus

$$|E_\theta|_{\max} = |E_2| \frac{b}{4r} \sqrt{\frac{2\rho_2}{\lambda}} \left| \sin\phi \left\{ \left[C(t_2') + C(t_2'') - C(t_1') - C(t_1'') \right] \right. \right.$$

$$\left. \left. - j \left[S(t_2') + S(t_2'') - S(t_1') - S(t_1'') \right] \right\} \right|$$

$$(12\text{-}34)$$

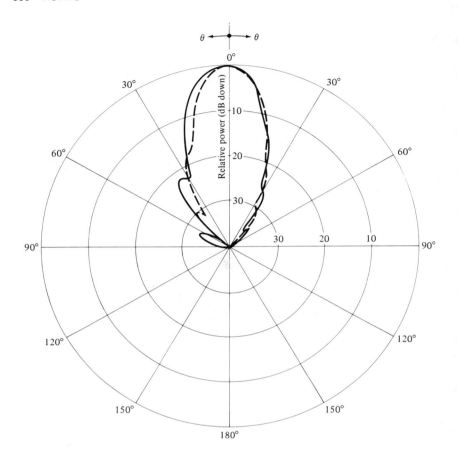

Figure 12.13 *H*-plane patterns of *H*-plane sectoral horn for constant length and different included angles.

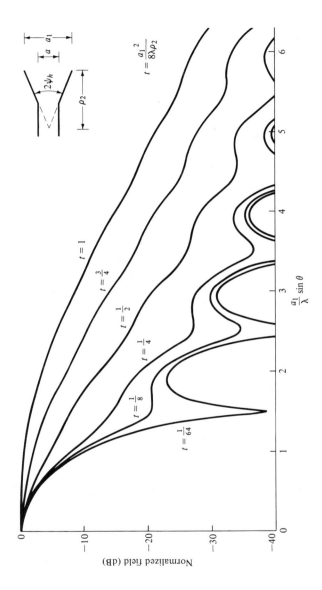

Figure 12.14 *H*-plane universal patterns for *H*-plane sectoral and pyramidal horns.

$$t_1' = \sqrt{\frac{1}{\pi k \rho_2}} \left(-\frac{ka_1}{2} - \frac{\pi}{a_1} \rho_2 \right) \tag{12-34a}$$

$$t_2' = \sqrt{\frac{1}{\pi k \rho_2}} \left(+\frac{ka_1}{2} - \frac{\pi}{a_1} \rho_2 \right) \tag{12-34b}$$

$$t_1'' = \sqrt{\frac{1}{\pi k \rho_2}} \left(-\frac{ka_1}{2} + \frac{\pi}{a_1} \rho_2 \right) = -t_2' = v \tag{12-34c}$$

$$t_2'' = \sqrt{\frac{1}{\pi k \rho_2}} \left(+\frac{ka_1}{2} + \frac{\pi}{a_1} \rho_2 \right) = -t_1' = u \tag{12-34d}$$

Since

$$C(-x) = -C(x) \tag{12-35a}$$

$$S(-x) = -S(x) \tag{12-35b}$$

$$|E_\theta|_{\max} = \left| E_2 \frac{b}{r} \sqrt{\frac{\rho_2}{2\lambda}} \left| \sin\phi \{ [C(u) - C(v)] - j[S(u) - S(v)] \} \right| \right.$$

$$\tag{12-36}$$

$$u = t_2'' = -t_1' = \sqrt{\frac{1}{\pi k \rho_2}} \left(+\frac{ka_1}{2} + \frac{\pi}{a_1} \rho_2 \right) = \frac{1}{\sqrt{2}} \left(\frac{\sqrt{\lambda \rho_2}}{a_1} + \frac{a_1}{\sqrt{\lambda \rho_2}} \right)$$

$$\tag{12-36a}$$

$$v = t_1'' = -t_2' = \sqrt{\frac{1}{\pi k \rho_2}} \left(-\frac{ka_1}{2} + \frac{\pi}{a_1} \rho_2 \right) = \frac{1}{\sqrt{2}} \left(\frac{\sqrt{\lambda \rho_2}}{a_1} - \frac{a_1}{\sqrt{\lambda \rho_2}} \right)$$

$$\tag{12-36b}$$

Similarly

$$|E_\phi|_{\max} = \left| E_2 \frac{b}{r} \sqrt{\frac{\rho_2}{2\lambda}} \left| \cos\phi \{ [C(u) - C(v)] - j[S(u) - S(v)] \} \right| \right.$$

$$\tag{12-37}$$

Thus

$$|\mathbf{E}|_{\max} = \sqrt{|E_\theta|_{\max}^2 + |E_\phi|_{\max}^2}$$

$$= |E_2| \frac{b}{r} \sqrt{\frac{\rho_2}{2\lambda}} \left\{ [C(u) - C(v)]^2 + [S(u) - S(v)]^2 \right\}^{1/2} \tag{12-38}$$

$$U_{\max} = |E_2|^2 \frac{b^2 \rho_2}{4\eta\lambda} \left\{ [C(u) - C(v)]^2 + [S(u) - S(v)]^2 \right\} \tag{12-39}$$

The total power radiated can be obtained by simply integrating the average power density over the mouth of the horn, and it is given by

$$P_{\text{rad}} = |E_2|^2 \frac{ba_1}{4\eta} \tag{12-40}$$

Using (12-39) and (12-40), the directivity for the *H*-plane sectoral horn can be written as

$$D_H = \frac{4\pi U_{max}}{P_{rad}} = \frac{4\pi b\rho_2}{a_1\lambda}$$

$$\times \left\{ [C(u) - C(v)]^2 + [S(u) - S(v)]^2 \right\}$$

(12-41)

where

$$u = \frac{1}{\sqrt{2}} \left(\frac{\sqrt{\lambda\rho_2}}{a_1} + \frac{a_1}{\sqrt{\lambda\rho_2}} \right)$$

(12-41a)

$$v = \frac{1}{\sqrt{2}} \left(\frac{\sqrt{\lambda\rho_2}}{a_1} - \frac{a_1}{\sqrt{\lambda\rho_2}} \right)$$

(12-41b)

The half-power beamwidth (HPBW) as a function of flare angle is plotted in Figure 12.15. The normalized directivity (relative to the constant aperture dimension *b*) for different horn lengths, as a function of aperture dimension a_1, is displayed in Figure 12.16. As for the *E*-plane sectoral horn, the HPBW exhibits a monotonic decrease and the directivity a monotonic increase up to a given flare; beyond that the trends are reversed.

If the values of a_1 (in λ), which correspond to the maximum directivities in Figure 12.16, are plotted versus their corresponding values of ρ_2 (in λ), it can be shown that each optimum directivity occurs when

$$a_1 \simeq \sqrt{3\lambda\rho_2}$$

(12-41c)

with a corresponding value of *t* equal to

$$t\Big|_{a_1 = \sqrt{3\lambda\rho_2}} = t_{op} = \frac{a_1^2}{8\lambda\rho_2}\Big|_{a_1 = \sqrt{3\lambda\rho_2}} = \frac{3}{8}$$

(12-41d)

The directivity of an *H*-plane sectoral horn can also be computed by using the following procedure [7].

1. Calculate *A* by

$$A = \frac{a_1}{\lambda}\sqrt{\frac{50}{\rho_h/\lambda}}$$

(12-42a)

2. Using this value of *A*, find the corresponding value of G_H from Figure 12.17. If the value of *A* is smaller than 2, then compute G_H

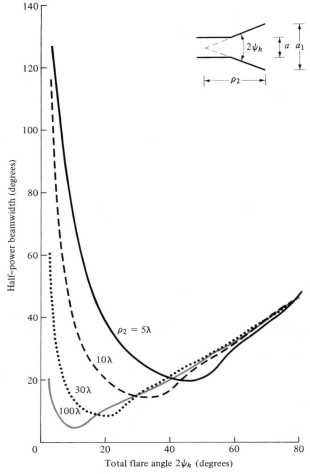

Figure 12.15   Half-power beamwidth of *H*-plane sectoral horn as a function of included angle and for different lengths.

using

$$G_H = \frac{32}{\pi} A \qquad (12\text{-}42b)$$

3. Calculate D_H by using the value of G_E from Figure 12.17 or from (12-42b). Thus

$$D_H = \frac{b}{\lambda} \frac{G_h}{\sqrt{\dfrac{50}{\rho_h/\lambda}}} \qquad (12\text{-}42c)$$

This is the actual directivity of the horn.

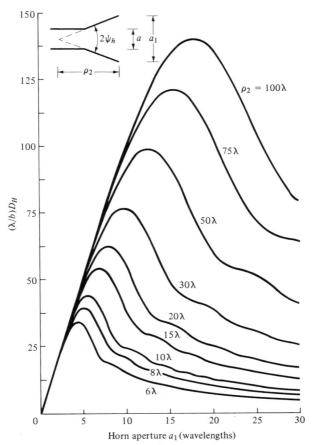

Figure 12.16   Normalized directivity of *H*-plane sectoral horn as a function of aperture size and for different lengths.

Example 12.4

An *H*-plane horn has dimensions of $a=0.5\lambda$, $b=0.25\lambda$, $a_1=5.5\lambda$, and $\rho_2=6\lambda$. Compute the directivity using (12-41) and (12-42c). Compare the answers.

SOLUTION
For this horn

$$u=\frac{1}{\sqrt{2}}\left(\frac{\sqrt{6}}{5.5}+\frac{5.5}{\sqrt{6}}\right)=1.9$$

$$v=\frac{1}{\sqrt{2}}\left(\frac{\sqrt{6}}{5.5}-\frac{5.5}{\sqrt{6}}\right)=-1.273$$

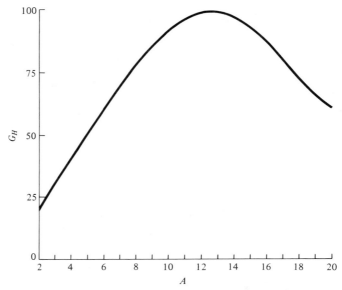

Figure 12.17 G_H as a function of A. (SOURCE: Adopted from data by E. H. Braun, "Some Data for the Design of Electromagnetic Horns," *IRE Trans. Antennas Propag.*, vol. AP-4, No. 1, January 1956. © (1956) IEEE)

Therefore (from Appendix IV)

$$C(1.9) = 0.394$$
$$C(-1.273) = -C(1.273) = -0.659$$
$$S(1.9) = 0.373$$
$$S(-1.273) = -S(1.273) = -0.669$$

Using (12-41)

$$D_H = \frac{4\pi(0.25)6}{5.5}\left[(0.394+0.659)^2 + (0.373+0.669)^2\right]$$
$$D_H = 7.52 = 8.763 \text{ dB}$$

To compute the directivity using (12-42c), the following parameters are computed:

$$\rho_h = \lambda\sqrt{(6)^2 + (5.5/2)^2} = 6.6\lambda$$
$$\sqrt{\frac{50}{\rho_h/\lambda}} = \sqrt{\frac{50}{6.6}} = 2.7524$$
$$A = 5.5(2.7524) = 15.14$$

For $A = 15.14$, $G_H = 91.8$ from Figure 12.17. Thus, using (12-42c)

$$D_H = \frac{0.25(91.8)}{2.7624} = 8.338 = 9.21 \text{ dB}$$

Although there is a good agreement between the results of (12-41) and (12-42c), they do not compare as well as those of Example 12.3.

12.4 PYRAMIDAL HORN

The most widely used horn is the one which is flared in both directions, as shown in Figure 12.18. It is widely referred to as a pyramidal horn, and its radiation characteristics are essentially a combination of the E- and H-plane sectoral horns.

12.4.1 Aperture Fields, Equivalent, and Radiated Fields

To simplify the analysis and to maintain a modeling that leads to computations that have been shown to correlate well with experimental data, the tangential components of the E- and H-fields over the aperture of the horn are approximated by

$$E_y'(x', y') = E_0 \cos\left(\frac{\pi}{a_1} x'\right) e^{-j[k(x'^2/\rho_2 + y'^2/\rho_1)/2]} \tag{12-43a}$$

$$H_x'(x', y') = -\frac{E_0}{\eta} \cos\left(\frac{\pi}{a_1} x'\right) e^{-j[k(x'^2/\rho_2 + y'^2/\rho_1)/2]} \tag{12-43b}$$

and the equivalent current densities by

$$J_y(x', y') = -\frac{E_0}{\eta} \cos\left(\frac{\pi}{a_1} x'\right) e^{-j[k(x'^2/\rho_2 + y'^2/\rho_1)/2]} \tag{12-44a}$$

$$M_x(x', y') = E_0 \cos\left(\frac{\pi}{a_1} x'\right) e^{-j[k(x'^2/\rho_2 + y'^2/\rho_1)/2]} \tag{12-44b}$$

The above expressions contain a cosinusoidal amplitude distribution in the x' direction and quadratic phase variations in both the x' and y' directions, similar to those of the sectoral E- and H-plane horns.

The N_θ, N_ϕ, L_θ and L_ϕ can now be formulated as before, and it can be shown that they are given by

$$N_\theta = -\frac{E_0}{\eta} \cos\theta \sin\phi I_1 I_2 \tag{12-45a}$$

$$N_\phi = -\frac{E_0}{\eta} \cos\phi I_1 I_2 \tag{12-45b}$$

$$L_\theta = E_0 \cos\theta \cos\phi I_1 I_2 \tag{12-45c}$$

$$L_\phi = -E_0 \sin\phi I_1 I_2 \tag{12-45d}$$

where

$$I_1 = \int_{-a_1}^{+a_1/2} \cos\left(\frac{\pi}{a} x'\right) e^{-jk[x'^2/(2\rho_1) - x'\sin\theta\cos\phi]} \, dx' \tag{12-45e}$$

$$I_2 = \int_{-b_1/2}^{+b_1/2} e^{-jk[y'^2/(2\rho_1) - y'\sin\theta\sin\phi]} \, dy' \tag{12-45f}$$

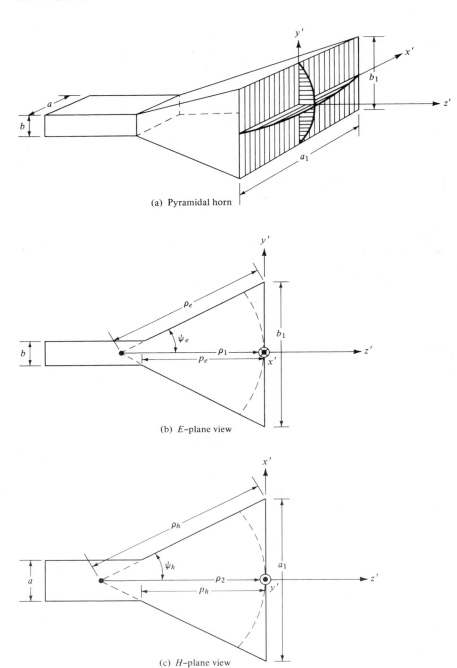

(a) Pyramidal horn

(b) E-plane view

(c) H-plane view

Figure 12.18 Pyramidal horn and coordinate system.

Using (12-23b), (12-25), (12-26), and (12-27), Equation (12-45e) can be expressed as

$$I_1 = \frac{1}{2}\sqrt{\frac{\pi\rho_2}{k}} \left(e^{j(k_x'^2\rho_2/2k)}\{[C(t_2') - C(t_1')] - j[S(t_2') - S(t_1')]\} \right.$$
$$\left. + e^{j(k_x''^2\rho_2/2k)}\{[C(t_2'') - C(t_1'')] - j[S(t_2'') - S(t_1'')]\} \right)$$

(12-46)

where t_1', t_2', k_x', t_1'', t_2'', and k_x'' are given by (12-26a)–(12-26c) and (12-27a)–(12-27c). Similarly, using (12-5)–(12-8d), I_2 of (12-45f) can be written as

$$I_2 = \sqrt{\frac{\pi\rho_1}{k}} \, e^{j(k_y^2\rho_1/2k)}\{[C(t_2) - C(t_1)] - j[S(t_2) - S(t_1)]\}$$

(12-47)

where k_y, t_1, and t_2 are given by (12-5a), (12-8a), and (12-8b).

Combining (12-45a)–(12-45d), the far-zone **E**- and **H**-field components of (11-10a)–(11-10c) reduce to

$$E_r = 0$$

(12-48a)

$$E_\theta = -j\frac{ke^{jkr}}{4\pi r}\left[L_\phi + \eta N_\theta\right]$$
$$= j\frac{kE_0 e^{-jkr}}{4\pi r}\left[\sin\phi(1 + \cos\theta)I_1 I_2\right]$$

(12-48b)

$$E_\phi = +j\frac{ke^{-jkr}}{4\pi r}\left[L_\theta - \eta N_\phi\right]$$
$$= j\frac{kE_0 e^{-jkr}}{4\pi r}\left[\cos\phi(\cos\theta + 1)I_1 I_2\right]$$

(12-48c)

where I_1 and I_2 are given by (12-46) and (12-47), respectively.

The fields radiated by a pyramidal horn, as given by (12-48a)–(12-48c), are valid for all angles of observation. An examination of these equations reveals that the principal E-plane pattern ($\phi = \pi/2$) of a pyramidal horn, aside from a normalization factor, is identical to the E-plane pattern of an E-plane sectoral horn. Similarly the H-plane ($\phi = 0$) is identical to that of an H-plane sectoral horn. Therefore the pattern of a pyramidal horn is very narrow in both principal planes and, in fact, in all planes. This is illustrated in Figure 12.19. The corresponding E-plane pattern is shown in Figure 12.4 and the H-plane pattern in Figure 12.12.

To demonstrate that the maximum radiation for a pyramidal horn is not necessarily directed along its axis, the three-dimensional field pattern

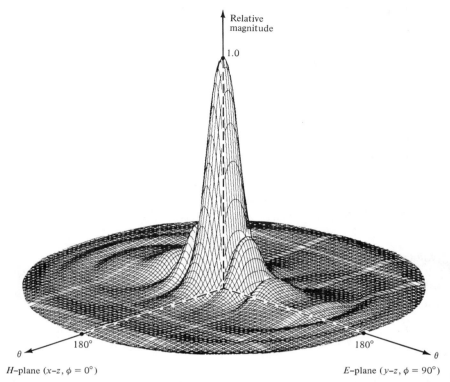

Relative
magnitude

1.0

θ ←——— 180°

H-plane $(x\text{-}z, \phi = 0°)$

180° ———→ θ

E-plane $(y\text{-}z, \phi = 90°)$

Figure 12.19   Three-dimensional field pattern of a pyramidal horn ($\rho_1 = \rho_2 = 6\lambda$, $a_1 = 5.5\lambda$, $b_1 = 2.75\lambda$, $a = 0.5\lambda$, $b = 0.25\lambda$).

for a horn with $\rho_1 = \rho_2 = 6\lambda$, $a_1 = 12\lambda$, $b_1 = 6\lambda$, $a = 0.50\lambda$ and $b = 0.25\lambda$ is displayed in Figure 12.20. The corresponding two-dimensional *E*- and *H*-plane patterns are shown in Figure 12.21. The maximum does not occur on axis because the phase error taper at the aperture is such that the rays emanating from the different parts of the aperture toward the axis are not in phase.

To physically construct a pyramidal horn, the dimension p_e of Figure 12.18(b) given by

$$p_e = (b_1 - b)\left[\left(\frac{\rho_e}{b_1}\right)^2 - \frac{1}{4}\right]^{1/2} \qquad (12\text{-}49a)$$

should be equal to the dimension p_h of Figure 12.18(c) given by

$$p_h = (a_1 - a)\left[\left(\frac{\rho_h}{a_1}\right)^2 - \frac{1}{4}\right]^{1/2} \qquad (12\text{-}49b)$$

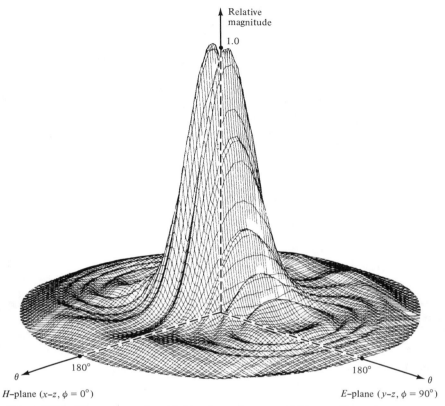

Figure 12.20 Three-dimensional field pattern of a pyramidal horn with maximum not on axis ($\rho_1 = \rho_2 = 6\lambda$, $a_1 = 12\lambda$, $b_1 = 6\lambda$, $a = 0.5\lambda$, $b = 0.25\lambda$).

The dimensions chosen for Figure 12.19 and 12.20 do satisfy these requirements. For the horn of Figure 12.19, $\rho_e = 6.1555\lambda$, $\rho_h = 6.6\lambda$, and $p_e = p_h = 5.4544\lambda$, whereas for that of Figure 12.20, $\rho_e = 6.7082\lambda$, $\rho_h = 8.4853\lambda$, and $p_e = p_h = 5.75\lambda$.

The fields of (12-48a)–(12-48c) provide accurate patterns for angular regions near the main lobe and its closest minor lobes. To accurately predict the field intensity of the pyramidal and other horns, especially in the minor lobes, diffraction techniques can be utilized [8]–[11]. These methods take into account diffractions that occur near the aperture edges of the horn. The diffraction contributions become more dominant in regions where the radiation of (12-48a)–(12-48c) is of very low intensity.

12.4.2 Directivity

As for the E- and H-plane sectoral horns, the directivity of the pyramidal configuration is vital to the antenna designer. The maximum radiation of the pyramidal horn is directed nearly along the z-axis ($\theta = 0$). It is a very simple exercise to show that $|E_\theta|_{\max}$, $|E_\phi|_{\max}$, and in turn $U_{\max}$ can be written, using (12-48b) and (12-48c), as

$$
|E_\theta|_{\max} = |E_0 \sin\phi| \frac{\sqrt{\rho_1 \rho_2}}{r} \left\{ [C(u) - C(v)]^2 + [S(u) - S(v)]^2 \right\}^{1/2}
$$

$$
\times \left\{ C^2\left(\frac{b_1}{\sqrt{2\lambda\rho_1}} \right) + S^2\left(\frac{b_1}{\sqrt{2\lambda\rho_1}} \right) \right\}^{1/2} \tag{12-50a}
$$

$$
|E_\phi|_{\max} = |E_0 \cos\phi| \frac{\sqrt{\rho_1 \rho_2}}{r} \left\{ [C(u) - C(v)]^2 + [S(u) - S(v)]^2 \right\}^{1/2}
$$

$$
\times \left\{ C^2\left(\frac{b_1}{\sqrt{2\lambda\rho_1}} \right) + S^2\left(\frac{b_1}{\sqrt{2\lambda\rho_1}} \right) \right\}^{1/2} \tag{12-50b}
$$

$$
U_{\max} = \frac{r^2}{2\eta} |\mathbf{E}|^2_{\max} = |E_0|^2 \frac{\rho_1 \rho_2}{2\eta} \left\{ [C(u) - C(v)]^2 + [S(u) - S(v)]^2 \right\}
$$

$$
\times \left\{ C^2\left(\frac{b_1}{\sqrt{2\lambda\rho_1}} \right) + S^2\left(\frac{b_1}{\sqrt{2\lambda\rho_1}} \right) \right\} \tag{12-50c}
$$

where u and v are defined by (12-41a) and (12-41b).

Since

$$
P_{\text{rad}} = |E_0|^2 \frac{a_1 b_1}{4\eta} \tag{12-51}
$$

the directivity for the pyramidal horn can be written as

$$
\boxed{
\begin{aligned}
D_p &= \frac{4\pi U_{\max}}{P_{\text{rad}}} = \frac{8\pi\rho_1\rho_2}{a_1 b_1} \left\{ [C(u) - C(v)]^2 + [S(u) - S(v)]^2 \right\} \\
&\times \left\{ C^2\left(\frac{b_1}{\sqrt{2\lambda\rho_1}} \right) + S^2\left(\frac{b_1}{\sqrt{2\lambda\rho_1}} \right) \right\}
\end{aligned}
}
$$

$$
\tag{12-52}
$$

which reduces to

$$
\boxed{D_p = \frac{\pi\lambda^2}{32\,ab} D_E D_H} \tag{12-52a}
$$

where D_E and D_H are the directivities of the E- and H-plane sectoral horns as given by (12-19) and (12-41), respectively. This is a well-known relationship and has been used extensively in the design of pyramidal horns.

The directivity (in dB) of a pyramidal horn, over isotropic, can also be approximated by [12]

$$
\boxed{D_0(\text{dB}) = 10\left[1.008 + \log_{10}\left(\frac{a_1 b_1}{\lambda^2} \right) \right] - (L_e + L_h)} \tag{12-53}
$$

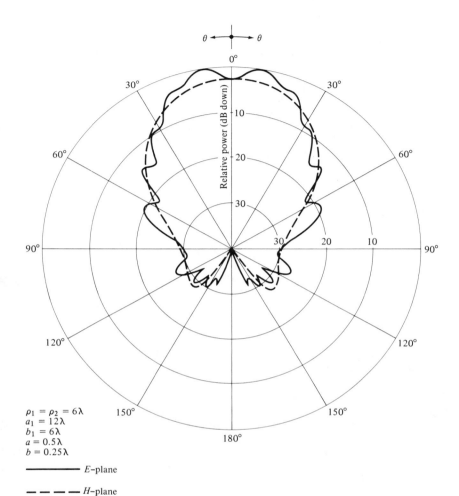

$\rho_1 = \rho_2 = 6\lambda$
$a_1 = 12\lambda$
$b_1 = 6\lambda$
$a = 0.5\lambda$
$b = 0.25\lambda$

—————— *E*-plane

— — — — *H*-plane

Figure 12.21   *E*- and *H*-plane amplitude patterns of a pyramidal horn with maximum not on-axis.

where L_e and L_h represent, respectively, the losses (in dB) due to phase errors in the *E*- and *H*-planes of the horn which are found plotted in Figure 12.22.

The directivity of a pyramidal horn can also be calculated by doing the following [7].

1. Calculate

$$A = \frac{a_1}{\lambda} \sqrt{\frac{50}{\rho_h/\lambda}} \qquad (12\text{-}54\text{a})$$

$$B = \frac{b_1}{\lambda} \sqrt{\frac{50}{\rho_e/\lambda}} \qquad (12\text{-}54\text{b})$$

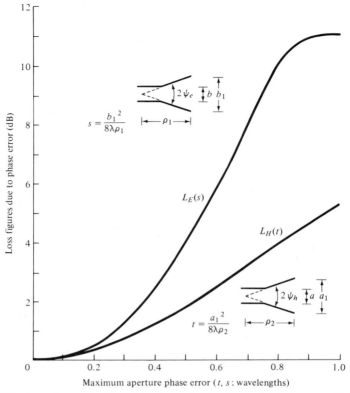

Figure 12.22   Loss figures for *E*- and *H*-planes due to phase errors. (SOURCE: W. C. Jakes, in H. Jasik (ed.), *Antenna Engineering Handbook*, McGraw-Hill, New York, 1961)

2. Using A and B, find G_H and G_E, respectively, from Figures 12.9 and 12.17. If the values of either A or B or both are smaller than 2, then calculate G_E and/or G_H by

$$G_E = \frac{32}{\pi} B \qquad (12\text{-}54c)$$

$$G_H = \frac{32}{\pi} A \qquad (12\text{-}54d)$$

3. Calculate D_p by using the values of G_E and G_H from Figures 12.9 and 12.17 or from (12-54c) and (12-54d). Thus

$$D_p = \frac{G_E G_H}{\dfrac{32}{\pi} \sqrt{\dfrac{50}{\rho_e/\lambda}} \sqrt{\dfrac{50}{\rho_h/\lambda}}} = \frac{G_E G_H}{10.1859 \sqrt{\dfrac{50}{\rho_e/\lambda}} \sqrt{\dfrac{50}{\rho_h/\lambda}}}$$

$$= \frac{\lambda^2 \pi}{32 ab} D_E D_H \qquad (12\text{-}54e)$$

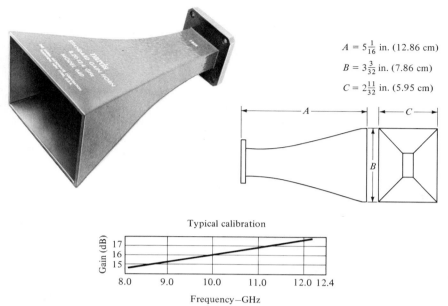

$A = 5\frac{1}{16}$ in. (12.86 cm)

$B = 3\frac{3}{32}$ in. (7.86 cm)

$C = 2\frac{11}{32}$ in. (5.95 cm)

Typical calibration

Figure 12.23   Typical standard gain X-band (8.2–12.4 GHz) pyramidal horn and its gain characteristics (courtesy of The NARDA Microwave Corporation).

where D_E and D_H are, respectively, the directivities of (12-20c) and (12-42c). This is the actual directivity of the horn. The above procedure has led to results accurate to within 0.01 dB for a horn with $\rho_e = \rho_h = 50\lambda$.

A typical X-band (8.2–12.4 GHz) horn is that shown in Figure 12.23. It is a lightweight precision horn antenna, which is usually cast of aluminum, and it can be used as a

1. standard for calibrating other antennas
2. feed for reflectors and lenses
3. pickup horn for sampling power
4. receiving and/or transmitting antenna

It possesses an exponential taper, and its dimensions and typical gain characteristics are indicated in the figure. The half-power beamwidth in both the E- and H-planes is about 28° while the side lobes in the E- and H-planes are, respectively, about 13 and 20 dB down.

Example 12.5

A pyramidal horn has dimensions of $\rho_1 = \rho_2 = 6\lambda$, $a_1 = 5.5\lambda$, $b_1 = 2.75\lambda$, $a = 0.5\lambda$, and $b = 0.25\lambda$.

(a) Check to see if such a horn can be constructed physically.
(b) Compute the directivity using (12-52a), (12-53), and (12-54e).

SOLUTION
From Example 12.3 and 12.4.

$$\rho_e = 6.1555\lambda$$
$$\rho_h = 6.6\lambda$$

Thus

$$p_e = (2.75 - 0.25)\lambda\sqrt{\left(\frac{6.1555}{2.75}\right)^2 - \frac{1}{4}} = 5.454\lambda$$

$$p_h = (5.5 - 0.5)\lambda\sqrt{\left(\frac{6}{5.5}\right)^2 - \frac{1}{4}} = 5.454\lambda$$

Therefore the horn can be constructed physically.

The directivity can be computed by utilizing the results of Examples 12.3 and 12.4. Using (12-52a) with the values of D_E and D_H computed using, respectively, (12-19) and (12-41) gives

$$D_p = \frac{\pi\lambda^2}{32ab} D_E D_H = \frac{\pi}{32(0.5)(0.25)}(12.79)(7.52) = 75.54 = 18.78 \text{ dB}$$

Utilizing the values of D_E and D_H computed using, respectively, (12-20c) and (12-42c), the directivity of (12-54e) is equal to

$$D_p = \frac{\pi\lambda^2}{32ab} D_E D_H = \frac{\pi}{32(0.5)0.25}(12.89)(8.338) = 84.41 = 19.26 \text{ dB}$$

For this horn

$$s = \frac{b_1^2}{8\lambda\rho_2} = \frac{(2.75)^2}{8(6)} = 0.1575$$

$$t = \frac{a_1^2}{8\lambda\rho_2} = \frac{(5.5)^2}{8(6)} = 0.63$$

For these values of s and t

$$L_E = 0.20 \text{ dB}$$
$$L_H = 2.75 \text{ dB}$$

from Figure 12.22. Using (12-53)

$$D_0 = 10\{1.008 + \log_{10}[5.5(2.75)]\} - (0.20 + 2.75) = 18.93 \text{ dB}$$

The agreement is best between the directivities of (12-52a) and (12-53).

12.4.3 Design Procedure

The pyramidal horn is widely used as a standard to make gain measurements of other antennas (see Section 15.4, Chapter 15), and as such it is often referred to as a *standard gain horn*. To design a pyramidal horn, one usually knows the desired gain G_0 and the dimensions a, b of the rectangular feed waveguide. The objective of the design is to determine the remaining dimensions ($a_1, b_1, \rho_e, \rho_h, p_e$ and p_h) that will lead to an optimum gain. The procedure that follows can be used to accomplish this [12].

The design equations are derived by first selecting values of b_1 and a_1 that lead, respectively, to optimum directivities for the E- and H-plane sectoral horns using (12-19a) and (12-41c). Since the overall efficiency (including both the antenna and aperture efficiencies) of a horn antenna is about 50% [12], the gain of the antenna can be related to its physical area. Thus it can be written using (11-39c), (11-40), (12-19a), and (12-41c) as

$$G_0 = \frac{1}{2}\frac{4\pi}{\lambda^2}(a_1 b_1) = \frac{2\pi}{\lambda^2}\sqrt{3\lambda\rho_2}\sqrt{2\lambda\rho_1} \simeq \frac{2\pi}{\lambda^2}\sqrt{3\lambda p_h}\sqrt{2\lambda p_e} \tag{12-55}$$

since for long horns $\rho_2 \simeq p_h$ and $\rho_1 \simeq p_e$. For a pyramidal horn to be physically realizable, p_e and p_h of (12-49a) and (12-49b) must be equal. Using this equality, it can be shown that (12-55) reduces to

$$\left(\sqrt{2\chi} - \frac{b}{\lambda}\right)^2 (2\chi - 1) = \left(\frac{G_0}{2\pi}\sqrt{\frac{3}{2\pi}}\frac{1}{\sqrt{\chi}} - \frac{a}{\lambda}\right)^2\left(\frac{G_0^2}{6\pi^3}\frac{1}{\chi} - 1\right) \tag{12-56}$$

where

$$\frac{\rho_e}{\lambda} = \chi \tag{12-56a}$$

$$\frac{\rho_h}{\lambda} = \frac{G_0^2}{8\pi^3}\left(\frac{1}{\chi}\right) \tag{12-56b}$$

Equation (12-56) is the horn design equation.

1. As a first step of the design, find the value of χ which satisfies (12-56) for a desired gain G_0 (dimensionless). Use an iterative technique and begin with a trial value of

$$\chi\,(\text{trial}) = \chi_1 = \frac{G_0}{2\pi\sqrt{2\pi}} \tag{12-57}$$

2. Once the correct χ has been found, determine ρ_e and ρ_h using (12-56a) and (12-56b), respectively.
3. Find the corresponding values of a_1 and b_1 using (12-19a) and (12-41c) or

$$a_1 = \sqrt{3\lambda\rho_2} \simeq \sqrt{3\lambda p_h} = \frac{G_0}{2\pi}\sqrt{\frac{3}{2\pi\chi}}\lambda \tag{12-58a}$$

$$b_1 = \sqrt{2\lambda\rho_1} \simeq \sqrt{2\lambda p_e} = \sqrt{2\chi}\lambda \tag{12-58b}$$

4. The values of p_e and p_h can also be found using (12-19a) and (12-41c).

Example 12.6

Design an optimum gain X-band (8.2–12.4 GHz) pyramidal horn so that its gain (above isotropic) at $f = 11$ GHz is 22.6 dB. The horn is fed by a WR 90 rectangular waveguide with inner dimensions of $a = 0.9$ in. (2.286 cm) and $b = 0.4$ in. (1.016 cm).

SOLUTION
Convert the gain G_0 from dB to a dimensionless quantity. Thus

$$G_0 \text{ (dB)} = 22.6 = 10 \log_{10} G_0 \Rightarrow G_0 = 10^{2.26} = 181.97$$

Since $f = 11 = $ GHz, $\lambda = 2.7273$ cm and

$a = 0.8382\lambda$
$b = 0.3725\lambda$

1. The initial value of χ is taken, using (12-57), as

$$\chi_1 = \frac{181.97}{2\pi\sqrt{2\pi}} = 11.5539$$

which does not satisfy (12-56) for the desired design specifications. After a few iterations, a more accurate value is $\chi = 11.1157$.

2. Using (12-56a) and (12-56b)

$$\rho_e = 11.1157\lambda = 30.316 \text{ cm} = 11.935 \text{ in.}$$
$$\rho_h = 12.0094\lambda = 32.753 \text{ cm} = 12.895 \text{ in.}$$

3. The corresponding values of a_1 and b_1 are

$$a_1 = 6.002\lambda = 16.370 \text{ cm} = 6.445 \text{ in.}$$
$$b_1 = 4.715\lambda = 12.859 \text{ cm} = 5.063 \text{ in.}$$

4. The values of p_e and p_h are equal to

$$p_e = p_h = 10.005\lambda = 27.286 \text{ cm} = 10.743 \text{ in.}$$

The derived design parameters agree closely with those of a commercial gain horn available in the market.

As a check, the gain of the designed horn was computed using (12-52a) and (12-53), assuming an antenna efficiency e_t of 100%, and (12-55). The values were

$G_0 \simeq D_0 = 22.4$ dB   for (12-52a)
$G_0 \simeq D_0 = 22.1$ dB   for (12-53)
$G_0 = 22.5$ dB   for (12-55)

All three computed values agree closely with the designed value of 22.6 dB.

12.5 CONICAL HORN

Another very practical microwave antenna is the conical horn shown in Figure 12.24. While the pyramidal, E-, and H-plane sectoral horns are usually fed by a rectangular waveguide, the feed of a conical horn is often a circular waveguide.

The first rigorous treatment of the fields radiated by a conical horn is that of Schorr and Beck [13]. The modes within the horn are found by introducing a spherical coordinate system and are in terms of spherical Bessel functions and Legendre polynomials. The analysis is too involved and will not be attempted here. However data, in the form of curves [14], will be presented which give a qualitative description of the performance of a conical horn.

Referring to Figure 12.25, it is apparent that the behavior of a conical horn is similar to that of a pyramidal or a sectoral horn. As the flare angle increases, the directivity for a given length horn increases until it reaches a maximum beyond which it begins to decrease. The decrease is a result of the dominance of the quadratic phase error at the aperture. In the same figure, an optimum directivity line is indicated.

The results of Figure 12.25 behave as those of Figures 12.8 and 12.16. When the horn aperture (d_m) is held constant and its length (L) is allowed to vary, the maximum directivity is obtained when the flare angle is zero ($\psi_c = 0$ or $L = \infty$). This is equivalent to a circular waveguide of diameter d_m. As for the pyramidal and sectoral horns, a lens is usually placed at the aperture of the conical horn to compensate for its quadratic phase error. The result is a narrower pattern as its flare increases.

The directivity (in dB) of a conical horn, with an aperture efficiency of ε_{ap} and aperture circumference C, can be computed using

$$D_c\,(\text{dB}) = 10\log_{10}\left[\varepsilon_{ap}\frac{4\pi}{\lambda^2}(\pi a^2)\right] = 10\log_{10}\left(\frac{C}{\lambda}\right)^2 - L(s) \qquad (12\text{-}59)$$

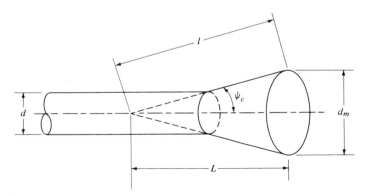

Figure 12.24 Geometry of conical horn.

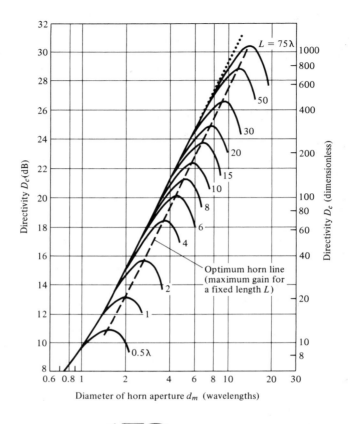

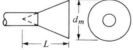

Figure 12.25 Directivity of a conical horn as a function of aperture diameter and for different axial horn lengths. (SOURCE: A. P. King, "The Radiation Characteristics of Conical Horn Antennas," *Proc. IRE*, vol. 38, pp. 249–251, March 1950. © (1950) IEEE)

where

$$L(s) = -10\log_{10}(\varepsilon_{ap})$$ (12-59a)

The first term in (12-59) represents the directivity of a uniform circular aperture whereas the second term, represented by (12-59a), is a correction figure to account for the loss in directivity due to the aperture efficiency. Usually the term in (12-59a) is referred to as *loss figure* which can be computed (in decibels) using [12]

$$L(s) \simeq (0.8 - 1.71s + 26.25s^2 - 17.79s^3)$$ (12-59b)

where s is the maximum phase deviation (in number of wavelengths), and it is given by

$$s = \frac{d_m^2}{8\lambda l} \tag{12-59c}$$

The directivity of a conical horn is optimum when its diameter is equal to

$$\boxed{d_m \simeq \sqrt{3l\lambda}} \tag{12-60}$$

which corresponds to a maximum aperture phase deviation of $s = 3/8$ (wavelengths) and a loss figure of about 2.9 dB (or an aperture efficiency of about 51%).

12.6 CORRUGATED HORN

The large emphasis placed on horn antenna research in the 1960s was inspired by the need to reduce spillover efficiency and cross-polarization losses and increase aperture efficiencies of large reflectors used in radio astronomy and satellite communications. In the 1970s high-efficiency and rotationally symmetric antennas were needed in microwave radiometry. Using conventional feeds, aperture efficiencies of 50–60% were obtained. However, efficiencies of the order of 75–80% can be obtained with improved feed systems utilizing corrugated horns.

The aperture techniques introduced in Chapter 11 can be used to compute the pattern of a horn antenna and would yield accurate results only around the main lobe and the first few minor lobes. The antenna pattern structure in the back lobe region is strongly influenced by diffractions from the edges, especially from those that are perpendicular to the E-field at the horn aperture. The diffractions lead to undesirable radiation not only in the back lobes but also in the main lobe and in the minor lobes. However, they dominate only in low-intensity regions.

In 1964 Kay [15] realized that grooves on the walls of a horn antenna would present the same boundary conditions to all polarizations and would taper the field distribution at the aperture in all the planes. The creation of the same boundary conditions on all four walls would eliminate the spurious diffractions at the edges of the aperture. For a square aperture, this would lead to an almost rotationally symmetric pattern with equal E- and H-plane beamwidths. A *corrugated (grooved)* pyramidal horn, with corrugations in the E-plane walls, is shown in Figure 12.26(a) with a side view in Figure 12.26(b). Since diffractions at the edges of the aperture in the H-plane are minimal, corrugations are usually not placed on the walls of that plane. Corrugations can also be placed in a conical horn forming a *conical corrugated* horn. However, instead of the corrugations being formed as shown in Figure 12.27(a), practically it is much easier to machine them to have the profile shown in Figure 12.27(b).

To form a very effective corrugated surface, it usually requires 10 or more slots (corrugations) per wavelength [16]. To simplify the analysis of an

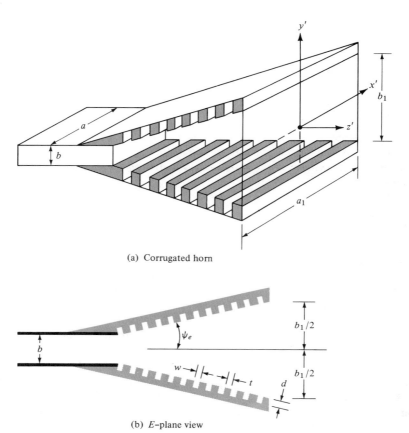

(a) Corrugated horn

(b) *E*-plane view

Figure 12.26 Pyramidal horn with corrugations in the *E*-plane.

infinite corrugated surface, the following assumptions are usually required:

1. The teeth of the corrugations are vanishingly thin.
2. Reflections from the base of the slot are only those of a TEM mode.

The second assumption is satisfied provided the width of the corrugation (w) is small compared to the free-space wavelength (λ_0) and the slot depth (d) (usually $w < \lambda_0/10$). For a corrugated surface satisfying the above assumptions, its approximate surface reactance is given by [17]

$$X = \frac{w}{w+t} \sqrt{\frac{\mu_0}{\varepsilon_0}} \tan(k_0 d) \qquad \text{(12-61)}$$

when

$$\frac{w}{w+t} \simeq 1 \qquad \text{(12-61a)}$$

which can be satisfied provided $t \leq w/10$.

(a) Corrugations perpendicular to surface

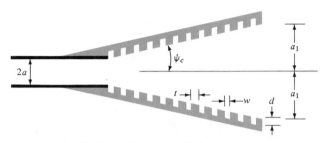

(b) Corrugations perpendicular to axis

Figure 12.27 Side view profiles of conical corrugated horns.

The surface reactance of a corrugated surface, used on the walls of a horn, must be capacitive in order for the surface to force to zero the tangential magnetic field parallel to the edge at the wall. Thus the surface will not support surface waves, will prevent illumination of the E-plane edges, and will diminish diffractions. This can be accomplished, according to (12-61), if $\lambda_0/4 < d < \lambda_0/2$ or more generally when $(2n+1)\lambda_0/4 < d < (n+1)\lambda_0/2$. Even though the cutoff depth is also a function of the slot width w, its influence is negligible if $w < \lambda_0/10$ and $\lambda_0/4 < d < \lambda_0/2$.

To study the performance of a corrugated surface, an analytical model was developed and parametric studies were performed [18]. Although the details are numerous, only the results will be presented here. In Figure 12.28(a) a corrugated surface is sketched and in Figure 12.28(b) its corresponding uncorrugated counterpart is shown.

For a free-space wavelength of $\lambda_0 = 8$ cm, the following have been plotted for point B in Figure 12.28(a) relative to point A in Figure 12.28(b):

1. In Figure 12.29(a) the surface current decay at B relative to that at $A[J_s(B)/J_s(A)]$ as a function of corrugation number (for 20 total corrugations) due to energy being forced away from the corrugations. As expected, no decay occurs for $d = 0.5\lambda_0$ and the most rapid decay is obtained for $d = 0.25\lambda_0$.

2. In Figure 12.29(b) the surface current decay at B relative to that in $A[J_s(B)/J_s(A)]$ as a function of the distance z from the onset of the

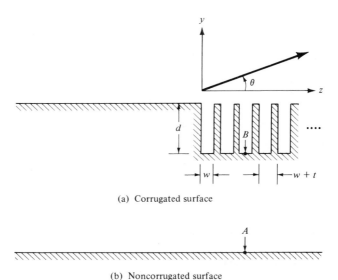

(a) Corrugated surface

(b) Noncorrugated surface

Figure 12.28 Geometry of corrugated and plane surfaces. (SOURCE: C. A. Mentzer and L. Peters, Jr., "Properties of Cutoff Corrugated Surfaces for Corrugated Horn Design," *IEEE Trans. Antennas Propag.*, vol. AP-22, No. 2, March 1974. © (1974) IEEE)

corrugations for four and eight corrugations per wavelength. The results indicate an almost independence of current decay as a function of corrugation density for the cases considered.

3. In Figure 12.29(c) the surface current decay at B relative to that in $A[J_s(B)/J_s(A)]$ as a function of the distance z from the onset of the corrugations for $w/(w+t)$ ratios ranging from 0.5 to 0.9. For $z < 4$ cm $= \lambda_0/2$, thinner corrugations [larger $w/(w+t)$ ratios] exhibit larger rates of decay. Beyond that point, the rate of decay is approximately constant. This would indicate that in a practical design thinner corrugations can be used at the onset followed by thicker ones, which are easier to construct.

The effect of the corrugations on the walls of a horn is to modify the electric field distribution in the E-plane from uniform (at the waveguide-horn junction) to cosine (at the aperture). Through measurements, it has been shown that the transition from uniform to cosine distribution takes place almost at the onset of the corrugations. For a horn of about 45 corrugations, the cosine distribution has been established by the fifth corrugation (from the onset) and the spherical phase front by the fifteenth [19]. The E- and H-plane amplitude and phase distributions at the aperture of the horn with 45 corrugations are shown in Figures 12.30(a) and (b). It is clear that the cosine distribution is well established.

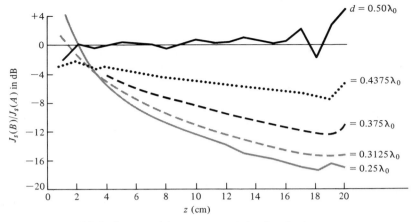

(a) Surface current decay on corrugated surface due to energy forced away from corrugations.

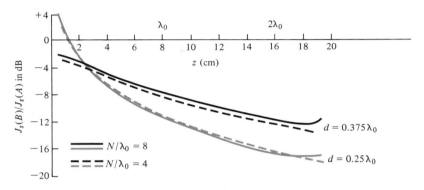

(b) Surface current decay on corrugations as a function of corrugation density.

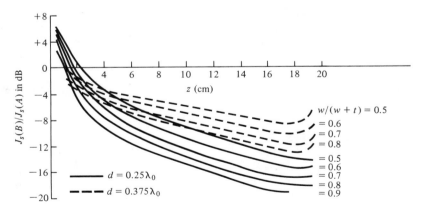

(c) Surface current decay on corrugations as a function of corrugation shape.

Figure 12.29 Surface current decays on corrugated surface. (SOURCE: C. A. Mentzer and L. Peters, Jr., "Properties of Cutoff Corrugated Surfaces for Corrugated Horn Design," *IEEE Trans. Antennas Propag.*, vol. AP-22, No. 2, March 1974. © (1974) IEEE)

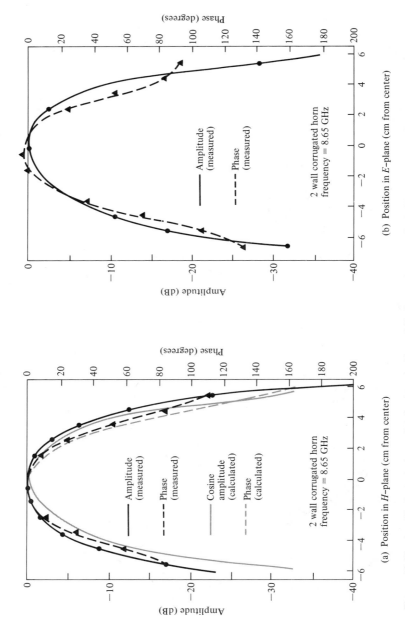

(b) Position in *E*-plane (cm from center)

(a) Position in *H*-plane (cm from center)

Figure 12.30 Amplitude and phase distributions in *H*- and *E*-planes. (SOURCE: C. A. Mentzer and L. Peters, Jr., "Pattern Analysis of Corrugated Horn Antennas," *IEEE Trans. Antennas Propag.*, vol. AP-24, No. 3, May 1976. © (1976) IEEE)

Referring to Figure 12.26(a), the field distribution at the aperture can be written as

$$E_y'(x', y') = E_0 \cos\left(\frac{\pi}{a_1}x'\right)\cos\left(\frac{\pi}{b_1}y'\right)e^{-j[k(x'^2/\rho_2 + y'^2/\rho_1)/2]} \qquad (12\text{-}62a)$$

$$H_x'(x', y') = -\frac{E_0}{\eta}\cos\left(\frac{\pi}{a_1}x'\right)\cos\left(\frac{\pi}{b_1}y'\right)e^{-j[k(x'^2/\rho_2 + y'^2/\rho_1)/2]} \qquad (12\text{-}62b)$$

corresponding to (12-43a) and (12-43b) of the uncorrugated pyramidal horn. Using the above distributions, the fields radiated by the horn can be computed in a manner analogous to that of the pyramidal horn of Section 12.4. Patterns have been computed and compare very well with measurements [19].

In Figure 12.31(a) the measured E-plane patterns of an uncorrugated square pyramidal horn (*referred to as the control horn*) and a corrugated square pyramidal horn are shown. The aperture size on each side was 3.5 in. ($2.96\lambda_0$ at 10 GHz) and the total flare angle in each plane was 50°. It is evident that the levels of the minor lobes and back lobes are much lower for the corrugated horn than those of the control horn. However the corrugated horn also exhibits a wider main beam for small angles; thus a larger 3-dB beamwidth (HPBW) but a lower 10-dB beamwidth. This is attributed to the absence of the diffracted fields from the edges of the corrugated horn which, for nearly on-axis observations, add to the direct wave contribution because of their in-phase relationship. The fact that the on-axis far-fields of the direct and diffracted fields are nearly in-phase is also evident from the pronounced on-axis maximum of the control horn. The E- and H-plane patterns of the corrugated horn are almost identical to those of Figure 12.31(a) over the frequency range from 8 to 14 GHz. These suggest that the main beam in the E-plane can be obtained from known H-plane patterns of horn antennas.

In Figure 12.31(b) the measured E-plane patterns of larger control and corrugated square pyramidal horns, having an aperture of 9.7 in. on each side ($8.2\lambda_0$ at 10 GHz) and included angles of 34° and 31° in the E- and H-planes, are shown. For this geometry, the pattern of the corrugated horn is narrower and its minor and back lobes are much lower than those of the corresponding control horn. The saddle formed on the main lobe of the control horn is attributed to the out-of-phase relations between the direct and diffracted rays. The diffracted rays are nearly absent from the corrugated horn and the minimum on-axis field is eliminated. The control horn is a thick-edged horn which has the same interior dimensions as the corrugated horn. The H-plane pattern of the corrugated horn is almost identical to the H-plane pattern of the corresponding control horn.

In Figures 12.31(c) and 12.31(d) the back lobe level and the 3-dB beamwidth for the smaller size control and corrugated horns, whose E-plane patterns are shown in Figure 12.31(a), are plotted as a function of frequency. All the observations made previously for that horn are well evident in these figures.

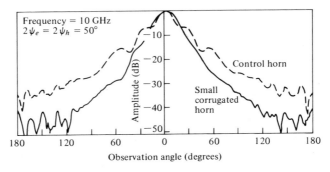

(a) Measured patterns of $2.96\lambda_0 \times 2.96\lambda_0$ pyramidal horns (E-plane)

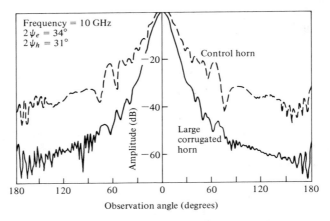

(b) Measured patterns of $8.2\lambda_0 \times 8.2\lambda_0$ pyramidal horns (E-plane)

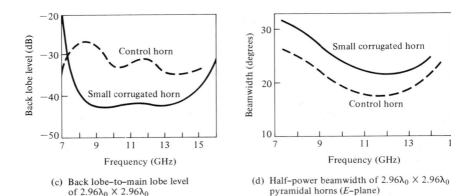

(c) Back lobe-to-main lobe level of $2.96\lambda_0 \times 2.96\lambda_0$ pyramidal horns (E-plane)

(d) Half-power beamwidth of $2.96\lambda_0 \times 2.96\lambda_0$ pyramidal horns (E-plane)

Figure 12.31   Radiation characteristics of small and large corrugated and uncorrugated (control) horns. (SOURCE: R. E. Lawrie and L. Peters, Jr., "Modifications of Horn Antennas for Low Side Lobe Levels," *IEEE Trans. Antennas Propag.*, vol. AP-14, No. 5, September 1966. © (1966) IEEE)

The presence of the corrugations, especially near the waveguide-horn junction, can affect the impedance and VSWR of the antenna. The usual practice is to begin the corrugations at a small distance away from the junction. This leads to low VSWR's over a broad band. Previously it was indicated that the width w of the corrugations must be small (usually $w < \lambda_0/10$) to approximate a corrugated surface. This would cause corona and other breakdown phenomena. However the large corrugated horn, whose E-plane pattern is shown in Figure 12.31(b), has been used in a system whose peak power was 20 kW at 10 GHz with no evidence of any breakdown phenomena.

12.7 PHASE CENTER

Each of the far-zone field components radiated by an antenna can be written, in general, as

$$\mathbf{E}_u = \hat{u} E(\theta, \phi) e^{j\psi(\theta,\phi)} \frac{e^{-jkr}}{r} \qquad (12\text{-}63)$$

where $\hat{u}$ is a unit vector. $E(\theta, \phi)$ and $\psi(\theta, \phi)$ represent, respectively, the (θ, ϕ) variations of the amplitude and phase.

In navigation, tracking, homing, landing, and other aircraft and aerospace systems, it is usually desirable to assign to the antenna a reference point such that for a given frequency, $\psi(\theta, \phi)$ of (12-63) is independent of θ and ϕ [i.e., $\psi(\theta, \phi) = $ constant]. The reference point that makes $\psi(\theta, \phi)$ independent of θ and ϕ is known as the *phase center* of the antenna [20]–[23]. When referenced to the phase center, the fields radiated by the antenna are spherical waves with ideal spherical wavefronts or equiphase surfaces.

For practical antennas such as arrays, reflectors, and others, a single phase center valid for all values of θ and ϕ does not exist. However, in many antenna systems a reference point can be found such that $\psi(\theta, \phi) = $ constant over most of the angular space, especially over the main lobe.

The need for the phase center can best be explained by examining the radiation characteristics of a paraboloidal reflector (parabola of revolution). Plane waves incident on a paraboloidal reflector focus at a single point which is known as the *focal point*. Conversely, spherical waves emanating from the focal point are reflected by the paraboloidal surface and form plane waves. Thus in the receiving mode all the energy is collected at a single point. In the transmitting mode, ideal plane waves are formed if the radiated waves have spherical wavefronts and emanate from a single point.

In practice, no antenna is a point source with ideal spherical equiphases. However many of them contain a point from which their radiation, over most of the angular space, seems to have spherical wave fronts. When such an antenna is used as a feed for a reflector, its phase center must be placed at the focal point.

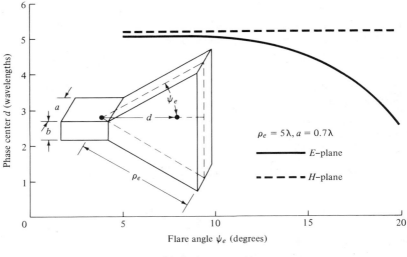

(a) E-plane sectoral horn

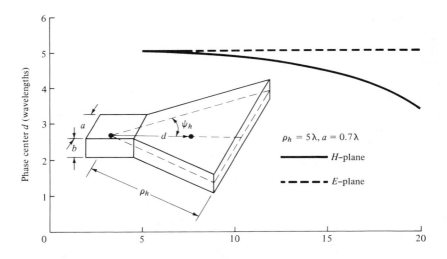

Figure 12.32　Phase center location, as a function of flare angle, for E- and H-plane sectoral horns. (SOURCE: Y. Y. Hu, "A Method of Determining Phase Centers and Its Applications to Electromagnetic Horns," *Journal of Franklin Institute*, vol. 271, pp. 31–39, January 1961)

The analytical formulations for locating the phase center of an antenna are usually very laborious and exist only for a limited number of configurations [20], [21], [23]. Experimental techniques [22], [24] are available to locate the phase center of an antenna.

The horn is a microwave antenna which is widely used as a feed for reflectors [25]. To perform as an efficient feed for reflectors, it is imperative that its phase center is known and it is located at the focal point of the reflector. Instead of presenting analytical formulations for the phase center of a horn, graphical data will be included to illustrate typical phase centers.

Usually the phase center of a horn is not located at its mouth (throat) or at its aperture but between its imaginary apex point and its aperture. The exact location depends on the dimensions of the horn, especially on its flare angle. For large flare angles, the phase center is closer to the apex. As the flare angle of the horn becomes smaller, the phase center moves toward the aperture of the horn.

Computed phase centers for an E-plane and an H-plane sectoral horn are displayed in Figures 12.32(a) and (b). It is apparent that for small flare angles, the E- and H-plane phase centers are identical. Although each specific design has its own phase center, the data of Figures 12.32(a) and (b) are typical. If the E- and H-phase centers of a pyramidal horn are not identical, its phase center can be taken to be the average of the two. Phase center nomographs for conical horns are available [23].

References

1. A. W. Love, *Electromagnetic Horn Antennas*, IEEE Press, New York, 1976.
2. R. F. Harrington, *Time-Harmonic Electromagnetic Fields*, McGraw-Hill, New York, 1961, pp. 208–213.
3. S. Silver (ed.), *Microwave Antenna Theory and Design*, MIT Radiation Laboratory Series, vol. 12, McGraw-Hill, New York, 1949, pp. 349–376.
4. M. Abramowitz and I. A. Stegun (eds.), *Handbook of Mathematical Functions*, National Bureau of Standards, United States Dept. of Commerce, June 1964.
5. J. Boersma, "Computation of Fresnel Integrals," *Math. Comp.*, vol. 14, p. 380, 1960.
6. Y.-B. Cheng, "Analysis of Aircraft Antenna Radiation for Microwave Landing System Using Geometrical Theory of Diffraction," MSEE Thesis, Dept. of Electrical Engineering, West Virginia University, pp. 208–211.
7. E. H. Braun, "Some Data for the Design of Electromagnetic Horns," *IRE Trans. Antennas Propag.*, vol. AP-4, No. 1, pp. 29–31, Jan. 1956.
8. P. M. Russo, R. C. Rudduck, and L. Peters, Jr., "A Method for Computing E-Plane Patterns of Horn Antennas," *IEEE Trans. Antennas Propag.*, vol. AP-13, No. 2, pp. 219–224, March 1965.
9. J. S. Yu, R. C. Rudduck, and L. Peters, Jr., "Comprehensive Analysis for E-Plane of Horn Antennas by Edge Diffraction Theory," *IEEE Trans. Antennas Propag.*, vol. AP-14, No. 2, pp. 138–149, March 1966.
10. M. A. K. Hamid, "Diffraction by a Conical Horn," *IEEE Trans. Antennas Propag.*, vol. AP-16, No. 5, pp. 520–528, Sept. 1966.

11. M. S. Narasimhan and M. S. Shehadri, "GTD Analysis of the Radiation Patterns of Conical Horns," *IEEE Trans. Antenna Propag.*, vol. AP-26, No. 6, pp. 774–778, Nov. 1978.

12. W. C. Jakes, "Horn Antennas," in *Antenna Engineering Handbook*, H. Jasik (ed.), McGraw-Hill, New York, 1961, Chapter 10.

13. M. G. Schorr and F. J. Beck, Jr., "Electromagnetic Field of a Conical Horn," *J. Appl. Phys.*, vol. 21, pp. 795–801, August 1950.

14. A. P. King, "The Radiation Characteristics of Conical Horn Antennas," *Proc. IRE*, vol. 38, pp. 249–251, March 1950.

15. A. F. Kay, "The Scalar Feed," AFCRL Rep. 64-347, AD601609, March 1964.

16. R. E. Lawrie and L. Peters, Jr., "Modifications of Horn Antennas for Low Side Lobe Levels," *IEEE Trans. Antennas and Propag.*, vol. AP-14, pp. 605–610, Sept. 1966.

17. R. S. Elliot, "On the Theory of Corrugated Plane Surfaces," *IRE Trans. Antennas and Propag.*, vol. AP-12, pp. 71–81, April 1954.

18. C. A. Mentzer and L. Peters, Jr., "Properties of Cutoff Corrugated Surfaces for Corrugated Horn Design," *IEEE Trans. Antennas and Propag.*, vol. AP-22, pp. 191–196, March 1974.

19. C. A. Mentzer and L. Peters, Jr., "Pattern Analysis of Corrugated Horn Antennas," *IEEE Trans. Antennas and Propag.*, vol. AP-24, pp. 304–309, May 1976.

20. Y. Y. Hu, "A Method of Determining Phase Centers and Its Applications to Electromagnetic Horns," *Journal of the Franklin Institute*, vol. 271, pp. 31–39, Jan. 1961.

21. E. R. Nagelberg, "Fresnel Region Phase Centers of Circular Aperture Antennas," *IEEE Trans. Antennas Propag.*, vol. AP-13, No. 3, pp. 479–480, May 1965.

22. M. Teichman, "Precision Phase Center Measurements of Horn Antennas," *IEEE Trans. Antennas Propag.*, vol. AP-18, No. 5, pp. 689–690, Sept. 1970.

23. I. Ohtera and H. Ujiie, "Nomographs for Phase Centers of Conical Corrugated and TE_{11} Mode Horns," *IEEE Trans. Antennas Propag.*, vol. AP-23, No. 6, pp. 858–859, Nov. 1975.

24. J. D. Dyson, "Determination of the Phase Center and Phase Patterns of Antennas," in *Radio Antennas for Aircraft and Aerospace Vehicles*, W. T. Blackband (ed.), AGARD Conference Proceedings, No. 15, Slough, England, Technivision Services, 1967.

25. W. M. Truman and C. A. Balanis, "Optimum Design of Horn Feeds for Reflector Antennas," *IEEE Trans. Antennas Propag.*, vol. AP-22, No. 4, pp. 585–586, July 1974.

PROBLEMS

12.1. Derive (12-1a)–(12-1e) by treating the *E*-plane horn as a radial waveguide.

12.2. Design an *E*-plane horn such that the maximum phase difference between two points at the aperture, one at the center and the other at the edge, is 120°. Assuming that the maximum length along its wall (ρ_e), measured from the aperture to its apex, is 10λ, find the
(a) maximum total flare angle of the horn
(b) largest dimension of the horn at the aperture
(c) directivity of the horn (dimensionless and in dB)

(d) gain of the antenna (in dB) when the reflection coefficient within the waveguide feeding the horn is 0.2. Assume only mismatch losses. The waveguide feeding the horn has dimensions of 0.5λ and 0.25λ.

12.3. For an E-plane horn with $\rho_1=6\lambda$, $b_1=3.47\lambda$, and $a=0.5\lambda$,
   (a) compute (in dB) its pattern at $\theta=0°$, $10°$, and $20°$ using the results of Figure 12.6. Show all the steps for one angle.
   (b) compute its directivity using (12-19) and (12-20c). Compare the answers.

12.4. Repeat Problem 12.3 for $\rho_1=6\lambda$, $b_1=6\lambda$, and $a=0.5\lambda$.

12.5. For an E-plane sectoral horn, plot b_1 (in λ) versus ρ_1 (in λ) using (12-19a). Verify, using the data of Figure 12.8, that the maximum directivities occur when (12-19a) is satisfied.

12.6. For an E-plane sectoral horn with $\rho_1=20\lambda$, $a=0.5\lambda$
   (a) find its optimum aperture dimensions for maximum normalized directivity
   (b) compute the total flare angle of the horn
   (c) *compute* its directivity, using (12-19), and compare it with the graphical answer
   (d) find its half-power beamwidth (in degrees)
   (e) compute the directivity using (12-20c)

12.7. An E-plane horn is fed by an X-band WR 90 rectangular waveguide with inner dimensions of 0.9 in. (2.286 cm) and $b=0.4$ in. (1.016 cm). Design the horn so that its maximum directivity at $f=11$ GHz is 30 (14.77 dB).

12.8. Derive (12-21a)–(12-21e) by treating the H-plane horn as a radial waveguide.

12.9. For an H-plane sectoral horn with $\rho_2=6\lambda$, $a_1=6\lambda$, and $b=0.25\lambda$ compute the
   (a) directivity (in dB) using (12-41), (12-42c) and compare the answers
   (b) normalized field strength (in dB) at $\theta=30°$, $45°$, and $90°$. Approximate it using linear interpolation.

12.10. For an H-plane sectoral horn, plot a_1 (in λ) versus ρ_2 (in λ) using (12-41c). Verify, using the data of Figure 12.16, that the maximum directivities occur when (12-41c) is satisfied.

12.11. An H-plane horn is fed by an X-band WR 90 rectangular waveguide with dimensions of $a=0.9$ in. (2.286 cm) and $b=0.4$ in. (1.016 cm). Design the horn so that its maximum directivity at $f=11$ GHz is 16.3 (12.12 dB).

12.12. Show that (12-49a) and (12-49b) must be satisfied in order for a pyramidal horn to be physically realizable.

12.13. A standard gain X-band (8.2–12.4 GHz) pyramidal horn has dimensions of $\rho_1 \simeq 13.5$ in. (34.29 cm), $\rho_2 \simeq 14.2$ in. (36.07 cm), $a_1=7.65$ in. (19.43 cm), $b_1=5.65$ in. (14.35 cm), $a=0.9$ in. (2.286 cm), and $b=0.4$ in. (1.016 cm).
   (a) Check to see if such a horn can be constructed physically.
   (b) Compute the directivity (in dB) at $f=8.2$, 10.3, 12.4 GHz using for each (12-52a), (12-53), and (12-54e). Compare the answers.

12.14. A standard gain X-band (8.2–12.4 GHz) pyramidal horn has dimensions of $\rho_1 \simeq 5.3$ in. (13.46 cm), $\rho_2 \simeq 6.2$ in. (15.75 cm), $a_1=3.09$ in. (7.85 cm), $b_1=2.34$ in. (5.94 cm), $a=0.9$ in. (2.286 cm), and $b=0.4$ in. (1.016 cm).
   (a) Check to see if such a horn can be constructed physically.
   (b) Compute the directivity (in dB) at $f=8.2$, 10.3, and 12.4 GHz using for each (12-52a), (12-53), and (12-54e). Compare the computed answers with the gains of Figure 12.23.

12.15. Repeat the design of the optimum X-band pyramidal horn of Example 12.6 so that the gain at $f=11$ GHz is 17.05 dB.

12.16. For a conical horn, plot d_m (in λ) versus l (in λ) using (12-60). Verify, using the data of Figure 12.25, that the maximum directivities occur when (12-60) is satisfied.

12.17. A conical horn has dimensions of $L=19.5$ in., $d_m=15$ in., and $d=2.875$ in.
   (a) Find the frequency (in GHz) which will result in maximum directivity for this horn. What is that directivity (in dB)?
   (b) Find the directivity (in dB) at 2.5 and 5 GHz.
   (c) Compute the cutoff frequency (in GHz) of the TE_{11}-mode which can exist inside the circular waveguide that is used to feed the horn.

12.18. Design an optimum gain conical horn, using (12-59)–(12-60), so that its gain (above isotropic) at $f=11$ GHz is 22.6 dB. Check your design with the data in Figure 12.25. Compare the design dimensions with those of the pyramidal horn of Example 12.6.

12.19. For an X-band pyramidal corrugated horn operating at 10.3 GHz, find the
   (a) smallest lower and upper limits of the corrugation depths
   (b) width w of each corrugation
   (c) width t of each corrugation tooth

12.20. Find the E- and H-plane phase centers (in λ) of
   (a) an E-plane ($\rho_e = 5\lambda$, $a = 0.7\lambda$)
   (b) an H-plane ($\rho_h = 5\lambda$, $a = 0.7\lambda$)
   sectoral horn with a total included angle of 30°.

Chapter 13
Reflectors and Lens
Antennas

13.1 INTRODUCTION

Reflector antennas, in one form or another, have been in use since the discovery of electromagnetic wave propagation in 1888 by Hertz. However the fine art of analyzing and designing reflectors of many various geometrical shapes did not forge ahead until the days of World War II when numerous radar applications evolved. Subsequent demands of reflectors for use in radio astronomy, microwave communication, and satellite tracking resulted in spectacular progress in the development of sophisticated analytical and experimental techniques in shaping the reflector surfaces and optimizing illumination over their apertures so as to maximize the gain. The use of reflector antennas for deep space communication, such as in the space program and especially their deployment on the surface of the moon, resulted in establishing the reflector antenna almost as a household word during the 1960s. Although reflector antennas take many geometrical configurations, some of the most popular shapes are the plane, corner, and curved reflectors (especially the paraboloid), as shown in Figure 13.1, each of which will be discussed in this chapter. Many articles on various phases of the analysis and design of curved reflectors have been published and some of the most referenced can be found in a book of reprinted papers [1].

The primary purpose of a lens is to converge expanding energy from a radiating source. Lens antennas are usually placed in front of another radiator (such as a slotted waveguide, dipole, horn, or reflector) to convert cylindrical or spherical waves into plane waves (constant phase parallel rays) and to provide higher directivities.

13.2 PLANE REFLECTOR

The simplest type of reflector is a plane reflector introduced to direct energy in a desired direction. The arrangement is that shown in Figure 13.1(a) which has been extensively analyzed in Section 4.7 when the radiating source is a vertical or horizontal linear element. It has been clearly demonstrated that the polarization of the radiating source and its position relative to the reflecting surface can be used to control the radiating properties (pattern, impedance, directivity) of the overall system. Image theory has been used to analyze the radiating characteristics of such a system. Although the infinite dimensions of the plane reflector are idealized, the results can be used as approximations for electrically large surfaces. The perturbations introduced by keeping the dimensions finite can be accounted for by using special methods such as the Geometrical Theory of Diffraction [2]–[5] which was introduced in Section 11.9.

13.3 CORNER REFLECTOR

To better collimate the energy in the forward direction, the geometrical shape of the plane reflector itself must be changed so as to prohibit radiation in the back and side directions. One arrangement which accomplishes that consists of two plane reflectors joined so as to form a corner, as shown in Figures 13.1(b) and in 13.2(a). This is known as the corner reflector. Because of its simplicity in construction, it has many unique applications. For example, if the reflector is used as a passive target for radar or communication applications, it will return the signal exactly in the same direction as it received it when its included angle is 90°. This is illustrated geometrically in Figure 13.2(b). Because of this unique feature, military ships and vehicles are designed with minimum sharp corners to reduce their detection by enemy radar. Corner reflectors are also widely used as receiving elements for home television.

In most practical applications, the included angle formed by the plates is usually 90°; however other angles are sometimes used. To maintain a given system efficiency, the spacing between the vertex and the feed element must increase as the included angle of the reflector decreases, and vice-versa. For reflectors with infinite sides, the gain increases as the included angle between the planes decreases. This, however, may not be true for finite size plates. For simplicity, in this chapter it will be assumed that the plates themselves are infinite in extent ($l = \infty$). However, since in practice the dimensions must be finite, guidelines on the size of the aperture (D_a), length (l), and height (h) will be given.

The feed element for a corner reflector is almost always a dipole or an array of collinear dipoles placed parallel to the vertex a distance s away, as shown in a perspective view in Figure 13.2(c). Greater bandwidth is obtained when the feed elements are cylindrical or biconical dipoles instead of

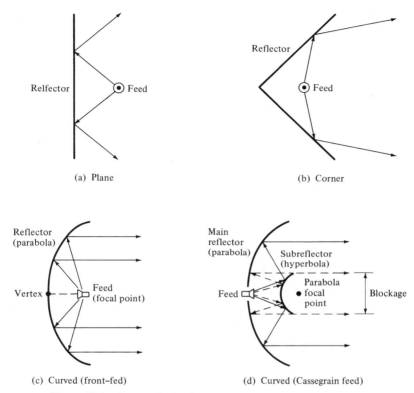

(a) Plane

(b) Corner

(c) Curved (front–fed)

(d) Curved (Cassegrain feed)

Figure 13.1 Geometrical configuration for some reflector systems.

thin wires. In many applications, especially when the wavelength is large compared to tolerable physical dimensions, the surfaces of the corner reflector are frequently made of grid wires rather than solid sheet metal, as shown in Figure 13.2(d). One of the reasons for doing that is to reduce wind resistance and overall system weight. The spacing (g) between wires is made a small fraction of a wavelength (usually $g \leq \lambda/10$). For wires that are parallel to length of the dipole, as is the case for the arrangement of Figure 13.2(d), the reflectivity of the grid-wire surface is as good as that of a solid surface.

In practice, the aperture of the corner reflector (D_a) is usually made between one and two wavelengths ($\lambda < D_a < 2\lambda$). The length of the sides of a 90° corner reflector is most commonly taken to be about twice the distance from the vertex to the feed ($l \simeq 2s$). For reflectors with smaller included angles, the sides are made larger. The feed-to-vertex distance (s) is usually taken to be between $\lambda/3$ and $2\lambda/3$ ($\lambda/3 < s < 2\lambda/3$). For each reflector, there is an optimum feed-to-vertex spacing. If the spacing becomes too small, the radiation resistance decreases and becomes comparable to the loss resistance of the system which leads to an inefficient antenna. For very

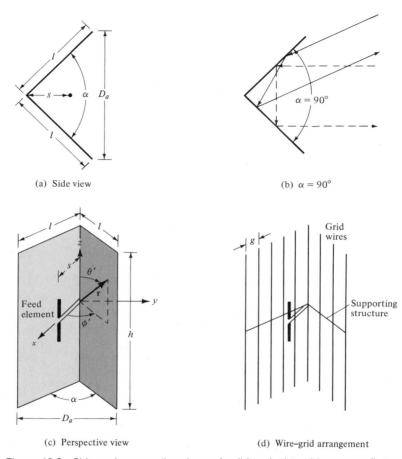

(a) Side view

(b) $\alpha = 90°$

(c) Perspective view

(d) Wire–grid arrangement

Figure 13.2 Side and perspective views of solid and wire-grid corner reflectors.

large spacing, the system produces undesirable multiple lobes, and it loses its directional characteristics. It has been experimentally observed that increasing the size of the sides does not greatly affect the beamwidth and directivity, but it increases the bandwidth and radiation resistance. The main lobe is somewhat broader for reflectors with finite sides compared to that of infinite dimensions. The height (h) of the reflector is usually taken to be about 1.2 to 1.5 times greater than the total length of the feed element in order to reduce radiation toward the back region from the ends.

The analysis for the field radiated by a source in the presence of a corner reflector is facilitated when the included angle (α) of the reflector is $\alpha = \pi/n$, where n is an integer ($\alpha = \pi, \pi/2, \pi/3, \pi/4$, etc.). For those cases ($\alpha = 180°, 90°, 60°, 45°$, etc.) it is possible to find a system of images, which when properly placed in the absence of the reflector plates, form an array that yields the same field within the space formed by the reflector plates as the actual system. The number of images, polarity, and position of each is controlled by the included angle of the corner reflector and the polarization of the feed element. In Figure 13.3 we display the geometrical and electrical arrangement of the images for corner reflectors with included angles of 90°, 60°, 45°, and 30° and a feed with perpendicular polarization. The procedure for finding the number, location, and polarity of the images is demonstrated graphically in Figure 13.4 for a corner reflector with a 90° included angle. It is assumed that the feed element is a linear dipole placed parallel to the vertex. A similar procedure can be followed for all other reflectors with an included angle of $\alpha = 180°/n$, where n is an integer.

13.3.1 90° Corner Reflector

The first corner reflector to be analyzed is the one with an included angle of 90°. Because its radiation characteristics are the most attractive, it has become the most popular.

Referring to the reflector of Figure 13.2(c) with its images in Figure 13.3(a), the total field of the system can be derived by summing the

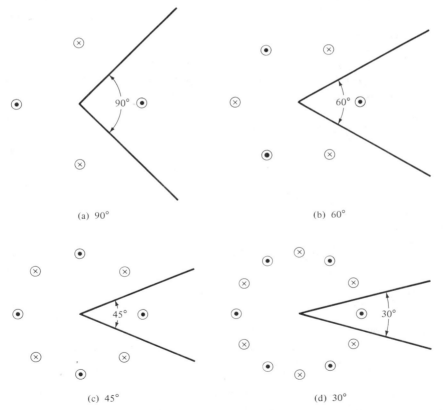

Figure 13.3   Corner reflectors and their images (with perpendicularly polarized feeds) for angles of 90°, 60°, 45°, and 30°.

contributions from the feed and its images. Thus

$$E(r,\theta,\phi)=E_1(r_1,\theta,\phi)+E_2(r_2,\theta,\phi)+E_3(r_3,\theta,\phi)+E_4(r_4,\theta,\phi)$$
$$(13\text{-}1)$$

In the far-zone, the normalized field can be written as

$$E(r,\theta,\phi)=f(\theta,\phi)\frac{e^{-jkr_1}}{r_1}-f(\theta,\phi)\frac{e^{-jkr_2}}{r_2}$$
$$+f(\theta,\phi)\frac{e^{-jkr_3}}{r_3}-f(\theta,\phi)\frac{e^{-jkr_4}}{r_4}$$

$$E(r,\theta,\phi)=[e^{-jks\cos\psi_1}-e^{-jks\cos\psi_2}$$

$$+e^{-jks\cos\psi_3}-e^{-jks\cos\psi_4}]f(\theta,\phi)\frac{e^{-jkr}}{r} \qquad (13\text{-}2)$$

where

$$\cos\psi_1=\hat{a}_x\cdot\hat{a}_r=\sin\theta\cos\phi \qquad (13\text{-}2a)$$
$$\cos\psi_2=\hat{a}_y\cdot\hat{a}_r=\sin\theta\sin\phi \qquad (13\text{-}2b)$$
$$\cos\psi_3=-\hat{a}_x\cdot\hat{a}_r=-\sin\theta\cos\phi \qquad (13\text{-}2c)$$
$$\cos\psi_4=-\hat{a}_y\cdot\hat{a}_r=-\sin\theta\sin\phi \qquad (13\text{-}2d)$$

since $\hat{a}_r=\hat{a}_x\sin\theta\cos\phi+\hat{a}_y\sin\theta\sin\phi+\hat{a}_z\cos\theta$. Equation (13-2) can also be written, using (13-2a)–(13-2d), as

$$E(r,\theta,\phi)=2[\cos(ks\sin\theta\cos\phi)-\cos(ks\sin\theta\sin\phi)]f(\theta,\phi)\frac{e^{-jkr}}{r}$$
$$(13\text{-}3)$$

where

$$0\leq\theta\leq\pi,\qquad \begin{array}{l}0\leq\phi\leq\alpha/2\\[4pt]2\pi-\alpha/2\leq\phi\leq2\pi\end{array} \qquad (13\text{-}3a)$$

Letting the field of a single isolated (radiating in free-space) element to be

$$E_0=f(\theta,\phi)\frac{e^{-jkr}}{r} \qquad (13\text{-}4)$$

(13-3) can be rewritten as

$$\boxed{\frac{E}{E_0}=\text{AF}(\theta,\phi)=2[\cos(ks\sin\theta\cos\phi)-\cos(ks\sin\theta\sin\phi)]} \qquad (13\text{-}5)$$

Equation (13-5) represents not only the ratio of the total field to that of an

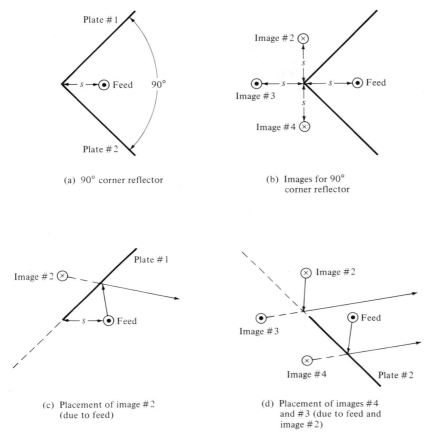

Figure 13.4 Geometrical placement and electrical polarity of images for a 90° corner reflector with a parallel polarized feed.

isolated element at the origin but also the array factor of the entire reflector system. In the azimuthal plane ($\theta = \pi/2$), (13-5) reduces to

$$\frac{E}{E_0} = AF(\theta = \pi/2, \phi) = 2[\cos(ks\cos\phi) - \cos(ks\sin\phi)] \tag{13-6}$$

To gain some insight into the performance of a corner reflector, in Figure 13.5 we display the normalized patterns for an $\alpha = 90°$ corner reflector for spacings of $s = 0.1\lambda$, 0.7λ, 0.8λ, 0.9λ, and 1.0λ. It is evident that for the small spacings the pattern consists of a single major lobe whereas multiple lobes appear for the larger spacings ($s > 0.7\lambda$). For $s = \lambda$ the pattern exhibits two lobes separated by a null along the $\phi = 0°$ axis.

Another parameter of performance for the corner reflector is the field strength along the symmetry axis ($\theta = 90°$, $\phi = 0°$) as a function of feed-to-vertex distance s [6]. The normalized (relative to the field of a single isolated

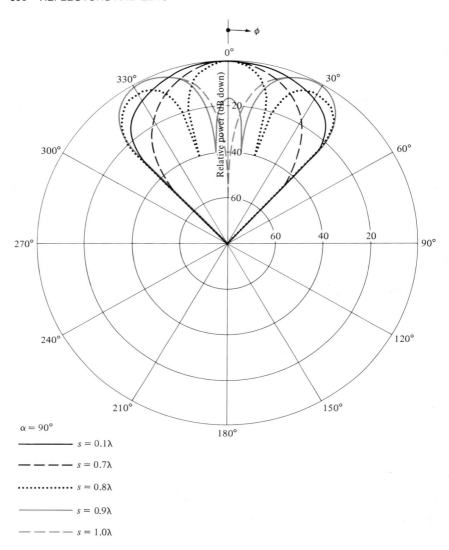

Figure 13.5   Normalized radiation amplitude patterns for $\alpha=90°$ corner reflector.

element) absolute field strength $|E/E_0|$ as a function of s/λ ($0 \leq s \leq 10\lambda$) for $\alpha = 90°$ is shown plotted in Figure 13.6. It is apparent that the first field strength peak is achieved when $s = 0.5\lambda$, and it is equal to 4. The field is also periodic with a period of $\Delta s/\lambda = 1.0$.

13.3.2   Other Corner Reflectors

A similar procedure can be used to derive the array factors and total fields for all other corner reflectors with included angles of $\alpha = 180°/n$. Referring

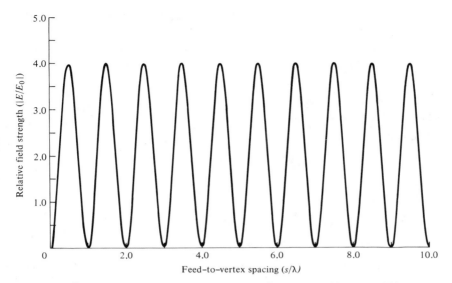

Figure 13.6   Relative field strength along the axis ($\theta=90°$, $\phi=0°$) of an $\alpha=90°$ corner reflector as a function of feed-to-vertex spacing.

to Figure 13.3, it can be shown that the array factors for $\alpha=60°$, $45°$, and $30°$ can be written as

$$\underline{\alpha=60°}$$
$$\mathrm{AF}(\theta,\phi)=4\sin\left(\frac{X}{2}\right)\left[\cos\left(\frac{X}{2}\right)-\cos\left(\sqrt{3}\,\frac{Y}{2}\right)\right] \tag{13-7}$$

$$\underline{\alpha=45°}$$
$$\mathrm{AF}(\theta,\phi)=2\left[\cos(X)+\cos(Y)-2\cos\left(\frac{X}{\sqrt{2}}\right)\cos\left(\frac{Y}{\sqrt{2}}\right)\right] \tag{13-8}$$

$$\underline{\alpha=30°}$$
$$\mathrm{AF}(\theta,\phi)=2\left[\cos(X)-2\cos\left(\frac{\sqrt{3}}{2}X\right)\cos\left(\frac{Y}{2}\right)\right.$$
$$\left.-\cos(Y)+2\cos\left(\frac{X}{2}\right)\cos\left(\frac{\sqrt{3}}{2}Y\right)\right] \tag{13-9}$$

where

$$X=ks\sin\theta\cos\phi \tag{13-9a}$$
$$Y=ks\sin\theta\sin\phi \tag{13-9b}$$

These are assigned, at the end of the chapter, as exercises to the reader (Problem 13.1).

It has also been shown [7] by using long filament wires as feeds, that the azimuthal plane ($\theta = \pi/2$) array factor for corner reflectors with $\alpha = 180°/n$, where n is an integer, can also be written as

n=even   (n=2,4,6,...)

$$\text{AF}(\phi) = 4n(-1)^{n/2}[J_n(ks)\cos(n\phi) + J_{3n}(ks)\cos(3n\phi)$$
$$+ J_{5n}(ks)\cos(5n\phi) + \cdots] \tag{13-10a}$$

n=odd   (n=1,3,5,...)

$$\text{AF}(\phi) = 4nj(-1)^{(n-1)/2}[J_n(ks)\cos(n\phi) - J_{3n}(ks)\cos(3n\phi)$$
$$+ J_{5n}(ks)\cos(5n\phi) + \cdots] \tag{13-10b}$$

where $J_m(x)$ is the Bessel function of the first kind of order m (see Appendix V).

When n is not an integer, the field must be found by retaining a sufficient number of terms of the infinite series. It has also been shown [7] that for all values of $n = m$ (integral or fractional) that the field can be written as

$$\text{AF}(\phi) = 4m[e^{jm\pi/2}J_m(ks)\cos(m\phi) + e^{j3m\pi/2}J_{3m}(ks)\cos(3m\phi) + \cdots]$$
$$\tag{13-11}$$

The array factor for a corner reflector, as given by (13-10a)–(13-11), has a form that is similar to the array factor for a uniform circular array, as given by (6-106). This should be expected since the feed sources and their images in Figure 13.3 form a circular array. The number of images increase as the included angle of the corner reflector decreases.

Patterns have been computed for corner reflectors with included angles of 60°, 45°, and 30°. It has been found that these corner reflectors have also single-lobed patterns for the smaller values of s, and they become narrower as the included angle decreases. Multiple lobes begin to appear when

$$s \approx 0.95\lambda \quad \text{for} \quad \alpha = 60°$$
$$s \approx 1.2\lambda \quad \text{for} \quad \alpha = 45°$$
$$s \approx 2.5\lambda \quad \text{for} \quad \alpha = 30°$$

The field strength along the axis of symmetry ($\theta = 90°$, $\phi = 0°$) as a function of the feed-to-vertex distance s, has been computed for reflectors with included angles of $\alpha = 60°$, 45°, and 30°. The results for $\alpha = 45°$ are shown in Figure 13.7.

For reflectors with $\alpha = 180°/n$, where n is an integer, the normalized field strength is periodic, and it vanishes at the end of each period. However when $\alpha = 180°/m$, where m is not an integer, the field strength is also

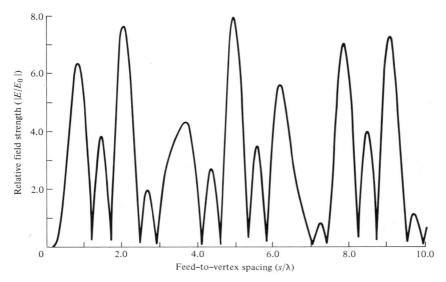

Figure 13.7 Relative field strength along the axis ($\theta = 90°$, $\phi = 0°$) for an $\alpha = 45°$ corner reflector as a function of feed-to-vertex spacing.

periodic, falls to minima, but never reaches zero. The period ($\Delta s/\lambda$) of the normalized field strength profile for the different reflectors is

PERIOD ($\Delta s/\lambda$)	REFLECTOR ANGLE (α-DEGREES)
1.0	90°
2.0	60°
16.69	45°
30.00	30°

The periodicity for $\alpha = 90°$ is displayed in Figure 13.6. For $\alpha = 45°$ it cannot be illustrated in Figure 13.7 because of its length. The $\alpha = 60°$ reflector exhibits a field strength profile which is similar to that of $\alpha = 90°$ while the $\alpha = 30°$ reflector profile is irregular and similar to that of $\alpha = 45°$.

It has also been found that the maximum field strength increases as the included angle of the reflector decreases. This is expected since a smaller angle reflector exhibits better directional characteristics because of the narrowness of its angle. The maximum values of $|E/E_0|$ for $\alpha = 60°$, $45°$, and $30°$ are approximately 5.2, 8, and 9, respectively. The first field strength peak, but not necessarily its ultimate maximum, is achieved when

$$s \simeq 0.65\lambda \quad \text{for} \quad \alpha = 60°$$
$$s \simeq 0.85\lambda \quad \text{for} \quad \alpha = 45°$$
$$s \simeq 1.20\lambda \quad \text{for} \quad \alpha = 30°$$

13.4 PARABOLIC REFLECTOR

The overall radiation characteristics (antenna pattern, antenna efficiency, polarization discrimination, etc.) of a reflector can be improved if the structural configuration of its surface is upgraded. It has been shown by geometrical optics that if a beam of parallel rays are incident upon a reflector whose geometrical shape is a parabola, the radiation will converge (focus) at a spot which is known as the *focal point*. In the same manner, if a point source is placed at the focal point, the rays reflected by a parabolic reflector will emerge as a parallel beam. This is one form of the principle of reciprocity, and it is demonstrated geometrically in Figure 13.1(c). The symmetrical point on the parabolic surface is known as the vertex. Rays that emerge in a parallel formation are usually said to be *collimated*. In practice, collimation is often used to describe the highly directional characteristics of an antenna even though the emanating rays are not exactly parallel. Since the transmitter (receiver) is placed at the focal point of the parabola, the configuration is usually known as *front-fed*.

The disadvantage of the front-fed arrangement is that the transmission line from the feed must usually be long enough to reach the transmitting or the receiving equipment, which is usually placed behind or below the reflector. This may necessitate the use of long transmission lines whose losses may not be tolerable in many applications, especially in low-noise receiving systems. In some applications, the transmitting or receiving equipment is placed at the focal point to avoid the need for long transmission lines. However, in some of these applications, especially for transmission that may require large amplifiers and for low-noise receiving systems where cooling and weatherproofing may be necessary, the equipment may be too heavy and bulky and will provide undesirable blockage.

Another arrangement that avoids placing the feed (transmitter and/or receiver) at the focal point is that shown in Figure 13.1(d), and it is known as the *Cassegrain feed*. Through geometrical optics, Cassegrain, a famous astronomer (hence its name), showed that incident parallel rays can be focused to a point by utilizing two reflectors. To accomplish this, the main (primary) reflector must be a parabola, the secondary reflector (subreflector) a hyperbola, and the feed placed along the axis of the parabola usually at or near the vertex. Cassegrain used this scheme to construct optical telescopes, and then its design was copied for use in radio frequency systems. For this arrangement, the rays that emanate from the feed illuminate the subreflector and are reflected by it in the direction of the primary reflector, as if they originated at the focal point of the parabola (primary reflector). The rays are then reflected by the primary reflector and are converted to parallel rays, provided the primary reflector is a parabola and the subreflector is a hyperbola. Diffractions occur at the edge of the subreflector and primary reflector, and they must be taken into account to accurately predict the overall system pattern, especially in regions of low intensity [8]–[10]. Even in regions of high intensity, diffractions must be included if an accurate formation of the fine ripple structure of the pattern is desired. With the Cassegrain-feed arrangement, the transmitting and/or receiving equipment can be placed behind the primary reflector. This scheme makes the system relatively more accessible for servicing and adjustment.

A parabolic reflector can take two different forms. One configuration is that of the parabolic right cylinder, shown in Figure 13.8(a), whose energy is collimated at a line that is parallel to the axis of the cylinder through the focal point of the reflector. The most widely used feed for this type of a reflector is a linear dipole, a linear array, or a slotted waveguide. The other reflector configuration is that of Figure 13.8(b) which is formed by rotating the parabola around its axis, and it is referred to as a paraboloid (parabola of revolution). A pyramidal or a conical horn has been widely utilized as a feed for this arrangement.

There are many other types of reflectors whose analysis is widely documented in the literature [11]–[13]. The spherical reflector, for example, has been utilized for radioastronomy and small earth station applications, because its beam can be efficiently scanned by moving its feed. An example of that is the 1000-ft (305-m) diameter spherical reflector at Arecibo, Puerto Rico [11] whose primary surface is built into the ground and scanning of the beam is accomplished by movement of the feed. For spherical reflectors a substantial blockage may be provided by the feed leading to unacceptable minor lobes levels, in addition to the inherent reduction in gain and less favorable cross-polarization discrimination.

To eliminate some of the deficiencies of the symmetric configurations, offset-parabolic reflector designs have been developed for single- and dual-reflector systems [13]. Because of the asymmetry of the system, the analysis is more complex. However the advent and advances of the computer technology have made the modeling and optimization of the offset reflector designs available and convenient. Offset reflector designs reduce aperture-blocking and VSWR. In addition, they lead to the use of larger f/d ratios

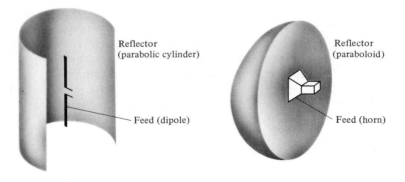

(a) Parabolic right cylinder   (b) Paraboloid

Figure 13.8   Parabolic right cylinder and paraboloid.

while maintaining acceptable structural rigidity, which provide an opportunity for improved feed-pattern shaping and better suppression of cross-polarized radiation emanating from the feed. However, offset-reflector configurations generate cross-polarized antenna radiation when illuminated by a linearly polarized primary-feed. Circularly polarized feeds eliminate depolarization, but they lead to squinting of the main beam from boresight. In addition, the structural asymmetry of the system is usually considered a major drawback.

Paraboloidal reflectors are the most widely used large aperture ground-based antennas [12]. The world's largest fully steerable reflector is the 100-m diameter radio telescope [14] of the Max Planck Institute for Radioastronomy at Effelsberg, West Germany, while the largest in the United States is the 64-m diameter [15] reflector at Goldstone, California built primarily for deep-space applications. When fed efficiently from the focal point, paraboloidal reflectors produce a high gain pencil beam with low side lobes and good cross-polarization discrimination characteristics. This type of an antenna is widely used for low-noise applications, such as in radioastronomy, and it is considered as a good compromise between performance and cost. To build a large reflector requires not only a large financial budget but also a difficult structural undertaking, because it must withstand severe weather conditions.

Cassegrain designs, employing dual reflector surfaces, are used in applications where pattern control is essential, such as in satellite ground-based systems, and have efficiencies of 65–80%. They supersede the performance of the single-reflector front-fed arrangement by about 10%. Using geometrical optics, the classical Cassegrain configuration, consisting of a paraboloid and a hyperboloid, is designed to achieve a uniform phase front in the aperture of the paraboloid. By employing good feed designs, this arrangement can achieve lower spillover and more uniform illumination of the main reflector. In addition, slight shaping of one or both of the dual-reflector's surfaces can lead to an aperture with almost uniform amplitude and phase with a substantial enhancement in gain [12]. Shaping techniques have been employed in dual-reflectors used in earth station applications. An example is the 10-m earth station dual-reflector antenna, shown in Figure 13.9, whose main reflector and subreflector are shaped.

For many years horns or waveguides, operating in a single mode, were used as feeds for reflector antennas. However because of radioastronomy and earth-station applications, considerable efforts have been placed in designing more efficient feeds to illuminate either the main reflector or the subreflector. It has been found that corrugated horns that support hybrid mode fields (combination of TE and TM modes) can be used as desirable feeds. Such feed elements match efficiently the fields of the feeds with the desired focal distribution produced by the reflector, and they can reduce cross-polarization. Dielectric cylinders and cones are other antenna structures that support hybrid modes [12]. Their structural configuration can also

Figure 13.9   Shaped 10-m earth station dual-reflector antenna (courtesy Andrew Corp.).

be used to support the subreflector and to provide attractive performance figures.

There are primarily two techniques that can be used to analyze the performance of a reflector system [16]. One technique is the *aperture distribution method* and the other the *current distribution method*. Both techniques will be introduced to show the similarities and differences.

13.4.1 Front-Fed Parabolic Reflector

Parabolic cylinders have widely been used as high-gain apertures fed by line sources. The analysis of a parabolic cylinder (single-curved) reflector is similar, but considerably simpler than that of a paraboidal (double-curved) reflector. The principal characteristics of aperture amplitude, phase, and polarization for a parabolic cylinder, as contrasted to those of a paraboloid, are as follows:

1. The amplitude taper, due to variations in distance from the feed to the surface of the reflector, is proportional to $1/\rho$ in a cylinder compared to $1/r^2$ in a paraboloid.
2. The focal region, where incident plane waves converge, is a line-source for a cylinder and a point-source for a paraboloid.
3. When the fields of the feed are linearly polarized parallel to the axis of the cylinder, no cross-polarized components are produced by the parabolic cylinder. That is not the case for a paraboloid.

Generally, parabolic cylinders, as compared to paraboloids, (1) are mechanically simpler to build, (2) provide larger aperture blockage, and (3) do not possess the attractive characteristics of a paraboloid. In this chapter, only paraboloidal reflectors will be examined.

SURFACE GEOMETRY

The surface of a paraboloidal reflector is formed by rotating a parabola about its axis. Its surface must be a paraboloid of revolution so that rays emanating from the focus of the reflector are transformed into plane waves. The design is based on optical techniques, and it does not take into account any deformations (diffractions) from the rim of the reflector. Referring to Figure 13.10 and choosing a plane perpendicular to the axis of the reflector through the focus, it follows that

$$OP + PQ = \text{constant} = 2f \tag{13-12}$$

Since

$$OP = r'$$
$$PQ = r'\cos\theta' \tag{13-13}$$

(13-12) can be written as

$$r'(1 + \cos\theta') = 2f \tag{13-14}$$

or

$$\boxed{r' = \frac{2f}{1 + \cos\theta'} = f\sec^2\left(\frac{\theta'}{2}\right) \qquad \theta \le \theta_0} \tag{13-14a}$$

Since a paraboloid is a parabola of revolution (about its axis), (13-14a) is also the equation of a paraboloid in terms of the spherical coordinates r', θ', ϕ'. Because of its rotational symmetry, there are no variations with respect to ϕ'.

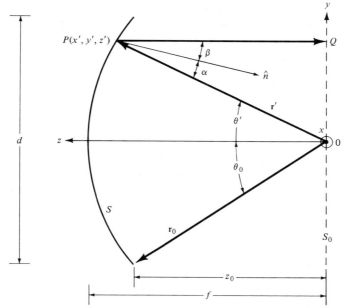

Figure 13.10 Two-dimensional configuration of a paraboloidal reflector.

Equation (13-14a) can also be written in terms of the rectangular coordinates x', y', z'. That is,

$$r' + r'\cos\theta' = \sqrt{(x')^2 + (y')^2 + (z')^2} + z' = 2f \tag{13-15}$$

or

$$(x')^2 + (y')^2 = 4f(f - z') \qquad \text{with } (x')^2 + (y')^2 \le (d/2)^2 \tag{13-15a}$$

In the analysis of parabolic reflectors, it is desirable to find a unit vector that is normal to the local tangent at the surface reflection point. To do this, (13-14a) is first expressed as

$$f - r'\cos^2\left(\frac{\theta'}{2}\right) = S = 0 \tag{13-16}$$

and then a gradient is taken to form a normal to the surface. That is,

$$\mathbf{N} = \nabla\left[f - r'\cos^2\left(\frac{\theta'}{2}\right)\right] = \hat{a}_{r'}\frac{\partial S}{\partial r'} + \hat{a}_{\theta'}\frac{1}{r'}\frac{\partial S}{\partial \theta'}$$

$$= -\hat{a}_{r'}\cos^2\left(\frac{\theta'}{2}\right) + \hat{a}_{\theta'}\cos\left(\frac{\theta'}{2}\right)\sin\left(\frac{\theta'}{2}\right) \tag{13-17}$$

A unit vector, normal to S, is formed from (13-17) as

$$\hat{n} = \frac{\mathbf{N}}{|\mathbf{N}|} = -\hat{a}_{r'}\cos\left(\frac{\theta'}{2}\right) + \hat{a}_{\theta'}\sin\left(\frac{\theta'}{2}\right) \tag{13-18}$$

To find the angle between the unit vector $\hat{n}$ which is normal to the surface at the reflection point, and a vector directed from the focus to the reflection point, we form

$$
\alpha = -\hat{a}_r' \cdot \hat{n} = -\hat{a}_r' \cdot \left[-\hat{a}_r' \cos\left(\frac{\theta'}{2}\right) + \hat{a}_\theta' \sin\left(\frac{\theta'}{2}\right) \right]
$$
$$
= \cos\left(\frac{\theta'}{2}\right)
$$

(13-19)

In a similar manner we can find the angle between the unit vector $\hat{n}$ and the z-axis. That is,

$$
\beta = -\hat{a}_z \cdot \hat{n} = -\hat{a}_z \cdot \left[-\hat{a}_r' \cos\left(\frac{\theta'}{2}\right) + \hat{a}_\theta' \sin\left(\frac{\theta'}{2}\right) \right]
$$

(13-20)

Using the transformation of (4-5), (13-20) can be written as

$$
\beta = -(\hat{a}_r' \cos\theta' - \hat{a}_\theta' \sin\theta') \cdot \left[-\hat{a}_r' \cos\left(\frac{\theta'}{2}\right) + \hat{a}_\theta' \sin\left(\frac{\theta'}{2}\right) \right]
$$
$$
= \cos\left(\frac{\theta'}{2}\right)
$$

(13-21)

which is identical to α of (13-19). This is nothing more than a verification of Snell's law of reflection at each differential area of the surface, which has been assumed to be flat locally.

Another expression that is usually very prominent in the analysis of reflectors is that relating the subtended angle θ_0 to the f/d ratio. From the geometry of Figure 13.10

$$
\theta_0 = \tan^{-1}\left(\frac{d/2}{z_0}\right)
$$

(13-22)

where z_0 is the distance along the axis of the reflector from the focal point to the edge of the rim. From (13-15a)

$$
z_0 = f - \frac{x_0^2 + y_0^2}{4f} = f - \frac{(d/2)^2}{4f} = f - \frac{d^2}{16f}
$$

(13-23)

Substituting (13-23) into (13-22) reduces it to

$$
\theta_0 = \tan^{-1}\left(\frac{\dfrac{d}{2}}{f - \dfrac{d^2}{16f}} \right) = \tan^{-1}\left(\frac{\dfrac{1}{2}\left(\dfrac{f}{d}\right)}{\left(\dfrac{f}{d}\right)^2 - \dfrac{1}{16}} \right)
$$

(13-24)

It can also be shown that another form of (13-24) is

$$\boxed{f = \left(\frac{d}{4}\right)\cot\left(\frac{\theta_0}{2}\right)}$$

(13-25)

INDUCED CURRENT DENSITY

To determine the radiation characteristics (pattern, gain, efficiency, polarization, etc.) of a parabolic reflector, the current density induced on its surface must be known.

The current density $\mathbf{J}_s$ can be determined by using

$$\mathbf{J}_s = \hat{n} \times \mathbf{H} = \hat{n} \times (\mathbf{H}_i + \mathbf{H}_r)$$

(13-26)

where $\mathbf{H}_i$ and $\mathbf{H}_r$ represent, respectively, the incident and reflected magnetic field components evaluated at the surface of the conductor, and $\hat{n}$ is a unit vector normal to the surface. If the reflecting surface can be approximated by an *infinite plane surface* (this condition is met locally for a parabola), then by the method of images

$$\hat{n} \times \mathbf{H}_i = \hat{n} \times \mathbf{H}_r$$

(13-27)

and (13-26) reduces to

$$\boxed{\mathbf{J}_s = \hat{n} \times (\mathbf{H}_i + \mathbf{H}_r) = 2\hat{n} \times \mathbf{H}_i = 2\hat{n} \times \mathbf{H}_r}$$

(13-28)

The current density approximation of (13-28) is known as the *physical-optics* approximation, and it is valid when the transverse dimensions of the reflector, radius of curvature of the reflecting object, and the radius of curvature of the incident wave are large compared to a wavelength.

If the reflecting surface is in the far-field of the source generating the incident waves, then (13-28) can also be written as

$$\boxed{\mathbf{J}_s = 2\hat{n} \times \mathbf{H}_i \simeq \frac{2}{\eta}\left[\hat{n} \times (\hat{s}_i \times \mathbf{E}_i)\right]}$$

(13-29)

or

$$\boxed{\mathbf{J}_s = 2\hat{n} \times \mathbf{H}_r \simeq \frac{2}{\eta}\left[\hat{n} \times (\hat{s}_r \times \mathbf{E}_r)\right]}$$

(13-29a)

where η is the intrinsic impedance of the medium, $\hat{s}_i$ and $\hat{s}_r$ are radial unit vectors along the ray paths of the incident and reflected waves (as shown in Figure 13.11), and $\mathbf{E}_i$ and $\mathbf{E}_r$ are the incident and reflected electric fields.

APERTURE DISTRIBUTION METHOD

It was pointed out earlier that the two most commonly used techniques in analyzing the radiation characteristics of reflectors are the *aperture distribution* and the *current distribution* methods.

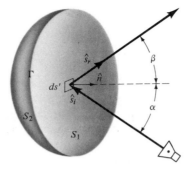

Figure 13.11   Reflecting surface with boundary Γ.

For the aperture distribution method, the field reflected by the surface of the paraboloid is first found over a plane which is normal to the axis of the reflector. Geometrical optics techniques (ray tracing) are usually employed to accomplish this. In most cases, the plane is taken through the focal point, and it is designated as the aperture plane, as shown in Figure 13.12. Equivalent sources are then formed over that plane. Usually it is assumed that the equivalent sources are zero outside the projected area of the reflector on the aperture plane. These equivalent sources are then used to compute the radiated fields utilizing the aperture techniques of Chapter 11.

For the *current distribution method*, the physical optics approximation of the induced current density $\mathbf{J}_s$ given by (13-28) ($\mathbf{J}_s \simeq 2\hat{n} \times \mathbf{H}_i$ where $\mathbf{H}_i$ is

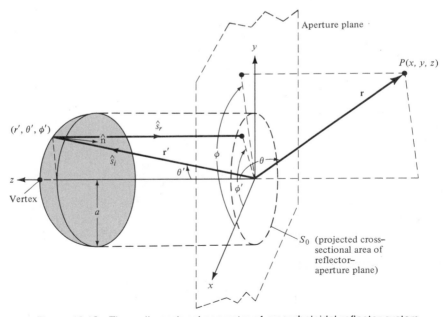

Figure 13.12   Three-dimensional geometry of a paraboloidal reflector system.

the incident magnetic field and $\hat{n}$ is a unit vector normal to the reflector surface) is formulated over the illuminated side of the reflector (S_1) of Figure 13.11. This current density is then integrated over the surface of the reflector to yield the far-zone radiation fields.

For the reflector of Figure 13.11, approximations that are common to both methods are:

1. The current density is zero on the shadow side (S_2) of the reflector.
2. The discontinuity of the current density over the rim (Γ) of the reflector is neglected.
3. Direct radiation from the feed and aperture blockage by the feed are neglected.

These approximations lead to accurate results, using either technique, for the radiated fields on the main beam and nearby minor lobes. To predict the pattern more accurately in all regions, especially the far minor lobes, geometrical diffraction techniques [8]–[10] can be applied. Because of the level of the material, it will not be included here. The interested reader can refer to the literature.

The advantage of the aperture distribution method is that the integration over the aperture plane can be performed with equal ease for any feed pattern or feed position [17]. The integration over the surface of the reflector as required for the current distribution method, becomes quite complex and time consuming when the feed pattern is asymmetrical and/or the feed is placed off-axis.

Let us assume that a y-polarized source with a gain function of $G_f(\theta', \phi')$ is placed at the focal point of a paraboloidal reflector. The radiated intensity of this source is given by

$$U(\theta', \phi') = \frac{P_t}{4\pi} G_f(\theta', \phi') \tag{13-30}$$

where P_t is the total radiated power. Referring to Figure 13.12, at a point r' in the far-zone of the source

$$U(\theta', \phi') = \frac{1}{2} \text{Re}[\mathbf{E}(\theta', \phi') \times \mathbf{H}^*(\theta', \phi')] = \frac{1}{2\eta} |\mathbf{E}(\theta', \phi')|^2 \tag{13-31}$$

or

$$|\mathbf{E}(\theta', \phi')| = [2\eta U(\theta', \phi')]^{1/2} = \left[\eta \frac{P_t}{2\pi} G_f(\theta', \phi')\right]^{1/2} \tag{13-31a}$$

The incident field, with a direction perpendicular to the radial distance, can then be written as

$$\mathbf{E}_i(r', \theta', \phi') = \hat{e}_i \left[\sqrt{\frac{\mu}{\varepsilon}} \frac{P_t}{2\pi} G_f(\theta', \phi')\right]^{1/2} \frac{e^{-jkr'}}{r'} = \hat{e}_i C_1 \sqrt{G_f(\theta', \phi')} \frac{e^{-jkr'}}{r'} \tag{13-32}$$

$$C_1 = \left(\frac{\mu}{\varepsilon}\right)^{1/4} \left(\frac{P_t}{2\pi}\right)^{1/2} \tag{13-32a}$$

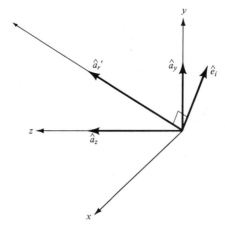

Figure 13.13   Unit vector alignment for a paraboloidal reflector system.

where $\hat{e}_i$ is a unit vector perpendicular to $\hat{a}_r'$ and parallel to the plane formed by $\hat{a}_r'$ and $\hat{a}_y$, as shown in Figure 13.13.

It can be shown [18] that on the surface of the reflector

$$\mathbf{J}_s = 2\sqrt{\frac{\varepsilon}{\mu}}\left[\hat{n}\times(\hat{s}_i\times\mathbf{E}_i)\right] = 2\sqrt{\frac{\varepsilon}{\mu}}\,C_1\sqrt{G_f(\theta',\phi')}\,\frac{e^{-jkr'}}{r'}\,\mathbf{u} \tag{13-33}$$

where

$$\mathbf{u} = \hat{n}\times(\hat{a}_r'\times\hat{e}_i) = (\hat{n}\cdot\hat{e}_i)\hat{a}_r' - (\hat{n}\cdot\hat{a}_r')\hat{e}_i \tag{13-33a}$$

which reduces to

$$\mathbf{u} = \left[-\hat{a}_x\sin\theta'\sin\left(\frac{\theta'}{2}\right)\sin\phi'\cos\phi'\right.$$
$$+\hat{a}_y\cos\left(\frac{\theta'}{2}\right)(\sin^2\phi'\cos\theta'+\cos^2\phi')$$
$$\left.-\hat{a}_z\cos\theta'\sin\phi'\sin\left(\frac{\theta'}{2}\right)\right]\bigg/\sqrt{1-\sin^2\theta'\sin^2\phi'} \tag{13-34}$$

To find the aperture field $\mathbf{E}_{ap}$ at the plane through the focal point, due to the reflector currents of (13-33), the reflected field $\mathbf{E}_r$ at r' (the reflection point) is first found. This is of the form

$$\mathbf{E}_r = \hat{e}_r C_1\sqrt{G_f(\theta',\phi')}\,\frac{e^{-jkr'}}{r'} \tag{13-35}$$

where $\hat{e}_r$ is a unit vector depicting the polarization of the reflected field. From (13-29a)

$$\mathbf{J}_s = 2\sqrt{\frac{\varepsilon}{\mu}}\left[\hat{n}\times(\hat{s}_r\times\mathbf{E}_r)\right] \tag{13-36}$$

Because $\hat{s}_r = -\hat{a}_z$, (13-36) can be written, using (13-35), as

$$\mathbf{J}_s = 2\sqrt{\frac{\varepsilon}{\mu}} \, C_1\sqrt{G_f(\theta', \phi')} \, \frac{e^{-jkr'}}{r'} \mathbf{u} \tag{13-37}$$

where

$$\mathbf{u} = \hat{n} \times (-\hat{a}_z \times \hat{e}_r) = -\hat{a}_z(\hat{n} \cdot \hat{e}_r) - \hat{e}_r \cos\left(\frac{\theta'}{2}\right) \tag{13-37a}$$

Since **u** in (13-37) and (13-37a) is the same as that of (13-33)–(13-34), it can be shown [18] through some extensive mathematical manipulations that

$$\hat{e}_r = \frac{\hat{a}_x \sin\phi' \cos\phi'(1 - \cos\theta') - \hat{a}_y(\sin^2\phi' \cos\theta' + \cos^2\phi')}{\sqrt{1 - \sin^2\theta' \sin^2\phi'}} \tag{13-38}$$

Thus the field $\mathbf{E}_r$ at the point of reflection r' is given by (13-35) where $\hat{e}_r$ is given by (13-38). At the plane passing through the focal point, the field is given by

$$\mathbf{E}_{ap} = \hat{e}_r C_1\sqrt{G_f(\theta', \phi')} \, \frac{e^{-jkr'(1+\cos\theta')}}{r'(1+\cos\theta')} = \hat{a}_x E_{xa} + \hat{a}_y E_{ya} \tag{13-39}$$

where E_{xa} and E_{ya} represent the x- and y-components of the reflected field over the aperture. For values of θ' close to 90°, (13-39) reduces to

$$\mathbf{E}_{ap} \simeq \hat{e}_r C_1\sqrt{G_f(\theta', \phi')} \, \frac{e^{-jkr'(1+\cos\theta')}}{r'} = \hat{a}_x E_{xa} + \hat{a}_y E_{ya} \tag{13-39a}$$

Using the reflected electric field components (E_{xa} and E_{ya}) as given by (13-39), an equivalent is formed at the aperture plane. That is,

$$\mathbf{J}_s = \hat{n} \times \mathbf{H}_a = -\hat{a}_z \times \left(\hat{a}_x \frac{E_{ay}}{\eta} - \hat{a}_y \frac{E_{ax}}{\eta}\right) = -\hat{a}_x \frac{E_{ax}}{\eta} - \hat{a}_y \frac{E_{ay}}{\eta} \tag{13-40a}$$

$$\mathbf{M}_s = -\hat{n} \times \mathbf{E}_a = -\hat{a}_z \times (\hat{a}_x E_{ax} + \hat{a}_y E_{ay}) = +\hat{a}_x E_{ay} - \hat{a}_y E_{ax} \tag{13-40b}$$

The radiated field can be computed using the (13-40a), (13-40b), and the formulations of Section 11.3. The integration is restricted only over the projected cross-sectional area S_0 of the reflector at the aperture plane shown dashed in Figure 13.12. That is,

$$E_{\theta s} = \frac{jke^{-jkr}}{4\pi r}(1 + \cos\theta) \iint_{S_0} (E_{ax}\cos\phi + E_{ay}\sin\phi)$$

$$\times e^{jk(x'\sin\theta\cos\phi + y'\sin\theta\sin\phi)} \, dx' \, dy' \tag{13-41a}$$

$$E_{\phi s} = \frac{jke^{-jkr}}{4\pi r}(1 + \cos\theta) \iint_{S_0} (-E_{ax}\sin\phi + E_{ay}\cos\phi)$$

$$\times e^{jk(x'\sin\theta\cos\phi + y'\sin\theta\sin\phi)} \, dx' \, dy' \tag{13-41b}$$

The aperture distribution method has been used to compute, using efficient numerical integration techniques, the radiation patterns of paraboloidal [17] and spherical [19] reflectors. The fields given by (13-41a) and (13-41b) represent only the secondary pattern due to scattering from the reflector. The total pattern of the system is represented by the sum of secondary pattern and the primary pattern of the feed element. For most feeds (such as horns), the primary pattern in the boresight (forward) direction of the reflector is of very low intensity and usually can be neglected.

To demonstrate the utility of the techniques, the principal E- and H-plane secondary patterns of a 35 GHz reflector, with an $f/d \simeq 0.82$ [$f = 8.062$ in. (20.48 cm), $d = 9.84$ in. (24.99 cm)] and fed by a conical dual-mode horn, were computed and they are displayed in Figure 13.14. Since the feed horn has identical E- and H-plane patterns and the reflector is fed symmetrically, the reflector E- and H-plane patterns are also identical and do not possess any cross-polarized components.

To simultaneously display the field intensity associated with each point in the aperture plane of the reflector, a computer generated plot was developed [19]. The field point locations, showing quantized contours of constant amplitude in the aperture plane, are illustrated in Figure 13.15.

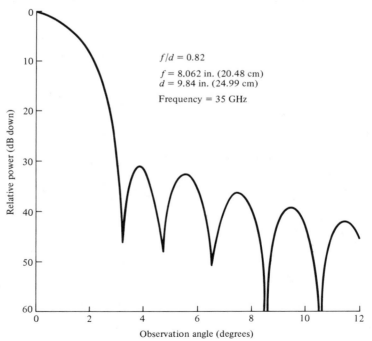

Figure 13.14 Principal E- or H-plane pattern of a symmetrical front-fed paraboloidal reflector (courtesy M. C. Bailey, NASA Langley Research Center).

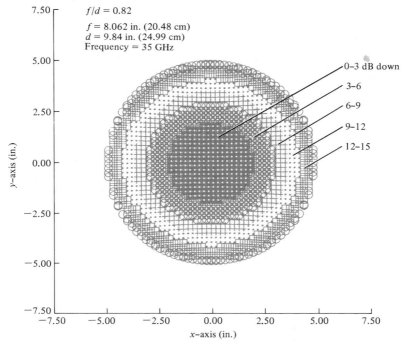

Figure 13.15   Field point locations of constant amplitude contours in the aperture plane of a symmetrical front-fed paraboloidal reflector (courtesy M. C.Bailey, NASA Langley Research Center).

The reflector system has an $f/d \simeq 0.82$ with the same physical dimensions [$f = 8.062$ in. (20.48 cm), $d = 9.84$ in. (24.99 cm)] and the same feed as the principal pattern of Figure 13.14. One symbol is used to represent each 3-dB region. The field intensity within the bounds of the reflector aperture plane is within the 0–15 dB range.

CROSS-POLARIZATION

The field reflected by the paraboloid, as represented by (13-35) and (13-38) of the aperture distribution method, contains x- and y-polarized components when the incident field is y-polarized. The y-component is designated as the principal polarization and the x-component as the cross-polarization. This is illustrated in Figure 13.16. It is also evident that symmetrical (with respect to the principal planes) cross-polarized components are 180° out of phase with one another. However for very narrow beam reflectors or for angles near the boresight axis ($\theta' \simeq 0$), the cross-polarized x-component diminishes and it vanishes on axis ($\theta' = 0$). A similar procedure can be used to show that for an incident x-polarized field, the reflecting surface decomposes the wave to a y-polarized field, in addition to its x-polarized component.

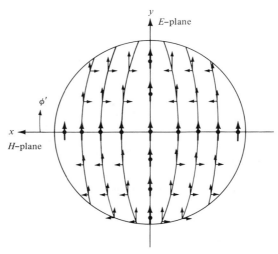

Figure 13.16 Principal (*y*-direction) and cross-polarization (*x*-direction) components of a paraboloidal reflector. (SOURCE: S. Silver (ed.), *Microwave Antenna Theory and Design* (MIT Radiation Lab. Series, vol. 12), McGraw-Hill, New York, 1949)

An interesting observation about the polarization phenomenon of a parabolic reflector can be made if we first assume that the feed element is an infinitesimal electric dipole ($l \ll \lambda$) with its length along the *y*-axis. For that feed, the field reflected by the reflector is given by (13-35) where from (4-110)

$$C_1\sqrt{G_f(\theta', \phi')} = j\eta \frac{kI_0 l}{4\pi} \sin\psi = j\eta \frac{kI_0 l}{4\pi} \sqrt{1 - \cos^2\psi}$$

$$= j\eta \frac{kI_0 l}{4\pi} \sqrt{1 - \sin^2\theta' \sin^2\phi'} \tag{13-42}$$

The angle ψ is measured from the *y*-axis toward the observation point.

When (13-42) is inserted in (13-35), we can write with the aid of (13-38) that

$$\mathbf{E}_r = \left[\hat{a}_x \sin\theta' \cos\phi'(1 - \cos\theta') - \hat{a}_y(\sin^2\phi' \cos\phi' + \cos^2\phi') \right]$$

$$\times j\eta \frac{kI_0 l}{4\pi} \frac{e^{-jkr'}}{r'} \tag{13-43}$$

Now let us assume that an infinitesimal magnetic dipole, with its length along the *x*-axis (or a small loop with its area parallel to the *y*-*z* plane) and with a magnetic moment of $-\hat{a}_x M$, is placed at the focal point and used as a feed. It can be shown [20]–[22] that the field reflected by the reflector has *x*- and *y*-components. However the *x*-component has a reverse sign to the *x*-component of the electric dipole feed. By adjusting the ratio of the electric to the magnetic dipole moments to be equal to $\sqrt{\mu/\varepsilon}$, the two cross-polarized reflected components (*x*-components) can be made equal in magnitude and for their sum to vanish (because of reverse signs). Thus a crossed electric

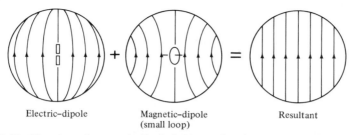

Electric–dipole   Magnetic–dipole   Resultant
                       (small loop)

Figure 13.17 Electric and magnetic dipole fields combined to form a Huygens' source with ideal feed polarization for reflector. (SOURCE: A. W. Love, "Some Highlights in Reflector Antenna Development," *Radio Science*, vol. 11, Nos. 8, 9, August–September 1976)

and magnetic dipole combination located at the focal point of a paraboloid can be used to induce currents on the surface of the reflector which are parallel everywhere. This is illustrated graphically in Figure 13.17.

The direction of the induced current flow will determine the far-field polarization of the antenna. Thus for the crossed electric and magnetic dipole combination feed, the far-field radiation will be free of cross-polarization. This type of feed is "ideal" in that it does not require that the surface of the reflector be solid but can be formed by closely space parallel conductors. Because of its ideal characteristics, it is usually referred to as a *Huygens' source*.

CURRENT DISTRIBUTION METHOD

The current distribution method was introduced as a technique that can be used to better approximate, as compared to the geometrical-optics (ray-tracing) method, the field scattered from a surface. Usually the main difficulty in applying this method is the approximation of the current density over the surface of the scatterer.

To analyze the reflector using this technique, we refer to the radiation integrals and auxiliary potential functions formulations of Chapter 3. While the two-step procedure of Figure 3.1 often simplifies the solution of most problems, the one-step formulation of Figure 3.1 is most convenient for the reflectors.

Using the potential function methods outlined in Chapter 3, and referring to the coordinate system of Figure 11.2(a), it can be shown [16] that the **E**- and **H**-fields radiated by the sources **J** and **M** can be written as

$$\mathbf{E} = \mathbf{E}_A + \mathbf{E}_F = -j\frac{1}{4\pi\omega\varepsilon} \int_V \left[(\mathbf{J} \cdot \nabla)\nabla + k^2\mathbf{J} + j\omega\varepsilon\mathbf{M} \times \nabla \right] \frac{e^{-jkR}}{R} \, dv'$$

$$(13\text{-}44\text{a})$$

$$\mathbf{H} = \mathbf{H}_A + \mathbf{H}_F = -j\frac{1}{4\pi\omega\mu} \int_V \left[(\mathbf{M} \cdot \nabla)\nabla + k^2\mathbf{M} - j\omega\mu\mathbf{J} \times \nabla \right] \frac{e^{-jkR}}{R} \, dv'$$

$$(13\text{-}44\text{b})$$

which for far-field observations reduce, according to the coordinate system of Figure 11.2(b), to

$$\mathbf{E} \simeq -j\frac{\omega\mu}{4\pi r}e^{-jkr}\int_V \left[\mathbf{J} - (\mathbf{J}\cdot\hat{a}_r)\hat{a}_r + \sqrt{\frac{\varepsilon}{\mu}}\,\mathbf{M}\times\hat{a}_r\right]e^{+jk\mathbf{r}'\cdot\hat{a}_r}dv' \quad (13\text{-}45a)$$

$$\mathbf{H} \simeq -j\frac{\omega\varepsilon}{4\pi r}e^{-jkr}\int_V \left[\mathbf{M} - (\mathbf{M}\cdot\hat{a}_r)\hat{a}_r - \sqrt{\frac{\mu}{\varepsilon}}\,\mathbf{J}\times\hat{a}_r\right]e^{+jk\mathbf{r}'\cdot\hat{a}_r}dv' \quad (13\text{-}45b)$$

If the current distributions are induced by electric and magnetic fields incident on a perfect electric conducting ($\sigma = \infty$) surface shown in Figure 13.18, the fields created by these currents are referred to as scattered fields. If the conducting surface is closed, the far-zone fields are obtained from (13-45a) and (13-45b) by letting $\mathbf{M} = 0$ and reducing the volume integral to a surface integral with the surface current density $\mathbf{J}$ replaced by the linear current density $\mathbf{J}_s$. Thus

$$E_s = -j\frac{\omega\mu}{4\pi r}e^{-jkr}\oiint_S \left[\mathbf{J}_s - (\mathbf{J}_s\cdot\hat{a}_r)\hat{a}_r\right]e^{+jk\mathbf{r}'\cdot\hat{a}_r}ds' \qquad (13\text{-}46a)$$

$$\mathbf{H}_s = +j\frac{\omega\sqrt{\mu\varepsilon}}{4\pi r}e^{-jkr}\oiint_S \left[\mathbf{J}_s \times \hat{a}_r\right]e^{+jk\mathbf{r}'\cdot\hat{a}_r}ds' \qquad (13\text{-}46b)$$

The electric and magnetic fields scattered by the closed surface of the reflector of Figure 13.11, and given by (13-46a) and (13-46b), are valid provided the source-density functions (current and charge) satisfy the equation of continuity. This would be satisfied if the scattering object is a smooth closed surface. For the geometry of Figure 13.11, the current distribution is discontinuous across the boundary Γ (being zero over the shadow area S_2) which divides the illuminated (S_1) and shadow (S_2) areas. It can be shown [16] that the equation of continuity can be satisfied if an appropriate line source distribution of charge is introduced along the boundary Γ. Therefore the total scattered field would be the sum of the (1)

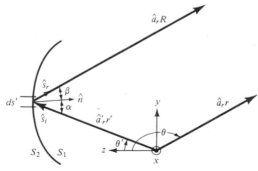

Figure 13.18 Geometrical arrangement of reflecting surface.

surface currents over the illuminated area, (2) surface charges over the illuminated area, and (3) line charge distribution over the boundary Γ.

The contributions from the surface charge density are taken into account by the current distribution through the equation of continuity. However it can be shown [16] that in the far-zone the contribution due to line-charge distribution cancels out the longitudinal component introduced by the surface current and charge distributions. Since in the far-zone the field components are predominantly transverse, the contribution due to the line-charge distribution need not be included and (13-46a)–(13-46b) can be applied to an open surface.

In this section, (13-46a) and (13-46b) will be used to calculate the field scattered from the surface of a parabolic reflector. Generally the field radiated by the currents on the shadow region of the reflector is very small compared to the total field, and the currents and field can be set equal to zero. The field scattered by the illuminated (concave) side of the parabolic reflector can be formulated, using the current distribution method, by (13-46a) and (13-46b) when the integration is restricted over the illuminated area.

The total field of the system can be obtained by a superposition of the radiation from the primary source in directions greater than θ_0 ($\theta > \theta_0$) and that scattered by the surface as obtained by using either the aperture distribution or the current distribution method.

Generally, edge effects are neglected. However the inclusion of diffracted fields [8]–[10] from the rim of the reflector not only introduce fields in the shadow region of the reflector, but also modify those present in the transition and lit regions. Any discontinuities introduced by geometrical optics methods along the transition region (between lit and shadow regions) are removed by the diffracted components.

The far-zone electric field of a parabolic reflector, neglecting the direct radiation, is given by (13-46a). When expanded, (13-46a) reduces, by referring to the geometry of Figure 13.18, to the two components of

$$E_\theta = -j\frac{\omega\mu}{4\pi r}e^{-jkr}\iint_{S_1} \hat{a}_\theta \cdot \mathbf{J}_s e^{+jk\mathbf{r}'\cdot\hat{a}_r}ds'$$

(13-47a)

$$E_\phi = -j\frac{\omega\mu}{4\pi r}e^{-jkr}\iint_{S_1} \hat{a}_\phi \cdot \mathbf{J}_s e^{+jk\mathbf{r}'\cdot\hat{a}_r}ds'$$

(13-47b)

According to the geometry of Figure 13.19

$$ds' = dW\,dN = (r'\sin\theta'\,d\phi')\left[r'\sec\left(\frac{\theta'}{2}\right)d\theta'\right]$$

$$= (r')^2\sin\theta'\sec\left(\frac{\theta'}{2}\right)d\theta'\,d\phi'$$

(13-48)

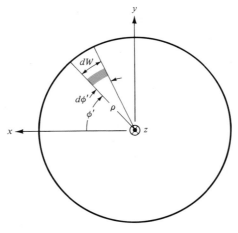

(a) Projected cross section

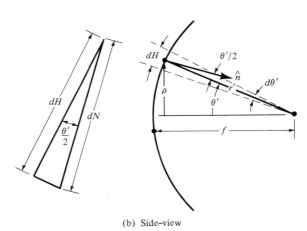

(b) Side–view

Figure 13.19 Projected cross section and side view of reflector.

since

$$dW = r' \sin\theta' \, d\phi' \tag{13-48a}$$

$$dH = -\hat{a}_r' \cdot d\mathbf{N} = -\hat{a}_r' \cdot \hat{n} \, dN$$

$$= -\hat{a}_r'\left[-\hat{a}_r'\cos\left(\frac{\theta'}{2}\right) - \hat{a}_\theta'\sin\left(\frac{\theta'}{2}\right)\right] dN = \cos\left(\frac{\theta'}{2}\right) dN \tag{13-48b}$$

$$dN = \sec\left(\frac{\theta'}{2}\right) dH = \sec\left(\frac{\theta'}{2}\right) r' \, d\theta' = r' \sec\left(\frac{\theta'}{2}\right) d\theta' \tag{13-48c}$$

Therefore, it can be shown that (13-47a) and (13-47b) can be expressed, with the aid of (13-37), (13-37a), and (13-48), as

$$\begin{bmatrix} E_\theta \\ E_\phi \end{bmatrix} = -j\frac{\omega\mu}{2\pi r}\sqrt{\frac{\varepsilon}{\mu}}\,C_1 e^{-jkr}\begin{bmatrix} \hat{a}_\theta\cdot\mathbf{I} \\ \hat{a}_\phi\cdot\mathbf{I} \end{bmatrix}$$

$$= -j\frac{\omega\mu e^{-jkr}}{2\pi r}\left[\sqrt{\frac{\varepsilon}{\mu}}\frac{P_t}{2\pi}\right]^{1/2}\begin{bmatrix} \hat{a}_\theta\cdot\mathbf{I} \\ \hat{a}_\phi\cdot\mathbf{I} \end{bmatrix}$$

(13-49)

where

$$\mathbf{I} = \mathbf{I}_t + \mathbf{I}_z$$

(13-49a)

$$\mathbf{I}_t = -\int_0^{2\pi}\int_0^{\theta_0}\hat{e}_r\cos\left(\frac{\theta'}{2}\right)\frac{\sqrt{G_f(\theta',\phi')}}{r'}\,e^{-jkr'[1-\sin\theta'\sin\theta\cos(\phi'-\phi)-\cos\theta'\cos\theta]}$$

$$\times(r')^2\sin\theta'\sec\left(\frac{\theta'}{2}\right)d\theta'\,d\phi'$$

(13-49b)

$$\mathbf{I}_z = -\hat{a}_z\int_0^{2\pi}\int_0^{\theta_0}(\hat{n}\cdot\hat{e}_r)\frac{\sqrt{G_f(\theta',\phi')}}{r'}\,e^{-jkr'[1-\sin\theta'\sin\theta\cos(\phi'-\phi)-\cos\theta'\cos\theta]}$$

$$\times(r')^2\sin\theta'\sec\left(\frac{\theta'}{2}\right)d\theta'\,d\phi'$$

(13-49c)

By comparing (13-49) with (13-35), the radiated field components formulated by the aperture distribution and current distribution methods lead to similar results provided the $\mathbf{I}_z$ contribution of (13-49c) is neglected. As the ratio of the aperture diameter to wavelength (d/λ) increases, the current distribution method results reduce to those of the aperture distribution and the angular pattern becomes more narrow.

For variations near the $\theta = \pi$ region, the $\mathbf{I}_z$ contribution becomes negligible because

$$\hat{a}_\theta\cdot\left[-\hat{a}_z(\hat{n}\cdot\hat{e}_r)\right] = \left[\hat{a}_x\sin\theta\cos\phi + \hat{a}_y\cos\theta\sin\phi - \hat{a}_z\sin\theta\right]\cdot\left[-\hat{a}_z(\hat{n}\cdot\hat{e}_r)\right]$$

$$= (\hat{n}\cdot\hat{e}_r)\sin\theta$$

(13-50a)

$$\hat{a}_\phi\cdot\left[-\hat{a}_z(\hat{n}\cdot\hat{e}_r)\right] = \left[-\hat{a}_x\sin\phi + \hat{a}_y\cos\phi\right]\cdot\left[-\hat{a}_z(\hat{n}\cdot\hat{e}_r)\right] = 0$$

(13-50b)

DIRECTIVITY AND APERTURE EFFICIENCY

In the design of antennas, the directivity is a very important figure-of-merit. The purpose of this section will be to examine the dependence of the directivity and aperture efficiency on the primary-feed pattern $G_f(\theta',\phi')$ and f/d ratio (or the included angle $2\theta_0$) of the reflector. To simplify the analysis, it will be assumed that the feed pattern $G_f(\theta',\phi')$ is circularly symmetric (not a function of ϕ') and that $G_f(\theta')=0$ for $\theta'>90°$.

The secondary pattern (formed by the surface of the reflector) is given by (13-49). Approximating the $\mathbf{I}$ of (13-49a) by $\mathbf{I}_t$, the total E-field in the $\theta = \pi$ direction is given by either E_θ or E_ϕ of (13-49). Assuming the feed is circularly symmetric, linearly polarized in the y-direction, and by neglecting cross-polarized contributions, it can be shown with the aid of (13-14a) that

(13-49) reduces to

$$E(r, \theta = \pi) = -j\frac{2\omega\mu f}{r}\left[\sqrt{\frac{\varepsilon}{\mu}}\frac{P_t}{2\pi}\right]^{1/2}e^{-jk(r+2f)}\int_0^{\theta_0}\sqrt{G_f(\theta')}\tan\left(\frac{\theta'}{2}\right)d\theta'$$

(13-51)

The power intensity (power/unit solid angle) in the forward direction $U(\theta = \pi)$ is given by

$$U(\theta = \pi) = \frac{1}{2}r^2\sqrt{\frac{\varepsilon}{\mu}}\,|\mathbf{E}(r, \theta = \pi)|^2$$

(13-52)

which by using (13-51) reduces to

$$U(\theta = \pi) = \frac{16\pi^2}{\lambda^2}f^2\frac{P_t}{4\pi}\left|\int_0^{\theta_0}\sqrt{G_f(\theta')}\tan\left(\frac{\theta'}{2}\right)d\theta'\right|^2$$

(13-52a)

The antenna directivity in the forward direction can be written, using (13-52a), as

$$D_o = \frac{4\pi U(\theta = \pi)}{P_t} = \frac{U(\theta = \pi)}{P_t/4\pi} = \frac{16\pi^2}{\lambda^2}f^2\left|\int_0^{\theta_0}\sqrt{G_f(\theta')}\tan\left(\frac{\theta'}{2}\right)d\theta'\right|^2$$

(13-53)

The focal length is related to the angular spectrum and aperture diameter d by (13-25). Thus (13-53) reduces to

$$D_o = \left(\frac{\pi d}{\lambda}\right)^2\left\{\cot^2\left(\frac{\theta_0}{2}\right)\left|\int_0^{\theta_0}\sqrt{G_f(\theta')}\tan\left(\frac{\theta'}{2}\right)d\theta'\right|^2\right\}$$

(13-54)

The factor $(\pi d/\lambda)^2$ is the directivity of a uniformly illuminated constant phase aperture; the remaining part is the aperture efficiency defined as

$$\varepsilon_{ap} = \cot^2\left(\frac{\theta_0}{2}\right)\left|\int_0^{\theta_0}\sqrt{G_f(\theta')}\tan\left(\frac{\theta'}{2}\right)d\theta'\right|^2$$

(13-55)

It is apparent by examining (13-55) that the aperture efficiency is a function of the subtended angle (θ_0) and the feed pattern $G_f(\theta')$ of the reflector. Thus for a given feed pattern, all paraboloids with the same f/d ratio have identical aperture efficiency.

To illustrate the variation of the aperture efficiency as a function of the feed pattern and the angular extent of the reflector, Silver [16] considered a class of feeds whose patterns are defined by

$$G_f(\theta') = \begin{cases} G_0^{(n)}\cos^n(\theta') & 0 \le \theta' \le \pi/2 \\ 0 & \pi/2 < \theta' \le \pi \end{cases}$$

(13-56)

where $G_0^{(n)}$ is a constant for a given value of n. Although idealistic, these patterns were chosen because (1) closed form solutions can be obtained, and (2) they often are used to represent a major part of the main lobe of many practical antennas. The intensity in the back region $(\pi/2 < \theta' \leq \pi)$ was assumed to be zero in order to avoid interference between direct radiation from the feed and scattered radiation from the reflector.

The constant $G_0^{(n)}$ can be determined from the relation

$$\oiint_S G_f(\theta')\, d\Omega = \oiint_S G_f(\theta') \sin\theta'\, d\theta'\, d\phi' = 4\pi \tag{13-57}$$

which for (13-56) becomes

$$G_0^{(n)} \int_0^{\pi/2} \cos^n\theta' \sin\theta'\, d\theta' = 2 \Rightarrow G_0^n = 2(n+1) \tag{13-58}$$

Substituting (13-56) and (13-58) into (13-55) leads, for the even values of $n = 2$ through $n = 8$, to

$$\varepsilon_{ap}(n=2) = 24\left\{\sin^2\left(\frac{\theta_0}{2}\right) + \ln\left[\cos\left(\frac{\theta_0}{2}\right)\right]\right\}^2 \cot^2\left(\frac{\theta_0}{2}\right) \tag{13-59a}$$

$$\varepsilon_{ap}(n=4) = 40\left\{\sin^4\left(\frac{\theta_0}{2}\right) + \ln\left[\cos\left(\frac{\theta_0}{2}\right)\right]\right\}^2 \cot^2\left(\frac{\theta_0}{2}\right) \tag{13-59b}$$

$$\varepsilon_{ap}(n=6) = 14\left\{2\ln\left[\cos\left(\frac{\theta_0}{2}\right)\right] + \frac{[1-\cos(\theta_0)]^3}{3}\right.$$

$$\left. + \frac{1}{2}\sin^2(\theta_0)\right\}^2 \cot^2\left(\frac{\theta_0}{2}\right) \tag{13-59c}$$

$$\varepsilon_{ap}(n=8) = 18\left\{\frac{1-\cos^4(\theta_0)}{4} - 2\ln\left[\cos\left(\frac{\theta_0}{2}\right)\right] - \frac{[1-\cos(\theta_0)]^3}{3}\right.$$

$$\left. - \frac{1}{2}\sin^2(\theta_0)\right\}^2 \cot^2\left(\frac{\theta_0}{2}\right) \tag{13-59d}$$

The variations of (13-59a)–(13-59d), as a function of the angular aperture of the reflector θ_0 or the f/d ratio, are shown plotted in Figure 13.20. It is apparent, from the graphical illustration, that for a given feed pattern ($n =$ constant)

1. There is only one reflector with a given angular aperture or f/d ratio which leads to a maximum aperture efficiency.
2. Each maximum aperture efficiency, shown by the dashed line Figure 13.20, is in the neighborhood of 82–83%.
3. Each maximum aperture efficiency, for any one of the given patterns, is almost the same as that of any of the others.

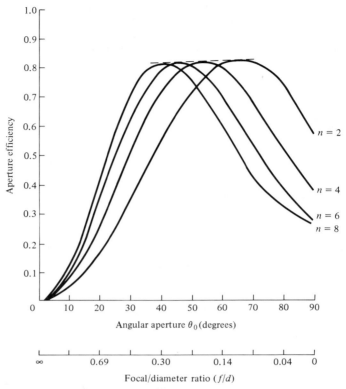

Figure 13.20 Aperture efficiency of reflector as a function of angular aperture (or f/d ratio) for different feed patterns. (SOURCE: S. Silver (ed.), *Microwave Antenna Theory and Design* (MIT Radiation Lab. Series, vol. 12), McGraw-Hill, New York, 1949.)

4. As the feed pattern becomes more directive (n increases),· the angular aperture of the reflector that leads to the maximum efficiency is smaller.

The aperture efficiency is generally the product of the

1. fraction of the total power that is radiated by the feed, intercepted, and collimated by the reflecting surface (generally known as spillover efficiency ε_s)
2. uniformity of the amplitude distribution of the feed pattern over the surface of the reflector (generally known as taper efficiency ε_t)
3. phase uniformity of the field over the aperture plane (generally known as phase efficiency ε_p)
4. polarization uniformity of the field over the aperture plane (generally known as polarization efficiency ε_x)
5. blockage efficiency ε_b
6. random error efficiency ε_r over the reflector surface

Thus in general

$$\boxed{\varepsilon_{ap} = \varepsilon_s \varepsilon_t \varepsilon_p \varepsilon_x \varepsilon_b \varepsilon_r}$$

(13-60)

For feeds with symmetrical patterns

$$\boxed{\varepsilon_s = \frac{\int_0^{\theta_0} G_f(\theta') \sin \theta' \, d\theta'}{\int_0^{\pi} G_f(\theta') \sin \theta' \, d\theta'}}$$

(13-61)

$$\boxed{\varepsilon_t = 2 \cot^2\left(\frac{\theta_0}{2}\right) \frac{\left| \int_0^{\theta_0} \sqrt{G_f(\theta')} \, \tan\left(\frac{\theta'}{2}\right) d\theta' \right|^2}{\int_0^{\theta_0} G_f(\theta') \sin \theta' \, d\theta'}}$$

(13-62)

which by using (13-25) can also be written as

$$\boxed{\varepsilon_t = 32 \left(\frac{f}{d}\right)^2 \frac{\left| \int_0^{\theta_0} \sqrt{G_f(\theta')} \, \tan\left(\frac{\theta'}{2}\right) d\theta' \right|^2}{\int_0^{\theta_0} G_f(\theta') \sin \theta' \, d\theta'}}$$

(13-62a)

Thus

1. $100(1 - \varepsilon_s)$=percent power loss due to energy from feed spilling past the main reflector
2. $100(1 - \varepsilon_t)$=percent power loss due to nonuniform amplitude distribution over the reflector surface
3. $100(1 - \varepsilon_p)$=percent power loss if the field over the aperture plane is not in phase everywhere.
4. $100(1 - \varepsilon_x)$=percent power loss if there are cross-polarized fields over the antenna aperture plane.
5. $100(1 - \varepsilon_b)$=percent power loss due to blockage provided by the feed or supporting struts (also by subreflector for a dual reflector).
6. $100(1 - \varepsilon_r)$=percent power loss due to random errors over the reflector surface.

An additional factor that reduces the antenna gain is the attenuation in the antenna feed and associated transmission line.
    For feeds with

1. symmetrical patterns
2. aligned phase centers
3. no cross-polarized field components

4. no blockage
5. no random surface error

the two main factors that contribute to the aperture efficiency are the spillover and nonuniform amplitude distribution losses. Because these losses depend primarily on the feed pattern, a compromise between spillover and taper efficiency must emerge. Very high spillover efficiency can be achieved by a narrow beam pattern with a low minor lobes at the expense of a very low taper efficiency. Uniform illumination and ideal taper efficiency can be obtained when the feed power pattern is

$$
G_f(\theta') = \begin{cases} \sec^4\left(\dfrac{\theta'}{2}\right) & 0 \le \theta' \le \theta_0 \\ 0 & \theta' > \theta_0 \end{cases} \tag{13-63}
$$

which is shown plotted in Figure 13.21. Although such a pattern is "ideal" and impractical to achieve, much effort has been devoted to develop feed designs which attempt to approximate it [12].

To develop guidelines for designing practical feeds which result in high aperture efficiencies, it is instructive to examine the relative field strength at the edges of the reflector's bounds ($\theta' = \theta_0$) for patterns that lead to optimum efficiencies. For the patterns of (13-56), when used with reflectors that result in optimum efficiencies as demonstrated graphically in Figure 13.20, the relative field strength at the edges of their angular bounds ($\theta' = \theta_0$) is shown plotted in Figure 13.22. Thus for $n = 2$ the field strength of the pattern at $\theta' = \theta_0$ is 8 dB down from the maximum. As the pattern becomes more narrow (n increases), the relative field strength at the edges for maximum efficiency is further reduced as illustrated in Figure 13.20. Since for $n = 2$ through $n = 10$ the field strength is between 8 to 10.5 dB down, for most practical feeds the figure used is 9–10 dB.

Another parameter to examine for the patterns of (13-56), when used with reflectors that lead to optimum efficiency, is the amplitude taper or

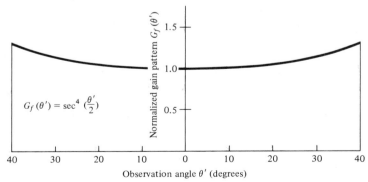

Figure 13.21 Normalized gain pattern of feed for uniform amplitude illumination of paraboloidal reflector with a total subtended angle of 80°.

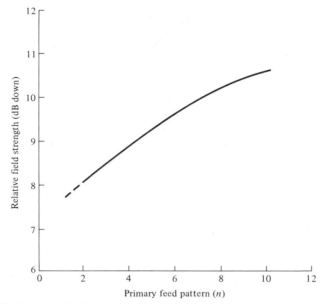

Figure 13.22   Relative field strength of feed pattern along reflector edge bounds as a function of primary feed pattern number ($\cos^n\theta$). (SOURCE: S. Silver (ed.), *Microwave Antenna Theory and Design* (MIT Radiation Lab. Series, vol. 12), McGraw-Hill, New York, 1949)

illumination of the main aperture of the reflector which is defined as the ratio of the field strength at the edge of the reflector surface to that at the vertex. The aperture illumination is a function of the feed pattern and the f/d ratio of the reflector. To obtain that, the ratio of the angular variation of the pattern toward the two points $[G_f(\theta'=0)/G_f(\theta'=\theta_0)]$ is multiplied by the space attenuation factor $(r'/r_0)^2$, where r' is the distance from the focal point to any point on the reflector and r_0 is the distance from the focal point to the edge of the reflector. For each of the patterns, the reflector edge illumination for maximum efficiency is 11 dB down from that at the vertex.

The results obtained with the idealized patterns of (13-56) should only be taken as typical, because it was assumed that

1. the field intensity for $\theta'>90°$ was zero
2. the feed was placed at the phase center of the system
3. the patterns were symmetrical
4. there were no cross-polarized field components
5. there was no blockage
6. there were no random errors at the surface of the reflector

Each factor can have a significant effect on the efficiency, and each has received much attention which is well documented in the open literature [1].

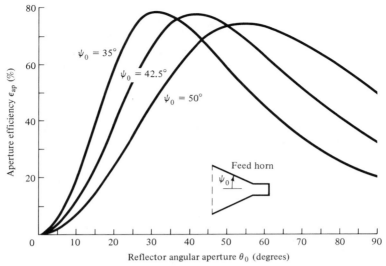

Figure 13.23 Parabolic reflector aperture efficiency as a function of angular aperture for $8\lambda \times 8\lambda$ square corrugated horn feed with total flare angles of $2\psi_0 = 70°$, $85°$, and $100°$.

In practice, maximum reflector efficiencies are in the 65–80% range. To demonstrate that, paraboloidal reflector efficiencies for square corrugated horns feeds were computed, and they are shown plotted in Figure 13.23. The corresponding amplitude taper and spillover efficiencies are displayed in Figure 13.24. Each of the horns had aperture dimensions of $8\lambda \times 8\lambda$, their patterns were assumed to be symmetrical (by averaging the E- and H-planes), and they were computed using the techniques of Section 12.6. From the plotted data, it is apparent that the maximum aperture efficiency for each feed pattern is in the range of 74–79%, and that the product of the taper and spillover efficiencies is approximately equal to the total aperture efficiency.

We would be remiss if we left the discussion of this section without reporting the gain of some of the largest reflectors that exist around the world [22]. The gains are shown in Figure 13.25 and include the 1000-ft (305-m) diameter spherical reflector [11] at Arecibo, Puerto Rico, the 100-m radio telescope [14] at Effelsberg, West Germany, the 64-m reflector [15] at Goldstone, California, the 22-m reflector at Krim, USSR, and the 12-m telescope at Kitt Peak, Arizona. The dashed portions of the curves indicate extrapolated values. For the Arecibo reflector, two curves are shown. The 215-m diameter curve is for a reduced aperture of the large reflector (305-m) for which a line feed at 1415 MHz was designed [11].

PHASE ERRORS
Any departure of the phase, over the aperture of the antenna, from uniform can lead to a significant diminution of its directivity [23]. For a paraboloidal

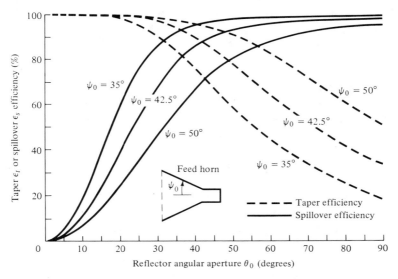

Figure 13.24 Parabolic reflector taper and spillover efficiencies as a function of reflector aperture for different corrugated horn feeds.

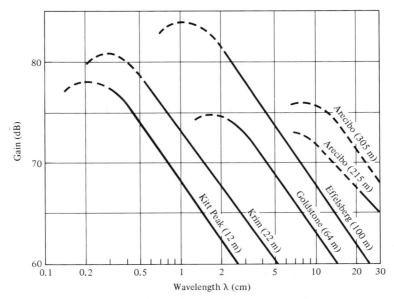

Figure 13.25 Gains of some worldwide large reflector antennas. (SOURCE: A. W. Love, "Some Highlights in Reflector Antenna Development," *Radio Science*, vol. 11, Nos. 8, 9, August–September 1976)

reflector system, phase errors result from [16]

1. displacement (defocusing) of the feed phase center from the focal point
2. deviation of the reflector surface from a parabolic shape or random errors at the surface of the reflector
3. departure of the feed wave fronts from spherical shape

The defocusing effect can be reduced by first locating the phase center of the feed antenna and then placing it at the focal point of the reflector. In Chapter 12 (Section 12.7) it was shown that the phase center for horn antennas, which are widely utilized as feeds for reflectors, is located between the aperture of the horn and the apex formed by the intersection of the inclined walls of the horn [24].

Very simple expressions have been derived [23] to predict the loss in directivity for rectangular and circular apertures when the peak values of the aperture phase deviation is known. When the phase errors are assumed to be relatively small, it is not necessary to know the exact amplitude or phase distribution function over the aperture.

Assuming the maximum radiation occurs along the axis of the reflector, and that the maximum phase deviation over the aperture of the reflector can be represented by

$$|\Delta\phi(z)| = |\phi(z) - \overline{\phi(z)}| \leq m, \qquad -1 \leq z \leq 1 \tag{13-64}$$

where $\phi(z)$ is the aperture phase function and $\overline{\phi(z)}$ is its average value, then the ratio of the directivity with (D) and without (D_0) phase errors can be written as [23]

$$\boxed{\frac{D}{D_0} = \frac{\text{directivity with phase error}}{\text{directivity without phase error}} \geq \left(1 - \frac{m^2}{2}\right)^2} \tag{13-65}$$

and the maximum fractional reduction in directivity as

$$\frac{\Delta D}{D_0} = \frac{D_0 - D}{D_0} \leq m^2 \left(1 - \frac{m^2}{4}\right) \tag{13-66}$$

Relatively simple expressions have also been derived [23] to compute the maximum possible change in half-power beamwidth.

Example 13.1

A 10-m diameter reflector, with an f/d ratio of 0.5, is operating at $f = 3$ GHz. The reflector is fed with an antenna whose primary pattern is symmetrical and which can be approximated by $G_f(\theta') = 6\cos^2\theta'$. Find its

(a) aperture efficiency
(b) overall directivity
(c) spillover and taper efficiencies
(d) directivity when the maximum aperture phase deviation is $\pi/8$ rad

SOLUTION

Using (13-24), half of the subtended angle of the reflector is equal to

$$\theta_0 = \tan^{-1}\left[\frac{0.5(0.5)}{(0.5)^2 - \frac{1}{16}}\right] = 53.13°$$

(a) The aperture efficiency is obtained using (13-59a). Thus

$$\varepsilon_{ap} = 24\{\sin^2(26.57°) + \ln[\cos(26.57°)]\}^2 \cot^2(26.57°)$$
$$= 0.75 = 75\%$$

which agrees with the data of Figure 13.20.

(b) The overall directivity is obtained by (13-54), or

$$D = 0.75[\pi(100)]^2 = 74,022.03 = 48.69 \text{ dB}$$

(c) The spillover efficiency is computed using (13-61) where the upper limit of the integral in the denominator has been replaced by $\pi/2$. Thus

$$\varepsilon_s = \frac{\int_0^{53.13°} \cos^2\theta' \sin\theta' d\theta'}{\int_0^{90°} \cos^2\theta' \sin\theta' d\theta'} = \frac{2\cos^3\theta'|_0^{53.13°}}{2\cos^3\theta'|_0^{90°}} = 0.784 = 78.4\%$$

In a similar manner, the taper efficiency is computed using (13-62). Since the numerator in (13-62) is identical in form to the aperture efficiency of (13-55), it can be found by multiplying (13-59a) by 2 and dividing by the denominator of (13-62). Thus

$$\varepsilon_t = \frac{2(0.75)}{1.568} = 0.9566 = 95.66\%$$

The product of ε_s and ε_t is equal to

$$\varepsilon_s \varepsilon_t = 0.784(0.9566) = 0.75$$

and it is identical to the total aperture efficiency computed above.

(d) The directivity for a maximum phase error of $m = \pi/8 = 0.3927$ rad can be computed using (13-65). Thus

$$\frac{D}{D_0} \geq \left(1 - \frac{m^2}{2}\right)^2 = \left[1 - \frac{(0.3927)^2}{2}\right]^2 = 0.8517 = -0.69 \text{ dB}$$

or $D \geq 0.8517 D_0 = 0.8517(74,022.03) = 63,046.94 = 48.0 \text{ dB}$

Surface roughness effects on the directivity of the antenna were first examined by Ruze [25] where he indicated that for any reflector antenna there is a wavelength (λ_{max}) at which the directivity reaches a maximum. This wavelength depends on the RMS deviation (σ) of the reflector surface from an ideal paraboloid. For a random roughness of Gaussian distribution, with correlation interval large compared to the wavelength, they are related

by

$$\lambda_{max} = 4\pi\sigma \tag{13-67}$$

Thus the directivity of the antenna, given by (13-54), is modified to include surface roughness and can be written as

$$D = \left(\frac{\pi d}{\lambda}\right)^2 \varepsilon_{ap} e^{-(4\pi\sigma/\lambda)^2} \tag{13-68}$$

Using (13-67), the maximum directivity of (13-68) can be written as

$$\boxed{D_{max} = 10^{2q}\varepsilon_{ap}\left(\frac{e^{-1}}{16}\right)} \tag{13-69}$$

where q is the index of smoothness defined by

$$\frac{d}{\sigma} = 10^{+q} \tag{13-70}$$

In decibels, (13-69) reduces to

$$\boxed{D_{max}(dB) = 20q - 16.38 + 10\log_{10}(\varepsilon_{ap})} \tag{13-71}$$

For an aperture efficiency of unity ($\varepsilon_{ap} = 1$), the directivity of (13-68) is plotted in Figure 13.26, as a function of (d/λ), for values of $q = 3.5$, 4.0, and

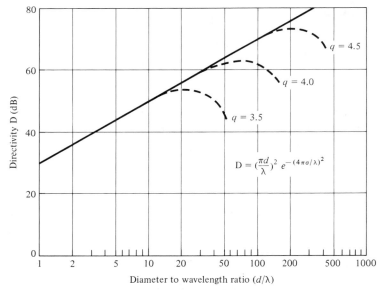

Figure 13.26   Reflector surface roughness effects on antenna directivity. (SOURCE: A. W. Love, "Some Highlights in Reflector Antenna Development," *Radio Science*, vol. 11, Nos. 8, 9, August–September 1976)

4.5. It is apparent that for each value of q and a given reflector diameter d, there is a maximum wavelength where the directivity reaches a maximum value. This maximum wavelength is given by (13-67).

FEED DESIGN

The widespread use of paraboloidal reflectors has stimulated interest in the development of feeds to improve the aperture efficiency and to provide greater discrimination against noise radiation from the ground. This can be accomplished by developing design techniques that permit the synthesis of feed patterns with any desired distribution over the bounds of the reflector, rapid cutoff at its edges, and very low minor lobes in all the other space. In recent years, the two main problems that concerned feed designers were aperture efficiency and low cross-polarization.

In the receiving mode, an ideal feed and a matched load would be one that would absorb all the energy intercepted by the aperture when uniform and linearly polarized plane waves are normally incident upon it. The feed field structure must be made to match the focal region field structure formed by the reflecting, scattering, and diffracting characteristics of the reflector. By reciprocity, an ideal feed in the transmitting mode would be one that radiates only within the solid angle of the aperture and establishes within it an identical outward traveling wave. For this ideal feed system, the transmitting and receiving mode field structures within the focal region are identical with only the direction of propagation reversed.

An optical analysis indicates that the focal region fields, formed by the reflection of linearly polarized plane waves incident normally on an axially symmetric reflector, are represented by the well-known Airy rings described mathematically by the amplitude distribution intensity of $[2J_1(u)/u]^2$. This description is incomplete, because it is a scalar solution, and it does not take into account polarization effects. In addition, it is valid only for reflectors with large f/d ratios, which are commonly used in optical systems, and it would be significantly in error for reflectors with f/d ratios of 0.25 to 0.5, which are commonly used in microwave applications.

A vector solution has been developed [26] which indicates that the fields near the focal region can be expressed by hybrid TE and TM modes propagating along the axis of the reflector. This representation provides a clear physical picture for the understanding of the focal region field formation. The boundary conditions of the hybrid modes indicate that these field structures can be represented by a spectrum of hybrid waves that are linear combinations of TE_{1n} and TM_{1n} modes of circular waveguides.

A single hollow pipe cannot simultaneously satisfy both the TE and TM modes because of the different radial periodicities. However, it has been shown that $\lambda/4$ deep annular slots on the inner surface of a circular pipe force the boundary conditions on $\mathbf{E}$ and $\mathbf{H}$ to be the same and provide a single anisotropic reactance surface which satisfies the boundary conditions on both TE and TM modes. This provided the genesis of hybrid mode

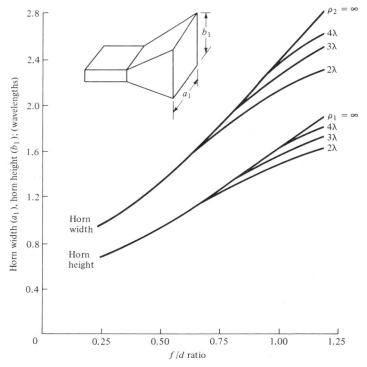

Figure 13.27 Optimum pyramidal horn dimensions versus f/d ratio for various horn lengths.

waveguide radiators [27] and corrugated horns [28]. Corrugated horns, whose aperture size and flare angle are such that at least 180° phase error over their aperture is assured, are known as "scalar" horns [29]. Design data for uncorrugated horns that can be used to maximize the aperture efficiency or to produce maximum power transmission to the feed have been calculated [30] and are shown in graphical form in Figure 13.27.

13.4.2 Cassegrain Reflectors

To improve the performance of large ground-based microwave reflector antennas for satellite tracking and communication, it has been proposed that a two-reflector system be utilized. The arrangement suggested was the Cassegrain dual-reflector system [31] of Figure 13.1(d), which was often utilized in the design of optical telescopes and it was named after its inventor. To achieve the desired collimation characteristics, the larger (main) reflector must be a paraboloid and the smaller (secondary) a hyperboloid. The use of a second reflector, which is usually referred to as the subreflector or subdish, gives an additional degree of freedom for achieving good performance in a number of different applications. For an accurate description of its performance, diffraction techniques must be used to take into account diffractions from the edges of the subreflector, especially when its diameter is small [32].

In general, the Cassegrain arrangement provides a variety of benefits, such as the

1. ability to place the feed in a convenient location
2. reduction of spillover and minor lobe radiation
3. ability to obtain an equivalent focal length much greater than the physical length
4. capability for scanning and/or broadening of the beam by moving one of the reflecting surfaces

To achieve good radiation characteristics, the subreflector or subdish must be several, at least a few, wavelengths in diameter. However, its presence introduces shadowing which is the principal limitation of its use as a microwave antenna. The shadowing can significantly degrade the gain of the system, unless the main reflector is several wavelengths in diameter. Therefore the Cassegrain is usually attractive for applications that require gains of 40 dB or greater. There are, however, a variety of techniques that can be used to minimize aperture blocking by the subreflector. Some of them are [31] (1) minimum blocking with simple Cassegrain, and (2) twisting Cassegrains for least blocking.

The first comprehensive published analysis of the Cassegrain arrangement as a microwave antenna is that by Hannan [31]. He uses geometrical optics to derive the geometrical shape of the reflecting surfaces, and he introduces the equivalence concepts of the virtual feed and the equivalent parabola. Although his analysis does not predict fine details, it does give reasonably good results. Refinements to his analysis have been introduced [32]–[34].

To improve the aperture efficiency, suitable modifications to the geometrical shape of the reflecting surfaces have been suggested [35]–[37]. The reshaping of the reflecting surfaces is used to generate desirable amplitude and phase distributions over one or both of the reflectors. The resultant system is usually referred to as *shaped* dual-reflector. The reflector antenna of Figure 13.9 is such a system. Shaped reflector surfaces, generated using analytical models, are illustrated in [37]. It also has been suggested [33] that a flange is placed around the subreflector to improve the aperture efficiency.

Because a comprehensive treatment of this arrangement can be very lengthy, only a brief introduction of the system will be presented here. The interested reader is referred to the referenced literature.

CLASSICAL CASSEGRAIN FORM

The operation of the Cassegrain arrangement can be introduced by referring to Figure 13.1(d) and assuming the system is operating in the receiving or transmitting mode. To illustrate the principle, a receiving mode will be adopted.

Let us assume that energy, in the form of parallel rays, is incident upon the reflector system. Energy intercepted by the main reflector, which has a large concave surface, is reflected toward the subreflector. Energy collected by the convex surface of the subdish is reflected by it, and it is directed toward the vertex of the main dish. If the incident rays are parallel, the main reflector is a paraboloid, and the subreflector is a hyperboloid, then the collected bundle of rays is focused at a single point. The receiver is then placed at this focusing point.

A similar procedure can be used to describe the system in the transmitting mode. The feed is placed at the focusing point, and it is usually sufficiently small so that the subdish is located in its far-field region. In addition, the subreflector is large enough that it intercepts most of the radiation from the feed. Using the geometrical arrangement of the paraboloid and the hyperboloid, the rays reflected by the main dish will be parallel. The amplitude taper of the emerging rays is determined by the feed pattern and the tapering effect of the geometry.

The geometry of the classical Cassegrain system, employing a concave paraboloid as the main dish and a convex hyperboloid as the subreflector, is simple and it can be described completely by only four independent parameters (two for each reflector). The analytical details can be found in [31].

To aid in the understanding and in predicting the essential performance of a Cassegrain, the concept of *virtual feed* [31] is useful. By this principle, the real feed and the subreflector are replaced by an equivalent system which consists of a virtual feed located at the focal point of the main reflector, as shown by the dashed lines of Figure 13.28(a). For analysis purposes then, the new system is a single-reflector arrangement with the original main dish, a different feed, and no subreflector.

The configuration of the virtual feed can be determined by finding the optical image of the real feed. This technique is only accurate when examining the effective aperture of the feed and when the dimensions of the real and virtual feeds are larger than a wavelength. In fact, for the classical Cassegrain arrangement of Figure 13.28(a), the virtual feed has a smaller effective aperture, and a corresponding broader beamwidth, than the real feed. The increase in beamwidth is a result of the convex curvature of the subreflector, and it can be determined by equating the ratio of the virtual to real-feed beamwidths to the ratio of the angles θ_v/θ_r.

The ability to obtain a different effective aperture for the virtual feed as compared to that of the real feed is useful in many applications such as in a monopulse antenna [31]. To maintain efficient and wideband performance and effective utilization of the main aperture, this system requires a large feed aperture, a corresponding long focal length, and a large antenna structure. The antenna dimensions can be maintained relatively small by employing the Cassegrain configuration which utilizes a large feed and a short focal length for the main reflector.

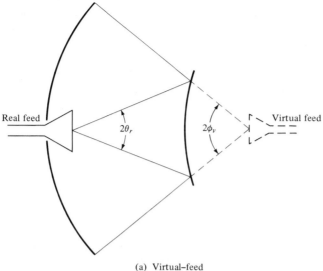

(a) Virtual–feed

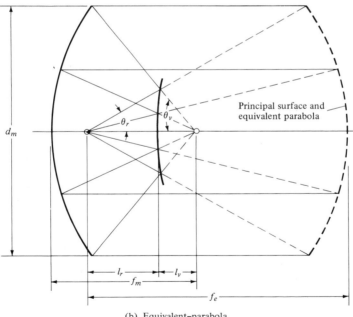

(b) Equivalent–parabola

Figure 13.28 Virtual-feed and equivalent parabola concepts. (SOURCE: P. W. Hannan, "Microwave Antennas Derived from the Cassegrain Telescope," *IRE Trans. Antennas Propag.* vol. AP-9, March 1961. © (1961) IEEE)

Although the concept of virtual feed can furnish useful qualitative information for a Cassegrain system, it is not convenient for an accurate quantitative analysis. Some of the limitations of the virtual feed concept can be overcome by the concept of the *equivalent parabola* [31].

By the technique of the equivalent parabola, the main dish and the subreflector are replaced by an equivalent focusing surface at a certain distance from the real focal point. This surface is shown dashed in Figure 13.28(b), and it is defined as [31] "the locus of intersection of incoming rays parallel to the antenna axis with the extension of the corresponding rays converging toward the real focal point." Based on simple geometrical optics ray tracing, the equivalent focusing surface for a Cassegrain configuration is a paraboloid whose focal length equals the distance from its vertex to the real focal point. This equivalent system also reduces to a single-reflector arrangement, which has the same feed but a different main reflector, and it is accurate when the subreflector is only a few wavelengths in diameter. More accurate results can be obtained by including diffraction patterns. It also has the capability to focus toward the real focal point an incoming plane wave, incident from the opposite direction, in exactly the same manner as the actual main dish and the subreflector.

CASSEGRAIN AND GREGORIAN FORMS

In addition to the classical Cassegrain forms, there are other configurations that employ a variety of main reflector and subreflector surfaces and include concave, convex, and flat shapes [31]. In one form, the main dish is held invariant while its feed beamwidth progressively increases and the axial dimensions of the antenna progressively decrease. In another form, the feed beamwidth is held invariant while the main reflector becomes progressively flatter and the axial dimensions progressively increase.

A series of configurations in which the feed beamwidth is progressively increased, while the overall antenna dimensions are held fixed, are shown in Figure 13.29. The first five are referred to as Cassegrain forms while the last two are Gregorian forms, whose configurations are similar to the Gregorian telescope. A number of parameter ranges, along with distinguishing characteristics, are indicated alongside each configuration sketch. The main dish for the fourth configuration has degenerated to a flat contour, the subreflector to a parabolic contour, and they can be separated by distances where the ray-tracing approximation is valid. For the fifth configuration, the subreflector has degenerated to a ridiculous extreme concave elliptical contour and the main dish to a convex parabolic form, with the former being larger than the latter.

For the last two configurations, which are referred to as Gregorian forms, the focal point of the main dish has moved to the region between the two dishes and the subreflector has attained a concave elliptical contour. When the overall size and the feed beamwidth of the classical Gregorian are identical to those of the classical Cassegrain, the Gregorian form requires a

	Illustration	θ_v/θ_r and f_e/f_m	f_m and f_c	e
Cassegrain reflector forms	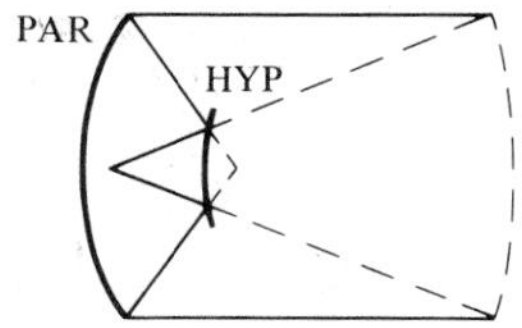 PAR / HYP — Convex subdish (classical form)	>1	>0	>1
	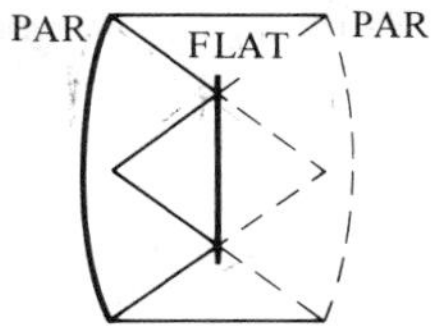 PAR FLAT PAR — Flat subdish	1	>0	∞
	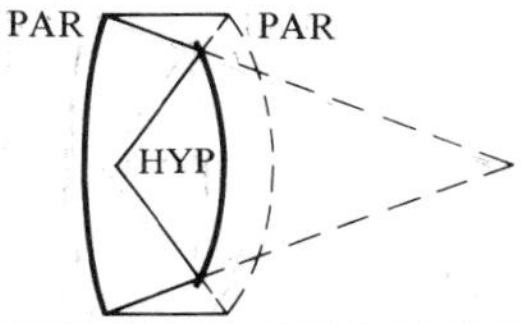 PAR PAR / HYP — Concave subdish	<1 >0	>0	<-1
	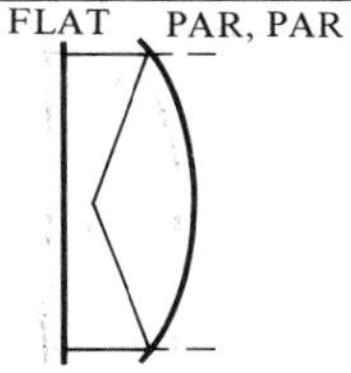 FLAT PAR, PAR — Flat main dish	0	∞	1
	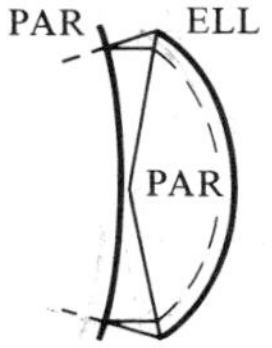 PAR ELL PAR — Convex main dish	<0 >-1	<0	<0 >-1
Gregorian reflector forms	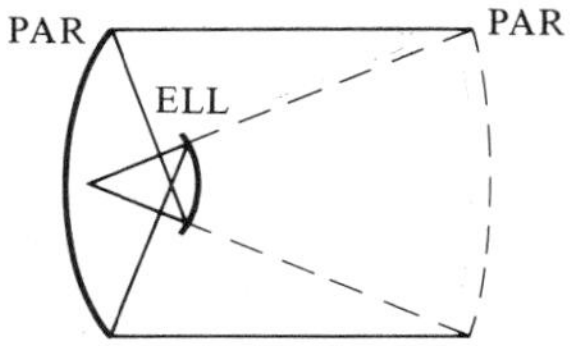 PAR ELL PAR — Feed in rear (classical form)	>1	>0	>0 <1
	PAR PAR ELL — Feed in front of main dish focus	<1	<0	>0 <1

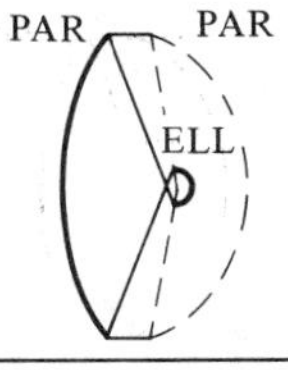

Figure 13.29 Series of Cassegrain and Gregorian reflector forms. (SOURCE: P. W. Hannan, "Microwave Antennas Derived from the Cassegrain Telescope," *IRE Trans. Antennas Propag.*, vol. AP-9, March 1961. © (1961) IEEE)

shorter focal length for the main dish. The feed for the second of the Gregorian forms has moved to a location between the focus of the main dish and the subreflector while the main dish has kept the same dimensions as the first form. In general, this configuration has several major disadvantages that make it unattractive for many antenna applications.

From the data in Figure 13.29, the relative sizes of the effective apertures of the virtual and real feeds can be inferred. When the subreflector is flat, the real and virtual feeds are identical. The virtual feeds of the Cassegrain configurations, which have a concave subreflector, possess smaller beamwidths and larger effective apertures than their corresponding real feeds. However, the virtual feed of the classical Gregorian configuration, which also has a concave subreflector, possesses an effective aperture which is smaller than that of the real feed.

The equivalent parabola concept is applicable to all the Cassegrain and Gregorian forms, and they are shown dashed in Figure 13.29. The classical Cassegrain and Gregorian configurations have equivalent focal lengths which are greater than the focal lengths of the corresponding main dishes. For the Cassegrain arrangement with the flat subreflector, the equivalent focal length is equal to the focal length of the main dish. In general, the equivalent focal lengths of the Cassegrain configurations which have a concave subreflector are shorter than the focal lengths of their corresponding main dishes. For the configuration with the flat main dish, the equivalent parabola is identical with the subreflector.

The equivalent parabola concept can also be used to determine the amplitude taper across the aperture of a Cassegrain arrangement. As for the front-fed configuration, the amplitude taper or aperture illumination is determined by the radiation pattern of the feed modified by the space attenuation factor of the reflector. The amplitude taper of a Cassegrain configuration is identical to that of a front-fed arrangement whose feed is the actual feed and whose focal length is the equivalent focal length. In other words, the process is identical to that of a front-fed configuration except that the equivalent f_e/d ratio is used.

13.5 SPHERICAL REFLECTOR

The discussion and results presented in the previous sections illustrate that a paraboloidal reflector is an ideal collimating device. However, despite all of its advantages and many applications it is severely handicapped in angular scanning. Although scanning can be accomplished by (1) mechanical rotation of the entire structure, and (2) displacement of the feed alone, it is thwarted by the large mechanical moment of inertia in the first case and by the large coma and astigmatism in the second. By contrast, the spherical reflector can make an ideal wide-angle scanner because of its perfectly symmetrical geometrical configuration. However, it is plagued by poor inherent collimating properties. If, for example, a point source is placed at

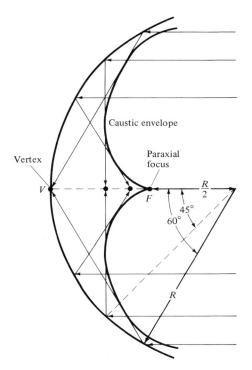

Figure 13.30 Spherical reflector geometry and rays that form a caustic.

the focus of the sphere, it does not produce plane waves. The departure of the reflected wavefront from a plane wave is known as spherical aberration, and it depends on the diameter and focal length of the sphere. By reciprocity, plane waves incident on a spherical reflector surface parallel to its axis do not converge at the focal point. However a spherical reflector has the capability of focusing plane waves incident at various angles by translating and orientating the feed and by illuminating different parts of the structural geometry. The 1000-ft diameter reflector [11] at Arecibo, Puerto Rico is a spherical reflector whose surface is built into the earth and the scanning is accomplished by movement of the feed.

The focusing characteristics of a typical spherical reflector is illustrated in Figure 13.30 for three rays. The point F in the figure is the paraxial focus, and it is equal to one-half the radius of the sphere. The caustic* surface is an epicycloid and is generated by the reflection of parallel rays. A degenerate line FV of this caustic is parallel to the incident rays and extends from

---

*A caustic is a point, a line, or a surface through which all the rays in a bundle pass and where the intensity is infinite. The caustic also represents the geometrical loci of all the centers of curvature of the wave surfaces. Examples of it include the focal line for cylindrical parabolic reflector and the focal point of a paraboloidal reflector.

the paraxial focus to the vertex of the reflector. If one draws a ray diagram of plane waves incident within a 120° cone, it will be shown that all energy must pass through the line FV. Thus, the line FV can be used for the placement of the feed for the interception of plane waves incident parallel to the axial line. It can thus be said that a spherical reflector possesses a line focus instead of a point. However, amplitude and phase corrections must be made in order to realize maximum antenna efficiency.

Ashmead and Pippard [38] proposed to reduce spherical aberration and to minimize path error by placing a point source feed not at the paraxial focus F (half radius of the sphere), as taught in optics, but displaced slightly toward the reflector. For an aperture of diameter d, the correct location for placing a point source is a distance f_0 from the vertex such that the maximum path error value is [38]

$$\Delta_{max} \simeq \frac{d^4}{200 f_0^{\,3}} \qquad\qquad (13\text{-}72)$$

and the maximum phase error does not differ from a paraboloid by more than one-eighth of a wavelength. This, however, leads to large f/d and to poor area utilization. A similar result was obtained by Li [39]. He stated that the total phase error (sum of maximum absolute values of positive and negative phase errors) over an aperture of radius a is least when the phase error at the edge of the aperture is zero. Thus the optimum focal length is

$$f_{op} = \frac{1}{4}\left(R + \sqrt{R^2 - a^2} \right) \qquad\qquad (13\text{-}73)$$

where

R = radius of the spherical reflector

a = radius of the utilized aperture

Thus when $R = 2a$, the optimum focal length is $0.4665R$ and the corresponding total phase error is $0.02643(R/\lambda)$ rad. Even though the optimum focal length leads to minimum total phase error over a prescribed aperture, it does not yield the best radiation pattern when the illumination is not uniform. For a tapered amplitude distribution, the focal length that yields the best radiation pattern will be somewhat longer, and in practice, it is usually determined by experiment. Thus for a given maximum aperture size there exists a maximum value of total allowable phase error, and it is given by [39]

$$\left(\frac{a}{R}\right)^4_{max} = 14.7 \frac{(\Delta/\lambda)_{total}}{(R/\lambda)} \qquad\qquad (13\text{-}74)$$

where (Δ/λ) is the total phase error in wavelengths.

Example 13.2

A spherical reflector having a 10-ft diameter is given. If at 11.2 GHz the maximum allowable phase error is $\lambda/16$, find the maximum permissible aperture.

SOLUTION
At $f = 11.2$ GHz

$$\lambda = 0.08788 \text{ ft}$$

$$\left(\frac{a}{R}\right)^4_{\max} = 14.7\left(\frac{1/16}{56.8957}\right) = 0.01615$$

$$a^4 \simeq 10.09$$

$$a = 1.78 \text{ ft}$$

To overcome the shortcoming of a point feed and minimize spherical aberration, Spencer, Sletten, and Walsh [40] were the first to propose the use of a line source feed. Instead of a continuous line source, a set of discrete feed elements can be used to reduce spherical aberration when they are properly placed along the axis in the vicinity of the paraxial focus. The number of elements, their position, and the portion of the reflector surface which they illuminate is dictated by the allowable wavefront distortion, size, and curvature of the reflector. This is shown in Figure 13.31. A single feed located near the paraxial focus will illuminate the central portion of the

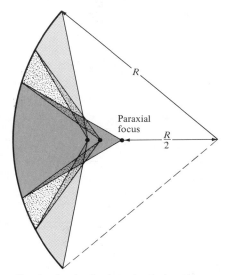

Figure 13.31   Reflector illumination by feed sections placed between paraxial focus and vertex. (SOURCE: A. C. Schell, "The Diffraction Theory of Large-Aperture Spherical Reflector Antennas," *IRE Trans. Antennas Propag.*, vol. AP-11, No. 4, July 1963. © (1963) IEEE)

reflector. If the reflector is large, additional feed elements along the axis toward the vertex will be needed to minimize the phase errors in the aperture. The ultimate feed design will be a compromise between a single element and a line-source distribution.

An extensive effort has been placed on the analysis and experiment of spherical reflectors, and most of it can be found well documented in a book of reprinted papers [1]. In addition, a number of two-dimensional patterns and aperture plane constant amplitude contours, for symmetrical and offset feeds, have been computed [19].

13.6 LENS ANTENNAS

Lens antennas are used in conjunction with transmitting and receiving element radiators. The collimating action of a lens antenna in the transmitting mode is shown in Figure 13.32(a). By reciprocity, incoming plane waves converge to a point located at the focal point of the lens as shown in Figure

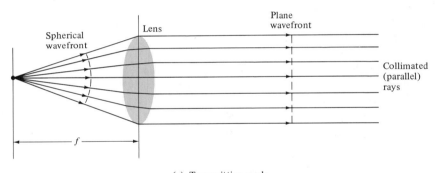

(a) Transmitting mode

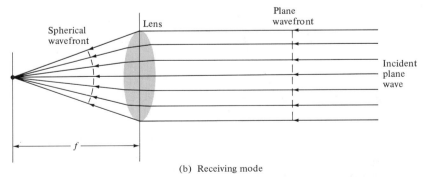

(b) Receiving mode

Figure 13.32 Collimating and converging actions of a lens in the transmitting and receiving modes.

13.32(b). If the source is placed away from the focal point, either in front or behind it, ideal collimation will not occur.

The collimating action by a lens antenna is similar to that performed by the human eye. Light rays striking the eye enter first the cornea (index of refraction $n = 1.33$), then the anterior chamber ($n = 1.33$), followed by the lens (graded n with $n = 1.41$ at the center and 1.39 at the periphery), and finally converge toward the retina. For most practical purposes, the ray bending action of the compound lens system of the eye can be reduced to a single equivalent *refractive* lens which has its optical center or nodal point situated 5 mm behind the anterior corneal surface and 15 mm in front of the retina.

Individuals with *emmetropia* (20/20 vision) do have their nodal point 15 mm in front of the retina, those with *hyperopia* (farsightedness) have it less than 15 mm, while those with *myopia* (nearsightedness) have it more than 15 mm.

Farsightedness, characterized by an abnormally short eyeball, forms the image of a distant object behind the retina in the resting eye. While this is self-corrected by the action of the eye lens, it impairs the vision of near objects which are seen more distant than normal. This hyperopic condition is remedied by placing an appropriate convex spherical lens before the eye.

Myopia (nearsightedness), characterized by an abnormally long eyeball, causes the image of a distant object to be formed in front of the retina in the resting eye. Because this defect cannot be self-corrected by the eye, it is remedied by placing an appropriate concave spherical lens before the eye. Near objects are in turn seen slightly closer than normal.

Lenses are primarily used in the microwave region, usually above 3 GHz, as collimating elements for high gain and narrow beam antennas. Although lenses and curved reflectors can be used for the same applications, the choice depends on many factors. Usually

1. the frequency range of the lenses is somewhat higher, because they become bulky and heavy at lower frequencies.
2. the mechanical tolerances on a lens are not as critical.
3. lenses do not provide aperture blockage, as reflectors do, since the source is not placed in front of it.
4. lens antennas can scan over an angle which is large compared to the on-axis beamwidth.
5. reflector antennas are simpler to design, because they have only one surface that obeys more elementary laws of geometric optics than the surfaces of the lens.
6. lenses have somewhat smaller gains (1–2 dB) than reflector antennas.
7. lenses provide reflections from both interfaces.
8. lenses are inherently lossy and some of them are structurally unstable.

Reflection losses from the interfaces can be reduced, if not completely eliminated, by special techniques. For flat surfaces this can be accomplished by the use of a nonreflecting surface coating of $\lambda/4$ thickness. Corrugations or other types of loadings may also be used. Reflections from a curved surface are more complicated, because they depend on the angle of incidence and the wave polarization. However, good results can be obtained by the use of a $\lambda/4$ matching coating on the curved surface.

The collimation action of diverging rays by a lens is accomplished by ray bending and wave velocity retardation or acceleration. The amount of bending and change in wave velocity is different at the various parts of the lens. However, the bending and wave velocity at each point must be such that the total phase of any ray along its path from the source to a plane in front of the lens is equal to that of any other ray. This requirement results in some very common lens shapes. The surface profile depends on the index of refraction (n) of the lens material.

Typically there are three general classes of lenses. One class requires an index of refraction greater than unity ($n>1$), another needs $n<1$, and the third has a variable index of refraction. The lenses with $n>1$ are made of natural dielectrics while those with $n<1$ require artificial media. The lenses with $n>1$ provide phase velocity retardation to the waves while those with $n<1$ introduce phase velocity acceleration.

The phase velocity acceleration of lenses with $n<1$ is accomplished by introducing structures where the phase velocity is greater than that of free-space. One structure that displays such a behavior is a parallel plate arrangement with the E-field parallel to the metallic plates. A square grid of parallel metallic plates form an "egg-crate" lens [42] which can be used for any wave polarization. Because the phase velocity in a waveguide is a function of frequency, lenses with $n<1$ are highly dispersive (with frequency bandwidths of 2 to 10%) while those with $n>1$ are relatively nondispersive (with frequency bandwidths over an octave).

If the source is two-dimensional (line-source), the lens geometry will be cylindrical, as shown in Figures 13.33(a) and 13.33(b). However, if the source is three-dimensional (point-source type), the lens will have rotational symmetry, as shown in Figures 13.33(c) and 13.33(d). The surface profiles must be such that cylindrical or spherical wave fronts from the source are converted to plane waves.

13.6.1 Lenses with $n>1$

All natural dielectrics have an index of refraction which is greater than unity. To achieve collimation with this type of material, one or both surfaces of the lens must be convex as shown in Figures 1.6(a) and 1.6(b). Collimation can also be achieved if one surface is convex and the other concave provided that the convex surface has a smaller radius of curvature as shown in Figure 1.6(c).

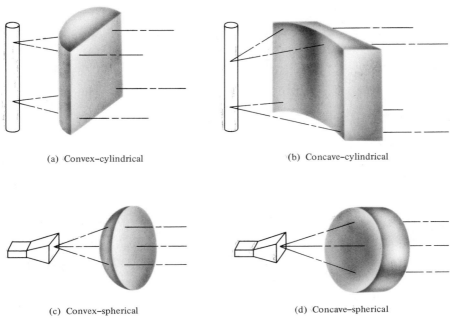

(a) Convex–cylindrical

(b) Concave–cylindrical

(c) Convex–spherical

(d) Concave–spherical

Figure 13.33 Cylindrical and spherical lenses for two- and three-dimensional sources.

The operation of a delay lens ($n>1$) can better be understood by referring to Figure 13.34. Choosing two different ray paths, P_1 and P_2, the total phase shift of P_1 from the source to the point x', $y'=0$ must be equal to that of path P_2 from the source to the point x', y'. Thus

$$k_0 f + k_1 x' = k_0 \sqrt{(f+x')^2 + (y')^2}$$

(13-75)

where f is the focal point of the lens surface. By expanding and collecting

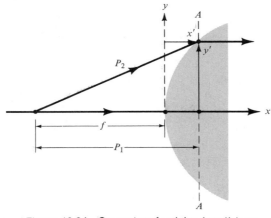

Figure 13.34 Geometry of a delay ($n>1$) lens.

terms, (13-75) reduces to

$$x'^2(n^2-1)+2fx'(n-1)-y'^2=0, \qquad n>1$$

(13-75a)

where

$$k_0 = \frac{2\pi}{\lambda_0} = \text{free-space phase constant}$$

$$k_1 = \frac{2\pi}{\lambda_1} = \text{lens material phase constant}$$

$$n = \frac{\lambda_0}{\lambda_1} = \text{index of refraction of lens material}$$

Equation (13-75a) represents the profile of a hyperbola. Three-dimensionally, it must be a hyperboloid.

Microwave lenses made of natural dielectrics, such as polystyrene, are very heavy. To reduce the weight, artificial dielectrics may be used. The artificial dielectrics can be produced by supporting small spheres or metal disks in a lattice arrangement [43]. To simulate better a true dielectric, the size of the spheres or disks and the spacing between them must be small compared to the wavelength.

The size, weight, and power loss by a lens can be reduced by *zoning* one of its surfaces. This is accomplished by a stepping procedure whereby parts of the dielectric material can be removed, as shown in Figures 13.35(a) and 13.35(b). The depth of each step must be such that the ray paths passing on each side of it differ by multiples of a full wavelength.

The discontinuities in the zoned lenses can introduce shadowing on the aperture illumination and scattering in undesired directions [42]. Such phenomena lead to reductions in gain and increases of minor lobe levels. These, however, can be minimized by good design techniques.

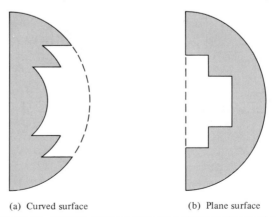

(a) Curved surface   (b) Plane surface

Figure 13.35 Zoning of the curved and plane surfaces of a lens.

13.6.2 Lenses with $n<1$

To achieve collimation with lenses with $n<1$, one or both surface profiles must be concave as shown in Figures 1.6(d) and 1.6(e). Collimation can also be accomplished with one surface concave and the other convex provided that the concave surface has a smaller radius of curvature, as shown in Figure 1.6(f).

The surface profile of an acceleration lens ($n<1$) can be derived by referring to Figure 13.36. Equating the phases of the two paths, P_1 and P_2, leads to

$$k_0 f = k_0 \sqrt{(f-x')^2 + (y')^2} + k_1 x' \qquad (13\text{-}76)$$

By expanding and collecting terms, (13-76) reduces to

$$\boxed{(1-n^2)x'^2 - 2f(1-n)x' + y'^2 = 0, \qquad n<1} \qquad (13\text{-}76a)$$

which is recognized as the equation for an ellipse. Three-dimensionally it must be an ellipsoid (ellipse of revolution).

Artificial dielectrics with $n<1$ can be simulated by the use of parallel metallic plates with the electric field parallel to the plates, as shown in Figures 13.37(a) and 13.37(b). Because the waves within the plates are constrained to follow linear paths, which are parallel to the plates and do not satisfy Snell's law of refraction, these lenses are referred to as *constrained* lenses [44], [45].

The wave velocity within the artificial accelerated lens of parallel plates is that of a waveguide TE_{10}-mode, and it is related to the index of refraction

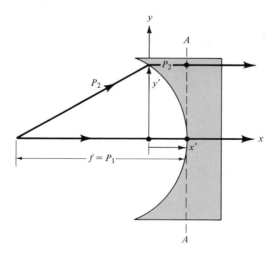

Figure 13.36 Geometry of accelerating ($n<1$) lens.

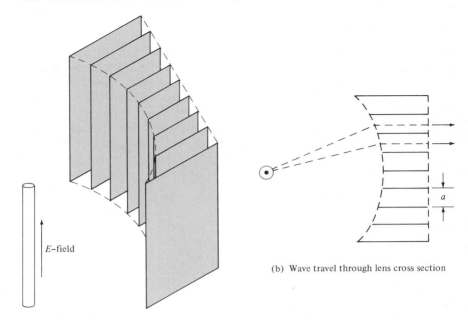

(a) Constrained lens with line source feed

(b) Wave travel through lens cross section

Figure 13.37 Parallel plate artificial constrained lens with $n<1$.

by

$$n = \frac{v_0}{v} = \sqrt{1 - \left(\frac{\lambda_0}{2a}\right)^2} \qquad (13\text{-}77)$$

It is apparent from (13-77) that the index of refraction and the wave velocity are variable, and they can be controlled by the plate spacing. The separation between the plates is usually $\lambda_0/2 < a < \lambda_0$. Smaller spacings are not utilized in order to avoid wave attenuation and to maintain a real index of refraction. In addition, electric field components perpendicular to the plates are undesirable in order not to excite TEM-mode fields with phase velocities equal to those in free-space.

13.6.3 Lenses with Variable Index of Refraction

Lenses with variable index of refraction can be built, and they have many practical applications. The most widely used configuration is the *Luneberg* lens [46]. It has a spherical shape, as shown in Figure 13.38(a), and its normalized index of refraction varies as a function of the radial distance from the center of the sphere according to

$$n(r) = \sqrt{2 - \left(\frac{r}{a}\right)^2} \qquad (13\text{-}78)$$

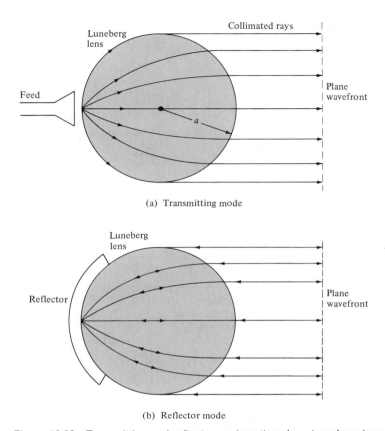

(a) Transmitting mode

(b) Reflector mode

Figure 13.38 Transmitting and reflector mode actions by a Luneberg lens.

where

r = radial distance from the center of the sphere

a = radius of the sphere

On the surface of the sphere ($r=a$), the index of refraction is unity while at its center ($r=0$) it is equal to $\sqrt{2}$.

Radiation from a point source located on the surface of the sphere is converted to plane waves exiting diametrically opposite the source. Thus one focal point is on the surface while the other is at infinity. With these collimation properties, the feed can be moved to any point on the surface, and the energy will emerge as plane waves diametrically opposite to the source. This behavior can be used effectively to scan the beam in any desired direction.

Another application of a Luneberg lens is to use it as a reflector. By adding a reflecting surface on one side, incident plane waves will converge at a point on the sphere where the reflector is located. The focused energy will be reradiated in the form of plane waves emerging on the other side and traveling in an opposite direction to the incident radiation. This mechanism is shown in Figure 13.38(b).

A Luneberg lens sphere, with the required index of refraction variation, can be made of artificial dielectric media. It can also be constructed using concentric spherical shells of solid dielectric material, each with different index of refraction.

The Luneberg lens is an ideal device for beam steering. It only requires that the feed be moved along the surface, and the beam will emerge from the other side without any loss in gain, beamwidth, and side lobe level. To avoid movement of the feed, a number of feeds can be placed on the surface and scanning will be accomplished by proper switching between feeds.

Beam steering can also be accomplished by an ordinary lens or a parabolic reflector. Both require that the source is moved along a plane passing through its focal point. Beam steering with an ordinary lens, and even more with a reflector, is limited to small scans. Large angle deviations produce decreased directivities due to increased beamwidths and minor lobe levels, and general beam deterioration. The maximum permissible scan angle is on the order of a few on-axis beamwidths. Reflectors with large f/d's have greater scan angles.

References

1. A. W. Love (ed.), *Reflector Antennas*, IEEE Press, New York, 1978.
2. Y. Obha, "On the Radiation of a Corner Reflector Finite in Width," *IEEE Trans. Antennas Propag.*, vol. AP-11, pp. 127–132, March 1963.
3. C. A. Balanis and L. Peters, Jr., "Equatorial Plane Pattern of an Axial-TEM Slot on a Finite Size Ground Plane," *IEEE Trans. Antennas Propag.*, vol. AP-17, pp. 351–353, May 1969.
4. C. A. Balanis, "Pattern Distortion due to Edge Diffractions," *IEEE Trans. Antennas Propag.*, vol. AP-18, pp. 551–563, July 1970.
5. C. A. Balanis, "Analysis of an Array of Line Sources Above a Finite Ground Plane," *IEEE Trans. Antennas Propag.*, vol. AP-19, pp. 181–185, March 1971.
6. D. Proctor, "Graphs Simplify Corner Reflector Antenna Design," *Microwaves*, vol. 14, No. 7, pp. 48,52, July 1975.
7. E. B. Moullin, *Radio Aerials*, Oxford University Press, 1949, Chapters 1 and 3.
8. P. A. J. Ratnasiri, R. G. Kouyoumjian, and P. H. Pathak, "The Wide Angle Side Lobes of Reflector Antennas," ElectroScience Laboratory, The Ohio State University, Technical Report 2183-1, March 23, 1970.
9. G. L. James and V. Kerdemelidis, "Reflector Antenna Radiation Pattern Analysis by Equivalent Edge Currents," *IEEE Trans. Antennas Propag.*, vol. AP-21, No. 1, pp. 19–24, Jan. 1973.
10. C. A. Mentzer and L. Peters, Jr., "A GTD Analysis of the Far-out Side Lobes of Cassegrain Antennas," *IEEE Trans. Antennas Propag.*, vol. AP-23, No. 5, pp. 702–709, Sept. 1975.
11. L. M. LaLonde and D. E. Harris, "A High Performance Line Source Feed for the AIO Spherical Reflector," *IEEE Trans. Antennas Propag.*, vol. AP-18, No. 1, pp. 41–48, 1970.

12. P. J. B. Clarricoats and G. T. Poulton, "High-Efficiency Microwave Reflector Antennas—A Review," *Proc. IEEE*, vol. 65, No. 10, pp. 1470–1502, Oct. 1977.

13. A. W. Rudge, "Offset-Parabolic-Reflector Antennas: A Review," *Proc. IEEE*, vol. 66, No. 12, pp. 1592–1618, Dec. 1978.

14. O. Hachenberg, B. H. Grahl, and R. Wielebinski, "The 100-Meter Radio Telescope at Effelsberg," *Proc. IEEE*, vol. 69, No. 9, pp. 1288–1295, 1973.

15. P. D. Potter, W. D. Merrick, and A. C. Ludwig, "Big Antenna Systems for Deep-Space Communications," *Astronautics and Aeronautics*, pp. 84–95, October 1966.

16. S. Silver (ed.), *Microwave Antenna Theory and Design*, McGraw-Hill, New York, 1949 (MIT Radiation Lab. Series, vol. 12).

17. J. F. Kauffman, W. F. Croswell, and L. J. Jowers, "Analysis of the Radiation Patterns of Reflector Antennas," *IEEE Trans. Antennas Propag.*, vol. AP-24, No. 1, pp. 53–65, January 1976.

18. R. E. Collin and F. J. Zucker (eds.), *Antenna Theory Part II*, McGraw-Hill, New York, 1969, pp. 36–48.

19. P. K. Agrawal, J. F. Kauffman, and W. F. Croswell, "Calculated Scan Characteristics of a Large Spherical Reflector Antenna," *IEEE Trans. Antennas Propag.*, vol. AP-27, No. 3, pp. 430–431, May 1979.

20. E. M. T. Jones, "Paraboloid Reflector and Hyperboloid Lens Antennas," *IRE Trans. Antennas Propag.*, vol. AP-2, No. 4, pp. 119–127, 1954.

21. I. Koffman, "Feed Polarization for Parallel Currents in Reflectors Generated by Conic Sections," *IEEE Trans. Antennas Propag.*, vol. AP-14, No. 1, pp. 37–40, 1966.

22. A. W. Love, "Some Highlights in Reflector Antenna Development," *Radio Science*, vol. 11, Nos. 8, 9, pp. 671–684, August-September 1976.

23. D. K. Cheng, "Effect of Arbitrary Phase Errors on the Gain and Beamwidth Characteristics of Radiation Pattern," *IRE Trans. Antennas Propag.*, vol. AP-3, pp. 145–147, July 1955.

24. Y. Y. Hu, "A Method of Determining Phase Centers and Its Application to Electromagnetic Horns," *J. Franklin Inst.*, pp. 31–39, Jan. 1961.

25. J. Ruze, "The Effect of Aperture Errors on the Antenna Radiation Pattern," *Nuevo Cimento Suppl.*, vol. 9, No. 3, pp. 364–380, 1952.

26. H. C. Minnett and B. MacA. Thomas, "Fields in the Image Space of Symmetrical Focusing Reflectors," *Proc. IEE*, vol. 115, pp. 1419–1430, Oct. 1968.

27. G. F. Koch, "Coaxial Feeds for High Aperture Efficiency and Low Spillover of Paraboloidal Reflector Antennas," *IEEE Trans. Antennas Propag.*, vol. AP-21, No. 3, pp. 164–169, March 1973.

28. R. E. Lawrie and L. Peters, Jr., "Modifications of Horn Antennas for Low Side Lobe Levels," *IEEE Trans. Antennas Propag.*, vol. AP-14, pp. 605–610, Sept. 1966.

29. A. J. Simmons and A. F. Kay, "The Scalar Feed-A High Performance Feed for Large Paraboloid Reflectors," *Design and Construction of Large Steerable Aerials*, IEE Conf. Publ. 21, pp. 213–217, 1966.

30. W. M. Truman and C. A. Balanis, "Optimum Design of Horn Feeds for Reflector Antennas," *IEEE Trans. Antennas Propag.*, vol. AP-22, No. 4, pp. 585–586, July 1974.

31. P. W. Hannan, "Microwave Antennas Derived from the Cassegrain Telescope," *IRE Trans. Antennas Propag.*, vol. AP-9, pp. 140–153, March 1961.

32. W. V. T. Rusch, "Scattering from a Hyperboloidal Reflector in a Cassegrain Feed System," *IEEE Trans. Antennas Propag.*, vol. AP-11, pp. 414–421, July 1963.
33. P. D. Potter, "Application of Spherical Wave Theory to Cassegrainian-fed Paraboloids," *IEEE Trans. Antennas Propag.*, vol. AP-15, pp. 727–736, Nov. 1967.
34. W. C. Wong, "On the Equivalent Parabola Technique to Predict the Performance Characteristics of a Cassegrain System with an Offset Feed," *IEEE Trans. Antennas Propag.*, vol. AP-21, pp. 335–339, May 1973.
35. V. Galindo, "Design of Dual-Reflector Antennas with Arbitrary Phase and Amplitude Distributions," *IEEE Trans. Antennas Propag.*, vol. AP-12, pp. 403–408, July 1964.
36. W. F. Williams, "High Efficiency Antenna Reflector," *Microwave Journal*, vol. 8, pp. 79–82, July 1965.
37. G. W. Collins, "Shaping of Subreflectors in Cassegrainian Antennas for Maximum Aperture Efficiency," *IEEE Trans. Antennas Propag.*, vol. AP-21, pp. 309–313, May 1973.
38. J. Ashmead and A. B. Pippard, "The Use of Spherical Reflectors as Microwave Scanning Aerials," *J. Inst. Elec. Eng.*, vol. 93, Part III-A, pp. 627–632, 1946.
39. T. Li, "A Study of Spherical Reflectors as Wide-Angle Scanning Antennas," *IRE Trans. Antennas Propag.*, vol. AP-7, pp. 223–226, July 1959.
40. R. C. Spencer, C. J. Sletten, and J. E. Walsh, "Correction of Spherical Aberration by a Phased Line Source," *Proceedings National Electronics Conference*, vol. 5, pp. 320–333, 1949.
41. A. C. Schell, "The Diffraction Theory of Large-Aperture Spherical Reflector Antennas," *IEEE Trans. Antennas Propag.*, vol. AP-11, pp. 428–432, July 1963.
42. H. Jasik (ed.), *Antenna Engineering Handbook* (Chapter 14 by S. B. Cohn), McGraw-Hill, New York, 1961, pp. 14–1 to 14–43.
43. H. J. Reich, J. G. Skalnik, P. F. Ordung, and H. L. Krauss, *Microwave Principles*, Van Nostrand, New York, 1957, pp. 144–148.
44. E. A. Wolff, *Antenna Analysis*, Wiley, New York, 1967, pp. 487–492.
45. J. D. Kraus, *Antennas*, McGraw-Hill, New York, 1950, pp. 382–404.
46. C. H. Walter, *Traveling Wave Antennas*, McGraw-Hill, New York, 1966, pp. 384–388.

PROBLEMS

13.1. For corner reflectors with included angles of $\alpha = 60°$, $45°$, and $30°$:
   (a) Derive the array factors of (13-7)–(13-9b).
   (b) Plot the field strength along the axis ($\theta = 90°$, $\phi = 0°$) as a function of the feed-to-vertex spacing.
   (c) Determine the period and the peak value of the normalized field strength profile.

13.2. For a parabolic reflector, derive (13-25) which relates the f/d ratio to its subtended angle.

13.3. Show that for a parabolic reflector
   (a) $0 \le f/d \le 0.25$ relates to $180° \ge \theta_0 > 90°$
   (b) $0.25 \le f/d \le \infty$ relates to $90° \ge \theta_0 > 0°$

13.4. Show that the directivity of a uniformly illuminated circular aperture of diameter d is equal to $(\pi d/\lambda)^2$.

13.5. Verify (13-33) and (13-33a).

13.6. Verify (13-49) and (13-54).

13.7. The 140-ft (42.672-m) paraboloidal reflector at the National Radio Astronomy Observatory, Green Bank, W. Va., has an f/d ratio of 0.4284. Determine the

    (a) subtended angle of the reflector

    (b) aperture efficiency assuming the feed pattern is symmetrical and its gain pattern is given by $2\cos^2(\theta'/2)$, where θ' is measured from the axis of the reflector

    (c) directivity of the entire system when the antenna is operating at 10 GHz, and it is illuminated by the feed pattern of part (b)

    (d) directivity of the entire system at 10 GHz when the reflector is illuminated by the feed pattern of part (b) and the maximum aperture phase deviation is $\pi/16$ rad

13.8. A paraboloidal reflector has an f/d ratio of 0.38. Determine

    (a) which $\cos^n\theta'$ symmetrical feed pattern will maximize its aperture efficiency

    (b) the directivity of the reflector when the focal length is 10λ

    (c) the value of the feed pattern *in dB* (relative to the main maximum) along the edges of the reflector

13.9. Verify that the ideal parabolic reflector feed pattern, for uniform amplitude taper and no spillover, is that represented by $\sec^4(\theta'/2)$.

13.10. The symmetrical feed pattern for a paraboloidal reflector is given by

$$G_f = \begin{cases} G_0\cos^4\left(\dfrac{\theta'}{2}\right) & 0\le\theta'\le\pi/2 \\ 0 & \text{elsewhere} \end{cases}$$

where G_0 is a constant.

    (a) Evaluate the constant G_0.

    (b) Derive an expression for the aperture efficiency.

    (c) Find the subtended angle of the reflector that will maximize the aperture efficiency. What is the maximum aperture efficiency?

13.11. Design pyramidal horn antennas that will maximize the aperture efficiency or produce maximum power transmission to the feed, for paraboloidal reflector with f/d ratios of

    (a) 0.50

    (b) 0.75

    (c) 1.00

13.12. Verify (13-75a) and (13-76a).

13.13. The plate separation of an artificial accelerated lens $(n<1)$ is equal to a. Plot the values of the effective index of refraction for the lens for $\lambda_0/2\le a\le\lambda_0$.

13.14. Plot the normalized values of the index of refraction for a Luneberg lens of radius $0\le r\le a$.

Chapter 14
Antenna Synthesis and Continuous Sources

14.1 INTRODUCTION

Thus far in the book we have concentrated primarily on the analysis and design of antennas. In the analysis problem an antenna model is chosen, and it is analyzed for its radiation characteristics (pattern, directivity, impedance, beamwidth, efficiency, polarization, and bandwidth). This is usually accomplished by initially specifying the current distribution of the antenna, and then analyzing it using standard procedures. If the antenna current is not known, it can usually be determined from integral equation formulations. Numerical techniques, such as the Moment Method of Chapter 7 (Section 7.5), can be used to numerically solve the integral equations.

In practice, it is often necessary to design an antenna system that will yield desired radiation characteristics. For example, a very common request is to design an antenna whose far-field pattern possesses nulls in certain directions. Other common requests are for the pattern to exhibit a desired distribution, narrow beamwidth and low side lobes, decaying minor lobes, and so forth. The task, in general, is to find not only the antenna configuration but also its geometrical dimensions and excitation distribution. The designed system should yield, either exactly or approximately, an acceptable radiation pattern, and it should satisfy other system constraints. This method of design is usually referred to as *synthesis*. Although synthesis, in its broadest definition, usually refers to antenna pattern synthesis, it is often used interchangeably with design. Since design methods have been outlined and illustrated previously, in this chapter we want to introduce and illustrate antenna pattern synthesis methods.

Antenna pattern synthesis usually requires that first an approximate analytical model be chosen to represent, either exactly or approximately, the desired pattern. The second step is to realize the analytical model by an antenna model. Generally speaking, antenna pattern synthesis can be classified into three categories. One group requires that the antenna patterns possess nulls in desired directions. The method introduced by Schelkunoff [1] can be used to accomplish this; it will be discussed in Section 14.3. Another category requires that the patterns exhibit a desired distribution in the entire visible region. This is referred to as *beam shaping*, and it can be accomplished using the Fourier transform [2] and the Woodward [3], [4] methods. They will be discussed and illustrated in Sections 14.4 and 14.5, respectively. A third group includes techniques that produce patterns with narrow beams and low side lobes. Some methods that accomplish this have already been discussed; namely the binomial method (Section 6.7.2) and the Dolph-Tschebyscheff method (also spelled Tchebyscheff or Chebyshev) of Section 6.7.3. Other techniques that belong in this family are the Taylor line-source (Tschebyscheff error) [5] and the Taylor line-source (one-parameter) [6]. They will be outlined and illustrated in Sections 14.6 and 14.7, respectively.

The synthesis methods will be utilized to design line-sources and linear arrays whose space factors [as defined by (4-58a)] and array factors [as defined by (6-52)] will yield desired far-field radiation patterns. The total pattern is formed by multiplying the space factor (or array factor) by the element factor (or element pattern) as dictated by (4-59) [or (6-5)]. For very narrow beam patterns, the total pattern is nearly the same as the space or array factor. This is demonstrated by the dipole antenna of Figure 4.4 whose element factor, as given by (4-58a), is $\sin\theta$; for values of θ near $90°$ ($\theta \simeq 90°$), $\sin\theta \simeq 1$.

The synthesis techniques will be followed with a brief discussion of some very popular line-source distributions (triangular, cosine, cosine-squared) and continuous aperture distributions (rectangular and circular).

14.2 CONTINUOUS SOURCES

Very long (in terms of a wavelength) arrays of discrete elements usually are more difficult to implement, more costly, and have narrower bandwidths. For such applications, antennas with continuous distributions would be convenient to use. A very long wire and a large reflector represent, respectively, antennas with continuous line and aperture distributions. Continuous distribution antennas usually have larger side lobes, are more difficult to scan, and in general, they are not as versatile as arrays of discrete elements. The characteristics of continuously distributed sources can be approximated by discrete-element arrays, and vice-versa, and their development follows and parallels that of discrete-element arrays.

14.2.1 Line-Source

Continuous line-source distributions are functions of only one coordinate, and they can be used to approximate linear arrays of discrete elements and vice-versa.

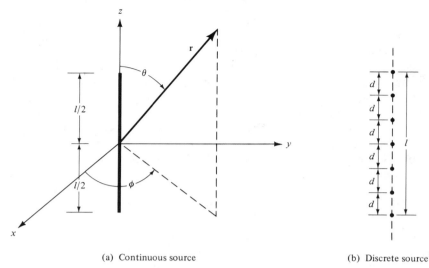

(a) Continuous source   (b) Discrete source

Figure 14.1   Continuous and discrete linear sources.

The array factor of a discrete-element array, placed along the z-axis, is given by (6-52) and (6-52a). As the number of elements increases in a fixed-length array, the source approaches a continuous distribution. In the limit, the array factor summation reduces to an integral. For a continuous distribution, the factor that corresponds to the array factor is known as the *space factor*. For a line-source distribution of length l placed symmetrically along the z-axis as shown in Figure 14.1(a), the space factor (SF) is given by

$$\text{SF}(\theta) = \int_{-l/2}^{+l/2} I_n(z') e^{j[kz'\cos\theta + \phi_n(z')]} \, dz' \tag{14-1}$$

where $I_n(z')$ and $\phi_n(z')$ represent, respectively, the amplitude and phase distributions along the source. For a constant phase distribution $\phi_n(z')=0$.

Equation (14-1) is a finite one-dimensional Fourier transform relating the far-field pattern of the source to its excitation distribution. Two-dimensional Fourier transforms are used to represent the space factors for two-dimensional source distributions. These relations are results of the angular spectrum concept for plane waves, introduced first by Booker and Clemmow [2], and it relates the angular spectrum of a wave to the excitation distribution of the source.

For a continuous source distribution, the total field is given by the product of the *element* and *space* factors as defined in (4-59). This is analogous to the pattern multiplication of (6-5) for arrays. *The type of current and its direction of flow on a source determine the element factor.* For a finite length linear dipole, for example, the total field of (4-58a) is obtained by summing the contributions of small infinitesimal elements which are used to represent the entire dipole. In the limit, as the infinitesimal lengths become very small, the summation reduces to an integration. In (4-58a), the factor outside the brackets is the element factor and the one within the brackets is the space factor and corresponds to (14-1).

14.2.2 Discretization of Continuous Sources

The radiation characteristics of continuous sources can be approximated by discrete-element arrays, and vice-versa. This is illustrated in Figure 14.1(b) whereby discrete elements, with a spacing d between them, are placed along the length of the continuous source. Smaller spacings between the elements yield better approximations, and they can even capture the fine details of the continuous distribution radiation characteristics. For example, the continuous line-source distribution $I_n(z')$ of (14-1) can be approximated by a discrete-element array whose element excitation coefficients, at the specified element positions within $-l/2 \le z' \le l/2$, are determined by the sampling of $I_n(z')e^{j\phi_n(z')}$. The radiation pattern of the digitized discrete-element array will approximate the pattern of the continuous source.

The technique can be used for the discretization of any continuous distribution. The accuracy increases as the element spacing decreases; in the limit, the two patterns will be identical. For large element spacing, the patterns of the two antennas will not match well. To avoid this, another method known as *root-matching* can be used [7]. Instead of sampling the continuous current distribution to determine the element excitation coefficients, the root-matching method requires that the nulls of the continuous distribution pattern also appear in the initial pattern of the discrete-element array. If the synthesized pattern using this method still does not yield (within an acceptable accuracy) the desired pattern, a perturbation technique [7] can then be applied to the distribution of the discrete-element array to improve its accuracy.

14.3 SCHELKUNOFF POLYNOMIAL METHOD

A method that is conducive to the synthesis of arrays whose patterns possess nulls in desired directions is that introduced by Schelkunoff [1]. To complete the design, this method requires information on the number of nulls and their locations. The number of elements and their excitation coefficients are then derived. The analytical formation of the techinque follows.

Referring to Figure 6.4, the array factor for an N-element, equally spaced, nonuniform amplitude, and progressive phase excitation is given by (6-52) as

$$\text{AF} = \sum_{n=1}^{N} a_n e^{j(n-1)(kd\cos\theta + \beta)} = \sum_{n=1}^{N} a_n e^{j(n-1)\psi} \qquad (14\text{-}2)$$

where a_n has been introduced to account for the nonuniform amplitude excitation of each element. The spacing between the elements is d and β is the progressive phase shift.

Letting

$$z = x + jy = e^{j\psi} = e^{j(kd\cos\theta + \beta)} \tag{14-3}$$

we can rewrite (14-2) as

$$AF = \sum_{n=1}^{N} a_n z^{n-1} = a_1 + a_2 z + a_3 z^2 + \cdots + a_N z^{N-1} \tag{14-4}$$

which is a polynomial of degree $(N-1)$. From the mathematics of complex variables and algebra, any polynomial of degree $(N-1)$ has $(N-1)$ roots and can be expressed as a product of $(N-1)$ linear terms. Thus we can write (14-4) as

$$\boxed{AF = a_n(z - z_1)(z - z_2)(z - z_3) \cdots (z - z_{N-1})} \tag{14-5}$$

where $z_1, z_2, z_3, \ldots, z_{N-1}$ are the roots, which may be complex, of the polynomial. The magnitude of (14-5) can be expressed as

$$\boxed{|AF| = |a_n||z - z_1||z - z_2||z - z_3| \cdots |z - z_{N-1}|} \tag{14-6}$$

Some very interesting observations can be drawn from (14-6) which can be used judiciously for the analysis and synthesis of arrays. Before tackling that phase of the problem, let us first return and examine the properties of (14-3).

The complex variable z of (14-3) can be written in another form as

$$z = |z|e^{j\psi} = |z| \angle\psi = 1 \angle\psi \tag{14-7}$$

$$\psi = kd\cos\theta + \beta = \frac{2\pi}{\lambda}d\cos\theta + \beta \tag{14-7a}$$

It is clear that for any value of d, θ, or β the magnitude of z lies always on a *unit* circle; however its phase will depend upon d, θ, and β. For $\beta = 0$, we have plotted in Figures 14.2(a)–(d) the value of z, magnitude and phase, as θ takes values of 0 to π rad. It is observed that for $d = \lambda/8$ the values of z, for all the physically observable angles of θ, only exist over the part of the circle shown in Figure 14.2(a). Any values of z outside that arc are not realizable by any observation angle θ for the spacing $d = \lambda/8$. We refer to the realizable part of the circle as the *visible region* and the remaining as the *invisible region*. In Figure 14.2(a) we also observe the path of the z values as θ changes from $0°$ to $180°$.

In Figures 14.2(b)–(d) we have plotted the values of z when the spacing between the elements is $\lambda/4$, $\lambda/2$, and $3\lambda/4$. It is obvious that the visible region can be extended by increasing the spacing between the elements. It requires a spacing of at least $\lambda/2$ to encompass, at least once, the entire

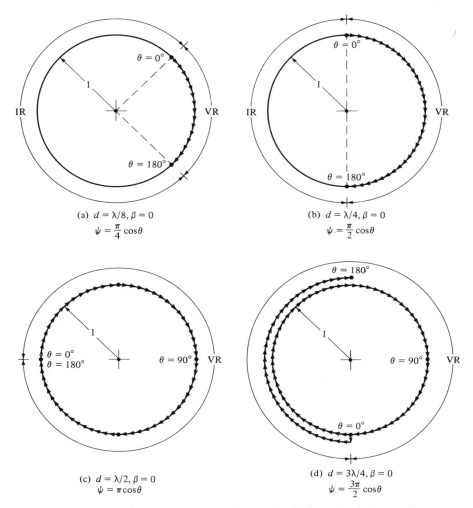

Figure 14.2 *Visible Region* (VR) and *Invisible Region* (IR) boundaries for complex variable z when $\beta = 0$.

circle. Any spacing greater than $\lambda/2$ leads to multiple values for z. In Figure 14.2(d) we have double values for z for half of the circle when $d = 3\lambda/4$.

To demonstrate the versatility of the arrays, in Figures 14.3(a)–(d) we have plotted the values of z for the same spacings as in Figures 14.2(a)–(d) but with a $\beta = \pi/4$. A comparison between the corresponding figures indicates that the overall visible region for each spacing has not changed but its relative position on the circle has rotated counterclockwise by an amount equal to β.

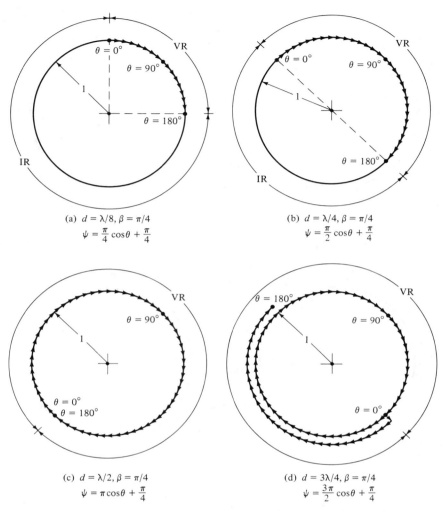

(a) $d = \lambda/8, \beta = \pi/4$
$\psi = \frac{\pi}{4}\cos\theta + \frac{\pi}{4}$

(b) $d = \lambda/4, \beta = \pi/4$
$\psi = \frac{\pi}{2}\cos\theta + \frac{\pi}{4}$

(c) $d = \lambda/2, \beta = \pi/4$
$\psi = \pi\cos\theta + \frac{\pi}{4}$

(d) $d = 3\lambda/4, \beta = \pi/4$
$\psi = \frac{3\pi}{2}\cos\theta + \frac{\pi}{4}$

Figure 14.3   *Visible Region* (VR) and *Invisible Region* (IR) boundaries for complex variable z when $\beta = \pi/4$.

We can conclude then that the overall extent of the visible region can be controlled by the spacing between the elements and its relative position on the circle by the progressive phase excitation of the elements. These two can be used effectively in the design of the array factors.

Now let us return to (14-6). The magnitude of the array factor, its form as shown in (14-6), has a geometrical interpretation. For a given value of z in the visible region of the unit circle, corresponding to a value of θ as determined by (14-3), $|AF|$ is proportional to the product of the distances between z and $z_1, z_2, z_3, \ldots, z_{N-1}$, the roots of AF. In addition, apart from a

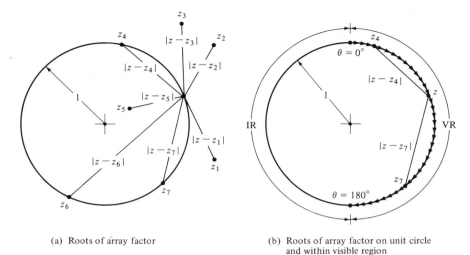

(a) Roots of array factor

(b) Roots of array factor on unit circle and within visible region

Figure 14.4 Array factor roots within and outside unit circle, and visible and invisible region.

constant, the phase of AF is equal to the sum of the phases between z and each of the zeros (roots). This is best demonstrated geometrically in Figure 14.4(a). If all the roots $z_1, z_2, z_3, \ldots, z_{N-1}$ are located in the visible region of the unit circle, then each one corresponds to a null in the pattern of $|AF|$ because as θ changes z changes and eventually passes through each of the z_n's. When it does, the length between z and that z_n is zero and (14-6) vanishes. When all the zeros (roots) are not on the visible region of the unit but some lie outside it and/or any other point not on the unit circle, then only those zeros on the visible region will contribute to the nulls of the pattern. This is shown geometrically in Figure 14.4(b). If no zeros exist in the visible region of the unit circle, then that particular array factor has no nulls for any value of θ. However, if a given zero lies on the unit circle but not in its visible region, that zero can be included in the pattern by changing the phase excitation β so that the visible region is rotated until it encompasses that root. Doing this, and not changing d, may exclude some other zero(s).

To demonstrate all the principles, we will consider an example along with some computations.

Example 14.1

Design a linear array with a spacing between the elements of $d = \lambda/4$ such that it has zeros at $\theta = 0°$, $90°$, and $180°$. Determine the number of elements, their excitation, and plot the derived pattern. Use Schelkunoff's method.

SOLUTION
For a spacing of $\lambda/4$ between the elements and a phase shift $\beta = 0°$, the visible region is shown in Figure 14.2(b). If the desired zeros of the array factor must occur at $\theta = 0°$, $90°$, and $180°$, then these correspond to $z = j, 1, -j$ on the unit circle. Thus a normalized form of the array factor is given by

$$AF = (z - z_1)(z - z_2)(z - z_3) = (z - j)(z - 1)(z + j)$$

$$AF = z^3 - z^2 + z - 1$$

Referring to (14-4), the above array factor and the desired radiation characteristics can be obtained when there are four elements and their excitation coefficients are equal to

$$a_1 = -1$$
$$a_2 = +1$$
$$a_3 = -1$$
$$a_4 = +1$$

To illustrate the method, we plotted in Figure 14.5 the pattern of that array; it clearly meets the desired specifications. Because of the symmetry of the array, the pattern of the left hemisphere is identical to that of the right.

14.4 FOURIER TRANSFORM METHOD

This method can be used to determine, given a complete description of the desired pattern, the excitation distribution of a continuous or a discrete source antenna system. The derived excitation will yield, either exactly or approximately, the desired antenna pattern. The pattern synthesis using this method is referred to as *beam shaping*.

14.4.1 Line-Source

For a continuous line-source distribution of length l, as shown in Figure 14.1, the normalized space factor of (14-1) can be written as

$$SF(\theta) = \int_{-l/2}^{l/2} I(z')e^{j(k\cos\theta - k_z)z'}\,dz' = \int_{-l/2}^{l/2} I(z')e^{j\xi z'}\,dz' \qquad (14\text{-}8)$$

$$\xi = k\cos\theta - k_z \Rightarrow \theta = \cos^{-1}\left(\frac{\xi + k_z}{k}\right) \qquad (14\text{-}8a)$$

where k_z is the excitation phase constant of the source. For a normalized uniform current distribution of the form $I(z') = I_0/l$, (14-8) reduces to

$$SF(\theta) = I_0 \frac{\sin\left[\dfrac{kl}{2}\left(\cos\theta - \dfrac{k_z}{k}\right)\right]}{\dfrac{kl}{2}\left(\cos\theta - \dfrac{k_z}{k}\right)} \qquad (14\text{-}9)$$

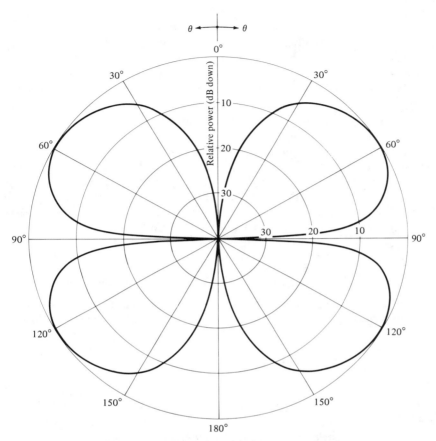

Figure 14.5 Amplitude radiation pattern of a four-element array of isotropic sources with a spacing of $\lambda/4$ between them, zero degrees progressive phase shift, and zeros at $\theta = 0°$, 90°, and 180°.

The observation angle θ of (14-9) will have real values (visible region) provided that $-(k + k_z) \leq \xi \leq (k - k_z)$ as obtained from (14-8a).

Since the current distribution of (14-8) extends only over $-l/2 \leq z' \leq l/2$ (and it is zero outside it), the limits can be extended to infinity and (14-8) can be written as

$$\boxed{\text{SF}(\theta) = \text{SF}(\xi) = \int_{-\infty}^{+\infty} I(z') e^{j\xi z'} dz'} \qquad \text{(14-10a)}$$

The form of (14-10a) is a Fourier transform, and it relates the excitation distribution $I(z')$ of a continuous source to its far-field space factor $\text{SF}(\theta)$.

The transform pair of (14-10a) is given by

$$I(z') = \frac{1}{2\pi} \int_{-\infty}^{+\infty} SF(\xi) e^{-jz'\xi} d\xi = \frac{1}{2\pi} \int_{-\infty}^{+\infty} SF(\theta) e^{-jz'\xi} d\xi \qquad \text{(14-10b)}$$

Whether (14-10a) represents the direct transform and (14-10b) the inverse transform, or vice-versa, does not matter here. The most important thing is that the excitation distribution and the far-field space factor are related by Fourier transforms.

Equation (14-10b) indicates that if $SF(\theta)$ represents the desired pattern, the excitation distribution $I(z')$ that will yield the exact desired pattern must in general exist for all values of z' ($-\infty \leq z' \leq \infty$). Since physically only sources of finite dimensions are realizable, the excitation distribution of (14-10b) is truncated at $z' = \pm l/2$ (beyond $z' = \pm l/2$ it is made zero). Thus the approximate source distribution is given by

$$I_a(z') \simeq \begin{cases} I(z') = \dfrac{1}{2\pi} \displaystyle\int_{-\infty}^{+\infty} SF(\xi) e^{-jz'\xi} d\xi & -l/2 \leq z' \leq l/2 \\ 0 & \text{elsewhere} \end{cases} \qquad \text{(14-11)}$$

and it yields an approximate pattern $SF(\theta)_a$. The approximate pattern is used to represent, within certain error, the desired pattern $SF(\theta)_d$. Thus

$$SF(\theta)_d \simeq SF(\theta)_a = \int_{-l/2}^{l/2} I_a(z') e^{j\xi z'} dz' \qquad \text{(14-12)}$$

It can be shown that, over all values of ξ, the synthesized approximate pattern $SF(\theta)_a$ yields the least mean square error or deviation from the desired pattern $SF(\theta)_d$. However that criterion is not satisfied when the values of ξ are restricted only in the visible region [8], [9].

To illustrate the principles of this design method, an example is taken.

Example 14.2

Determine the current distribution and the approximate radiation pattern of a line-source placed along the z-axis whose desired radiation pattern is symmetrical about $\theta = \pi/2$, and it is given by

$$SF(\theta) = \begin{cases} 1 & \pi/4 \leq \theta \leq 3\pi/4 \\ 0 & \text{elsewhere} \end{cases}$$

This is referred to as a sectoral pattern, and it is widely used in radar search and communication applications.

SOLUTION
Since the pattern is symmetrical, $k_z = 0$. The values of ξ, as determined by (14-8a), are given by $k/\sqrt{2} \geq \xi \geq -k/\sqrt{2}$. In turn, the current distribution

is given by (14-10b) or

$$I(z') = \frac{1}{2\pi} \int_{-\infty}^{+\infty} \mathrm{SF}(\xi) e^{-jz'\xi} d\xi$$

$$= \frac{1}{2\pi} \int_{-k/\sqrt{2}}^{k/\sqrt{2}} e^{-jz'\xi} d\xi = \frac{k}{\pi\sqrt{2}} \left[\frac{\sin\left(\frac{kz'}{\sqrt{2}}\right)}{\frac{kz'}{\sqrt{2}}} \right]$$

and it exists over all values of z' ($-\infty \le z' \le \infty$). Over the extent of the line source, the current distribution is approximated by

$$I_a(z') \simeq I(z'), \qquad -l/2 \le z' \le l/2$$

If the derived current distribution $I(z')$ is used in conjunction with (14-10a) and it is assumed to exist over all values of z', the exact and desired sectoral pattern will result. If however it is truncated at $z' = \pm l/2$ (and assumed to be zero outside), then the desired pattern is approximated by (14-12) or

$$\mathrm{SF}(\theta)_d \simeq \mathrm{SF}(\theta)_a = \int_{-l/2}^{l/2} I_a(z') e^{j\xi z'} dz'$$

$$= \frac{1}{\pi} \left\{ S_i \left[\frac{l}{\lambda} \pi \left(\cos\theta + \frac{1}{\sqrt{2}} \right) \right] - S_i \left[\frac{l}{\lambda} \pi \left(\cos\theta - \frac{1}{\sqrt{2}} \right) \right] \right\}$$

where $S_i(x)$ is the sine integral of (4-68b).

The approximate current distribution (normalized so that its maximum is unity) is plotted in Figure 14.6(a) for $l = 5\lambda$ and $l = 10\lambda$. The corresponding approximate normalized patterns are shown in Figure 14.6(b) where they are compared with the desired pattern. A very good reconstruction is indicated. The longer line source ($l = 10\lambda$) provides a better realization. The side lobes are about 0.102 (-19.83 dB) for $l = 5\lambda$ and 0.081 (-21.83 dB) for $l = 10\lambda$ (relative to the pattern at $\theta = 90°$).

14.4.2 Linear Array

The array factor of an N-element linear array of equally spaced elements and nonuniform excitation is given by (14-2). If the reference point is taken at the physical center of the array, the array factor can also be written as

Odd Number of Elements ($N = 2M + 1$)

$$AF(\theta) = AF(\psi) = \sum_{m=-M}^{M} a_m e^{jm\psi} \qquad (14\text{-}13a)$$

Even Number of Elements ($N=2M$)

$$AF(\theta)=AF(\psi)= \sum_{m=-M}^{-1} a_m e^{j[(2m+1)/2]\psi} + \sum_{m=1}^{M} a_m e^{j[(2m-1)/2]\psi}$$

(14-13b)

where

$$\psi = kd\cos\theta + \beta$$

(14-13c)

For an odd number of elements ($N=2M+1$), the elements are placed at

$$z'_m = md, \qquad m=0,\pm 1,\pm 2,\ldots,\pm M$$

(14-13d)

and for an even number ($N=2M$) at

$$z'_m = \begin{cases} \dfrac{2m-1}{2}d, & 1\le m\le M \\[2mm] \dfrac{2m+1}{2}d, & -M\le m\le -1 \end{cases}$$

(14-13e)

An odd number of elements must be utilized to synthesize a desired pattern whose average value, over all angles, is not equal to zero. The $m=0$ term of (14-13a) is analogous to the d.c. term in a Fourier series expansion of functions whose average value is not zero.

In general, the array factor of an antenna is a periodic function of ψ, and it must repeat for every 2π radians. In order for the array factor to satisfy the periodicity requirements for real values of θ (visible region), then $2kd=2\pi$ or $d=\lambda/2$. The periodicity and visible region requirement of $d=\lambda/2$ can be relaxed; in fact, it can be made $d<\lambda/2$. However, the array factor $AF(\psi)$ must be made pseudoperiodic by using fill-in functions, as is customarily done in Fourier series analysis. Such a construction will lead to nonunique solutions, because each new fill-in function will result in a different solution. In addition, spacings smaller than $\lambda/2$ lead to superdirective arrays that are undesirable and impractical. If $d>\lambda/2$, the derived patterns exhibit undesired grating lobes; in addition, they must be restricted to satisfy the periodicity requirements.

If $AF(\psi)$ represents the desired array factor, the excitation coefficients of the array can be obtained by the Fourier formula of

Odd Number of Elements ($N=2M+1$)

$$a_m = \frac{1}{T}\int_{-T/2}^{T/2} AF(\psi)e^{-jm\psi}\,d\psi = \frac{1}{2\pi}\int_{-\pi}^{\pi} AF(\psi)e^{-jm\psi}\,d\psi$$

(14-14a)

$$-M\le m\le M$$

Even Number of Elements ($N = 2M$)

$$a_m = \begin{cases} \dfrac{1}{T} \displaystyle\int_{-T/2}^{T/2} AF(\psi) e^{-j[(2m+1)/2]\psi}\, d\psi \\[6pt] = \dfrac{1}{2\pi} \displaystyle\int_{-\pi}^{\pi} AF(\psi) e^{-j[(2m+1)/2]\psi}\, d\psi \\[4pt] \qquad\qquad -M \le m \le -1 \qquad (14\text{-}14b) \\[8pt] \dfrac{1}{T} \displaystyle\int_{-T/2}^{T/2} AF(\psi) e^{-j[(2m-1)/2]\psi}\, d\psi = \\[6pt] \dfrac{1}{2\pi} \displaystyle\int_{-\pi}^{\pi} AF(\psi) e^{-j[(2m-1)/2]\psi}\, d\psi \\[4pt] \qquad\qquad 1 \le m \le M \qquad (14\text{-}14c) \end{cases}$$

Simplifications in the forms of (14-13a)–(14-13b) and (14-14a)–(14-14c) can be obtained when the excitations are symmetrical about the physical center of the array.

Example 14.3

Determine the excitation coefficients and the resultant pattern for a broadside discrete element array whose array factor will closely approximate the desired symmetrical sectoral pattern of Example 14.2. Use 11 elements with a spacing of $d = \lambda/2$ between them. Repeat the design for 21 elements.

SOLUTION
Since the array is broadside, the progressive phase shift between the elements as required by (6-18a) is zero ($\beta = 0$). Since the pattern is nonzero only for $\pi/4 \le \theta \le 3\pi/4$, the corresponding values of ψ are obtained from (14-13c) or $\pi/\sqrt{2} \ge \psi \ge -\pi/\sqrt{2}$. The excitation coefficients are obtained from (14-14a) or

$$a_m = \frac{1}{2\pi} \int_{-\pi/\sqrt{2}}^{\pi/\sqrt{2}} e^{-jm\psi}\, d\psi = \frac{1}{\sqrt{2}} \left[\frac{\sin\left(\dfrac{m\pi}{\sqrt{2}}\right)}{\dfrac{m\pi}{\sqrt{2}}} \right]$$

and they are symmetrical about the physical center of the array $[a_m(-z'_m) = a_m(z'_m)]$. The corresponding array factor is given by (14-13a).
The normalized excitation coefficients are

$$\begin{array}{lll}
a_0 = 1.0000 & a_{\pm 4} = 0.0578 & a_{\pm 8} = -0.0496 \\
a_{\pm 1} = 0.3582 & a_{\pm 5} = -0.0895 & a_{\pm 9} = 0.0455 \\
a_{\pm 2} = -0.2170 & a_{\pm 6} = 0.0518 & a_{\pm 10} = -0.0100 \\
a_{\pm 3} = 0.0558 & a_{\pm 7} = 0.0101 &
\end{array}$$

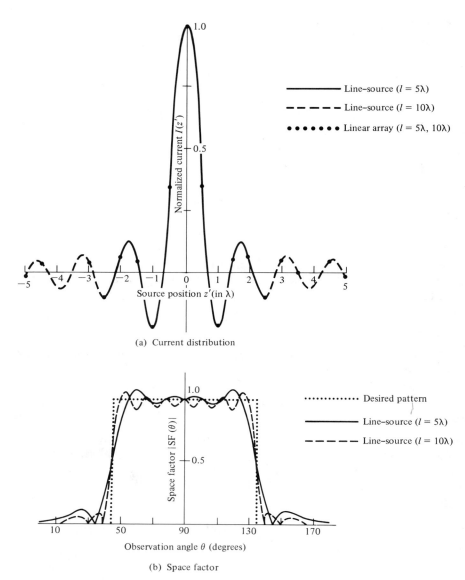

(a) Current distribution

(b) Space factor

Figure 14.6   Normalized current distribution, desired pattern, and synthesized patterns using the Fourier transform method.

They are displayed graphically by a dot (•) in Figure 14.6(a) where they are compared with the continuous current distribution of Example 14.2. It is apparent that at the element positions, the line-source and linear array excitation values are identical. This is expected since the two antennas are of the same length (for $N = 11$, $d = \lambda/2 \Rightarrow l = 5\lambda$ and for $N = 21$, $d = \lambda/2 \Rightarrow l = 10\lambda$).

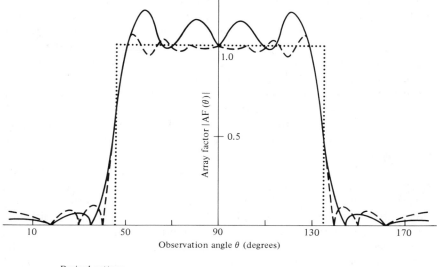

Figure 14.7 Desired array factor and synthesized normalized patterns for linear array of 11 and 21 elements using the Fourier transform method.

The corresponding normalized array factors are displayed in Figure 14.7. As it should be expected, the larger array ($N = 21$, $d = \lambda/2$) provides a better reconstruction of the desired pattern. The side lobe levels, relative to the value of the pattern at $\theta = 90°$, are 0.061 (-24.29 dB) for $N = 11$ and 0.108 (-19.33 dB) for $N = 21$.

Discrete element linear arrays only approximate continuous line-sources. Therefore, their patterns shown in Figure 14.7 do not approximate as well the desired pattern as the corresponding patterns of the line-source distributions shown in Figure 14.6(b).

Whenever the desired pattern contains discontinuities or its values in a given region change very rapidly, the reconstruction pattern will exhibit oscillatory overshoots which are referred to as *Gibbs's phenomena*. Since the desired sectoral patterns of Examples 14.2 and 14.3 are discontinuous at $\theta = \pi/4$ and $3\pi/4$, the reconstructed patterns displayed in Figures 14.6(b) and 14.7 exhibit these oscillatory overshoots.

14.5 WOODWARD METHOD

A very popular antenna pattern synthesis method used for beam shaping was introduced by Woodward [3], [4], [10]. The synthesis is accomplished by sampling the desired pattern at various discrete locations. Associated with each pattern sample is a harmonic current whose corresponding field is referred to as a *composing function*. For a line-source, each composing function is of an $a_m \sin(\psi_m)/\psi_m$ form whereas for a linear array it takes an $a_m \sin(N\phi_m)/N\sin(\phi_m)$ form. The excitation coefficient a_m of each harmonic current is such that its field strength is equal to the amplitude of the desired pattern at its corresponding sampled point. The total excitation of the source is comprised of a finite summation of space harmonics. The corresponding synthesized pattern is represented by a finite summation of composing functions with each term representing the field of a current harmonic.

The analytical formulation of this method is similar to the Shannon sampling theorem used in communications which states that "if a function $g(t)$ is band-limited, with its highest frequency being f_h, the function $g(t)$ can be reconstructed using samples taken at a frequency f_s. To faithfully reproduce the original function $g(t)$, the sampling frequency f_s should be at least twice the highest frequency f_h ($f_s = 2f_h$) or the function should be sampled at points separated by no more than $\Delta t = 1/f_s = 1/2f_h = T_h/2$ where T_h is the period of the highest frequency f_h." In a similar manner, the radiation pattern of an antenna can be synthesized by sampling functions whose samples are separated by λ/l rad, where l is the length of the source [9], [10].

14.5.1 Line-Source

Let the current distribution of a continuous source be represented, within $-l/2 \le z' \le l/2$, by a finite summation of normalized sources each of constant amplitude and linear phase of the form

$$i_m(z') = \frac{a_m}{l} e^{-jkz'\cos\theta_m}, \qquad -l/2 \le z' \le l/2 \tag{14-15}$$

As it will be shown later, θ_m represents the angles where the desired pattern will be sampled. The total current $I(z')$ is given by a finite summation of $2M$ (even samples) or $2M+1$ (odd samples) current sources each of the form of (14-15). Thus

$$\boxed{I(z') = \frac{1}{l} \sum_{m=-M}^{M} a_m e^{-jkz'\cos\theta_m}} \tag{14-16}$$

where

$$m = \pm 1, \pm 2, \ldots, \pm M \text{ (for } 2M \text{ even number of samples)}$$

$$\tag{14-16a}$$

$$m = 0, \pm 1, \pm 2, \ldots, \pm M \text{ (for } 2M+1 \text{ odd number of samples)}$$

Associated with each current source of (14-15) is a corresponding field pattern of the form given by (14-9) or

$$s_m(\theta) = a_m \left\{ \frac{\sin\left[\frac{kl}{2}(\cos\theta - \cos\theta_m)\right]}{\frac{kl}{2}(\cos\theta - \cos\theta_m)} \right\} \tag{14-17}$$

whose maximum occurs when $\theta = \theta_m$. The total pattern is obtained by summing $2M$ (even samples) or $2M+1$ (odd samples) terms each of the form given by (14-17). Thus

$$SF(\theta) = \sum_{m=-M}^{M} a_m \left\{ \frac{\sin\left[\frac{kl}{2}(\cos\theta - \cos\theta_m)\right]}{\frac{kl}{2}(\cos\theta - \cos\theta_m)} \right\} \tag{14-18}$$

The maximum of each individual term in (14-18) occurs when $\theta = \theta_m$, and it is equal to $SF(\theta = \theta_m)$. In addition, when one term in (14-18) attains its maximum value at its sample at $\theta = \theta_m$, all other terms of (14-18) which are associated with the other samples are zero at $\theta = \theta_m$. In other words, all sampling terms (composing functions) of (14-18) are zero at all sampling points other than at their own. Thus at each sampling point the total field is equal to that of the sample. This is one of the most appealing properties of this method. If the desired space factor is sampled at $\theta = \theta_m$, the excitation coefficients a_m can be made equal to its value at the sample points θ_m. Thus

$$kz'\Delta\big|_{|z'|=l} = 2\pi \Rightarrow \Delta = \frac{\lambda}{l} \tag{14-19a}$$

The reconstructed pattern is then given by (14-18), and it will approximate closely the desired pattern.

In order for the synthesized pattern to satisfy the periodicity requirements of 2π for real values of θ (visible region) and to faithfully reconstruct the desired pattern, each sample should be separated by

$$kz'\Delta\big|_{|z'|=l} = 2\pi \Rightarrow \Delta = \frac{\lambda}{l} \tag{14-19a}$$

The location of each sample is given by

$$\cos\theta_m = m\Delta = m\left(\frac{\lambda}{l}\right) \Rightarrow \theta_m = \cos^{-1}\left(m\frac{\lambda}{l}\right) \tag{14-19b}$$

Therefore, M should be the closest integer to $M \leq l/\lambda$.

As long as the location of each sample is determined by (14-19b), the pattern value at the sample points is determined solely by that of one sample and it is not correlated to the field of the other samples.

Example 14.4

Repeat the design of Example 14.2 for $l = 5\lambda$ using the Woodward synthesis method.

SOLUTION

Since $l = 5\lambda$, $M = 5$ and the sampling separation is 0.2. The total number of sampling points is 11. The angles where the sampling is performed are given, according to (14-19b), by

$$\theta_m = \cos^{-1}\left(m\frac{\lambda}{l}\right) = \cos^{-1}(0.2m), \qquad m = 0, \pm 1, \ldots, \pm 5$$

The angles and the excitation coefficients at the sample points are listed below.

m	θ_m	$a_m = SF(\theta_m)_d$	m	θ_m	$a_m = SF(\theta_m)_d$
0	90°	1			
1	78.46°	1	-1	101.54°	1
2	66.42°	1	-2	113.58°	1
3	53.13°	1	-3	126.87°	1
4	36.87°	0	-4	143.13°	0
5	0°	0	-5	180°	0

The computed pattern is shown in Figure 14.8(a) where it is compared with the desired pattern. A good reconstruction is indicated. The side lobe level, relative to the value of the pattern at $\theta = 90°$, is 0.160 (-15.92 dB).

To demonstrate the synthesis of the pattern using the sampling concept, we have plotted in Figure 14.8(b) all seven nonzero composing functions $s_m(\theta)$ used for the reconstruction of the $l = 5\lambda$ line-source pattern of Figure 14.8(a). Each nonzero $s_m(\theta)$ composing function was computed using (14-17) for $m = 0, \pm 1, \pm 2, \pm 3$. It is evident that at each sampling point all the composing functions are zero, except the one that represents that sample. Thus the value of the desired pattern at each sampling point is determined solely by the maximum value of a single composing function. The angles where the composing functions attain their maximum values are listed in the previous table.

14.5.2 Linear Array

The Woodward method can also be implemented to synthesize discrete linear arrays. The technique is similar to the Woodward method for line sources except that the pattern of each sample, as given by (14-17), is replaced by the array factor of a uniform array as given by (6-10c). If the elements are placed at the sampling points, the pattern of each sample can

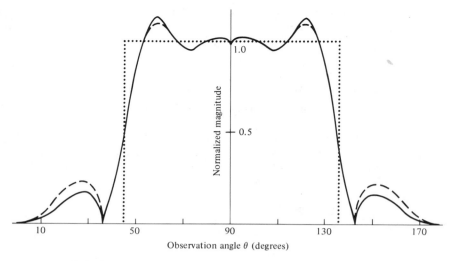

Observation angle θ (degrees)

··········· Desired pattern

———— Line-source $|SF(\theta)|$
$(l = 5\lambda)$

— — — — Linear array $|AF(\theta)|$
$(N = 11, d = \lambda/2)$

(a) Normalized amplitude patterns

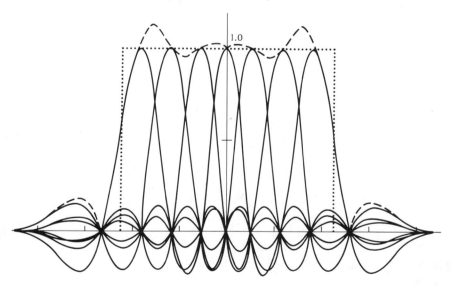

··········· Desired pattern

— — — — Line-source $|SF(\theta)|$
$(l = 5\lambda)$

———— Composing functions $s_m(\theta)$
$m = 0, \pm 1, \pm 2, \pm 3$

(b) Composing functions for line-source $(l = 5\lambda)$.

Figure 14.8 Desired and synthesized patterns, and composing functions for Woodward designs.

677

be written as

$$f_m(\theta) = a_m \frac{\sin\left[\frac{N-1}{2} kd(\cos\theta - \cos\theta_m)\right]}{(N-1)\sin\left[\frac{1}{2} kd(\cos\theta - \cos\theta_m)\right]} \tag{14-20}$$

$l = (N-1)d$ assumes that the array does not extend beyond the outer samples, as shown in Figure 14.1(b). The total array factor can be written as a superposition of $2M$ or $2M+1$ terms each of the form of (14-20). Thus

$$AF(\theta) = \sum_{m=-M}^{M} a_m \frac{\sin\left[\frac{N-1}{2} kd(\cos\theta - \cos\theta_m)\right]}{(N-1)\sin\left[\frac{1}{2} kd(\cos\theta - \cos\theta_m)\right]} \tag{14-21}$$

As for the line sources, the excitation coefficients of the array elements at the sample points are equal to the value of the desired array factor at the sample points. That is,

$$a_m = AF(\theta = \theta_m)_d \tag{14-22}$$

The sample points are taken at

$$\cos\theta_m = m\frac{\lambda}{l} = \frac{m\lambda}{(N-1)d} \Rightarrow \theta_m = \cos^{-1}\left[m\frac{\lambda}{(N-1)d}\right] \tag{14-23}$$

The normalized current excitation of each element is given by

$$I_n(z') = \frac{1}{N} \sum_{m=-M}^{M} a_m e^{-jkz_n'\cos\theta_m} \tag{14-24}$$

where z_n' indicates the position of the nth element (element in question).

Example 14.5

Repeat the design of Example 14.4 for an array of 11 elements with an element spacing of $d = \lambda/2$.

SOLUTION

Since the number of elements ($N=11$) is identical to the number of samples in Example 14.4, the excitation coefficients are identical. Using the values of a_m as listed in Example 14.4, the computed array factor pattern using (14-21) is shown in Figure 14.8(a). A good synthesis of the desired pattern is displayed. The side lobe level, relative to the pattern value at $\theta = 90°$, is

0.221 (-13.1 dB). The agreement between the line-source and the linear array Woodward designs are also good.

In general, the Fourier transform synthesis method yields reconstructed patterns whose mean-square error (or deviation) from the desired pattern is a minimum. However, the Woodward synthesis method reconstructs patterns whose values at the sampled points are identical to the ones of the desired pattern; it does not have any control of the pattern between the sample points, and it does not yield a pattern with least mean-square deviation.

Ruze [9] points out that the least-mean-square error design is not necessarily the best. The particular application will dictate the preference between the two. However, the Fourier transform method is best suited for reconstruction of desired patterns which are analytically simple and which allow the integrations to be performed in closed form. Today, with the advent of high-speed computers, this is not a major restriction since integration can be performed (with high efficiency) numerically. In contrast, the Woodward method is more flexible, and it can be used to synthesize any desired pattern. In fact, it can even be used to reconstruct patterns which, because of their complicated nature, cannot be expressed analytically. Measured patterns, either of analog or digital form, can also be synthesized using the Woodward method.

14.6 TAYLOR LINE-SOURCE (TSCHEBYSCHEFF ERROR)

In Chapter 6 we discussed the classic Dolph-Tschebyscheff array design which yields, for a given side lobe level, the smallest possible first null beamwidth (or the smallest possible side lobe level for a given first null beamwidth). Another classic design that is closely related to it, but is more applicable for continuous distributions, is that by Taylor [5] (this method is different from that by Taylor [6] which will be discussed in the next section).

The Taylor design [5] yields a pattern that displays an optimum compromise between beamwidth and side lobe level. In an ideal design, the minor lobes are maintained at an equal and specific level. Since the minor lobes are of equal ripple and extend to infinity, this implies an infinite power. More realistically, however, the technique as introduced by Taylor leads to a pattern whose first few minor lobes (closest to the main lobe) are maintained at an equal and specified level; the remaining lobes decay monotonically. Practically, even the level of the closest minor lobes exhibits a slight monotomic decay. This decay is a function of the space u over which these minor lobes are required to be maintained at an equal level. As this space increases, the rate of decay of the closest minor lobes decreases. For a very large space of u (over which the closest minor lobes are required to have an equal ripple), the rate of decay is negligible. It should be pointed out, however, that the other method by Taylor [6] (of Section 14.7) yields minor lobes, all of which decay monotomically.

The details of the analytical formulation are somewhat complex (for the average reader) and lengthy, and they will not be included here. The interested reader is referred to the literature [5], [11]. Instead, a succinct outline of the salient points of the method and of the design procedure will be included. The design is for far-field patterns, and it is based on the formulation of (14-1).

Ideally the normalized space factor that yields a pattern with equal-ripple minor lobes is given by

$$\text{SF}(\theta) = \frac{\cosh\left[\sqrt{(\pi A)^2 - u^2}\right]}{\cosh(\pi A)} \tag{14-25}$$

$$u = \pi \frac{l}{\lambda} \cos\theta \tag{14-25a}$$

whose maximum value occurs when $u = 0$. A is a constant which is related to the maximum desired side lobe level R_0 by

$$\cosh(\pi A) = R_0 \text{ (dimensionless)} \tag{14-26}$$

The space factor of (14-25) can be derived from the Dolph-Tschebyscheff array formulation of Section 6.7.3, if the number of elements of the array are allowed to become infinite.

Since (14-25) is ideal and cannot be realized physically, Taylor [5] suggested that it be approximated (within a certain error) by a space factor comprised of a product of factors whose roots are the zeros of the pattern. Because of its approximation to the ideal Tschebyscheff design, it is also referred to as *Tschebyscheff error*. The Taylor space factor is given by

$$\text{SF}(u, A, \bar{n}) = \frac{\sin(u)}{u} \frac{\displaystyle\prod_{n=1}^{\bar{n}-1}\left[1 - \left(\frac{u}{u_n}\right)^2\right]}{\displaystyle\prod_{n=1}^{\bar{n}-1}\left[1 - \left(\frac{u}{n\pi}\right)^2\right]} \tag{14-27}$$

$$u = \pi v = \pi \frac{l}{\lambda} \cos\theta \tag{14-27a}$$

$$u_n = \pi v_n = \pi \frac{l}{\lambda} \cos\theta_n \tag{14-27b}$$

where θ_n represents the locations of the nulls. The parameter $\bar{n}$ is a constant chosen by the designer so that the minor lobes for $|v| = |u/\pi| \leq \bar{n}$ are maintained at a nearly constant voltage level of $1/R_0$; for $|v| = |u/\pi| > \bar{n}$ the envelope, through the maxima of the remaining minor lobes, decays at a rate of $1/v = \pi/u$. In addition, the nulls of the pattern for $|v| \geq \bar{n}$ occur at integer values of v.

In general, there are $\bar{n}-1$ inner nulls for $|v|<\bar{n}$ and an infinite number of outer nulls for $|v|\geq\bar{n}$. To provide a smooth transition between the inner and the outer nulls (at the expense of slight beam broadening), Taylor introduced a parameter σ. It is usually referred to as the scaling factor, and it spaces the inner nulls so that they blend smoothly with the outer ones. In addition, it is the factor by which the beamwidth of the Taylor design is greater than that of the Dolph-Tschebyscheff, and it is given by

$$\sigma = \frac{\bar{n}}{\sqrt{A^2+\left(\bar{n}-\frac{1}{2}\right)^2}} \tag{14-28}$$

The location of the nulls are obtained using

$$u_n = \pi v_n = \pi \frac{l}{\lambda}\cos\theta_n = \begin{cases} \pm\pi\sigma\sqrt{A^2+\left(n-\frac{1}{2}\right)^2} & 1\leq n<\bar{n} \\ \pm n\pi & \bar{n}\leq n\leq\infty \end{cases} \tag{14-29}$$

The normalized line-source distribution, which will yield the desired pattern, is given by

$$I(z') = \frac{1}{l}\left[1+2\sum_{p=1}^{\bar{n}-1}\mathrm{SF}(p,A,\bar{n})\cos\left(2\pi p\frac{z'}{l}\right)\right] \tag{14-30}$$

The coefficients $\mathrm{SF}(p,A,\bar{n})$ represent samples of the Taylor pattern, and they can be obtained from (14-27) with $u=\pi p$. They can also be found using

$$\mathrm{SF}(p,A,\bar{n}) = \begin{cases} \dfrac{[(\bar{n}-1)!]^2}{(\bar{n}-1+p)!(\bar{n}-1-p)!}\displaystyle\prod_{m=1}^{\bar{n}-1}\left[1-\left(\frac{\pi p}{u_m}\right)^2\right] & |p|<\bar{n} \\ 0 & |p|\geq\bar{n} \end{cases} \tag{14-30a}$$

with $\mathrm{SF}(-p,A,\bar{n})=\mathrm{SF}(p,A,\bar{n})$.

The half-power beamwidth is given approximately by [8]

$$\Theta_0 \simeq 2\sin^{-1}\left\{\frac{\lambda\sigma}{\pi l}\left[\left(\cosh^{-1}R_0\right)^2-\left(\cosh^{-1}\frac{R_0}{\sqrt{2}}\right)^2\right]^{1/2}\right\} \tag{14-31}$$

14.6.1 Design Procedure

To initiate a Taylor design, you must

1. specify the normalized maximum tolerable side lobe level $1/R_0$ of the pattern.

2. choose a positive integer value for $\bar{n}$ such that for $|v| = |(l/\lambda)\cos\theta|$ $\leq \bar{n}$ the normalized level of the minor lobes is nearly constant at $1/R_0$. For $|v| > \bar{n}$, the minor lobes decrease monotonically. In addition, for $|v| < \bar{n}$ there exist $(\bar{n} - 1)$ nulls. The position of all the nulls is found using (14-29). Small values of $\bar{n}$ yield source distributions which are maximum at the center and monotonically decrease toward the edges. In contrast, large values of $\bar{n}$ result in sources which are peaked simultaneously at the center and at the edges, and they yield sharper main beams. Therefore, very small and very large values of $\bar{n}$ should be avoided. Typically the value of $\bar{n}$ should be at least 3 and at least 6 for designs with side lobes of -25 and -40 dB, respectively.

To complete the design, you do the following:

1. Determine A using (14-26), σ using (14-28), and the nulls using (14-29).
2. Compute the space factor using (14-27), the source distribution using (14-30) and (14-30a), and the half-power beamwidth using (14-31).

Example 14.6

Design a -20-dB Taylor distribution line-source with $\bar{n} = 5$. Plot the pattern and the current distribution for $l = 7\lambda (-7 \leq v = u/\pi \leq 7)$.

SOLUTION
For a -20-dB side lobe level

$$R_0 \text{ (dimensionless)} = 10$$

Using (14-26)

$$A = \frac{1}{\pi}\cosh^{-1}(10) = 0.95277$$

and by (14-28)

$$\sigma = \frac{5}{\sqrt{(0.95277)^2 + (5 - 0.5)^2}} = 1.0871$$

The nulls are given by (14-29) or

$$v_n = u_n/\pi = \pm 1.17, \pm 1.932, \pm 2.91, \pm 3.943, \pm 5.00, \pm 6.00, \pm 7.00,\ldots$$

The corresponding null angles for $l = 7\lambda$ are

$$\theta_n = 80.38°(99.62°), 73.98°(106.02°), 65.45°(114.55°),$$

$$55.71°(124.29°), 44.41°(135.59°), \text{ and } 31.00°(149.00°)$$

The half-power beamwidth for $l = 7\lambda$ is found using (14-31), or

$$\Theta_0 \simeq 7.95°$$

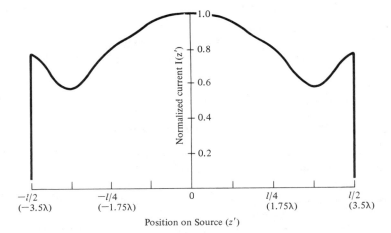

(a) Current distribution

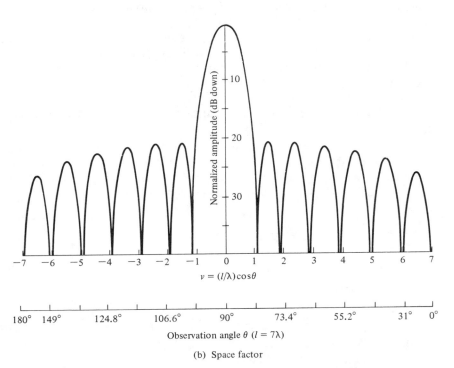

(b) Space factor

Figure 14.9 Normalized current distribution and far-field space factor pattern for a −20-dB side lobe and $\bar{n}=5$ Taylor (Tschebyscheff error) line-source of $l=7\lambda$.

The source distribution, as computed using (14-30) and (14-30a), is displayed in Figure 14.9(a). The corresponding radiation pattern for $-7 \leq v = u/\pi \leq 7$ ($0° \leq \theta \leq 180°$ for $l = 7\lambda$) is shown in Figure 14.9(b).

All the computed parameters compare well with results reported in [5] and [11].

14.7 TAYLOR LINE-SOURCE (ONE-PARAMETER)

The Dolph-Tschebyscheff array design of Section 6.7.3 yields minor lobes of equal intensity while the Taylor (Tschebyscheff error) produces a pattern whose inner minor lobes are maintained at a constant level and the remaining ones decrease monotonically. For some applications, such as radar and low-noise systems, it is desirable to sacrifice some beamwidth and low inner minor lobes to have all the minor lobes decay as the angle increases on either side of the main beam. In radar applications this is preferable because interfering or spurious signals would be reduced further when they try to enter through the decaying minor lobes. Thus any significant contributions from interfering signals would be through the pattern in the vicinity of the major lobe. Since in practice it is easier to maintain pattern symmetry around the main lobe, it is also possible to recognize that such signals are false targets. In low-noise applications, it is also desirable to have minor lobes that decay away from the main beam in order to diminish the radiation accepted through them from the relatively "hot" ground.

A continuous line-source distribution which yields decaying minor lobes and, in addition, controls the amplitude of the side lobe is that introduced by Taylor [6] in an unpublished classic memorandum. It is referred to as the Taylor (one-parameter) design and its source distribution is given by

$$I_n(z') = \begin{cases} J_0\left[j\pi B \sqrt{1 - \left(\dfrac{2z'}{l}\right)^2} \right] & -l/2 \leq z' \leq +l/2 \\ 0 & \text{elsewhere} \end{cases}$$

(14-32)

where J_0 is the Bessel function of the first kind of order zero, l is the total length of the continuous source [see Figure 14.1(a)], and B is a constant to be determined from the specified side lobe level.

The space factor associated with (14-32) can be obtained by using (14-1). After some intricate mathematical manipulations, utilizing Gegenbauer's finite integral and Gegenbauer polynomials [12], the space factor for a Taylor amplitude distribution line-source with uniform phase [$\phi_n(z') =$

$\phi_0 = 0$] can be written as

$$
SF(\theta) = \begin{cases} l\dfrac{\sinh\left[\sqrt{(\pi B)^2 - u^2}\right]}{\sqrt{(\pi B)^2 - u^2}}, & u^2 < (\pi B)^2 \\[4mm] l\dfrac{\sin\left[\sqrt{u^2 - (\pi B)^2}\right]}{\sqrt{u^2 - (\pi B)^2}}, & u^2 > (\pi B)^2 \end{cases}
\tag{14-33}
$$

where

$$
u = \pi \frac{l}{\lambda} \cos \theta
$$

B = constant determined from side lobe level
l = line-source dimension

The derivation of (14-33) is assigned as an exercise to the reader (Problem 14.15). When $(\pi B)^2 > u^2$, (14-33) represents the region near the main lobe. The minor lobes are represented by $(\pi B)^2 < u^2$ in (14-33). Either form of (14-33) can be obtained from the other by knowing that (see Appendix VI)

$$
\sin(jx) = j\sinh(x)
$$
$$
\sinh(jx) = j\sin(x)
\tag{14-34}
$$

When $u = 0$ ($\theta = \pi/2$ and maximum radiation), the pattern height is equal to

$$
(SF)_{max} = \frac{\sinh(\pi B)}{\pi B} = H_0
\tag{14-35}
$$

For $u^2 \gg (\pi B)^2$, (14-33) reduces to

$$
E(\theta) = \frac{\sin\left[\sqrt{u^2 - (\pi B)^2}\right]}{\sqrt{u^2 - (\pi B)^2}} \simeq \frac{\sin(u)}{u} \qquad u \gg \pi B
\tag{14-36}
$$

and it is identical to the pattern of a uniform distribution. The maximum height H_1 of the side lobe of (14-36) is $H_1 = 0.217233$ (or 13.2 dB down from the maximum), and it occurs when (see Appendix I)

$$
\left[u^2 - (\pi B)^2\right]^{1/2} \simeq u = 4.494
\tag{14-37}
$$

Using (14-35), the maximum voltage height of the side lobe (relative to the maximum H_0 of the major lobe) is equal to

$$
\frac{H_1}{H_0} = \frac{1}{R_0} = \frac{0.217233}{\sinh(\pi B)/(\pi B)}
\tag{14-38}
$$

or

$$R_0 = \frac{1}{0.217233} \frac{\sinh(\pi B)}{\pi B} = 4.603 \frac{\sinh(\pi B)}{\pi B} \qquad (14\text{-}38a)$$

Equation (14-38a) can be used to find the constant B when the intensity ratio R_0 of the major-to-the-side lobe is specified. Values of B for typical side lobes levels are

SIDE LOBE LEVEL (dB)	-10	-15	-20	-25	-30	-35	-40
B	$j0.4597$	0.3558	0.7386	1.0229	1.2761	1.5136	1.7415

The disadvantage of designing an array with decaying minor lobes as compared to a design with equal minor lobe level (Dolph-Tschebyscheff), is that it yields about 12 to 15% greater half-power beamwidth. However such a loss in beamwidth is a small penalty to pay when the extreme minor lobes decrease as $1/u$.

To illustrate the principles, let us consider an example.

Example 14.7

Given a continuous line-source whose total length is 4λ. Design a Taylor distribution array whose side lobe is 30 dB down from the maximum of the major lobe.

(a) Find the constant B.
(b) Plot the pattern (in dB) of the continuous line-source distribution.
(c) For a spacing of $\lambda/4$ between the elements, find the number of discrete isotropic elements needed to approximate the continuous source. Assume that the two extreme elements are placed at the edges of the continuous line source.
(d) Find the normalized coefficients of the discrete array of part (c).
(e) Write the array factor of the discrete array of parts (c) and (d).
(f) Plot the array factor (in dB) of the discrete array of part (e).
(g) For a corresponding Dolph-Tschebyscheff array, find the normalized coefficients of the discrete elements.
(h) Compare the patterns of the Taylor continuous line-source distribution and discretized array, and the corresponding Dolph-Tschebyscheff discrete element array.

SOLUTION
For a -30 dB maximum side lobe, the voltage ratio of the major-to-the-side lobe level is equal to

$$30 = 20\log_{10}(R_0) \Rightarrow R_0 = 31.62$$

(a) The constant B is obtained using (14-38a) or

$$R_0 = 31.62 = 4.603 \frac{\sinh(\pi B)}{\pi B} \Rightarrow B = 1.2761$$

(b) The normalized space factor pattern is obtained using (14-33), and it is shown plotted in Figure 14.10.

(c) For $d = \lambda/4$ and with elements at the extremes, the number of elements is 17.

(d) The coefficients are obtained using (14-32). Since we have an odd number of elements, their positioning and excitation coefficients

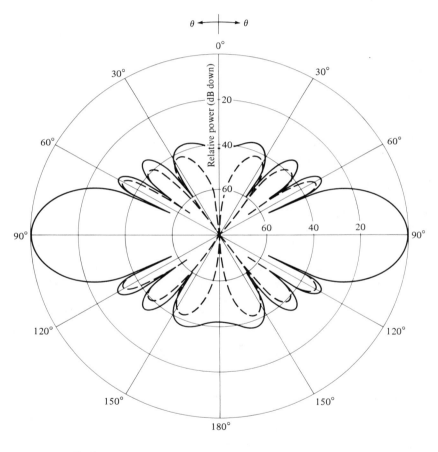

$\theta \longleftarrow \bigg|\longrightarrow \theta$

—————— Continuous
$(l = 4\lambda)$

— — — — Discretized
$(l = 4\lambda, d = \lambda/4, N = 17)$

Figure 14.10 Far-field amplitude patterns of continuous and discretized Taylor (one-parameter) distributions.

are those shown in Figure 6.14(b). Thus the total excitation coefficient of the center element is

$$2a_1 = I_n(z')\big|_{z'=0} = J_0(j4.009) = 11.400 \Rightarrow a_1 = 5.70$$

The coefficients of the elements on either side of the center element are identical (because of symmetry), and they are obtained from

$$a_2 = I(z')\big|_{z'=\pm\lambda/4} = J_0(j3.977) = 11.106$$

The coefficients of the other elements are obtained in a similar manner, and they are given by

$$a_3 = 10.192$$
$$a_4 = 8.889$$
$$a_5 = 7.195$$
$$a_6 = 5.426$$
$$a_7 = 3.694$$
$$a_8 = 2.202$$
$$a_9 = 1.000$$

(e) The array factor is given by (6-61b) and (6-61c), or

$$(\text{AF})_{17} = \sum_{n=1}^{9} a_n \cos[2(n-1)u]$$

$$u = \pi \frac{d}{\lambda} \cos\theta = \frac{\pi}{4}\cos\theta$$

where the coefficients (a_n's) are those found in part (d).

(f) The normalized pattern (in dB) of the discretized distribution (discrete element array) is shown in Figure 14.10.

(g) The normalized coefficients of a 17-element Dolph-Tschebyscheff array, with -30-dB side lobes, are obtained using the method outlined in the Design Section on pages 247–249 of Section 6.7.3 are given by

UNNORMALIZED	NORMALIZED
$a_1 = 2.858$	$a_{1n} = 1.680$
$a_2 = 5.597$	$a_{2n} = 3.290$
$a_3 = 5.249$	$a_{3n} = 3.086$
$a_4 = 4.706$	$a_{4n} = 2.767$
$a_5 = 4.022$	$a_{5n} = 2.364$
$a_6 = 3.258$	$a_{6n} = 1.915$
$a_7 = 2.481$	$a_{7n} = 1.459$
$a_8 = 1.750$	$a_{8n} = 1.029$
$a_9 = 1.701$	$a_{9n} = 1.000$

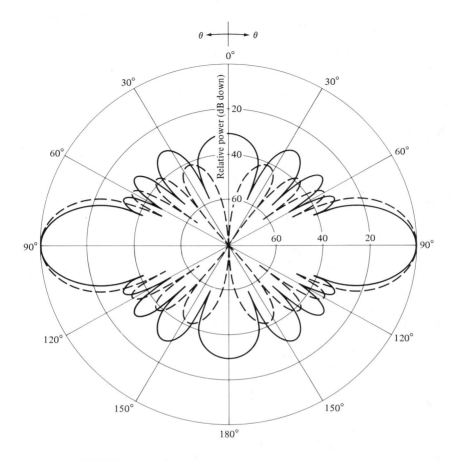

———————— Dolph–Tschebyscheff

— — — — Taylor (one–parameter); Discretized

Figure 14.11 Far-field amplitude patterns of Taylor (discretized) and Dolph-Tschebyscheff distributions ($l=4\lambda$, $d=\lambda/4$, $N=17$).

As with the discretized Taylor distribution array, the coefficients are symmetrical, and the form of the array factor is that given in part (e).

(h) The normalized pattern (in dB) is plotted in Figure 14.11 where it is compared with that of the discretized Taylor distribution. From the patterns in Figures 14.10 and 14.11 it can be concluded that

1. the main lobe of the continuous line-source Taylor design is well approximated by the discretized distribution with a $\lambda/4$ spacing between the elements. Even the minor lobes are well represented, and a better approximation can be obtained with more elements and smaller spacing between them.

2. the Taylor distribution array pattern has a wider main lobe than the corresponding Dolph-Tschebyscheff, but it displays decreasing minor lobes away from the main beam.

A larger spacing between the elements does not approximate the continuous distribution as accurately. The design of Taylor and Dolph-Tschebyscheff arrays for $l=4\lambda$ and $d=\lambda/2(N=9)$ is assigned as a problem at the end of the chapter (Problem 14.16).

To qualitatively assess the performance between uniform, binomial, Dolph-Tschebyscheff, and Taylor (one-parameter) array designs, the amplitude distribution of each has been plotted in Figure 14.12(a). It is assumed that $l=4\lambda$, $d=\lambda/4$, $N=17$, and the maximum side lobe is 30 dB down. The coefficients are normalized with respect to the amplitude of the corresponding element at the center of that array.

The binomial design possesses the smoothest amplitude distribution (between 1 and 0) from the center to the edges (the amplitude at the edges is vanishingly small). Because of this characteristic, the binomial array will display the smallest side lobes followed, in order, by the Taylor, Tschebyscheff, and the uniform arrays. In contrast, the uniform array will possess the smallest half-power beamwidth followed, in order, by the Tschebyscheff, Taylor, and binomial arrays. As a rule of thumb, the array with the smoothest amplitude distribution (from the center to the edges) will have the smallest side lobes and the larger half-power beamwidths. The best design is a trade-off between side lobe level and beamwidth.

14.8 TRIANGULAR, COSINE, AND COSINE-SQUARED AMPLITUDE DISTRIBUTIONS

Some other very common and simple line-source amplitude distributions are those of the triangular, cosine, cosine-squared, cosine on-a-pedestal, cosine-squared on-a-pedestal, Gaussian, inverse taper, and edge. Instead of including many details, the pattern, half-power beamwidth, first null beamwidth, magnitude of side lobes, and directivity for uniform, triangular, cosine, and cosine-squared amplitude distributions (with constant phase) are summarized in Table 14.1 [13], [14].

The normalized coefficients for a uniform, triangular, cosine, and cosine-squared arrays of $l=4\lambda$, $d=\lambda/4$, $N=17$ are shown plotted in Figure 14.12(b). The array with the smallest side lobes and the larger half-power beamwidth is the cosine-squared, because it possesses the smoothest distribution. It is followed, in order, by the triangular, cosine, and uniform distributions. This is verified by examining the characteristics in Table 14.1.

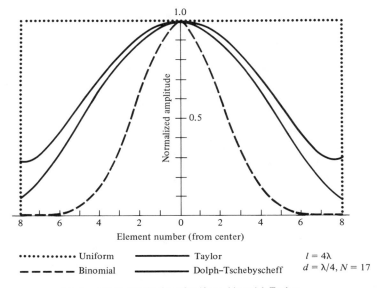

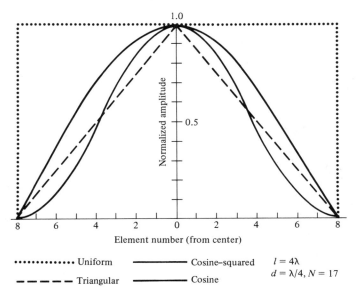

Element number (from center)

(a) Amplitude distribution of uniform, binomial, Taylor,
and Dolph–Tschebyscheff discrete–element arrays

(b) Amplitude distribution of uniform, triangular, cosine,
and cosine squared discrete–element arrays

Figure 14.12 Amplitude distribution of nonuniform amplitude linear arrays.

Table 14.1 RADIATION CHARACTERISTICS FOR LINE SOURCES AND LINEAR ARRAYS WITH UNIFORM, TRIANGULAR, COSINE, AND COSINE-SQUARED DISTRIBUTIONS

DISTRIBUTION	UNIFORM	TRIANGULAR	COSINE	COSINE-SQUARED
Distribution I_n (analytical)	I_0	$I_1\left(1 - \dfrac{2}{l}\lvert z'\rvert\right)$	$I_2\cos\left(\dfrac{\pi}{l}z'\right)$	$I_3\cos^2\left(\dfrac{\pi}{l}z'\right)$
Distribution (graphical)				
Space factor (SF) $u = \left(\dfrac{\pi l}{\lambda}\right)\sin\theta$	$I_0 l\,\dfrac{\sin(u)}{u}$	$I_1\dfrac{l}{2}\left[\dfrac{\sin\left(\dfrac{u}{2}\right)}{\dfrac{u}{2}}\right]^2$	$I_2 l\,\dfrac{\pi}{2}\dfrac{\cos(u)}{(\pi/2)^2 - u^2}$	$I_3\dfrac{l}{2}\dfrac{\sin(u)}{u}\left[\dfrac{\pi^2}{\pi^2 - u^2}\right]$
Space factor |SF|				
Half-power beamwidth (degrees) $l \gg \lambda$	$\dfrac{50.6}{(l/\lambda)}$	$\dfrac{73.4}{(l/\lambda)}$	$\dfrac{68.8}{(l/\lambda)}$	$\dfrac{83.2}{(l/\lambda)}$

First null beamwidth (degrees) $l \gg \lambda$	$\dfrac{114.6}{(l/\lambda)}$	$\dfrac{229.2}{(l/\lambda)}$	$\dfrac{171.9}{(l/\lambda)}$	$\dfrac{229.2}{(l/\lambda)}$
First side lobe max. (to main max.) (dB)	-13.2	-26.4	-23.2	-31.5
Directivity factor (l large)	$2\left(\dfrac{l}{\lambda}\right)$	$0.75\left[2\left(\dfrac{l}{\lambda}\right)\right]$	$0.810\left[2\left(\dfrac{l}{\lambda}\right)\right]$	$0.667\left[2\left(\dfrac{l}{\lambda}\right)\right]$

Cosine on-a-pedestal distribution is obtained by the superposition of the uniform and the cosine distributions. Thus it can be represented by

$$I_n(z') = \begin{cases} I_0 + I_2 \cos\left(\dfrac{\pi}{l}z'\right), & -l/2 \le z' \le l/2 \\ 0 & \text{elsewhere} \end{cases} \tag{14-39}$$

where I_0 and I_2 are constants. The space factor pattern of such a distribution is obtained by the addition of the patterns of the uniform and the cosine distributions found in Table 14.1. That is,

$$\text{SF}(\theta) = I_0 l \frac{\sin(u)}{u} + I_2 \frac{\pi l}{2} \frac{\cos u}{(\pi/2)^2 - u^2} \tag{14-40}$$

A similar procedure is used to represent and analyze a cosine-squared on-a-pedestal distribution.

14.9 LINE-SOURCE PHASE DISTRIBUTIONS

The amplitude distributions of the previous section were assumed to have uinform phase variations throughout the physical extent of the source. Practical radiators (such as reflectors, lenses, horns, etc.) have nonuniform phase fronts caused by one or more of the following:

1. displacement of the reflector feed from the focus
2. distortion of the reflector or lens surface
3. feeds whose wave fronts are not ideally cylindrical or spherical (as they are usually presumed to be)
4. physical geometry of the radiator

These are usually referred to *phase errors*, and they are more evident in radiators with tilted beams.

To simplify the analytical formulations, most of the phase fronts are represented with linear, quadratic, or cubic distributions. Each of the phase distributions can be associated with each of the amplitude distributions. In (14-1), the phase distribution of the source is represented by $\phi_n(z')$. For linear, quadratic, and cubic phase variations, $\phi_n(z')$ takes the form of

linear: $\qquad \phi_1(z') = \beta_1 \dfrac{2}{l} z',$ $\qquad\qquad -l/2 \le z' \le l/2 \tag{14-41a}$

quadratic: $\qquad \phi_2(z') = \beta_2 \left(\dfrac{2}{l}\right)^2 z'^2,$ $\qquad -l/2 \le z' \le l/2 \tag{14-41b}$

cubic: $\qquad \phi_3(z') = \beta_3 \left(\dfrac{2}{l}\right)^3 z'^3,$ $\qquad -l/2 \le z' \le l/2 \tag{14-41c}$

and it is shown plotted in Figure 14.13. The quadratic distribution is used to represent the phase variations at the aperture of horn and defocused (along the symmetry axis) reflector and lens antennas.

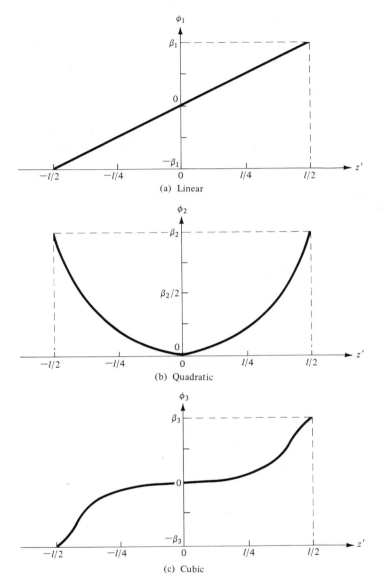

Figure 14.13 Linear, quadratic, and cubic phase variations.

The space factor patterns corresponding to the phase distributions of (14-41a)–(14-41c) can be obtained by using (14-1). Because the analytical formulations become lengthy and complex, especially for the quadratic and cubic distributions, they will not be included here. Instead, a general guideline of their effects will be summarized [13], [14].

Linear phase distributions have a tendency to tilt the main beam of an antenna by an angle θ_0 and to form an asymmetrical pattern. The pattern of this distribution can be obtained by replacing the u (for uniform phase) in Table 14.1 by $(u - \theta_0)$. In general, the half-power beamwidth of the tilted pattern is increased by $1/\cos\theta_0$ while the directivity is decreased by $\cos\theta_0$. This becomes more apparent by realizing that the projected length of the line source toward the maximum is reduced by $\cos\theta_0$. Thus the effective length of the source is reduced.

Quadratic phase errors lead primarily to a reduction of directivity, and an increase in side lobe level on either side of the main lobe. The symmetry of the original pattern is maintained. In addition, for moderate phase variations, ideal nulls in the patterns disappear. Thus the minor lobes blend into each other and into the main beam, and they represent shoulders of the main beam instead of appearing as separate lobes. Analytical formulations for quadratic phase distributions were introduced in Chapter 12 on horn antennas.

Cubic phase distributions introduce not only a tilt in the beam but also decrease the directivity. The newly formed patterns are asymmetrical. The minor lobes on one side are increased in magnitude and those on the other side are reduced in intensity.

14.10 CONTINUOUS APERTURE SOURCES

Space factors for aperture (two-dimensional) sources can be introduced in a similar manner as in Section 14.2.1 for line-sources.

14.10.1 Rectangular Aperture

Referring to the geometry of Figure 6.20(b), the space factor for a two-dimensional rectangular distribution along the x-y plane is given by

$$\text{SF} = \int_{-l_y/2}^{l_y/2} \int_{-l_x/2}^{l_x/2} A_n(x', y') e^{j[kx'\sin\theta\cos\phi + ky'\sin\theta\sin\phi + \phi_n(x', y')]} dx' dy'$$

(14-42)

where l_x and l_y are, respectively, the linear dimensions of the rectangular aperture along the x and y axes. $A_n(x', y')$ and $\phi_n(x', y')$ represent, respectively, the amplitude and phase distributions on the aperture.

For many practical antennas (such as waveguides, horns, etc.) the aperture distribution (amplitude and phase) is separable. That is,

$$A_n(x', y') = I_x(x') I_y(y') \tag{14-42a}$$

$$\phi_n(x', y') = \phi_x(x') + \phi_y(y') \tag{14-42b}$$

so that (14-42) can be written as

$$SF = S_x S_y \tag{14-43}$$

where

$$S_x = \int_{-l_x/2}^{l_x/2} I_x(x') e^{j[kx'\sin\theta\cos\phi + \phi_x(x')]} dx' \tag{14-43a}$$

$$S_y = \int_{-l_y/2}^{l_y/2} I_y(y') e^{j[ky'\sin\theta\sin\phi + \phi_y(y')]} dy' \tag{14-43b}$$

which is analogous to the array factor of (6-77)–(6-77b) for discrete-element arrays.

The evaluation of (14-42) can be accomplished either analytically or graphically. If the distribution is separable, as in (14-42a) and (14-42b), the evaluation can be performed using the results of a line-source distribution.

The total field of the aperture antenna is equal to the product of the element and space factors. As for the line sources, the element factor for apertures depends on the type of current density and its orientation.

14.10.2 Circular Aperture

The space factor for a circular aperture can be obtained in a similar manner as for the rectangular distribution. Referring to the geometry of Figure 6.29, the space factor for a circular aperture with radius a can be written as

$$SF(\theta, \phi) = \int_0^{2\pi} \int_0^a A_n(\rho', \phi') e^{j[k\rho'\sin\theta\cos(\phi - \phi') + \zeta_n(\rho', \phi')]} \rho' \, d\rho' \, d\phi' \tag{14-44}$$

where ρ' is the radial distance ($0 \le \rho' \le a$), ϕ' is the azimuthal angle over the aperture ($0 \le \phi' \le 2\pi$ for $0 \le \rho' \le a$), and $A_n(\rho', \phi')$ and $\zeta_n(\rho', \phi')$ represent, respectively, the amplitude and phase distributions over the aperture. Equation (14-44) is analogous to the array factor of (6-97a) for discrete elements.

If the aperture distribution has uniform phase $[\zeta_n(\rho', \phi') = \zeta_0 = 0]$ and azimuthal amplitude symmetry $[A_n(\rho', \phi') = A_n(\rho')]$, (14-44) reduces, by using (5-39), to

$$SF(\theta) = 2\pi \int_0^a A_n(\rho') J_0(k\rho' \sin\theta) \rho' \, d\rho' \tag{14-45}$$

where $J_0(x)$ is the Bessel function of the first kind and of order zero.

Many practical antennas, such as a parabolic reflector, have distributions that taper toward the edges of the apertures. These distributions can be approximated reasonably well by functions of the form

$$A_n(\rho') = \begin{cases} \left[1 - \left(\dfrac{\rho'}{a} \right)^2 \right]^n & 0 \le \rho' \le a, \quad n = 0, 1, 2, 3, \ldots \\ 0 & \text{elsewhere} \end{cases} \tag{14-46}$$

For $n = 0$, (14-46) reduces to a uniform distribution.

Table 14.2 RADIATION CHARACTERISTICS FOR CIRCULAR APERTURES AND CIRCULAR PLANAR ARRAYS WITH CIRCULAR SYMMETRY AND TAPERED DISTRIBUTION

DISTRIBUTION	UNIFORM	RADIAL TAPER	RADIAL TAPER SQUARED
Distribution (analytical)	$I_0\left[1-\left(\dfrac{\rho'}{a}\right)^2\right]^0$	$I_1\left[1-\left(\dfrac{\rho'}{a}\right)^2\right]^1$	$I_2\left[1-\left(\dfrac{\rho'}{a}\right)^2\right]^2$
Distribution (graphical)			
Space factor (SF) $u=\left(2\pi\dfrac{a}{\lambda}\right)\sin\theta$	$I_0 2\pi a^2 \dfrac{J_1(u)}{u}$	$I_1 4\pi a^2 \dfrac{J_2(u)}{u}$	$I_2 16\pi a^2 \dfrac{J_3(u)}{u}$
Half-power beamwidth (degrees) $a\gg\lambda$	$\dfrac{29.2}{(a/\lambda)}$	$\dfrac{36.4}{(a/\lambda)}$	$\dfrac{42.1}{(a/\lambda)}$
First null beamwidth (degrees) $a\gg\lambda$	$\dfrac{69.9}{(a/\lambda)}$	$\dfrac{93.4}{(a/\lambda)}$	$\dfrac{116.3}{(a/\lambda)}$
First side lobe max. (to main max.) (dB)	-17.6	-24.6	-30.6
Directivity factor	$\left(\dfrac{2\pi a}{\lambda}\right)^2$	$0.75\left(\dfrac{2\pi a}{\lambda}\right)^2$	$0.56\left(\dfrac{2\pi a}{\lambda}\right)^2$

The radiation characteristics of circular apertures or planar circular arrays with distributions of (14-46) with $n=0,1,2$ are shown tabulated in Table 14.2 [14]. It is apparent, as before, that distributions with lower taper toward the edges (larger values of n) have smaller side lobes but larger beamwidths. In design, a compromise between side lobe level and beamwidth is necessary.

References

1. S. A. Schelkunoff, "A Mathematical Theory of Linear Arrays," *Bell System Technical Journal*, vol. 22, pp. 80–107, 1943.
2. H. G. Booker and P. C. Clemmow, "The Concept of an Angular Spectrum of Plane Waves, and Its Relation to That of Polar Diagram and Aperture Distribu-

tion," *Proc. IEE* (London), Paper No. 922, Radio Section, vol. 97, pt. III, pp. 11–17, Jan. 1950.

3. P. M. Woodward, "A Method for Calculating the Field over a Plane Aperture Required to Produce a Given Polar Diagram," *J. IEE*, vol. 93, pt. IIIA, pp. 1554–1558, 1946.

4. P. M. Woodward and J. D. Lawson, "The Theoretical Precision with Which an Arbitrary Radiation-Pattern May Be Obtained from a Source of a Finite Size," *J. IEE*, vol. 95, pt. III, no. 37, pp. 363–370, Sept. 1948.

5. T. T. Taylor, "Design of Line-Source Antennas for Narrow Beamwidth and Low Sidelobes," *IRE Trans. Antennas Propag.*, vol. AP-3, No. 1, pp. 16–28, Jan. 1955.

6. T. T. Taylor, "One Parameter Family of Line Sources Producing Modified $\sin(\pi u)/\pi u$ Patterns," Hughes Aircraft Co. Tech. Mem. 324, Culver City, Calif., Contract AF 19(604)-262-F-14, Sept. 4, 1953.

7. R. S. Elliott, "On Discretizing Continuous Aperture Distributions," *IEEE Trans. Antennas Propag.*, vol. AP-25, No. 5, pp. 617–621, Sept. 1977.

8. R. C. Hansen (ed.), *Microwave Scanning Antennas*, vol. I, Academic Press, New York, 1964, p. 56.

9. J. Ruze, "Physical Limitations on Antennas," MIT Research Lab., Electronics Tech. Rept. 248, Oct. 30, 1952.

10. M. I. Skolnik, *Introduction to Radar Systems*, McGraw-Hill, New York, 1962, pp. 320–330.

11. R. S. Elliott, "Design of Line Source Antennas for Narrow Beamwidth and Asymmetric Low Sidelobes," *IEEE Trans. Antennas Propag.*, vol. AP-23, No. 1, pp. 100–107, Jan. 1975.

12. G. N. Watson, *A Treatise on the Theory of Bessel Functions*, 2nd Ed., Cambridge University Press, London, pp. 50 and 379, 1966.

13. S. Silver (ed.), *Microwave Antenna Theory and Design*, MIT Radiation Laboratory Series, Vol. 12, McGraw-Hill, New York, 1965, Chapter 6, pp. 169–199.

14. H. Jasik (ed.), *Antenna Engineering Handbook*, McGraw-Hill, New York, 1961, pp. 2-25 to 2-46.

PROBLEMS

14.1. A three-element array is placed along the z-axis. Assuming the spacing between the elements is $d = \lambda/4$ and the relative amplitude excitation is equal to $a_1 = 1$, $a_2 = 2$, $a_3 = 1$,

    (a) find the angles where the array factor vanishes when $\beta = 0$, $\pi/2$, π, and $3\pi/2$

    (b) plot the relative pattern for each array factor

    Use Schelkunoff's method.

14.2. Design a linear array of isotropic elements placed along the z-axis such that the zeros of the array factor occur at $\theta = 0°$, $60°$, and $120°$. Assume that the elements are spaced $\lambda/4$ apart and that the progressive phase shift between them is $0°$.

    (a) Find the required number of elements.

    (b) Determine their excitation coefficients.

    (c) Write the array factor.

    (d) Plot the array factor pattern to verify the validity of the design.

14.3. The z-plane array factor of an array of isotropic elements placed along the z-axis is given by

$$AF = z(z^4 - 1)$$

Determine the
(a) number of elements of the array. If there are any elements with zero excitation coefficients (null elements), so indicate
(b) position of each element (including that of null elements) along the z axis
(c) magnitude and phase (in degrees) excitation of each element
(d) angles where the pattern will vanish when the total array length (including null elements) is 2λ

Use Schelkunoff's method.

14.4. Repeat the Fourier transform design of Example 14.2 for a line source along the z-axis whose sectoral pattern is given by

$$SF(\theta) = \begin{cases} 1 & 60° \le \theta \le 120° \\ 0 & \text{elsewhere} \end{cases}$$

Use $l = 5\lambda$ and 10λ. Compare the reconstructed patterns with the desired one.

14.5. Repeat the Fourier transform design of Problem 14.4 for a linear array with a spacing of $d = \lambda/2$ between the elements and
(a) $N = 11$ elements
(b) $N = 21$ elements

14.6. Repeat the design of Problem 14.4 using the Woodward method for line-sources.

14.7. Repeat the design of Problem 14.5 using the Woodward method for linear arrays.

14.8. Design, using the Woodward method, a line-source of $l = 5\lambda$ whose space factor pattern is given by

$$SF(\theta) = \sin^3 \theta \qquad 0° \le \theta \le 180°$$

Determine the current distribution and compare the reconstructed pattern with the desired pattern.

14.9. Repeat the design of Problem 14.8 for a linear array of $N = 11$ elements with a spacing of $d = \lambda/2$ between them.

14.10. In target-search, grounding-mapping radars, and in airport beacons it is desirable to have the echo power received from a target, of constant cross section, to be independent of its range R.

Generally, the far-zone field radiated by an antenna is given by

$$|E(R, \theta, \phi)| = C_0 \frac{|F(\theta, \phi)|}{R}$$

where C_0 is a constant. According to the geometry of the figure

$$R = h/\sin\theta = h\csc\theta$$

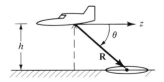

For a constant value of ϕ, the radiated field expression reduces to

$$|E(R,\theta,\phi=\phi_0)| = C_0\frac{|F(\theta,\phi=\phi_0)|}{R} = C_1\frac{|f(\theta)|}{R}$$

A constant value of field strength can be maintained provided the radar is flying at a constant altitude h and the far-field antenna pattern is equal to

$$f(\theta) = C_2\csc(\theta)$$

This is referred to as a cosecant pattern, and it is used to compensate for the range variations. For very narrow beam antennas, the total pattern is approximately equal to the space or array factor. Design a line-source, using the Woodward method, whose space factor is given by

$$SF(\theta) = \begin{cases} 0.342\csc(\theta), & 20° \le \theta \le 60° \\ 0 & \text{elsewhere} \end{cases}$$

Plot the synthesized pattern for $l = 20\lambda$, and compare it with the desired pattern.

14.11. Repeat the design of Problem 14.10 for a linear array of $N=41$ elements with a spacing of $d = \lambda/2$ between them.

14.12. For some radar search applications, it is more desirable to have an antenna which has a square beam for $0 \le \theta \le \theta_0$, a cosecant pattern for $\theta_0 \le \theta \le \theta_m$, and it is zero elsewhere. Design a line-source, using the Woodward method, with a space factor of

$$SF(\theta) = \begin{cases} 1 & 15° \le \theta \le 20° \\ 0.342\csc(\theta) & 20° \le \theta \le 60° \\ 0 & \text{elsewhere} \end{cases}$$

Plot the reconstructed pattern for $l = 20\lambda$, and compare it with the desired pattern.

14.13. Repeat the design of Problem 14.12, using the Woodward method, for a linear array of 41 elements with a spacing of $d = \lambda/2$ between them.

14.14. Design a Taylor (Tschebyscheff error) line-source with a
  (a) -25-dB side lobe level and $\bar{n} = 5$
  (b) -20-dB side lobe level and $\bar{n} = 10$
  For each, find the half-power beamwidth and plot the normalized current distribution and the reconstructed pattern when $l = 10\lambda$.

14.15. Derive (14-33) using (14-1), (14-32), and Gegenbauer's finite integral and polynomials.

14.16. Repeat the design of Example 14.7 for an array with $l = 4\lambda$, $d = \lambda/2$, $N = 9$.

14.17. Design a broadside five-element, -40-dB side lobe level Taylor (one-parameter) distribution array of isotropic sources. The elements are placed along the x-axis with a spacing of $\lambda/4$ between them. Determine the
  (a) normalized excitation coefficients (amplitude and phase) of each element
  (b) array factor

14.18. Derive the space factors for uniform, triangular, cosine, and cosine squared line-source continuous distributions. Compare with the results in Table 14.1.

14.19. Compute the half-power beamwidth, first null beamwidth, first side lobe level (in dB), and directivity of a linear array of closely spaced elements with overall length of 4λ when its amplitude distribution is
  (a) uniform   (b) triangular
  (c) cosine   (d) cosine squared

14.20. Derive the space factors for the uniform, radial taper, and radial taper-squared circular aperture continuous distributions. Compare with the results in Table 14.2.

14.21. Compute the half-power beamwidth, first null beamwidth, first side lobe level (in dB), and gain factor of a circular planar array of closely spaced elements, with radius of 2λ when its amplitude distribution is
    (a) uniform
    (b) radial taper
    (c) radial taper-squared

Chapter 15
Antenna Measurements

15.1 INTRODUCTION

In the previous fourteen chapters, analytical methods have been outlined which can be used to analyze, synthesize, and numerically compute the radiation characteristics of antennas. Often many antennas, because of their complex structural configuration and excitation method, cannot be investigated analytically. Although the number of radiators that fall into this category has diminished, because special analytical methods (such as the GTD and the Moment Method) have been developed during the past few years, there still is a fair number that have not nor cannot be examined analytically. In addition, experimental results are needed often to validate theoretical data.

Experimental investigations suffer from a number of drawbacks such as:

1. For pattern measurements, the distance to the far-field region ($r > 2D^2/\lambda$) is too long even for outside ranges. It also becomes difficult to keep unwanded reflections from the ground and the surrounding objects below acceptable levels.
2. In many cases, it may be impractical to move the antenna from the operating environment to the measuring site.
3. For some antennas, such as phased arrays, the time required to measure the necessary characteristics may be enormous.
4. Outside measuring systems provide an uncontrolled environment, and they do not possess an all-weather capability.
5. Enclosed measuring systems usually cannot accommodate large antenna systems (such as ships, aircraft, large spacecraft, etc.).
6. Measurement techniques, in general, are expensive.

Some of the above shortcomings can be overcome by using special techniques, such as the far-field pattern prediction from near-field measurements [1]–[4], scale model measurements, and automated commercial equipment specifically designed for antenna measurements and utilizing computer assisted techniques.

Because of the accelerated progress made in aerospace/defense related systems (with increasingly small design margins), more accurate measurement methods were necessary. To accommodate these requirements, improved instrumentation and measuring techniques were developed which include tapered anechoic chambers [5], compact and extrapolation ranges [2], near-field probing techniques [2]-[4], improved polarization techniques and swept-frequency measurements [6], indirect measurements of antenna characteristics, and automated test systems.

The parameters that often best describe an antenna system's performance are the pattern (amplitude and phase), gain, directivity, efficiency, impedance, current distribution, and polarization. Each of these topics will be addressed briefly in this chapter. A more extensive and exhaustive treatment of these and other topics can be found in the *IEEE Standard Test Procedures for Antennas* [7], in a summarized journal paper [8], and in a book on microwave antenna measurements [6]. Most of the material in this chapter is drawn from these three sources. The author recommends that the IEEE publication on test procedures for antennas becomes part of the library of every practicing antenna and microwave engineer.

15.2 ANTENNA RANGES

The testing and evaluation of antennas are performed in antenna ranges. Typically there exist indoor and outdoor ranges, and limitations are associated with both of them. Outdoor ranges are not protected from environmental conditions whereas indoor facilities are limited by space restrictions. Because some of the antenna characteristics are measured in the receiving mode and require far-field criteria, the ideal field incident upon the test antenna should be a uniform plane wave. To meet this specification, a large space is usually required and it limits the value of indoor facilities.

15.2.1 Reflection Ranges

In general, there are two basic types of antenna ranges: the *reflection* and the *free-space* ranges. The reflection ranges, if judiciously designed [9], can create a constructive interference in the region of the test antenna which is referred to as the "quiet zone." This is accomplished by designing the ranges so that specular reflections from the ground, as shown in Figure 15.1, combine constructively with direct rays.

Usually it is desirable for the illuminating field to have a small and symmetric amplitude taper. This can be achieved by adjusting the transmitting antenna height while maintaining constant that of the receiving antenna. These ranges are of the outdoor type, where the ground is the reflecting surface, and they are usually employed in the UHF region for

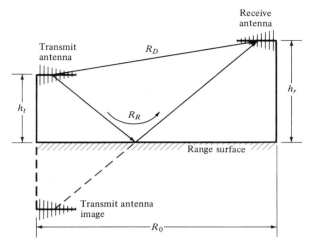

Figure 15.1 Geometrical arrangement for reflection range. (SOURCE: L. H. Hemming and R. A. Heaton, "Antenna Gain Calibration on a Ground Reflection Range," *IEEE Trans. Antennas Propag.*, vol. AP-21, No. 4, pp. 532–537, July 1973. © (1973) IEEE)

measurements of patterns of moderately broad antennas. They are also used for systems operating in the UHF to the 16-GHz frequency region.

15.2.2 Free-Space Ranges

Free-space ranges are designed to suppress the contributions from the surrounding environment and include *elevated ranges*, *slant ranges* [10], *compact ranges* [2], *anechoic chambers*, and *near-field measurements* [4].

ELEVATED RANGES

Elevated ranges are usually designed to operate mostly over smooth terrains. The antennas are mounted on towers or roofs of adjacent buildings. These ranges are used to test physically large antennas. A geometrical configuration is shown in Figure 15.2(a). The contributions from the surrounding environment are usually reduced or eliminated by [7]

1. carefully selecting the directivity and side lobe level of the source antenna
2. clearing the line-of-sight between the antennas
3. redirecting or absorbing any energy that is reflected from the range surface and/or from any obstacles that cannot be removed
4. utilizing special signal processing techniques such as modulation tagging of the desired signal or by using short pulses

In some applications, such as between adjacent mountains or hilltops, the ground terrain may be irregular. For these cases, it is more difficult to locate the specular reflection points (points that reflect energy toward the

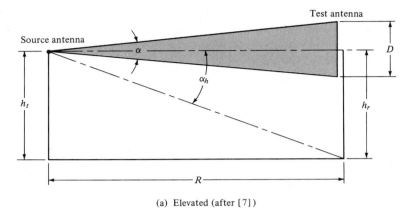

(a) Elevated (after [7])

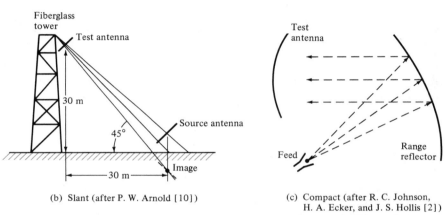

(b) Slant (after P. W. Arnold [10])

(c) Compact (after R. C. Johnson, H. A. Ecker, and J. S. Hollis [2])

Figure 15.2 Geometries of elevated, slant, and compact ranges. (SOURCES: *IEEE Standard Test Procedures for Antennas*, IEEE Std 149–1979, published by IEEE, Inc., 1979, distributed by Wiley; P. W. Arnold, "The 'Slant' Antenna Range", *IEEE Trans. Antennas Propag.*, vol. AP-14, pp. 658–659, Sept. 1966. © 1966 (IEEE) and R. C. Johnson, H. A. Ecker, and J. S. Hollis, "Determination of Far-Field Antenna Patterns from Near-Field Measurements", *Proc. IEEE*, vol. 61, No. 12, pp. 1668–1694, Dec. 1973. © (1973) IEEE).

test antenna). To take into account the irregular surface, scaled drawings of the vertical profile of the range are usually constructed from data obtained from the U.S. Geological Survey. The maps show ground contours [11], and they give sufficient details which can be used to locate the specular reflection points, determine the level of energy reflected toward the test antenna, and make corrections if it is excessive.

SLANT RANGES
Slant ranges [10] are designed so that the test antenna, along with its positioner, are mounted at a fixed height on a nonconducting tower while the source (transmitting) antenna is placed near the ground, as shown in

Figure 15.2(b). The source antenna is positioned so that the pattern maximum, of its free-space radiation, is oriented toward the center of the test antenna. The first null is usually directed toward the ground specular reflection point to suppress reflected signals. Slant ranges, in general, are more compact than elevated ranges in that they require less land.

COMPACT RANGES

Microwave antenna test measurements often require that the radiator under test be illuminated by a uniform plane wave. This is usually achieved only in the far-field region which, in many cases, dictates very large distances. The requirement of plane wave illumination can be achieved by a technique that requires smaller distances and the use of a reflector. To accomplish this, the source antenna is used as an offset feed that illuminates a paraboloidal reflector. The illuminated reflector converts the impinging spherical waves into plane waves [2]. The geometrical arrangement is shown in Figure 15.2(c). This technique leads to far-field pattern simulation, it requires smaller distances than conventional methods, and it is referred to as a *compact range*. Usually the linear dimensions of the reflector are three to four times greater than those of the test antenna.

The major drawbacks of compact ranges are aperture blockage, direct radiation from the source to the test antenna, diffractions from the edges of the reflector and feed support, depolarization coupling between the two antennas, and wall reflections. The use of an offset feed eliminates aperture blockage and reduces diffractions. Direct radiation and diffractions can be reduced further if a reflector with a long focal length is chosen. With such a reflector, the feed can then be mounted below the test antenna and the depolarization effects associated with curved surfaces are reduced. Undesirable radiation toward the test antenna can also be minimized by the use of high-quality absorbing material.

ANECHOIC CHAMBERS

To provide a controlled environment, an all-weather capability, and security, and to minimize electromagnetic interference, indoor anechoic chambers have been developed. By this method, the testing is performed inside a chamber whose walls are covered with RF absorbers. The availability of high-quality RF absorbing material, with improved electrical characteristics, has provided the impetus for development and proliferation of the anechoic chambers. Anechoic chambers are mostly utilized in the microwave region, but materials have been developed [12] which provide a reflection coefficient of -40 dB at normal incidence at frequencies as low as 100 MHz. The use of the anechoic chamber at the lower range of the frequency spectrum is limited by the availability of RF absorbers whose thicknesses increase as the frequency decreases. An RF absorber that meets the minimum electrical requirements at the lower frequencies possesses improved performance at higher frequencies.

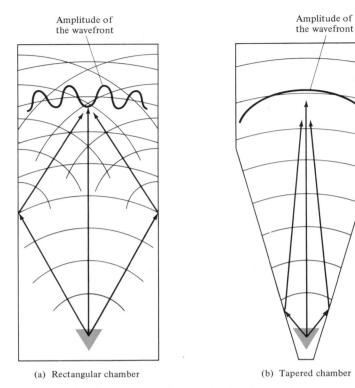

(a) Rectangular chamber   (b) Tapered chamber

Figure 15.3　Rectangular and tapered anechoic chambers and the corresponding side-wall specular reflections. (SOURCE: W. H. Kummer and E. S. Gillespie, "Antenna measurements—1978," *Proc. IEEE*, vol. 66, No. 4, pp. 483–507, April 1978. © (1978) IEEE)

Presently there are two basic types of anechoic chamber designs; the *rectangular* and the *tapered chamber*. The design of each is based on geometrical optics techniques, and each attempts to reduce or to minimize specular reflections. The geometrical configuration of each, which depicts also specular reflection points, is shown in Figures 15.3(a) and 15.3(b).

The rectangular chamber [13] is usually designed to simulate free-space conditions and maximize the volume of the quiet zone. The design takes into account the pattern and location of the source, the frequency of operation, and it assumes that the receiving antenna at the test point is isotropic. Reflected energy is minimized by the use of high-quality RF absorbers. Despite the use of RF absorbing material, significant specular reflections can occur, especially at large angles of incidence.

Tapered anechoic chambers [14] take the form of a pyramidal horn. They begin with a tapered chamber which leads to a rectangular configuration at the test region as shown in Figure 15.3(b). At the lower end of the frequency band at which the chamber is designed, the source is usually placed near the apex so that the reflections from the side walls, which contribute to the region of the test antenna, occur near the source antenna. For such paths, the phase difference between the direct radiation and that reflected from the walls near the source can be made very small by properly locating the source antenna near the apex. Thus the direct and reflected rays near the test antenna region add vectorially and provide a relatively smooth amplitude illumination taper. This can be illustrated by ray tracing techniques.

As the frequency of operation increases, it becomes increasingly difficult to place the source so close to the apex and the phase difference between the direct and specularly reflected rays can be maintained below an acceptable level. For such applications, reflections from the walls of the chamber are suppressed by using as sources high-gain antennas whose radiation toward the walls is minimal. In addition, the source is moved away from the apex, and it is placed closer to the end of the tapering section so as to simulate a rectangular chamber.

NEAR-FIELD MEASUREMENTS
The dimensions of a conventional test range can be reduced by making measurements in the near-field, and then using analytical methods to transform the measured near-field data to compute the far-field radiation characteristics [2]–[4]. Such techniques are usually used to measure patterns, and they are often performed indoors. Therefore, they provide a controlled environment and an all-weather capability, the measuring system is time and cost effective, and the computed patterns are as accurate as those measured in a far-field range. However such methods require more complicated and expensive systems, more extensive calibration procedures, more sophisticated computer software, and the patterns are not obtained in real time.

The near-field measured data (usually amplitude and phase distributions) are measured by a scanning field probe over a preselected surface which may be a plane, a cylinder, or a sphere. The measured data are then transformed to the far-field using analytical Fourier transform methods. The complexity of the analytical transformations increases from the plane to the cylindrical, and from the cylindrical to the spherical surfaces. The choice is primarily determined by the antenna to be measured.

The planar system is better suited for high-gain antennas, especially planar phased arrays, and it requires the least amount of computations and no movement of the antenna. Although the cylindrical system requires about 50% more computations than the planar, for many antennas its measuring, positioning, and probe equipment are least expensive. The spherical system requires the most expensive computation, antenna, and probe positioning equipment which can become quite significant for large antenna systems. This system is best suited for measurements for low-gain and omnidirectional antennas.

15.3 RADIATION PATTERNS

The radiation patterns (amplitude and phase), polarization, and gain of an antenna, which are used to characterize its radiation capabilities, are measured on the surface of a constant radius sphere. Any position on the sphere is identified using the standard spherical coordinate system of Figure 15.4. Since the radial distance is maintained fixed, only the two angular coordinates (θ, ϕ) are needed for positional identification. A representation of the radiation characteristics of the radiator as a function of θ and ϕ for a constant radial distance and frequency, is defined as the *pattern* of the antenna.

In general, the pattern of an antenna is three-dimensional. Because it is impractical to measure a three-dimensional pattern, a number of two-dimensional patterns, as defined in Section 2.2, are measured. They are used to construct a three-dimensional pattern. The number of two-dimensional patterns needed to construct faithfully a three-dimensional graph is determined by the functional requirements of the description, and the available time and funds. The minimum number of two-dimensional patterns is two, and they are usually chosen to represent the orthogonal principal *E*- and *H*-plane patterns, as defined in Section 2.2.

A two-dimensional pattern is also referred to as a *pattern cut*, and it is obtained by fixing one of the angles (θ or ϕ) while varying the other. For

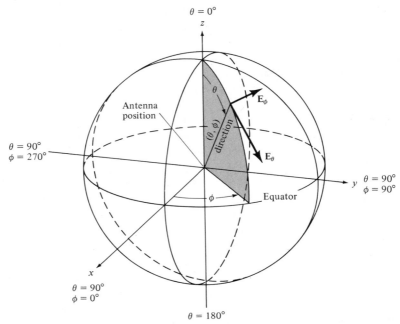

Figure 15.4 Spherical coordinate system geometry. (SOURCE: *IEEE Standard Test Procedures for Antennas*, IEEE Std 149-1979, published by IEEE, Inc., 1979, distributed by Wiley)

example, by referring to Figure 15.4, pattern cuts can be obtained by fixing ϕ_j ($0 \le \phi_j \le 2\pi$) and varying θ ($0 \le \theta \le 180°$). These are referred to as elevation patterns, and they are also displayed in Figure 2.12. Similarly θ can be maintained fixed ($0 \le \theta_i \le \pi$) while ϕ is varied ($0 \le \phi \le 2\pi$). These are designated as azimuthal patterns. Part ($0 \le \phi \le \pi/2$) of the $\theta_i = \pi/2$ azimuthal pattern is displayed in Figure 2.12.

The patterns of an antenna can be measured in the transmitting or receiving mode. The mode is dictated by the application. However, if the radiator is reciprocal, as is the case for most practical antennas, then either the transmitting or receiving mode can be utilized. For such cases, the receiving mode is selected. The analytical formulations upon which an amplitude pattern is based, along with the advantages and disadvantages for making measurements in the transmitting or receiving mode, are found in Section 3.8. The analytical basis of a phase pattern is discussed in Section 12.7. Unless otherwise specified, it will be assumed here that the measurements are performed in the receiving mode.

15.3.1 Instrumentation

The instrumentation required to accomplish a measuring task depends largely on the functional requirements of the design. An antenna range instrumentation must be designed to operate over a wide range of frequencies, and it usually can be classified into five categories [7]:

1. source antenna and transmitting system
2. receiving system
3. positioning system
4. recording system
5. data-processing system

A block diagram of a system that possess these capabilities is shown in Figure 15.5.

The source antennas are usually log-periodic antennas for frequencies below 1 GHz, families of parabolas with broadband feeds for frequencies above 400 MHz, and even large horn antennas. The system must be capable of controlling the polarization. Continuous rotation of the polarization can be accomplished by mounting a linearly polarized source antenna on a polarization positioner. Antennas with circular polarization can also be designed, such as crossed log-periodic arrays, which are often used in measurements.

The transmitting RF source must be selected so that it has [7] frequency control, frequency stability, spectral purity, power level, and modulation. The receiving system could be as simple as a bolometer detector, followed possibly by an amplifier, and a recorder. More elaborate and expensive receiving systems that provide greater sensitivity, precision, and dynamic range can be designed. One such system is a heterodyne receiving system [7], which uses double conversion and phase locking, and it can be used for

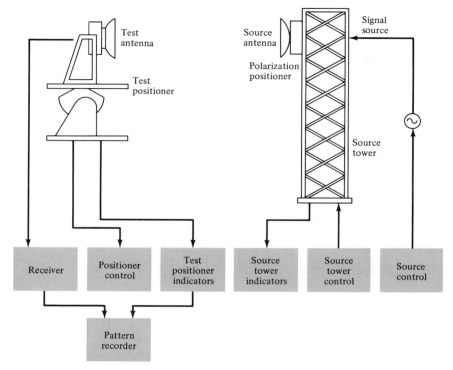

Figure 15.5 Instrumentation for typical antenna-range measuring system. (SOURCE: *IEEE Standard Test Procedures for Antennas*, IEEE Std 149-1979, published by IEEE, Inc., 1979, distributed by Wiley)

amplitude measurements. A dual-channel heterodyne system design is also available [7], and it can be used for phase measurements.

To achieve the desired plane cuts, the mounting structures of the system must have the capability to rotate in various planes. This can be accomplished by utilizing rotational mounts (pedestals), two of which are shown in Figure 15.6. Tower-model elevation-over-azimuth pedestals are also available [7].

There are primarily two types of recorders; one that provides a linear (rectangular) plot and the other a polar plot. The polar plots are most popular because they provide a better visualization of the radiation distribution in space. Usually the recording equipment is designed to graph the relative pattern. Absolute patterns are obtained by making, in addition, gain measurements which will be discussed in the next section. The recording instrumentation is usually calibrated to record relative field or power patterns. Power pattern calibrations are in decibels with dynamic ranges of 0–60 dB. For most applications, a 40-dB dynamic range is usually adequate and it provides sufficient resolution to examine the pattern structure of the main lobe and the minor lobes.

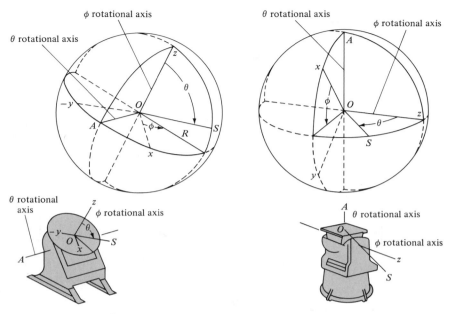

(a) Azimuth–over–elevation positioner   (b) Elevation–over–azimuth positioner

Figure 15.6   Azimuth-over-elevation and elevation-over-azimuth rotational mounts. (SOURCE: *IEEE Standard Test Procedures for Antennas*, IEEE Std 149-1979, published by IEEE, Inc., 1979, distributed by Wiley)

In an indoor antenna range, the recording equipment is usually placed in a room that adjoins the anechoic chamber. To provide a free-interference environment, the chamber is closed during measurements. To monitor the procedures, windows or closed-circuit TV is utilized. In addition, the recording equipment is connected, through synchronous servo-amplifier systems, to the rotational mounts (pedestals) as shown in Figure 15.7. The system can record rectangular or polar plots. Positioned references are recorded simultaneously with measurements, and they are used for angular positional identification. As the rotational mount moves, the pattern is graphed simultaneously by the recorder on a moving chart. One of the axes of the chart is used to record the amplitude of the pattern while the other identifies the relative position of the radiator. Usually ink-writing recording systems are preferred to electric, thermal, pressure-sensitive, and photographic systems because of their simplicity, reproducibility, and economy.

15.3.2   Amplitude Pattern

The total amplitude pattern of an antenna is described by the vector sum of the two orthogonally polarized radiated field components. The pattern on a conventional antenna range can be measured using the system of Figure 15.5 or Figure 15.7 with an appropriate detector. The receiver may be a

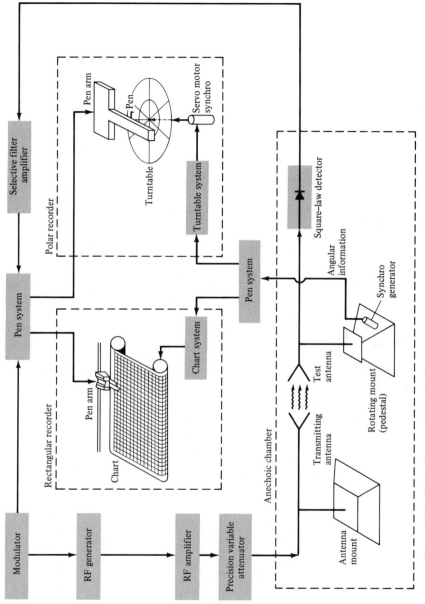

Figure 15.7 Block diagram of a typical instrumentation for measuring rectangular and polar antenna patterns.

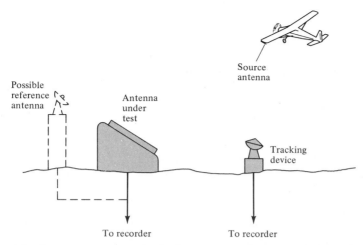

Figure 15.8   System arrangement for *in situ* antenna pattern measurements. (SOURCE: *IEEE Standard Test Procedures for Antennas*, IEEE Std 149-1979, published by IEEE, Inc., 1979, distributed by Wiley)

simple bolometer (followed possibly by an amplifier), a double conversion phase-locking heterodyne system [7, Fig. 14], or any other design.

In many applications, the movement of the antenna to the antenna range can be significantly altered by the operational environment. Therefore, in some cases, antenna pattern measurements must be made *in situ* to preserve the environmental performance characteristics. A typical system arrangement that can be used to accomplish this is shown in Figure 15.8. The source is mounted on an airborne vehicle, which is maneuvered through space around the test antenna and in its far-field, to produce a plane wave and to provide the desired pattern cuts. The tracking device provides to the recording equipment the angular position data of the source relative to a reference direction. The measurements can be conducted either by a point-by-point or by a continuous method. Usually the continuous technique is preferred.

15.3.3 Phase Measurements

Phase measurements are based on the analytical formulations of Section 12.7. The phase pattern of the field, in the direction of the unit vector $\hat{u}$, is given by the $\psi(\theta, \phi)$ phase function of (12-63). For linear polarizations $\hat{u}$ is real, and it may represent $\hat{a}_\theta$ or $\hat{a}_\phi$ in the direction of θ or ϕ.

The phase of an antenna is periodic, and it is defined in multiples of $360°$. In addition, the phase is a relative quantity, and a reference must be provided during measurements for comparison.

Two basic system techniques that can be used to measure phase patterns at short and long distances from the antenna are shown, respectively, in Figures 15.9(a) and 15.9(b). For the design of Figure 15.9(a), a

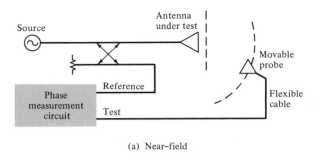

(a) Near–field

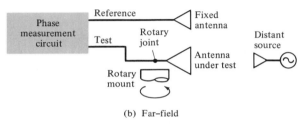

(b) Far–field

Figure 15.9 Near-field and far-field phase pattern measuring systems. (SOURCE: *IEEE Standard Test Procedures for Antennas*, IEEE Std 149-1979, published by IEEE, Inc., 1979, distributed by Wiley)

reference signal is coupled from the transmission line, and it is used to compare, in an appropriate network, the phase of the received signal. For large distances, this method does not permit a direct comparison between the reference and the received signal. In these cases, the arrangement of Figure 15.9(b) can be used in which the signal from the source antenna is received simultaneously by a fixed antenna and the antenna under test. The phase pattern is recorded as the antenna under test is rotated while the fixed antenna serves as a reference. The phase measuring circuit may be the dual-channel heterodyne system of [7] (Fig. 15).

15.4 GAIN MEASUREMENTS

The most important figure-of-merit that describes the performance of a radiator is the gain. There are various techniques and antenna ranges that are used to measure the gain. The choice of either depends largely on the frequency of operation.

Usually free-space ranges are used to measure the gain above 1 GHz. In addition, microwave techniques, which utilize waveguide components, can be utilized. At lower frequencies, it is more difficult to simulate free-space conditions because of the longer wavelengths. Therefore between

0.1–1 GHz, ground-reflection ranges are utilized. Scale models can also be used in this frequency range. However, since the conductivity and loss factors of the structures cannot be scaled conveniently, the efficiency of the full scale model must be found by other methods to determine the gain of the antenna. This is accomplished by multiplying the directivity by the efficiency to result in the gain. Below 0.1 GHz, directive antennas are physically large and the ground effects become increasingly pronounced. Usually the gain at these frequencies is measured *in situ*. Antenna gains are not usually measured at frequencies below 1 MHz. Instead, measurements are conducted on the field strength of the ground wave radiated by the antenna.

Usually there are two basic methods that can be used to measure the gain of an electromagnetic radiator: *absolute-gain* and *gain-transfer* (or *gain-comparison*) measurements. The absolute-gain method is used to calibrate antennas that can then be used as standards for gain measurements, and it requires no *a priori* knowledge of the gains of the antennas. Gain-transfer methods must be used in conjunction with standard gain antennas to determine the absolute gain of the antenna under test.

The two antennas that are most widely used and universally accepted as gain standards are the resonant $\lambda/2$ dipole (with a gain of about 2.1 dB) and the pyramidal horn antenna (with a gain ranging from 12–25 dB). Both antennas possess linear polarizations. The dipole, in free-space, exhibits a high degree of polarization purity. However, because of its broad pattern, its polarization may be suspect in other than reflection-free environments. Pyramidal horns usually possess, in free-space, slightly elliptical polarization (axial ratio of about 40 to infinite dB). However, because of their very directive patterns, they are less affected by the surrounding environment.

15.4.1 Absolute-Gain Measurements

There are a number of techniques that can be employed to make absolute-gain measurements. A very brief review of each will be included here. More details can be found in [6]–[8]. All of these methods are based on Friis transmission formula [as given by (2-105)] which assumes that the measuring system employs, each time, two antennas (as shown in Figure 2.22). The antennas are separated by a distance R, and it must satisfy the far-field criterion of each antenna. For polarization matched antennas, aligned for maximum directional radiation, (2-105) reduces to (2-106).

TWO-ANTENNA METHOD
Equation (2-106) can be written in a logarithmic decibel form as

$$(G_{ot})_{\text{dB}} + (G_{or})_{\text{dB}} = 20 \log_{10} \left(\frac{4\pi R}{\lambda} \right) + 10 \log_{10} \left(\frac{P_r}{P_t} \right) \tag{15-1}$$

where

$(G_{ot})_{\text{dB}}$ = gain of the transmitting antenna   (dB)

$(G_{or})_{\text{dB}}$ = gain of the receiving antenna   (dB)

P_r = received power   (W)

P_t = transmitted power   (W)

R = antenna separation   (m)

λ = operating wavelength   (m)

If the transmitting and receiving antennas are identical $(G_{ot} = G_{or})$, (15-1) reduces to

$$(G_{ot})_{\text{dB}} = (G_{or})_{\text{dB}} = \frac{1}{2}\left[20\log_{10}\left(\frac{4\pi R}{\lambda}\right) + 10\log_{10}\left(\frac{P_r}{P_t}\right)\right]$$ (15-2)

By measuring R, λ, and the ratio of P_r/P_t, the gain of the antenna can be found. At a given frequency, this can be accomplished using the system of Figure 15.10(a). The system is simple and the procedure straightforward. For continuous multifrequency measurements, such as for broadband antennas, the swept frequency instrumentation of Figure 15.10(b) can be utilized.

THREE-ANTENNA METHOD

If the two antennas in the measuring system are not identical, three antennas (a, b, c) must be employed and three measurements must be made (using all combinations of the three) to determine the gain of each of the three. Three equations (one for each combination) can be written, and each takes the form of (15-1). Thus

(a-b Combination)

$$(G_a)_{\text{dB}} + (G_b)_{\text{dB}} = 20\log_{10}\left(\frac{4\pi R}{\lambda}\right) + 10\log_{10}\left(\frac{P_{rb}}{P_{ta}}\right)$$ (15-3a)

(a-c Combination)

$$(G_a)_{\text{dB}} + (G_c)_{\text{dB}} = 20\log_{10}\left(\frac{4\pi R}{\lambda}\right) + 10\log_{10}\left(\frac{P_{rc}}{P_{ta}}\right)$$ (15-3b)

(b-c Combination)

$$(G_b)_{\text{dB}} + (G_c)_{\text{dB}} = 20\log_{10}\left(\frac{4\pi R}{\lambda}\right) + 10\log_{10}\left(\frac{P_{rc}}{P_{tb}}\right)$$ (15-3c)

From these three equations, the gains $(G_a)_{\text{dB}}$, $(G_b)_{\text{dB}}$, and $(G_c)_{\text{dB}}$ can be determined provided R, λ, and the ratios of P_{rb}/P_{ta}, P_{rc}/P_{ta}, and P_{rc}/P_{tb} are measured.

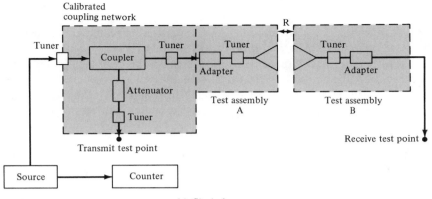

(a) Single frequency

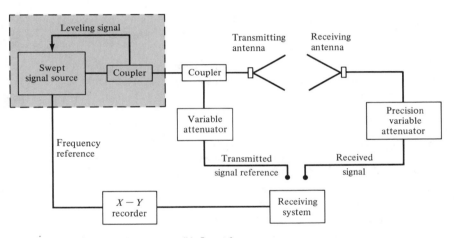

(b) Swept frequency

Figure 15.10 Typical two- and three-antenna measuring systems for single and swept frequency measurements. (SOURCE: J. S. Hollis, T. J. Lyon, and L. Clayton, Jr., *Microwave Antenna Measurements*, Scientific-Atlanta, Inc., Atlanta, Georgia, July 1970)

The two- and three-antenna methods are both subject to errors. Care must be utilized so

1. the system is frequency stable
2. the antennas meet the far-field criteria
3. the antennas are aligned for boresight radiation
4. all the components are impedance and polarization matched
5. there is a minimum of proximity effects and multipath interference

Impedance and polarization errors can be accounted for by measuring the appropriate complex reflection coefficients and polarizations and then correcting accordingly the measured power ratios. The details for these corrections can be found in [7], [8]. There are no rigorous methods to account for proximity effects and multipath interference. These, however, can be minimized by maintaining the antennas separated by at least a distance of $2D^2/\lambda$, as is required by the far-field criteria, and by utilizing RF absorbers to reduce unwanted reflections. The interference pattern that is created by the multiple reflections from the antennas themselves, especially at small separations, is more difficult to remove. It usually manifests itself as a cyclic variation in the measured antenna gain as a function of separation.

EXTRAPOLATION METHOD

The extrapolation method is an absolute-gain method, which can be used with the three-antenna method, and it was developed [15] to rigorously account for possible errors due to proximity, multipath, and nonidentical antennas. If none of the antennas used in the measurements are circularly polarized, the method yields the gains and polarizations of all three antennas. If only one antenna is circularly polarized, this method yields only the gain and polarization of the circularly polarized antenna. The method fails if two or more antennas are circularly polarized.

The method requires both amplitude and phase measurements when the gain and the polarization of the antennas is to be determined. For the determination of gains, amplitude measurements are sufficient. The details of this method can be found in [8] and [15].

GROUND-REFLECTION RANGE METHOD

A method that can be used to measure the gain of moderately broad beam antennas, usually for frequencies below 1 GHz, has been reported [16]. The method takes into account the specular reflections from the ground (using the system geometry of Figure 15.1), and it can be used with some restrictions and modifications with the two- or three-antenna methods. As described here, the method is applicable to linear antennas that couple only the electric field. Modifications must be made for loop radiators. Using this method, it is recommended that the linear vertical radiators be placed in a horizontal position when measurements are made. This is desired because the reflection coefficient of the earth, as a function of incidence angle, varies very rapidly for vertically polarized waves. Smoother variations are exhibited for horizontally polarized fields. Circularly and elliptically polarized antennas are excluded, because the earth exhibits different reflective properties for vertical and horizontal fields.

To make measurements using this technique, the system geometry of Figure 15.1 is utilized. Usually it is desirable that the height of the receiving antenna h_r be much smaller than the range R_0 ($h_r \ll R_0$). Also the height of the transmitting antenna is adjusted so that the field of the receiving antenna occurs at the maximum that is nearest to the ground. Doing this, each of the gain equations of the two- or three-antenna methods take the form of

$$(G_a)_{dB} + (G_b)_{dB} = 20\log_{10}\left(\frac{4\pi R_D}{\lambda}\right) + 10\log_{10}\left(\frac{P_r}{P_t}\right)$$

$$- 20\log_{10}\left(\sqrt{D_A D_B} + \frac{rR_D}{R_r}\right) \qquad (15\text{-}4)$$

D_a and D_b are the directive gains (relative to their respective maximum values) along R_D, and they can be determined from amplitude patterns measured prior to the gain measurements. R_D, R_r, λ, and P_r/P_t are also measured. The only quantity that needs to be determined is the factor r which is a function of the radiation patterns of the antennas, the frequency of operation, and the electrical and geometrical properties of the antenna range.

The factor r can be found by first repeating the above measurements but with the transmitting antenna height adjusted so that the field at the receiving antenna is minimum. The quantities measured with this geometry are designated by the same letters as before but with a prime (′) to distinguish them from those of the previous measurement.

By measuring or determining the parameters

1. R_r, R_D, P_r, D_a, and D_b at a height of the transmitting antenna such that the receiving antenna is at the first maximum of the pattern
2. R_r', R_D', P_r', D_a', and D_b' at a height of the transmitting antenna such that the receiving antenna is at a field minimum

it can be shown [16] that r can be determined from

$$r = \left(\frac{R_r R_r'}{R_D R_D'}\right)\left[\frac{\sqrt{(P_r/P_r')(D_a'D_b')}\,R_D - \sqrt{D_a D_b}\,R_D'}{\sqrt{(P_r/P_r')}\,R_r + R_r'}\right] \qquad (15\text{-}5)$$

Now all parameters included in (15-4) can either be measured or computed from measurements. The free-space range system of Figure 15.10(a) can be used to perform these measurements.

15.4.2 Gain-Transfer (Gain-Comparison) Measurements

The method most commonly used to measure the gain of an antenna is the gain-transfer method. This technique utilizes a gain standard (with a known gain) to determine absolute gains. Initially relative gain measurements are performed, which when compared with the known gain of the standard antenna, yield absolute values. The method can be used with free-space and reflection ranges, and for *in situ* measurements.

The procedure requires two sets of measurements. In one set, using the test antenna as the receiving antenna, the received power (P_T) into a matched load is recorded. In the other set, the test antenna is replaced by the standard gain antenna and the received power (P_S) into a matched load is recorded. In both sets, the geometrical arrangement is maintained intact (other than replacing the receiving antennas), and the input power is maintained the same.

Writing two equations of the form of (15-1) or (15-4), for free-space or reflection ranges, it can be shown that they reduce to [7]

$$(G_T)_{db} = (G_S)_{dB} + 10 \log_{10}\left(\frac{P_T}{P_S}\right) \tag{15-6}$$

where $(G_T)_{dB}$ and $(G_S)_{dB}$ are the gains (in dB) of the test and standard gain antennas.

System disturbance during replacement of the receiving antennas can be minimized by mounting the two receiving antennas back-to-back on either side of the axis of an azimuth positioner and connecting both of them to the load through a common switch. One antenna can replace the other by a simple, but very precise, 180° rotation of the positioner. Connection to the load can be interchanged by proper movement of the switch.

If the test antenna is not too dissimilar from the standard gain antenna, this method is less affected by proximity effects and multipath interference. Impedance and polarization mismatches can be corrected by making proper complex reflection coefficient and polarization measurements [8].

If the test antenna is circularly or elliptically polarized, gain measurements using the gain-transfer method can be accomplished by at least two different methods. One way would be to design a standard gain antenna that possesses circular or elliptical polarization. This approach would be attractive in mass productions of power-gain measurements of circularly or elliptically polarized antennas.

The other approach would be to measure the gain with two orthogonal linearly polarized standard gain antennas. Since circularly and elliptically polarized waves can be decomposed to linear (vertical and horizontal) components, the total power of the wave can be separated into two orthogonal linearly polarized components. Thus the total gain of the circularly or elliptically polarized test antenna can be written as

$$(G_T)_{dB} = 10 \log_{10}(G_{TV} + G_{TH}) \tag{15-7}$$

G_{TV} and G_{TH} are, respectively, the partial power gains with respect to vertical-linear and horizontal-linear polarizations.

G_{TV} is obtained, using (15-6), by performing a gain-transfer measurement with the standard gain antenna possessing vertical polarization. The measurements are repeated with the standard gain antenna oriented for horizontal polarization. This allows the determination of G_{TH}. Usually a single linearly polarized standard gain antenna (a linear $\lambda/2$ resonant dipole or a pyramidal horn) can be used, by rotating it by 90°, to provide both vertical and horizontal polarizations. This approach is very convenient, especially if the antenna possesses good polarization purity in the two orthogonal planes.

The techniques outlined above yield good results provided the transmitting and standard gain antennas exhibit good linear polarization purity. Errors will be introduced if either one of them possesses a polarization with a finite axial ratio. In addition, these techniques are accurate if the tests can be performed in a free-space, a ground-reflection, or an extrapolation range. These requirements place a low-frequency limit of 50 MHz.

Below 50 MHz, the ground has a large effect on the radiation characteristics of the antenna, and it must be taken into account. It usually requires that the measurements are performed on full scale models and *in situ*. Techniques that can be used to measure the gain of large HF antennas have been devised [17]–[19].

15.5 DIRECTIVITY MEASUREMENTS

If the directivity of the antenna cannot be found using solely analytical techniques, it can be computed using measurements of its radiation pattern. One of the methods is based on the approximate expressions of (2-28) by Kraus or (2-32b) by Tai and Pereira, whereas the other relies on the numerical techniques that were developed in Section 2.6. The computations can be performed very efficiently and economically with modern computational facilities and numerical techniques.

The simplest, but least accurate method, requires that the following procedure is adopted:

1. Measure the two principal *E*- and *H*-plane patterns of the test antenna.
2. Determine the half-power beamwidths (in degrees) of the *E*- and *H*-plane patterns.
3. Compute the directivity using either (2-28) or (2-32b).

The method is usually employed to obtain rough estimates of directivity. It is more accurate when the pattern exhibits only one major lobe, and its minor lobes are negligible.

The other method requires that the directivity be computed using (2-35) where P_{rad} is evaluated numerically using (2-43). The $F(\theta_i, \phi_j)$ function represents the radiation intensity or radiation pattern, as defined by (2-42), and it will be obtained by measurements. U_{max} in (2-35) represents the maximum radiation intensity of $F(\theta, \phi)$ in all space, as obtained by the measurements.

The radiation pattern is measured by sampling the field over a sphere of radius r. The pattern is measured in two-dimensional plane cuts with ϕ_j constant ($0 \leq \phi_j \leq 2\pi$) and θ variable ($0 \leq \theta \leq \pi$), as shown in Figure 2.12, or with θ_i fixed ($0 \leq \theta_i \leq \pi$) and ϕ variable ($0 \leq \phi \leq 2\pi$). The first are referred to as elevation or great-circle cuts, whereas the second represent azimuthal or conical cuts. Either measuring method can be used. Equation (2-43) is written in a form that is most convenient for elevation or great-circle cuts. However, it can be rewritten to accommodate azimuthal or conical cuts.

The spacing between measuring points is largely controlled by the directive properties of the antenna and the desired accuracy. The method is most accurate for broad beam antennas. However, with the computer facilities and the numerical methods now available, this method is very attractive even for highly directional antennas. To maintain a given accuracy, the number of sampling points must increase as the pattern becomes more directional. The pattern data is recorded digitally on tape, and it can be entered to a computer at a later time. If on-line computer facilities are available, the measurements can be automated to provide essentially real-time computations.

The above discussion assumes that all the radiated power is contained in a single polarization, and the measuring probe possesses that polarization. If the antenna is linearly polarized and the field is represented by both θ and ϕ components, the partial directivities $D_\theta(\theta, \phi)$ and $D_\phi(\theta, \phi)$ must each be found. This is accomplished from pattern measurements with the probe positioned, respectively, to sample the θ and ϕ components. The total directivity is then given by

$$D_0 = D_\theta + D_\phi \tag{15-8}$$

where

$$D_\theta = \frac{4\pi (U_{\max})_\theta}{(P_{\text{rad}})_\theta + (P_{\text{rad}})_\phi} \tag{15-8a}$$

$$D_\phi = \frac{4\pi (U_{\max})_\phi}{(P_{\text{rad}})_\theta + (P_{\text{rad}})_\phi} \tag{15-8b}$$

$(U_{\max})_\theta$, $(P_{\text{rad}})_\theta$ and $(U_{\max})_\phi$, $(P_{\text{rad}})_\phi$ represent the maximum radiation intensity and radiated power as contained in the two orthogonal θ and ϕ field components, respectively.

The same technique can be used to measure the field intensity and to compute the directivity of any antenna that possess two orthogonal polarizations. Many antennas have only one polarization (θ or ϕ). This is usually accomplished by design and/or proper selection of the coordinate system. In this case, the desired polarization is defined as the primary polarization. Ideally, the other polarization should be zero. However, in practice, it is non-vanishing, but it is very small. Usually it is referred to as the cross-polarization, and for good designs it is usually below -40 dB.

The directivity of circularly or elliptically polarized antennas can also be measured. Precautions must be taken [7] as to which component represents the primary polarization and which the cross-polarization contribution.

15.6 RADIATION EFFICIENCY

The radiation efficiency is defined as the ratio of the total power radiated by the antenna to the total power accepted by the antenna at its input terminals during radiation. System factors, such as impedance and/or polarization mismatches, do not contribute to the radiation efficiency because it is an inherent property of the antenna.

The radiation efficiency can also be defined, using the direction of maximum radiation as reference, as

$$\text{radiation efficiency} = \frac{\text{gain}}{\text{directivity}} \tag{15-9}$$

where directivity and gain, as defined in Sections 2.5 and 2.7, imply that they are measured or computed in the direction of maximum radiation. Using techniques that were outlined in Sections 15.4 and 15.5 for the measurements of the gain and directivity, the radiation efficiency can then be computed using (15-9).

If the antenna is very small and simple, it can be represented as a series network as shown in Figures 2.18(b) or 2.19(b). For antennas that can be represented by such a series network, the radiation efficiency can also be defined by (2-86) and it can be computed by another method [20]. For these antennas, the real part of the input impedance is equal to the total antenna resistance which consists of the radiation resistance and the loss resistance.

The radiation resistance accounts for the radiated power. For many simple antennas (dipole, loops, etc.), it can be found by analytically or numerically integrating the pattern, relating it to the radiated power and to the radiation resistance by a relation similar to (4-18). The loss resistance accounts for the dissipated power, and it is found by measuring the input impedance (input resistance − radiation resistance = loss resistance).

Because the loss resistance of antennas coated with lossy dielectrics or antennas over lossy ground cannot be represented in series with the radiation resistance, this method cannot be used to determine their radiation efficiency. The details of this method can be found in [20].

15.7 IMPEDANCE MEASUREMENTS

Associated with an antenna there are two types of impedances: a *self-* and a *mutual* impedance. When the antenna is radiating into an unbounded medium and there is no coupling between it and other antennas or surrounding obstacles, the self-impedance is also the driving-point impedance of the antenna. If there is coupling between the antenna under test and other sources or obstacles, the driving-point impedance is a function of its self-impedance and the mutual impedances between it and the other sources or obstacles. In practice, the driving-point impedance is usually referred to as the input impedance. The definitions and the analytical formulations that underlie the self-, mutual, and input impedances are presented in Chapter 7.

To attain maximum power transfer between a source or a source-transmission line and an antenna (or between an antenna and a receiver or transmission line-receiver), a conjugate match is usually desired. In some applications, this may not be the most ideal match. For example, in some receiving systems minimum noise is attained if the antenna impedance is lower than the load impedance. However, in some transmitting systems, maximum power transfer is attained if the antenna impedance is greater than the load impedance. If conjugate matching does not exist, the power lost can be computed [7] using

$$\frac{P_{\text{lost}}}{P_{\text{available}}} = \left| \frac{Z_{\text{ant}} - Z_{\text{cct}}^*}{Z_{\text{ant}} + Z_{\text{cct}}} \right|^2 \tag{15-10}$$

where

Z_{ant} = input impedance of the antenna

Z_{cct} = input impedance of the circuits which are connected to the antenna at its input terminals

When a transmission line is associated with the system, as is usually the case, the matching can be performed at either end of the line. In practice, however, the matching is performed near the antenna terminals, because it usually minimizes line losses and voltage peaks in the line and maximizes the useful bandwidth of the system.

In a mismatched system, the degree of mismatch determines the amount of incident or available power which is reflected at the input antenna terminals into the line. The degree of mismatch is a function of the antenna input impedance and the characteristic impedance of the line. These are related to the input reflection coefficient and the input VSWR at the antenna input terminals by the standard transmission line relationships of

$$\frac{P_{\text{refl}}}{P_{\text{inc}}} = |\Gamma|^2 = \frac{|Z_{\text{ant}} - Z_c|^2}{|Z_{\text{ant}} + Z_c|^2} = \left| \frac{\text{VSWR} - 1}{\text{VSWR} + 1} \right|^2 \tag{15-11}$$

where

$\Gamma = |\Gamma| e^{j\gamma}$ = voltage reflection coefficient at the antenna input terminals

VSWR = voltage standing wave ratio at the antenna input terminals

Z_c = characteristic impedance of the transmission line

Equation (15-11) shows a direct relationship between the antenna input impedance (Z_{ant}) and the VSWR. In fact, if Z_{ant} is known, the VSWR can be computed using (15-11). In practice, however, that is not the case. What is usually measured is the VSWR, and it alone does not provide sufficient information to uniquely determine the complex input impedance. To overcome this, the usual procedure is to measure the VSWR, and to compute the magnitude of the reflection coefficient using (15-11). The phase of the reflection coefficient can be determined by locating a voltage maximum or a first voltage minimum (from the antenna input terminals) in the transmission line. Since in practice the minima can be measured more accurately than the maxima, they are usually preferred. In addition, the first minimum is usually chosen unless the distance from it to the input terminals is too small to measure accurately. The phase γ of the reflection coefficient is then computed using [21]

$$\gamma = 2\beta x_n \pm (2n-1)\pi = \frac{4\pi}{\lambda_g} x_n \pm (2n-1)\pi, \qquad n = 1,2,3,\ldots \quad (15\text{-}12)$$

where

$n =$ the voltage minimum from the input terminals (i.e., $n = 1$ is used to locate the first voltage minimum)

$x_n =$ distance from the input terminals to the nth voltage minimum

$\lambda_g =$ wavelength measured inside the input transmission line (it is twice the distance between two voltage minima or two voltage maxima)

Once the reflection coefficient is completely described by its magnitude and phase, it can be used to determine the antenna impedance by

$$Z_{\text{ant}} = Z_c \left[\frac{1+\Gamma}{1-\Gamma} \right] = Z_c \left[\frac{1+|\Gamma|e^{j\gamma}}{1-|\Gamma|e^{j\gamma}} \right] \quad (15\text{-}13)$$

Other methods, utilizing impedance bridges, slotted lines, and broadband swept-frequency network analyzers, can be utilized to determine the antenna impedance [21]–[23].

The input impedance is generally a function of frequency, geometry, method of excitation, and proximity to its surrounding objects. Because of its strong dependence on the environment, it should usually be measured *in situ* unless the antenna possesses very narrow beam characteristics.

Mutual impedances, which take into account interaction effects, are usually best described and measured by the cross-coupling coefficients S_{mn} of the device's (antenna's) scattering matrix. The coefficients of the scattering matrix can then be related to the coefficients of the impedance matrix [24].

15.8 CURRENT MEASUREMENTS

The current distribution along an antenna is another very important antenna parameter. A complete description of its amplitude and phase permit the calculation of the radiation pattern.

There are a number of techniques that can be used to measure the current distribution [25]–[28]. One of the simplest methods requires that a small sampling probe, usually a small loop, be placed near the radiator. On the sampling probe, a current is induced which is proportional to the current of the test antenna.

The indicating meter can be connected to the loop in many different ways [25]. If the wavelength is very long, the meter can be consolidated into one unit with the measuring loop. At smaller wavelengths, the meter can be connected to a crystal rectifier. In order not to disturb the field distribution near the radiator, the rectifier is attached to the meter using long leads. To reduce the interaction between the measuring instrumentation and the test antenna and to minimize induced currents on the leads, the wires are wound on a dielectric support rod to form a helical choke. Usually the diameter of each turn, and spacing between them, is about $\lambda/50$. The dielectric rod can also be used as a support for the loop. To prevent a dc short circuit on the crystal rectifier, a bypass capacitor is placed along the circumference of the loop.

There are many other methods, some of them more elaborate and accurate, and the interested reader can refer to the literature [25]–[28].

15.9 POLARIZATION MEASUREMENTS

The polarization of a wave was defined in Section 2.12 as the curve traced by the instantaneous electric field, at a given frequency, in a plane perpendicular to the direction of wave travel. The far-field polarization of an antenna is usually measured at distances where the field radiated by the antenna forms, in a small region, a plane wave that propagates in the outward radial direction.

In a similar manner, the polarization of the antenna is defined as the curve traced by the instantaneous electric field radiated by the antenna in a plane perpendicular to the radial direction, as shown in Figure 15.11(a). The locus is usually an ellipse. In a spherical coordinate system, which is usually adopted in antennas, the polarization ellipse is formed by the orthogonal electric field components of E_θ and E_ϕ. The sense of rotation, also referred to as the sense of polarization, is defined by the sense of rotation of the wave as it is observed along the direction of propagation [see Figure 15.11(b)].

The general polarization of an antenna is characterized by the axial ratio (AR), the sense of rotation (CW or CCW, RH or LH), and the tilt angle τ. The tilt angle is used to identify the spatial orientation of the ellipse, and it is usually measured clockwise from the reference direction. This is demonstrated in Figure 15.11(a) where τ is measured clockwise with respect to $\hat{a}_\theta$, for a wave traveling in the outward radial direction.

Care must be exercised in the characterization of the polarization of a receiving antenna. If the tilt angle of an incident wave that is polarization

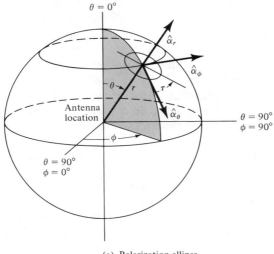

(a) Polarization ellipse

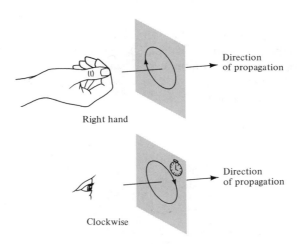

(b) Sense of rotation

Figure 15.11 Polarization ellipse and sense of rotation for antenna coordinate system. (SOURCE: *IEEE Standard Test Procedures for Antennas*, IEEE Std 149-1979, published by IEEE, Inc., 1979, distributed by Wiley)

matched to the receiving antenna is τ_m, it is related to the tilt angle τ_t of a wave transmitted by the same antenna by

$$\tau_t = 180° - \tau_m \qquad (15\text{-}14)$$

if a single coordinate system and one direction of view are used to characterize the polarization. If the receiving antenna has a polarization that is different from that of the incident wave, the polarization loss factor (PLF) of Section 2.12.2 can be used to account for the mismatch losses.

The polarization of a wave and/or an antenna can best be displayed and visualized on the surface of a Poincaré sphere [29]. Each polarization occupies a unique point on the sphere, as shown in Figure 15.12. If one of the two points on the Poincaré sphere is used to define the polarization of the incident wave and the other the polarization of the receiving antenna, the angular separation can be used to determine the polarization losses. The procedure requires that the complex polarization ratios of each are determined, and they are used to compute the polarization efficiency in a number of different ways. The details of this procedure are well documented, and they can be found in [7] and [8].

Practically it is very difficult to design radiators that maintain the same polarization state in all parts of its pattern. A complete description requires a number of measurements in all parts of the pattern. The number of measurements is determined by the required degree of polarization description.

There are a number of techniques that can be used to measure the polarization state of a radiator [7], [8], and they can be classified into three main categories:

1. Those that yield partial polarization information. They do not yield a unique point on the Poincaré sphere.
2. Those that yield complete polarization information but require a polarization standard for comparison. They are referred to as comparison methods.

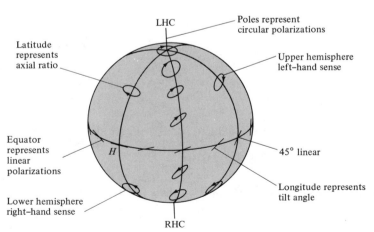

Figure 15.12 Polarization representation on Poincaré sphere. (SOURCE: W. H. Kummer and E. S. Gillespie, "Antenna Measurements—1978," *Proc. IEEE*, vol. 66, No. 4, pp. 483–507, April 1978. © (1978) IEEE)

3. Those that yield complete polarization information and require no *a priori* polarization knowledge or no polarization standard. They are designated as absolute methods.

The method selected depends on such factors as the type of antenna, the required accuracy, and the time and funds available. A complete description requires not only the polarization ellipse (axial ratio and tilt angle), but also its sense of rotation (CW or CCW, RH or LH).

In this text, a method will be discussed which can be used to determine the polarization ellipse (axial ratio and tilt angle) of an antenna but not its sense of rotation. This technique is referred to as the *polarization-pattern method*. The sense of polarization or rotation can be found by performing auxiliary measurements or by using other methods [7].

To perform the measurements, the antenna under test can be used either in the transmitting or in the receiving mode. Usually the transmitting mode is adopted. The method requires that a linearly polarized antenna, usually a dipole, be used to probe the polarization in the plane that contains the direction of the desired polarization. The arrangement is shown in Figure 15.13(a). The dipole is rotated in the plane of the polarization, which is taken to be normal to the direction of the incident field, and the output voltage of the probe is recorded.

If the test antenna is linearly polarized, the output voltage response will be proportional to $\sin \psi$ (which is the far-zone field pattern of an infinitesimal dipole). The pattern forms a figure-eight, as shown in Figure 15.13(b), where ψ is the rotation angle of the probe relative to a reference direction. For an elliptically polarized test antenna, the nulls of the figure-eight are filled and a dumbbell polarization curve (usually referred to as *polarization pattern*) is generated, as shown in Figure 15.13(b). The dashed curve represents the polarization ellipse.

The polarization ellipse is tangent to the polarization pattern, and it can be used to form the axial ratio and the tilt angle of the test antenna. The polarization pattern will be a circle, as shown in Figure 15.13(b), if the test antenna is circularly polarized. Ideally, this process must be repeated at every point of the antenna pattern. Usually it is performed at a number of points that describe sufficiently well the polarization of the antenna at the major and the minor lobes.

The sense of rotation can be determined by performing auxiliary measurements. One method requires that the responses of two circularly polarized antennas, one responsive to CW and the other to CCW rotation, be compared [25]. The sense of rotation corresponds to the sense of polarization of the antenna with the more intense response.

Another method would be to use a dual-polarized probe antenna, such as a dual-polarized horn, and to record simultaneously the amplitude polarization pattern and the relative phase between the two orthogonal polarizations. This is referred to as the *phase-amplitude* method, and it can be accomplished using the instrumentation of Figure 15.14. Double-

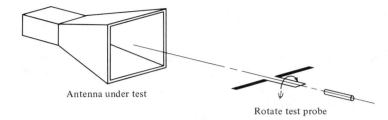

(a) Measuring system

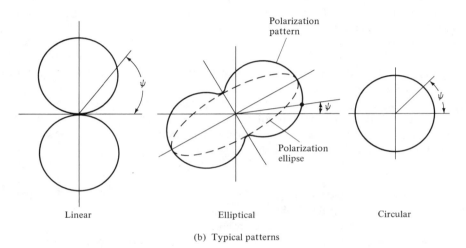

(b) Typical patterns

Figure 15.13 Polarization measuring system and typical patterns.

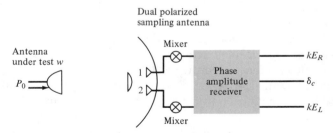

Figure 15.14 System configuration for measurements of polarization amplitude and phase. (SOURCE: W. H. Kummer and E. S. Gillespie, "Antenna Measurements—1978," *Proc. IEEE*, vol. 66, No. 4, pp. 483–507, April 1978. © (1978) IEEE)

conversion phase-locked receivers can be used to perform the amplitude and phase comparison measurements.

Another absolute polarization method, which can be used to completely describe the polarization of a test antenna, is referred to as the *three-antenna* method [7], [8]. As its name implies, it requires three antennas, two of which must not be circularly polarized. There are a number of transfer methods [7], [8], but they require calibration standards for complete description of the polarization state.

15.10 SCALE MODEL MEASUREMENTS

In many applications (such as with antennas on ships, aircraft, large spacecraft, etc.), the antenna and its supporting structure are so immense in weight and/or size that they cannot be moved or accommodated by the facilities of a measuring antenna range. In addition, a movement of the structure to an antenna range can eliminate or introduce environmental effects. To satisfy these system requirements, *in situ* measurements are usually executed.

A technique that can be used to perform antenna measurements associated with large structures is *geometrical scale modeling*. Geometrical modeling is employed to

1. physically accommodate, with small ranges or enclosures, measurements that can be related to large structures
2. provide experimental control over the measurements
3. minimize costs associated with large structures and corresponding experimental parametric studies

Geometrical scale modeling by a factor of n (n smaller or greater than unity) requires the following scaling.

GEOMETRICAL SCALE MODEL

SCALED PARAMETERS		UNCHANGED PARAMETERS	
Length:	$l' = l/n$	Permittivity:	$\varepsilon' = \varepsilon$
Time:	$t' = t/n$	Permeability:	$\mu' = \mu$
Wavelength:	$\lambda' = \lambda/n$	Velocity:	$v' = v$
Capacitance:	$C' = C/n$	Impedance:	$Z' = Z$
Inductance:	$L' = L/n$	Antenna gain:	$G_0' = G_0$
Echo area:	$A_e' = A_e/n^2$		
Frequency:	$f' = nf$		
Conductivity:	$\sigma' = n\sigma$		

The primed parameters represent the scaled model while the unprimed represent the full scale model.

For a geometrical scale model, all the linear dimensions of the antenna and its associated structure are divided by n whereas the operating frequency and the conductivity of the antenna material and its structure are multiplied by n. In practice, the scaling factor n is usually chosen greater than unity.

Ideal scale modeling for antenna measurements requires exact replicas, both physically and electrically, of the full scale structures. In practice, however, this is closely approximated. The most difficult scaling is that of the conductivity. If the full scale model possesses excellent conductors, even better conductors will be required in the scaled models. At microwave and millimeter wave frequencies this can be accomplished by utilizing clean polished surfaces, free of films and other residues.

Geometrical scaling is often used for pattern measurements. However, it can also be employed to measure gain, directivity, radiation efficiency, input and mutual impedances, and so forth. For gain measurements, the inability to properly scale the conductivity can be overcome by measuring the directivity and the antenna efficiency and multiplying the two to determine the gain. Scalings that permit additional parameter changes are available [30]. The changes must satisfy the theorem of similitude.

References

1. J. Brown and E. V. Jull, "The Prediction of Aerial Patterns from Near-Field Measurements," *IEE (London)*, Paper No. 3469E, pp. 635–644, Nov. 1961.
2. R. C. Johnson, H. A. Ecker, and J. S. Hollis, "Determination of Far-Field Antenna Patterns from Near-Field Measurements," *Proc. IEEE*, vol. 61, No. 12, pp. 1668–1694, Dec. 1973.
3. D. T. Paris, W. M. Leach, Jr., and E. B. Joy, "Basic Theory of Probe-Compensated Near-Field Measurements," *IEEE Trans. Antennas Propag.*, vol. AP-26, No. 3, pp. 373–379, May 1978.
4. E. B. Joy, W. M. Leach, Jr., G. P. Rodrigue, and D. T. Paris, "Applications of Probe-Compensated Near-Field Measurements," *IEEE Trans. Antennas Propag.*, vol. AP-26, No. 3, pp. 379–389, May 1978.
5. E. F. Buckley, "Modern Microwave Absorbers and Applications," Emerson & Cuming, Inc., Canton, Mass.
6. J. S. Hollis, T. J. Lyon, and L. Clayton, Jr., *Microwave Antenna Measurements*, Scientific-Atlanta, Inc., Atlanta, Georgia, July 1970.
7. *IEEE Standard Test Procedures for Antennas*, IEEE Std 149-1979, published by IEEE, Inc., 1979, distributed by Wiley-Interscience.
8. W. H. Kummer and E. S. Gillespie, "Antenna Measurements—1978," *Proc. IEEE*, vol. 66, No. 4, pp. 483–507, April 1978.
9. L. H. Hemming and R. A. Heaton, "Antenna Gain Calibration on a Ground Reflection Range," *IEEE Trans. Antennas Propag.*, vol. AP-21, No. 4, pp. 532–537, July 1973.
10. P. W. Arnold, "The 'Slant' Antenna Range," *IEEE Trans. Antennas Propag.*, vol. AP-14, pp. 658–659, Sept. 1966.
11. A. W. Moeller, "The Effect of Ground Reflections on Antenna Test Range Measurements," *Microwave Journal*, vol. 9, pp. 47–54, March 1966.

12. W. H. Emerson, "Electromagnetic Wave Absorbers and Anechoic Chambers Through the Years," *IEEE Trans. Antennas Propag.*, vol. AP-21, pp. 484–490, July 1973.

13. M. R. Gillette and P. R. Wu, "RF Anechoic Chamber Design Using Ray Tracing," *1977 Int. IEEE/AP-S Symp. Dig.*, pp. 246–252, June 1977.

14. W. H. Emerson and H. B. Sefton, "An Improved Design for Indoor Ranges," *Proc. IEEE*, vol. 53, pp. 1079–1081, August 1965.

15. A. C. Newell, R. C. Baird, and P. F. Wacker, "Accurate Measurement of Antenna Gain and Polarization at Reduced Distances by an Extrapolation Technique," *IEEE Trans. Antennas Propag.*, vol. AP-21, No. 4, pp. 418–431, July 1973.

16. L. H. Hemming and R. A. Heaton, "Antenna Gain Calibration on a Ground Reflection Range," *IEEE Trans. Antennas Propag.*, vol. AP-21, pp. 532–537, July 1973.

17. R. G. FitzGerrell, "Gain Measurements of Vertically Polarized Antennas over Imperfect Ground," *IEEE Trans. Antennas Propag.*, vol. AP-15, pp. 211–216, March 1967.

18. R. G. FitzGerrell, "The Gain of a Horizontal Half-Wave Dipole over Ground," *IEEE Trans. Antennas Propag.*, vol. AP-15, pp. 569–571, July 1967.

19. R. G. FitzGerrell, "Limitations on Vertically Polarized Ground-Based Antennas as Gain Standards," *IEEE Trans. Antennas Propag.*, vol. AP-23, pp. 284–286, March 1975.

20. E. H. Newman, P. Bohley, and C. H. Walter, "Two Methods for the Measurement of Antenna Efficiency," *IEEE Trans. Antennas Propag.*, vol. AP-23, pp. 457–461, July 1975.

21. M. Sucher and J. Fox, *Handbook of Microwave Measurements*, vol. I, Polytechnic Press of the Polytechnic Institute of Brooklyn, New York, 1963.

22. C. G. Montgomery, *Techniques of Microwave Measurements*, vol. II, MIT Radiation Laboratory Series, vol. 11, McGraw-Hill, New York, 1947, Chapter 8.

23. ANSI/IEEE Std 148-1959 (Reaff 1971).

24. R. E. Collin, *Foundations for Microwave Engineering*, McGraw-Hill, New York, 1966, pp. 170–179.

25. J. D. Kraus, *Antennas*, McGraw-Hill, New York, 1950.

26. G. Barzilai, "Experimental Determination of the Distribution of Current and Charge Along Cylindrical Antennas," *Proc. IRE* (Waves and Electrons Section), pp. 825–829, July 1949.

27. T. Morita, "Current Distributions on Transmitting and Receiving Antennas," *Proc. IRE*, pp. 898–904, Aug. 1950.

28. A. F. Rashid, "Quasi-Near-Zone Field of a Monopole Antenna and the Current Distribution of an Antenna on a Finite Conductive Earth," *IEEE Trans. Antennas Propagation*, vol. AP-18, No. 1, pp. 22–28, Jan. 1970.

29. H. G. Booker, V. H. Rumsey, G. A. Deschamps, M. I. Kales, and J. I. Bonhert, "Techniques for Handling Elliptically Polarized Waves with Special Reference to Antennas," *Proc. IRE*, vol. 39, pp. 533–552, May 1951.

30. G. Sinclair, "Theory of Models of Electromagnetic Systems," *Proc. IRE*, vol. 36, pp. 1364–1370, Nov. 1948.

Appendix I

$$f(x) = \frac{\sin(x)}{x}$$

x	$\sin(x)/x$	x	$\sin(x)/x$	x	$\sin(x)/x$
0.0	1.00000	5.1	-0.18153	10.2	-0.06861
0.1	0.99833	5.2	-0.16990	10.3	-0.07453
0.2	0.99335	5.3	-0.15703	10.4	-0.07960
0.3	0.98507	5.4	-0.14310	10.5	-0.08378
0.4	0.97355	5.5	-0.12828	10.6	-0.08705
0.5	0.95885	5.6	-0.11273	10.7	-0.08941
0.6	0.94107	5.7	-0.09661	10.8	-0.09083
0.7	0.92031	5.8	-0.08010	10.9	-0.09132
0.8	0.89670	5.9	-0.06337	11.0	-0.09091
0.9	0.87036	6.0	-0.04657	11.1	-0.08960
1.0	0.84147	6.1	-0.02986	11.2	-0.08743
1.1	0.81019	6.2	-0.01340	11.3	-0.08443
1.2	0.77670	6.3	0.00267	11.4	-0.08064
1.3	0.74120	6.4	0.01821	11.5	-0.07613
1.4	0.70389	6.5	0.03309	11.6	-0.07093
1.5	0.66500	6.6	0.04720	11.7	-0.06513
1.6	0.62473	6.7	0.06042	11.8	-0.05877
1.7	0.58333	6.8	0.07266	11.9	-0.05194
1.8	0.54103	6.9	0.08383	12.0	-0.04471
1.9	0.49805	7.0	0.09385	12.1	-0.03716
2.0	0.45465	7.1	0.10267	12.2	-0.02936
2.1	0.41105	7.2	0.11023	12.3	-0.02140
2.2	0.36750	7.3	0.11650	12.4	-0.01336
2.3	0.32422	7.4	0.12145	12.5	-0.00531
2.4	0.28144	7.5	0.12507	12.6	0.00267
2.5	0.23939	7.6	0.12736	12.7	0.01049
2.6	0.19827	7.7	0.12833	12.8	0.01809
2.7	0.15829	7.8	0.12802	12.9	0.02539
2.8	0.11964	7.9	0.12645	13.0	0.03232
2.9	0.08250	8.0	0.12367	13.1	0.03883
3.0	0.04704	8.1	0.11974	13.2	0.04485
3.1	0.01341	8.2	0.11472	13.3	0.05034
3.2	-0.01824	8.3	0.10870	13.4	0.05525
3.3	-0.04780	8.4	0.10174	13.5	0.05954
3.4	-0.07516	8.5	0.09394	13.6	0.06317
3.5	-0.10022	8.6	0.08540	13.7	0.06613
3.6	-0.12292	8.7	0.07620	13.8	0.06838
3.7	-0.14320	8.8	0.06647	13.9	0.06993
3.8	-0.16101	8.9	0.05629	14.0	0.07076
3.9	-0.17635	9.0	0.04579	14.1	0.07087
4.0	-0.18920	9.1	0.03507	14.2	0.07028
4.1	-0.19958	9.2	0.02423	14.3	0.06901
4.2	-0.20752	9.3	0.01338	14.4	0.06706
4.3	-0.21306	9.4	0.00264	14.5	0.06448
4.4	-0.21627	9.5	-0.00791	14.6	0.06129
4.5	-0.21723	9.6	-0.01816	14.7	0.05753
4.6	-0.21602	9.7	-0.02802	14.8	0.05326
4.7	-0.21275	9.8	-0.03740	14.9	0.04852
4.8	-0.20753	9.9	-0.04622	15.0	0.04335
4.9	-0.20050	10.0	-0.05440		
5.0	-0.19179	10.1	-0.06189		

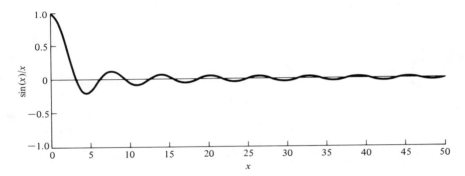

Figure I-1   Plot of $\sin(x)/x$ function.

Appendix II

$$f_N(x) = \left| \frac{\sin(Nx)}{N\sin(x)} \right|$$

$$N = 1, 3, 5, 10, 20$$

x	$f_1(x)$	$f_3(x)$	$f_5(x)$	$f_{10}(x)$	$f_{20}(x)$
0.0	1.00000	1.00000	1.00000	1.00000	1.00000
0.1	1.00000	0.98671	0.96045	0.84287	0.45540
0.2	1.00000	0.94737	0.84711	0.45769	0.19047
0.3	1.00000	0.88356	0.67508	0.04775	0.04727
0.4	1.00000	0.79780	0.46700	0.19434	0.12703
0.5	1.00000	0.69353	0.24966	0.20001	0.05674
0.6	1.00000	0.57490	0.04998	0.04948	0.04751
0.7	1.00000	0.44664	0.10890	0.10198	0.07688
0.8	1.00000	0.31387	0.21100	0.13792	0.02007
0.9	1.00000	0.18186	0.24958	0.05261	0.04794
1.0	1.00000	0.05590	0.22792	0.06465	0.05425
1.1	1.00000	0.05900	0.15833	0.11221	0.00050
1.2	1.00000	0.15826	0.05996	0.05757	0.04858
1.3	1.00000	0.23793	0.04465	0.04361	0.03957
1.4	1.00000	0.29481	0.13334	0.10052	0.01375
1.5	1.00000	0.32666	0.18807	0.06519	0.04953
1.6	1.00000	0.33220	0.19796	0.02880	0.02758
1.7	1.00000	0.31120	0.16104	0.09695	0.02668
1.8	1.00000	0.26451	0.08464	0.07712	0.05092
1.9	1.00000	0.19398	0.01588	0.01584	0.01566
2.0	1.00000	0.10243	0.11966	0.10040	0.04097
2.1	1.00000	0.00649	0.20382	0.09692	0.05309
2.2	1.00000	0.12844	0.24737	0.00109	0.00109
2.3	1.00000	0.25856	0.23480	0.11348	0.06047
2.4	1.00000	0.39167	0.15888	0.13407	0.05687
2.5	1.00000	0.52244	0.02216	0.02211	0.02192
2.6	1.00000	0.64568	0.16301	0.14792	0.09570
2.7	1.00000	0.75646	0.37615	0.22378	0.06537
2.8	1.00000	0.85038	0.59143	0.08087	0.07785
2.9	1.00000	0.92368	0.78152	0.27738	0.20750
3.0	1.00000	0.97345	0.92161	0.70013	0.10799
3.1	1.00000	0.99769	0.99309	0.97172	0.88885
3.1415	1.00000	1.00000	1.00000	1.00000	1.00000

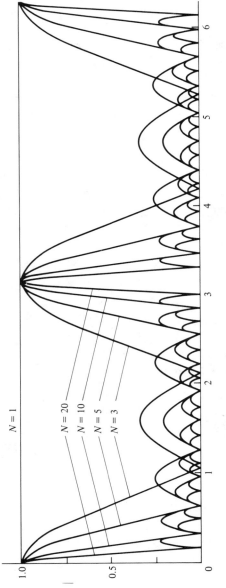

Figure II-1   Curves of $|\sin(Nx)/N\sin(x)|$ function.

Appendix III
Cosine and Sine Integrals

$$S_i(x) = \int_0^x \frac{\sin(\tau)}{\tau}\, d\tau \tag{III-1}$$

$$C_i(x) = -\int_x^\infty \frac{\cos(\tau)}{\tau}\, d\tau = \int_\infty^x \frac{\cos(\tau)}{\tau}\, d\tau \tag{III-2}$$

$$C_{in}(x) = \int_0^x \frac{1 - \cos(\tau)}{\tau}\, d\tau \tag{III-3}$$

$$C_{in}(x) = \ln(\gamma x) - C_i(x) = \ln(\gamma) + \ln(x) - C_i(x)$$

$$C_{in}(x) = \ln(1.781) + \ln(x) - C_i(x) = 0.5772 + \ln(x) - C_i(x) \tag{III-4}$$

x	$S_i(x)$	$C_i(x)$	$C_{in}(x)$	x	$S_i(x)$	$C_i(x)$	$C_{in}(x)$
0.0	0.0	$-\infty$	0.0	5.0	1.54993	-0.19003	2.37647
0.1	0.09994	-1.72787	0.00228	5.1	1.53125	-0.18348	2.38972
0.2	0.19956	-1.04220	0.00977	5.2	1.51367	-0.17525	2.40091
0.3	0.29850	-0.64917	0.02220	5.3	1.49731	-0.16551	2.41021
0.4	0.39646	-0.37881	0.03952	5.4	1.48230	-0.15439	2.41778
0.5	0.49311	-0.17778	0.06164	5.5	1.46872	-0.14205	2.42380
0.6	0.58813	-0.02227	0.08845	5.6	1.45667	-0.12867	2.42844
0.7	0.68122	0.10051	0.11981	5.7	1.44620	-0.11441	2.43188
0.8	0.77209	0.19828	0.15558	5.8	1.43736	-0.09944	2.43430
0.9	0.86047	0.27607	0.19557	5.9	1.43018	-0.08393	2.43588
1.0	0.94608	0.33740	0.23960	6.0	1.42469	-0.06806	2.43682
1.1	1.02868	0.38487	0.28744	6.1	1.42087	-0.05198	2.43727
1.2	1.10805	0.42046	0.33886	6.2	1.41871	-0.03587	2.43742
1.3	1.18396	0.44574	0.39363	6.3	1.41817	-0.01989	2.43744
1.4	1.25622	0.46201	0.45146	6.4	1.41922	-0.00418	2.43748
1.5	1.32468	0.47036	0.51211	6.5	1.42179	0.01110	2.43770
1.6	1.38918	0.47173	0.57527	6.6	1.42582	0.02582	2.43824
1.7	1.44959	0.46697	0.64066	6.7	1.43120	0.03985	2.43925
1.8	1.50581	0.45681	0.70797	6.8	1.43787	0.05308	2.44084
1.9	1.55777	0.44194	0.77691	6.9	1.44570	0.06539	2.44313
2.0	1.60541	0.42298	0.84717	7.0	1.45460	0.07669	2.44621
2.1	1.64870	0.40051	0.91842	7.1	1.46443	0.08691	2.45019
2.2	1.68762	0.37508	0.99038	7.2	1.47509	0.09596	2.45512
2.3	1.72221	0.34718	1.06273	7.3	1.48644	0.10379	2.46108
2.4	1.75248	0.31729	1.13517	7.4	1.49834	0.11036	2.46812
2.5	1.77852	0.28587	1.20742	7.5	1.51068	0.11563	2.47627
2.6	1.80039	0.25334	1.27917	7.6	1.52331	0.11960	2.48555
2.7	1.81821	0.22008	1.35017	7.7	1.53611	0.12225	2.49597
2.8	1.83210	0.18649	1.42013	7.8	1.54894	0.12359	2.50754
2.9	1.84219	0.15290	1.48881	7.9	1.56167	0.12364	2.52022
3.0	1.84865	0.11963	1.55598	8.0	1.57419	0.12243	2.53401
3.1	1.85166	0.08699	1.62141	8.1	1.58637	0.12002	2.54885
3.2	1.85140	0.05526	1.68489	8.2	1.59810	0.11644	2.56469
3.3	1.84808	0.02468	1.74624	8.3	1.60928	0.11177	2.58149
3.4	1.84191	-0.00452	1.80529	8.4	1.61981	0.10607	2.59916
3.5	1.83312	-0.03213	1.86189	8.5	1.62960	0.09943	2.61763
3.6	1.82195	-0.05797	1.91591	8.6	1.63857	0.09194	2.63682
3.7	1.80862	-0.08190	1.96723	8.7	1.64665	0.08368	2.65664
3.8	1.79339	-0.10378	2.01578	8.8	1.65379	0.07476	2.67699
3.9	1.77650	-0.12350	2.06147	8.9	1.65993	0.06528	2.69777
4.0	1.75820	-0.14098	2.10427	9.0	1.66504	0.05535	2.71887
4.1	1.73874	-0.15617	2.14415	9.1	1.66908	0.04507	2.74020
4.2	1.71837	-0.16901	2.18110	9.2	1.67205	0.03456	2.76165
4.3	1.69732	-0.17951	2.21512	9.3	1.67393	0.02391	2.78310
4.4	1.67583	-0.18766	2.24626	9.4	1.67473	0.01325	2.80446
4.5	1.65414	-0.19349	2.27457	9.5	1.67446	0.00268	2.82561
4.6	1.63246	-0.19705	2.30010	9.6	1.67316	-0.00771	2.84647
4.7	1.61100	-0.19839	2.32295	9.7	1.67084	-0.01780	2.86693
4.8	1.58997	-0.19760	2.34322	9.8	1.66757	-0.02752	2.88690
4.9	1.56956	-0.19478	2.36101	9.9	1.66338	-0.03676	2.90630

x	$S_i(x)$	$C_i(x)$	$C_{in}(x)$	x	$S_i(x)$	$C_i(x)$	$C_{in}(x)$
10.0	1.65835	-0.04546	2.92504	15.0	1.61819	0.04628	3.23877
10.1	1.65253	-0.05352	2.94306	15.1	1.62226	0.04102	3.25067
10.2	1.64600	-0.06089	2.96028	15.2	1.62575	0.03543	3.26287
10.3	1.63883	-0.06751	2.97665	15.3	1.62865	0.02955	3.27530
10.4	1.63112	-0.07332	2.99212	15.4	1.63093	0.02345	3.28792
10.5	1.62294	-0.07828	3.00666	15.5	1.63258	0.01719	3.30064
10.6	1.61439	-0.08237	3.02022	15.6	1.63359	0.01085	3.31343
10.7	1.60556	-0.08555	3.03279	15.7	1.63396	0.00447	3.32619
10.8	1.59654	-0.08781	3.04435	15.8	1.63370	-0.00187	3.33888
10.9	1.58743	-0.08915	3.05491	15.9	1.63280	-0.00812	3.35143
11.0	1.57831	-0.08956	3.06446	16.0	1.63130	-0.01420	3.36379
11.1	1.56927	-0.08907	3.07302	16.1	1.62921	-0.02007	3.37588
11.2	1.56042	-0.08769	3.08061	16.2	1.62657	-0.02566	3.38767
11.3	1.55182	-0.08546	3.08726	16.3	1.62339	-0.03093	3.39909
11.4	1.54356	-0.08240	3.09301	16.4	1.61973	-0.03583	3.41011
11.5	1.53571	-0.07857	3.09792	16.5	1.61563	-0.04031	3.42066
11.6	1.52835	-0.07401	3.10202	16.6	1.61112	-0.04433	3.43073
11.7	1.52155	-0.06879	3.10538	16.7	1.60627	-0.04786	3.44027
11.8	1.51535	-0.06297	3.10806	16.8	1.60111	-0.05087	3.44925
11.9	1.50981	-0.05661	3.11014	16.9	1.59572	-0.05334	3.45765
12.0	1.50497	-0.04978	3.11169	17.0	1.59014	-0.05524	3.46545
12.1	1.50087	-0.04257	3.11277	17.1	1.58443	-0.05657	3.47265
12.2	1.49755	-0.03504	3.11348	17.2	1.57865	-0.05732	3.47923
12.3	1.49501	-0.02729	3.11389	17.3	1.57285	-0.05749	3.48519
12.4	1.49327	-0.01938	3.11408	17.4	1.56711	-0.05708	3.49055
12.5	1.49234	-0.01141	3.11414	17.5	1.56146	-0.05610	3.49530
12.6	1.49221	-0.00344	3.11414	17.6	1.55597	-0.05458	3.49947
12.7	1.49286	0.00443	3.11417	17.7	1.55070	-0.05252	3.50309
12.8	1.49430	0.01214	3.11431	17.8	1.54568	-0.04997	3.50616
12.9	1.49647	0.01961	3.11462	17.9	1.54097	-0.04694	3.50874
13.0	1.49936	0.02676	3.11518	18.0	1.53661	-0.04348	3.51085
13.1	1.50292	0.03355	3.11607	18.1	1.53264	-0.03962	3.51253
13.2	1.50711	0.03989	3.11733	18.2	1.52909	-0.03540	3.51382
13.3	1.51188	0.04574	3.11903	18.3	1.52600	-0.03088	3.51478
13.4	1.51716	0.05104	3.12121	18.4	1.52339	-0.02610	3.51545
13.5	1.52290	0.05576	3.12393	18.5	1.52128	-0.02111	3.51588
13.6	1.52905	0.05984	3.12722	18.6	1.51969	-0.01596	3.51612
13.7	1.53552	0.06327	3.13112	18.7	1.51863	-0.01071	3.51623
13.8	1.54225	0.06602	3.13565	18.8	1.51810	-0.00540	3.51626
13.9	1.54917	0.06806	3.14083	18.9	1.51810	-0.00010	3.51626
14.0	1.55621	0.06940	3.14666	19.0	1.51863	0.00515	3.51629
14.1	1.56330	0.07002	3.15316	19.1	1.51967	0.01029	3.51640
14.2	1.57036	0.06993	3.16031	19.2	1.52122	0.01528	3.51663
14.3	1.57733	0.06914	3.16812	19.3	1.52324	0.02006	3.51704
14.4	1.58414	0.06767	3.17656	19.4	1.52572	0.02459	3.51768
14.5	1.59072	0.06554	3.18561	19.5	1.52862	0.02883	3.51858
14.6	1.59701	0.06278	3.19524	19.6	1.53192	0.03274	3.51979
14.7	1.60296	0.05943	3.20541	19.7	1.53557	0.03628	3.52133
14.8	1.60850	0.05554	3.21609	19.8	1.53954	0.03943	3.52325
14.9	1.61360	0.05113	3.22723	19.9	1.54377	0.04215	3.52557
				20.0	1.54824	0.04442	3.52831

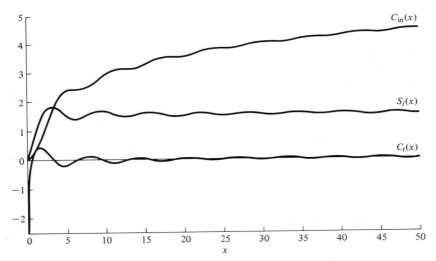

Figure III-1   Plots of sine and cosine integrals.

Appendix IV
Fresnel Integrals

$$C_0(x) = \int_0^x \frac{\cos(\tau)}{\sqrt{2\pi\tau}} d\tau \tag{IV-1}$$

$$S_0(x) = \int_0^x \frac{\sin(\tau)}{\sqrt{2\pi\tau}} d\tau \tag{IV-2}$$

$$C(x) = \int_0^x \cos\left(\frac{\pi}{2}\tau^2\right) d\tau \tag{IV-3}$$

$$S(x) = \int_0^x \sin\left(\frac{\pi}{2}\tau^2\right) d\tau \tag{IV-4}$$

$$C_1(x) = \int_x^\infty \cos(\tau^2) d\tau \tag{IV-5}$$

$$S_1(x) = \int_x^\infty \sin(\tau^2) d\tau \tag{IV-6}$$

$$C(x) - jS(x) = \int_0^x e^{-j(\pi/2)\tau^2} d\tau = \int_0^{(\pi/2)x^2} \frac{e^{-j\tau}}{\sqrt{2\pi\tau}} d\tau$$

$$C(x) - jS(x) = C_0\left(\frac{\pi}{2}x^2\right) - jS_0\left(\frac{\pi}{2}x^2\right) \tag{IV-7}$$

$$C_1(x) - jS_1(x) = \int_x^\infty e^{-j\tau^2} d\tau = \sqrt{\frac{\pi}{2}} \int_{x^2}^\infty \frac{e^{-j\tau}}{\sqrt{2\pi\tau}} d\tau$$

$$C_1(x) - jS_1(x) = \sqrt{\frac{\pi}{2}} \left\{ \int_0^\infty \frac{e^{-j\tau}}{\sqrt{2\pi\tau}} d\tau - \int_0^{x^2} \frac{e^{-j\tau}}{\sqrt{2\pi\tau}} d\tau \right\}$$

$$C_1(x) - jS_1(x) = \sqrt{\frac{\pi}{2}} \left\{ \left[\frac{1}{2} - j\frac{1}{2}\right] - \left[C_0(x^2) - jS_0(x^2)\right] \right\}$$

$$C_1(x) - jS_1(x) = \sqrt{\frac{\pi}{2}} \left\{ \left[\frac{1}{2} - C_0(x^2)\right] - j\left[\frac{1}{2} - S_0(x^2)\right] \right\} \tag{IV-8}$$

x	$C_1(x)$	$S_1(x)$	$C(x)$	$S(x)$
0.0	0.62666	0.62666	0.0	0.0
0.1	0.52666	0.62632	0.10000	0.00052
0.2	0.42669	0.62399	0.19992	0.00419
0.3	0.32690	0.61766	0.29940	0.01412
0.4	0.22768	0.60536	0.39748	0.03336
0.5	0.12977	0.58518	0.49234	0.06473
0.6	0.03439	0.55532	0.58110	0.11054
0.7	-0.05672	0.51427	0.65965	0.17214
0.8	-0.14119	0.46092	0.72284	0.24934
0.9	-0.21606	0.39481	0.76482	0.33978
1.0	-0.27787	0.31639	0.77989	0.43826
1.1	-0.32285	0.22728	0.76381	0.53650
1.2	-0.34729	0.13054	0.71544	0.62340
1.3	-0.34803	0.03081	0.63855	0.68633
1.4	-0.32312	-0.06573	0.54310	0.71353
1.5	-0.27253	-0.15158	0.44526	0.69751
1.6	-0.19886	-0.21861	0.36546	0.63889
1.7	-0.10790	-0.25905	0.32383	0.54920
1.8	-0.00871	-0.26682	0.33363	0.45094
1.9	0.08680	-0.23918	0.39447	0.37335
2.0	0.16520	-0.17812	0.48825	0.34342
2.1	0.21359	-0.09141	0.58156	0.37427
2.2	0.22242	0.00743	0.63629	0.45570
2.3	0.18833	0.10054	0.62656	0.55315
2.4	0.11650	0.16879	0.55496	0.61969
2.5	0.02135	0.19614	0.45742	0.61918
2.6	-0.07518	0.17454	0.38894	0.54999
2.7	-0.14816	0.10789	0.39249	0.45292
2.8	-0.17646	0.01329	0.46749	0.39153
2.9	-0.15021	-0.08181	0.56237	0.41014
3.0	-0.07621	-0.14690	0.60572	0.49631
3.1	0.02152	-0.15883	0.56160	0.58181
3.2	0.10791	-0.11181	0.46632	0.59335
3.3	0.14907	-0.02260	0.40570	0.51929
3.4	0.12691	0.07301	0.43849	0.42965
3.5	0.04965	0.13335	0.53257	0.41525
3.6	-0.04819	0.12973	0.58795	0.49231
3.7	-0.11929	0.06258	0.54195	0.57498
3.8	-0.12649	-0.03483	0.44810	0.56562
3.9	-0.06469	-0.11030	0.42233	0.47521
4.0	0.03219	-0.12048	0.49842	0.42052
4.1	0.10690	-0.05815	0.57369	0.47580
4.2	0.11228	0.03885	0.54172	0.56320
4.3	0.04374	0.10751	0.44944	0.55400
4.4	-0.05287	0.10038	0.43833	0.46227
4.5	-0.10884	0.02149	0.52602	0.43427
4.6	-0.08188	-0.07126	0.56724	0.51619
4.7	0.00810	-0.10594	0.49143	0.56715
4.8	0.08905	-0.05381	0.43380	0.49675
4.9	0.09277	0.04224	0.50016	0.43507
5.0	0.01519	0.09874	0.56363	0.49919

x	$C_1(x)$	$S_1(x)$	$C(x)$	$S(x)$
5.1	-0.07411	0.06405	0.49979	0.56239
5.2	-0.09125	-0.03004	0.43889	0.49688
5.3	-0.01892	-0.09235	0.50778	0.44047
5.4	0.07063	-0.05976	0.55723	0.51403
5.5	0.08408	0.03440	0.47843	0.55369
5.6	0.00641	0.08900	0.45171	0.47004
5.7	-0.07642	0.04296	0.53846	0.45953
5.8	-0.06919	-0.05135	0.52984	0.54604
5.9	0.01998	-0.08231	0.44859	0.51633
6.0	0.08245	-0.01181	0.49953	0.44696
6.1	0.03946	0.07180	0.54950	0.51647
6.2	-0.05363	0.06018	0.46761	0.53982
6.3	-0.07284	-0.03144	0.47600	0.45555
6.4	0.00835	-0.07765	0.54960	0.49649
6.5	0.07574	-0.01326	0.48161	0.54538
6.6	0.03183	0.06872	0.46899	0.46307
6.7	-0.05828	0.04658	0.54674	0.49150
6.8	-0.05734	-0.04600	0.48307	0.54364
6.9	0.03317	-0.06440	0.47322	0.46244
7.0	0.06832	0.02077	0.54547	0.49970
7.1	-0.00944	0.06977	0.47332	0.53602
7.2	-0.06943	0.00041	0.48874	0.45725
7.3	-0.00864	-0.06793	0.53927	0.51894
7.4	0.06582	-0.01521	0.46010	0.51607
7.5	0.02018	0.06353	0.51601	0.46070
7.6	-0.06137	0.02367	0.51564	0.53885
7.7	-0.02580	-0.05958	0.46278	0.48202
7.8	0.05828	-0.02668	0.53947	0.48964
7.9	0.02638	0.05752	0.47598	0.53235
8.0	-0.05730	0.02494	0.49980	0.46021
8.1	-0.02238	-0.05752	0.52275	0.53204
8.2	0.05803	-0.01870	0.46384	0.48589
8.3	0.01387	0.05861	0.53775	0.49323
8.4	-0.05899	0.00789	0.47092	0.52429
8.5	-0.00080	-0.05881	0.51417	0.46534
8.6	0.05767	0.00729	0.50249	0.53693
8.7	-0.01616	0.05515	0.48274	0.46774
8.8	-0.05079	-0.02545	0.52797	0.52294
8.9	0.03461	-0.04425	0.46612	0.48856
9.0	0.03526	0.04293	0.53537	0.49985
9.1	-0.04951	0.02381	0.46661	0.51042
9.2	-0.01021	-0.05338	0.52914	0.48135
9.3	0.05354	0.00485	0.47628	0.52467
9.4	-0.02020	0.04920	0.51803	0.47134
9.5	-0.03995	-0.03426	0.48729	0.53100
9.6	0.04513	-0.02599	0.50813	0.46786
9.7	0.00837	0.05086	0.49549	0.53250
9.8	-0.04983	-0.01094	0.50192	0.46758
9.9	0.02916	-0.04124	0.49961	0.53215

x	$C_1(x)$	$S_1(x)$	$C(x)$	$S(x)$
10.0	0.02554	0.04298	0.49989	0.46817
10.1	-0.04927	0.00478	0.49961	0.53151
10.2	0.01738	-0.04583	0.50186	0.46885
10.3	0.03233	0.03621	0.49575	0.53061
10.4	-0.04681	0.01094	0.50751	0.47033
10.5	0.01360	-0.04563	0.48849	0.52804
10.6	0.03187	0.03477	0.51601	0.47460
10.7	-0.04595	0.00848	0.47936	0.52143
10.8	0.01789	-0.04270	0.52484	0.48413
10.9	0.02494	0.03850	0.47211	0.50867
11.0	-0.04541	-0.00202	0.52894	0.49991
11.1	0.02845	-0.03492	0.47284	0.49079
11.2	0.01008	0.04349	0.52195	0.51805
11.3	-0.03981	-0.01930	0.48675	0.47514
11.4	0.04005	-0.01789	0.50183	0.52786
11.5	-0.01282	0.04155	0.51052	0.47440
11.6	-0.02188	-0.03714	0.47890	0.51755
11.7	0.04164	0.00962	0.52679	0.49525
11.8	-0.03580	0.02267	0.47489	0.49013
11.9	0.00977	-0.04086	0.51544	0.52184
12.0	0.02059	0.03622	0.49993	0.47347
12.1	-0.03919	-0.01309	0.48426	0.52108
12.2	0.03792	-0.01555	0.52525	0.49345
12.3	-0.01914	0.03586	0.47673	0.48867
12.4	-0.00728	-0.03966	0.50951	0.52384
12.5	0.02960	0.02691	0.50969	0.47645
12.6	-0.03946	-0.00421	0.47653	0.50936
12.7	0.03445	-0.01906	0.52253	0.51097
12.8	-0.01783	0.03475	0.49376	0.47593
12.9	-0.00377	-0.03857	0.48523	0.51977
13.0	0.02325	0.03064	0.52449	0.49994
13.1	-0.03530	-0.01452	0.48598	0.48015
13.2	0.03760	-0.00459	0.49117	0.52244
13.3	-0.03075	0.02163	0.52357	0.49583
13.4	0.01744	-0.03299	0.48482	0.48173
13.5	-0.00129	0.03701	0.49103	0.52180
13.6	-0.01421	-0.03391	0.52336	0.49848
13.7	0.02639	0.02521	0.48908	0.47949
13.8	-0.03377	-0.01313	0.48534	0.51781
13.9	0.03597	-0.00002	0.52168	0.50737
14.0	-0.03352	0.01232	0.49996	0.47726
14.1	0.02749	-0.02240	0.47844	0.50668
14.2	-0.01916	0.02954	0.51205	0.51890
14.3	0.00979	-0.03357	0.51546	0.48398
14.4	-0.00043	0.03472	0.48131	0.48819
14.5	-0.00817	-0.03350	0.49164	0.52030
14.6	0.01553	0.03052	0.52113	0.50538
14.7	-0.02145	-0.02640	0.50301	0.47856
14.8	0.02591	0.02168	0.47853	0.49869
14.9	-0.02903	-0.01683	0.49971	0.52136
15.0	0.03103	0.01217	0.52122	0.49926

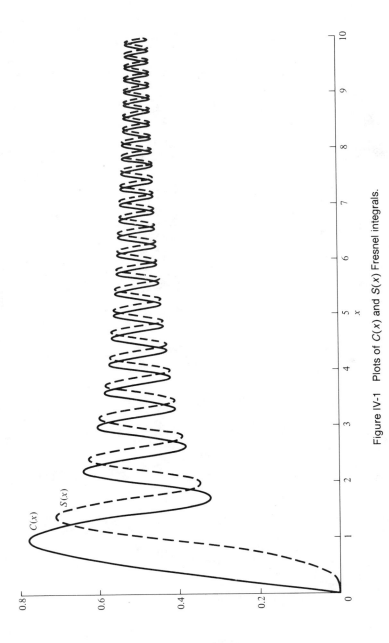

Figure IV-1 Plots of $C(x)$ and $S(x)$ Fresnel integrals.

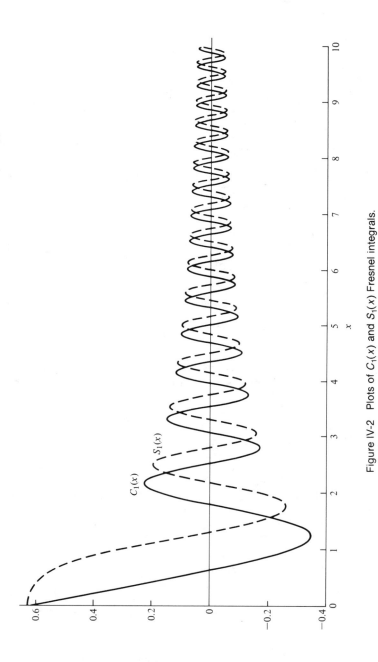

Figure IV-2 Plots of $C_1(x)$ and $S_1(x)$ Fresnel integrals.

Appendix V
Bessel Functions

Bessel's equation can be written as

$$x^2\frac{d^2y}{dx^2} - x\frac{dy}{dx} + (x^2 - p^2)y = 0 \tag{V-1}$$

Using the method of Frobenius, we can write its solutions as

$$y(x) = A_1 J_p(x) + B_1 J_{-p}(x), \qquad p \neq 0 \text{ or integer} \tag{V-2}$$

or

$$y(x) = A_2 J_n(x) + B_2 Y_n(x), \qquad p = n = 0 \text{ or integer} \tag{V-3}$$

where

$$J_p(x) = \sum_{m=0}^{\infty} \frac{(-1)^m (x/2)^{2m+p}}{m!(m+p)!} \tag{V-4}$$

$$J_{-p}(x) = \sum_{m=0}^{\infty} \frac{(-1)^m (x/2)^{2m-p}}{m!(m-p)!} \tag{V-5}$$

$$Y_p(x) = \frac{J_p(x)\cos(p\pi) - J_{-p}(x)}{\sin(p\pi)} \tag{V-6}$$

$$m! = \Gamma(m+1) \tag{V-7}$$

$J_p(x)$ is referred to as the Bessel function of the first kind of order p, $Y_p(x)$ as the Bessel function of the second kind of order p, and $\Gamma(x)$ as the gamma function.

When $p = n =$ integer, using (V-5) and (V-7) it can be shown that

$$J_{-n}(x) = (-1)^n J_n(x) \tag{V-8}$$

and no longer are the two Bessel functions independent of each other. Therefore a second solution is required and it is given by (V-3). It can also be shown that

$$Y_n(x) = \lim_{p \to n} Y_p(x) = \lim_{p \to n} \frac{J_p(x)\cos(p\pi) - J_{-p}(x)}{\sin(p\pi)} \tag{V-9}$$

When the argument of the Bessel function is negative and $p = n$, using (V-4) leads to

$$J_n(-x) = (-1)^n J_n(x) \tag{V-10}$$

In many applications, Bessel functions of small and large arguments are required. Using asymptotic methods, it can be shown that

$$\left.\begin{array}{l} J_0(x) \simeq 1 \\[2mm] Y_0(x) \simeq \dfrac{2}{\pi}\ln\left(\dfrac{\gamma x}{2}\right) \\[2mm] \gamma = 1.781 \end{array}\right\} \; x \to 0 \tag{V-11}$$

$$J_p(x) \simeq \frac{1}{p!}\left(\frac{x}{2}\right)^p \quad \left.\begin{array}{l} \\ \\ \end{array}\right\} \; x \to 0$$

$$Y_p(x) \simeq -\frac{(p-1)!}{\pi}\left(\frac{2}{x}\right)^p \quad \left.\begin{array}{l} \\ \end{array}\right] \; p > 0$$

(V-12)

and

$$J_p(x) \simeq \sqrt{\frac{2}{\pi x}} \; \cos\left(x - \frac{\pi}{4} - \frac{p\pi}{2}\right) \quad \left.\begin{array}{l} \\ \\ \\ \\ \end{array}\right\}$$

$$Y_p(x) \simeq \sqrt{\frac{2}{\pi x}} \; \sin\left(x - \frac{\pi}{4} - \frac{p\pi}{2}\right) \quad \begin{array}{l} \\ \end{array}$$ $x \to \infty$

(V-13)

For wave propagation it is often convenient to introduce Hankel functions defined as

$$H_p^{(1)}(x) = J_p(x) + jY_p(x) \tag{V-14}$$

$$H_p^{(2)}(x) = J_p(x) - jY_p(x) \tag{V-15}$$

where $H_p^{(1)}(x)$ is the Hankel function of the first kind of order p and $H_p^{(2)}(x)$ is the Hankel function of the second kind of order p. For large arguments

$$H_p^{(1)}(x) \simeq \sqrt{\frac{2}{\pi x}} \; e^{j[x - p(\pi/2) - \pi/4]}, \qquad x \to \infty \tag{V-16}$$

$$H_p^{(2)}(x) \simeq \sqrt{\frac{2}{\pi x}} \; e^{-j[x - p(\pi/2) - \pi/4]}, \qquad x \to \infty \tag{V-17}$$

A derivative can be taken using either

$$\frac{d}{dx}\left[Z_p(\alpha x)\right] = \alpha Z_{p-1}(\alpha x) - \frac{p}{x} Z_p(\alpha x) \tag{V-18}$$

or

$$\frac{d}{dx}\left[Z_p(\alpha x)\right] = -\alpha Z_{p+1}(\alpha x) + \frac{p}{x} Z_p(\alpha x) \tag{V-19}$$

where Z_p can be a Bessel function (J_p, Y_p) or a Hankel function $[H_p^{(1)}$ or $H_p^{(2)}]$.

A useful identity relating Bessel functions and their derivatives is given by

$$J_p(x)Y_p'(x) - Y_p(x)J_p'(x) = \frac{2}{\pi x} \tag{V-20}$$

and it is referred to as the Wronskian. The prime (') indicates a derivative. Also

$$J_p(x)J'_{-p}(x) - J_{-p}(x)J_p'(x) = -\frac{2}{\pi x}\sin(p\pi) \tag{V-21}$$

Some useful integrals of Bessel functions are

$$\int x^{p+1} J_p(\alpha x)\, dx = \frac{1}{\alpha} x^{p+1} J_{p+1}(\alpha x) + C \qquad\qquad (V\text{-}22)$$

$$\int x^{1-p} J_p(\alpha x)\, dx = -\frac{1}{\alpha} x^{1-p} J_{p-1}(\alpha x) + C \qquad\qquad (V\text{-}23)$$

$$\int x^3 J_0(x)\, dx = x^3 J_1(x) - 2x^2 J_2(x) + C \qquad\qquad (V\text{-}24)$$

$$\int x^6 J_1(x)\, dx = x^6 J_2(x) - 4x^5 J_3(x) + 8x^4 J_4(x) + C \qquad\qquad (V\text{-}25)$$

$$\int J_3(x)\, dx = -J_2(x) - \frac{2}{x} J_1(x) + C \qquad\qquad (V\text{-}26)$$

$$\int x J_1(x)\, dx = -x J_0(x) + \int J_0(x)\, dx + C \qquad\qquad (V\text{-}27)$$

$$\int x^{-1} J_1(x)\, dx = -J_1(x) + \int J_0(x)\, dx + C \qquad\qquad (V\text{-}28)$$

$$\int J_2(x)\, dx = -2J_1(x) + \int J_0(x)\, dx + C \qquad\qquad (V\text{-}29)$$

$$\int x^m J_n(x)\, dx = x^m J_{n+1}(x) - (m-n-1)\int x^{m-1} J_{n+1}(x)\, dx \qquad (V\text{-}30)$$

$$\int x^m J_n(x)\, dx = -x^m J_{n-1}(x) + (m+n-1)\int x^{m-1} J_{n-1}(x)\, dx \qquad (V\text{-}31)$$

$$J_1(x) = \frac{2}{\pi} \int_0^{\pi/2} \sin(x\sin\theta)\sin\theta\, d\theta \qquad\qquad (V\text{-}32)$$

$$\frac{1}{x} J_1(x) = \frac{2}{\pi} \int_0^{\pi/2} \cos(x\sin\theta)\cos^2\theta\, d\theta \qquad\qquad (V\text{-}33)$$

$$J_2(x) = \frac{2}{\pi} \int_0^{\pi/2} \cos(x\sin\theta)\cos2\theta\, d\theta \qquad\qquad (V\text{-}34)$$

$$J_n(x) = \frac{j^{-n}}{2\pi} \int_0^{2\pi} e^{jx\cos\phi} e^{jn\phi}\, d\phi \qquad\qquad (V\text{-}35)$$

$$J_n(x) = \frac{j^{-n}}{\pi} \int_0^{\pi} \cos(n\phi) e^{jx\cos\phi}\, d\phi \qquad\qquad (V\text{-}36)$$

$$J_n(x) = \frac{1}{\pi} \int_0^{\pi} \cos(x\sin\phi - n\phi)\, d\phi \qquad\qquad (V\text{-}37)$$

$$J_{2n}(x) = \frac{2}{\pi} \int_0^{\pi/2} \cos(x\sin\phi)\cos(2n\phi)\, d\phi \qquad\qquad (V\text{-}38)$$

$$J_{2n}(x) = (-1)^n \frac{2}{\pi} \int_0^{\pi/2} \cos(x\cos\phi)\cos(2n\phi)\, d\phi \qquad\qquad (V\text{-}39)$$

The integrals

$$\int_0^x J_0(\tau)\,d\tau \quad \text{and} \quad \int_0^x Y_0(\tau)\,d\tau \tag{V-40}$$

often appear in solutions of problems but cannot be integrated in closed form. Graphs and tables for each, obtained using numerical techniques, are included.

x	$J_0(x)$	$J_1(x)$	$Y_0(x)$	$Y_1(x)$
0.0	1.00000	0.0	$-\infty$	$-\infty$
0.1	0.99750	0.04994	-1.53424	-6.45895
0.2	0.99003	0.09950	-1.08110	-3.32382
0.3	0.97763	0.14832	-0.80727	-2.29310
0.4	0.96040	0.19603	-0.60602	-1.78087
0.5	0.93847	0.24227	-0.44452	-1.47147
0.6	0.91201	0.28670	-0.30851	-1.26039
0.7	0.88120	0.32900	-0.19066	-1.10325
0.8	0.84629	0.36884	-0.08680	-0.97814
0.9	0.80752	0.40595	0.00563	-0.87313
1.0	0.76520	0.44005	0.08826	-0.78121
1.1	0.71962	0.47090	0.16216	-0.69812
1.2	0.67113	0.49829	0.22808	-0.62114
1.3	0.62009	0.52202	0.28654	-0.54852
1.4	0.56686	0.54195	0.33789	-0.47915
1.5	0.51183	0.55794	0.38245	-0.41231
1.6	0.45540	0.56990	0.42043	-0.34758
1.7	0.39799	0.57777	0.45203	-0.28473
1.8	0.33999	0.58152	0.47743	-0.22366
1.9	0.28182	0.58116	0.49682	-0.16441
2.0	0.22389	0.57673	0.51038	-0.10703
2.1	0.16661	0.56829	0.51829	-0.05168
2.2	0.11036	0.55596	0.52078	0.00149
2.3	0.05554	0.53987	0.51807	0.05228
2.4	0.00251	0.52019	0.51041	0.10049
2.5	-0.04838	0.49710	0.49807	0.14592
2.6	-0.09681	0.47082	0.48133	0.18836
2.7	-0.14245	0.44161	0.46050	0.22763
2.8	-0.18504	0.40972	0.43592	0.26354
2.9	-0.22432	0.37544	0.40791	0.29594
3.0	-0.26005	0.33906	0.37686	0.32467
3.1	-0.29206	0.30092	0.34310	0.34963
3.2	-0.32019	0.26134	0.30705	0.37071
3.3	-0.34430	0.22066	0.26909	0.38785
3.4	-0.36430	0.17923	0.22962	0.40101
3.5	-0.38013	0.13738	0.18902	0.41019
3.6	-0.39177	0.09547	0.14771	0.41539
3.7	-0.39923	0.05383	0.10607	0.41667
3.8	-0.40256	0.01282	0.06450	0.41411
3.9	-0.40183	-0.02724	0.02338	0.40782
4.0	-0.39715	-0.06604	-0.01694	0.39793
4.1	-0.38868	-0.10328	-0.05609	0.38459
4.2	-0.37657	-0.13865	-0.09375	0.36801
4.3	-0.36102	-0.17190	-0.12960	0.34839
4.4	-0.34226	-0.20278	-0.16334	0.32597
4.5	-0.32054	-0.23106	-0.19471	0.30100
4.6	-0.29614	-0.25655	-0.22346	0.27375
4.7	-0.26933	-0.27908	-0.24939	0.24450
4.8	-0.24043	-0.29850	-0.27230	0.21356
4.9	-0.20974	-0.31470	-0.29205	0.18125

x	$J_0(x)$	$J_1(x)$	$Y_0(x)$	$Y_1(x)$
5.0	-0.17760	-0.32758	-0.30852	0.14786
5.1	-0.14434	-0.33710	-0.32160	0.11374
5.2	-0.11029	-0.34322	-0.33125	0.07919
5.3	-0.07580	-0.34596	-0.33744	0.04455
5.4	-0.04121	-0.34534	-0.34017	0.01013
5.5	-0.00684	-0.34144	-0.33948	-0.02376
5.6	0.02697	-0.33433	-0.33544	-0.05681
5.7	0.05992	-0.32415	-0.32816	-0.08872
5.8	0.09170	-0.31103	-0.31775	-0.11923
5.9	0.12203	-0.29514	-0.30437	-0.14808
6.0	0.15065	-0.27668	-0.28819	-0.17501
6.1	0.17729	-0.25587	-0.26943	-0.19981
6.2	0.20175	-0.23292	-0.24831	-0.22228
6.3	0.22381	-0.20809	-0.22506	-0.24225
6.4	0.24331	-0.18164	-0.19995	-0.25956
6.5	0.26009	-0.15384	-0.17324	-0.27409
6.6	0.27404	-0.12498	-0.14523	-0.28575
6.7	0.28506	-0.09534	-0.11619	-0.29446
6.8	0.29310	-0.06522	-0.08643	-0.30019
6.9	0.29810	-0.03490	-0.05625	-0.30292
7.0	0.30008	-0.00468	-0.02595	-0.30267
7.1	0.29905	0.02515	0.00418	-0.29948
7.2	0.29507	0.05433	0.03385	-0.29342
7.3	0.28822	0.08257	0.06277	-0.28459
7.4	0.27860	0.10962	0.09068	-0.27311
7.5	0.26634	0.13525	0.11731	-0.25913
7.6	0.25160	0.15921	0.14243	-0.24280
7.7	0.23456	0.18131	0.16580	-0.22432
7.8	0.21541	0.20136	0.18723	-0.20388
7.9	0.19436	0.21918	0.20652	-0.18172
8.0	0.17165	0.23464	0.22352	-0.15806
8.1	0.14752	0.24761	0.23809	-0.13315
8.2	0.12222	0.25800	0.25012	-0.10724
8.3	0.09601	0.26574	0.25951	-0.08060
8.4	0.06916	0.27079	0.26622	-0.05348
8.5	0.04194	0.27312	0.27021	-0.02617
8.6	0.01462	0.27276	0.27146	0.00108
8.7	-0.01252	0.26972	0.27000	0.02801
8.8	-0.03923	0.26407	0.26587	0.05436
8.9	-0.06525	0.25590	0.25916	0.07987
9.0	-0.09033	0.24531	0.24994	0.10431
9.1	-0.11424	0.23243	0.23834	0.12747
9.2	-0.13675	0.21741	0.22449	0.14911
9.3	-0.15765	0.20041	0.20857	0.16906
9.4	-0.17677	0.18163	0.19074	0.18714
9.5	-0.19393	0.16126	0.17121	0.20318
9.6	-0.20898	0.13952	0.15018	0.21706
9.7	-0.22180	0.11664	0.12787	0.22866
9.8	-0.23228	0.09284	0.10453	0.23789
9.9	-0.24034	0.06837	0.08038	0.24469

x	$J_0(x)$	$J_1(x)$	$Y_0(x)$	$Y_1(x)$
10.0	-0.24594	0.04347	0.05567	0.24902
10.1	-0.24903	0.01840	0.03066	0.25084
10.2	-0.24962	-0.00662	0.00558	0.25019
10.3	-0.24772	-0.03132	-0.01930	0.24707
10.4	-0.24337	-0.05547	-0.04375	0.24155
10.5	-0.23665	-0.07885	-0.06753	0.23370
10.6	-0.22764	-0.10123	-0.09042	0.22363
10.7	-0.21644	-0.12240	-0.11219	0.21144
10.8	-0.20320	-0.14217	-0.13264	0.19729
10.9	-0.18806	-0.16035	-0.15158	0.18132
11.0	-0.17119	-0.17679	-0.16885	0.16371
11.1	-0.15277	-0.19133	-0.18428	0.14464
11.2	-0.13299	-0.20385	-0.19773	0.12431
11.3	-0.11207	-0.21426	-0.20910	0.10294
11.4	-0.09021	-0.22245	-0.21829	0.08074
11.5	-0.06765	-0.22838	-0.22523	0.05794
11.6	-0.04462	-0.23200	-0.22987	0.03477
11.7	-0.02133	-0.23330	-0.23218	0.01145
11.8	0.00197	-0.23229	-0.23216	-0.01179
11.9	0.02505	-0.22898	-0.22983	-0.03471
12.0	0.04769	-0.22345	-0.22524	-0.05710
12.1	0.06967	-0.21575	-0.21844	-0.07874
12.2	0.09077	-0.20598	-0.20952	-0.09942
12.3	0.11080	-0.19426	-0.19859	-0.11895
12.4	0.12956	-0.18071	-0.18578	-0.13714
12.5	0.14689	-0.16549	-0.17121	-0.15384
12.6	0.16261	-0.14874	-0.15506	-0.16888
12.7	0.17659	-0.13066	-0.13750	-0.18213
12.8	0.18870	-0.11143	-0.11870	-0.19347
12.9	0.19885	-0.09125	-0.09887	-0.20282
13.0	0.20693	-0.07032	-0.07821	-0.21008
13.1	0.21289	-0.04885	-0.05692	-0.21521
13.2	0.21669	-0.02707	-0.03524	-0.21817
13.3	0.21830	-0.00518	-0.01336	-0.21895
13.4	0.21773	0.01660	0.00848	-0.21756
13.5	0.21499	0.03805	0.03008	-0.21402
13.6	0.21013	0.05896	0.05122	-0.20839
13.7	0.20322	0.07914	0.07169	-0.20074
13.8	0.19434	0.09839	0.09130	-0.19116
13.9	0.18358	0.11653	0.10986	-0.17975
14.0	0.17108	0.13338	0.12719	-0.16664
14.1	0.15695	0.14879	0.14314	-0.15198
14.2	0.14137	0.16261	0.15754	-0.13592
14.3	0.12449	0.17473	0.17028	-0.11862
14.4	0.10649	0.18503	0.18123	-0.10026
14.5	0.08755	0.19343	0.19030	-0.08104
14.6	0.06787	0.19986	0.19742	-0.06115
14.7	0.04764	0.20426	0.20252	-0.04079
14.8	0.02708	0.20660	0.20557	-0.02016
14.9	0.00639	0.20688	0.20655	0.00053
15.0	-0.01422	0.20511	0.20546	0.02107

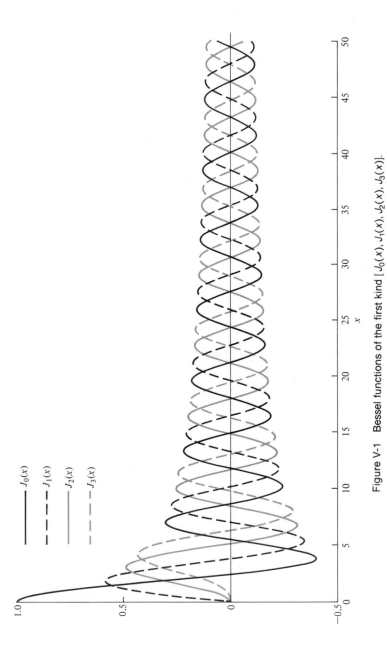

Figure V-1   Bessel functions of the first kind [$J_0(x)$, $J_1(x)$, $J_2(x)$, $J_3(x)$].

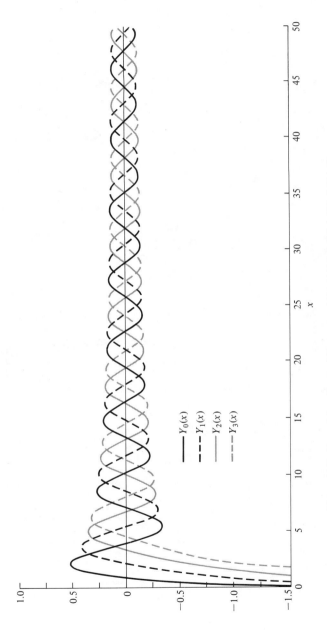

Figure V-2 Bessel functions of the second kind [$Y_0(x), Y_1(x), Y_2(x), Y_3(x)$].

$J_1(x)/x$ FUNCTION

x	$J_1(x)/x$	x	$J_1(x)/x$	x	$J_1(x)/x$
0.0	0.50000	5.0	-0.06552	10.0	0.00435
0.1	0.49938	5.1	-0.06610	10.1	0.00182
0.2	0.49750	5.2	-0.06600	10.2	-0.00065
0.3	0.49440	5.3	-0.06528	10.3	-0.00304
0.4	0.49007	5.4	-0.06395	10.4	-0.00533
0.5	0.48454	5.5	-0.06208	10.5	-0.00751
0.6	0.47783	5.6	-0.05970	10.6	-0.00955
0.7	0.46999	5.7	-0.05687	10.7	-0.01144
0.8	0.46105	5.8	-0.05363	10.8	-0.01316
0.9	0.45105	5.9	-0.05002	10.9	-0.01471
1.0	0.44005	6.0	-0.04611	11.0	-0.01607
1.1	0.42809	6.1	-0.04194	11.1	-0.01724
1.2	0.41524	6.2	-0.03757	11.2	-0.01820
1.3	0.40156	6.3	-0.03303	11.3	-0.01896
1.4	0.38710	6.4	-0.02838	11.4	-0.01951
1.5	0.37196	6.5	-0.02367	11.5	-0.01986
1.6	0.35618	6.6	-0.01894	11.6	-0.02000
1.7	0.33986	6.7	-0.01423	11.7	-0.01994
1.8	0.32306	6.8	-0.00959	11.8	-0.01969
1.9	0.30587	6.9	-0.00506	11.9	-0.01924
2.0	0.28836	7.0	-0.00067	12.0	-0.01862
2.1	0.27061	7.1	0.00354	12.1	-0.01783
2.2	0.25271	7.2	0.00755	12.2	-0.01688
2.3	0.23473	7.3	0.01131	12.3	-0.01579
2.4	0.21674	7.4	0.01481	12.4	-0.01457
2.5	0.19884	7.5	0.01803	12.5	-0.01324
2.6	0.18108	7.6	0.02095	12.6	-0.01180
2.7	0.16356	7.7	0.02355	12.7	-0.01029
2.8	0.14633	7.8	0.02582	12.8	-0.00871
2.9	0.12946	7.9	0.02774	12.9	-0.00707
3.0	0.11302	8.0	0.02933	13.0	-0.00541
3.1	0.09707	8.1	0.03057	13.1	-0.00373
3.2	0.08167	8.2	0.03146	13.2	-0.00205
3.3	0.06687	8.3	0.03202	13.3	-0.00039
3.4	0.05271	8.4	0.03224	13.4	0.00124
3.5	0.03925	8.5	0.03213	13.5	0.00282
3.6	0.02652	8.6	0.03172	13.6	0.00434
3.7	0.01455	8.7	0.03100	13.7	0.00578
3.8	0.00337	8.8	0.03001	13.8	0.00713
3.9	-0.00699	8.9	0.02875	13.9	0.00838
4.0	-0.01651	9.0	0.02726	14.0	0.00953
4.1	-0.02519	9.1	0.02554	14.1	0.01055
4.2	-0.03301	9.2	0.02363	14.2	0.01145
4.3	-0.03998	9.3	0.02155	14.3	0.01222
4.4	-0.04609	9.4	0.01932	14.4	0.01285
4.5	-0.05135	9.5	0.01697	14.5	0.01334
4.6	-0.05578	9.6	0.01453	14.6	0.01369
4.7	-0.05938	9.7	0.01202	14.7	0.01389
4.8	-0.06219	9.8	0.00947	14.8	0.01396
4.9	-0.06423	9.9	0.00691	14.9	0.01388
				15.0	0.01367

$\int_0^x J_0(\tau)\, d\tau$ AND $\int_0^x Y_0(\tau)\, d\tau$ FUNCTIONS

x	$\int_0^x J_0(\tau)\, d\tau$	$\int_0^x Y_0(\tau)\, d\tau$	x	$\int_0^x J_0(\tau)\, d\tau$	$\int_0^x Y_0(\tau)\, d\tau$
0.0	0.00000	0.00000	5.0	0.71531	0.19971
0.1	0.09991	-0.21743	5.1	0.69920	0.16818
0.2	0.19933	-0.34570	5.2	0.68647	0.13551
0.3	0.29775	-0.43928	5.3	0.67716	0.10205
0.4	0.39469	-0.50952	5.4	0.67131	0.06814
0.5	0.48968	-0.56179	5.5	0.66891	0.03413
0.6	0.58224	-0.59927	5.6	0.66992	0.00035
0.7	0.67193	-0.62409	5.7	0.67427	-0.03284
0.8	0.75834	-0.63786	5.8	0.68187	-0.06517
0.9	0.84106	-0.64184	5.9	0.69257	-0.09630
1.0	0.91973	-0.63706	6.0	0.70622	-0.12595
1.1	0.99399	-0.62447	6.1	0.72263	-0.15385
1.2	1.06355	-0.60490	6.2	0.74160	-0.17975
1.3	1.12813	-0.57911	6.3	0.76290	-0.20344
1.4	1.18750	-0.54783	6.4	0.78628	-0.22470
1.5	1.24144	-0.51175	6.5	0.81147	-0.24338
1.6	1.28982	-0.47156	6.6	0.83820	-0.25931
1.7	1.33249	-0.42788	6.7	0.86618	-0.27239
1.8	1.36939	-0.38136	6.8	0.89512	-0.28252
1.9	1.40048	-0.33260	6.9	0.92470	-0.28966
2.0	1.42577	-0.28219	7.0	0.95464	-0.29377
2.1	1.44528	-0.23071	7.1	0.98462	-0.29486
2.2	1.45912	-0.17871	7.2	1.01435	-0.29295
2.3	1.46740	-0.12672	7.3	1.04354	-0.28811
2.4	1.47029	-0.07526	7.4	1.07190	-0.28043
2.5	1.46798	-0.02480	7.5	1.09917	-0.27002
2.6	1.46069	0.02420	7.6	1.12508	-0.25702
2.7	1.44871	0.07132	7.7	1.14941	-0.24159
2.8	1.43231	0.11617	7.8	1.17192	-0.22392
2.9	1.41181	0.15839	7.9	1.19243	-0.20421
3.0	1.38756	0.19765	8.0	1.21074	-0.18269
3.1	1.35992	0.23367	8.1	1.22671	-0.15959
3.2	1.32928	0.26620	8.2	1.24021	-0.13516
3.3	1.29602	0.29502	8.3	1.25112	-0.10966
3.4	1.26056	0.31996	8.4	1.25939	-0.08335
3.5	1.22330	0.34090	8.5	1.26494	-0.05650
3.6	1.18467	0.35775	8.6	1.26777	-0.02940
3.7	1.14509	0.37044	8.7	1.26787	-0.00230
3.8	1.10496	0.37896	8.8	1.26528	0.02451
3.9	1.06471	0.38335	8.9	1.26005	0.05078
4.0	1.02473	0.38366	9.0	1.25226	0.07625
4.1	0.98541	0.38000	9.1	1.24202	0.10069
4.2	0.94712	0.37250	9.2	1.22946	0.12385
4.3	0.91021	0.36131	9.3	1.21473	0.14552
4.4	0.87502	0.34665	9.4	1.19799	0.16550
4.5	0.84186	0.32872	9.5	1.17944	0.18361
4.6	0.81100	0.30779	9.6	1.15927	0.19969
4.7	0.78271	0.28413	9.7	1.13772	0.21360
4.8	0.75721	0.25802	9.8	1.11499	0.22523
4.9	0.73468	0.22977	9.9	1.09134	0.23448
			10.0	1.06701	0.24129

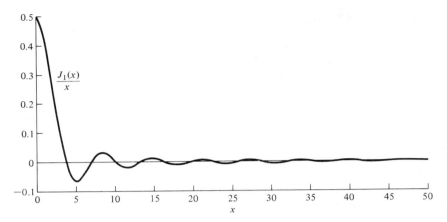

Figure V-3   Plot of $J_1(x)/x$ function.

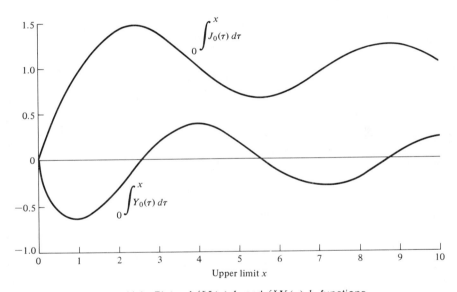

Figure V-4   Plots of $\int_0^x J_0(\tau)\,d\tau$ and $\int_0^x Y_0(\tau)\,d\tau$ functions.

Appendix VI
Identities

VI.1   TRIGONOMETRIC

1. Sum or difference:
   a. $\sin(x+y)=\sin x \cos y + \cos x \sin y$
   b. $\sin(x-y)=\sin x \cos y - \cos x \sin y$
   c. $\cos(x+y)=\cos x \cos y - \sin x \sin y$
   d. $\cos(x-y)=\cos x \cos y + \sin x \sin y$
   e. $\tan(x+y)=\dfrac{\tan x + \tan y}{1-\tan x \tan y}$
   f. $\tan(x-y)=\dfrac{\tan x - \tan y}{1+\tan x \tan y}$
   g. $\sin^2 x + \cos^2 x = 1$
   h. $\tan^2 x - \sec^2 x = -1$
   i. $\cot^2 x - \csc^2 x = -1$

2. Sum or difference into products:
   a. $\sin x + \sin y = 2\sin\frac{1}{2}(x+y)\cos\frac{1}{2}(x-y)$
   b. $\sin x - \sin y = 2\cos\frac{1}{2}(x+y)\sin\frac{1}{2}(x-y)$
   c. $\cos x + \cos y = 2\cos\frac{1}{2}(x+y)\cos\frac{1}{2}(x-y)$
   d. $\cos x - \cos y = -2\sin\frac{1}{2}(x+y)\sin\frac{1}{2}(x-y)$

3. Products into sum or differences:
   a. $2\sin x \cos y = \sin(x+y)+\sin(x-y)$
   b. $2\cos x \sin y = \sin(x+y)-\sin(x-y)$
   c. $2\cos x \cos y = \cos(x+y)+\cos(x-y)$
   d. $2\sin x \sin y = -\cos(x+y)+\cos(x-y)$

4. Double and half-angles:
   a. $\sin 2x = 2\sin x \cos x$
   b. $\cos 2x = \cos^2 x - \sin^2 x = 2\cos^2 x - 1 = 1 - 2\sin^2 x$
   c. $\tan 2x = \dfrac{2\tan x}{1-\tan^2 x}$
   d. $\sin\dfrac{1}{2}x = \pm\sqrt{\dfrac{1-\cos x}{2}}$ or $2\sin^2\theta = 1 - \cos 2\theta$
   e. $\cos\dfrac{1}{2}x = \pm\sqrt{\dfrac{1+\cos x}{2}}$ or $2\cos^2\theta = 1 + \cos 2\theta$
   f. $\tan\dfrac{1}{2}x = \pm\sqrt{\dfrac{1-\cos x}{1+\cos x}} = \dfrac{\sin x}{1+\cos x} = \dfrac{1-\cos x}{\sin x}$

5. Series:
   a. $\sin x = \dfrac{e^{jx}-e^{-jx}}{2j} = x - \dfrac{x^3}{3!} + \dfrac{x^5}{5!} - \dfrac{x^7}{7!} + \cdots$
   b. $\cos x = \dfrac{e^{jx}+e^{-jx}}{2} = 1 - \dfrac{x^2}{2!} + \dfrac{x^4}{4!} - \dfrac{x^6}{6!} + \cdots$
   c. $\tan x = \dfrac{e^{jx}-e^{-jx}}{j(e^{jx}+e^{-jx})} = x + \dfrac{x^3}{3} + \dfrac{2x^5}{15} + \dfrac{17x^7}{315} + \cdots$

VI.2 HYPERBOLIC

1. Definitions:
   a. Hyperbolic sine: $\sinh x = \frac{1}{2}(e^x + e^{-x})$
   b. Hyperbolic cosine: $\cosh x = \frac{1}{2}(e^x + e^{-x})$
   c. Hyperbolic tangent: $\tanh x = \dfrac{\sinh x}{\cosh x}$
   d. Hyperbolic cotangent: $\coth x = \dfrac{1}{\tanh x} = \dfrac{\cosh x}{\sinh x}$
   e. Hyperbolic secant: $\operatorname{sech} x = \dfrac{1}{\cosh x}$
   f. Hyperbolic cosecant: $\operatorname{csch} x = \dfrac{1}{\sinh x}$
2. Sum or difference:
   a. $\cosh(x+y) = \cosh x \cosh y + \sinh x \sinh y$
   b. $\sinh(x-y) = \sinh x \cosh y - \cosh x \sinh y$
   c. $\cosh(x-y) = \cosh x \cosh y - \sinh x \sinh y$
   d. $\tanh(x+y) = \dfrac{\tanh x + \tanh y}{1 + \tanh x \tanh y}$
   e. $\tanh(x-y) = \dfrac{\tanh x - \tanh y}{1 - \tanh x \tanh y}$
   f. $\cosh^2 x - \sinh^2 x = 1$
   g. $\tanh^2 x + \operatorname{sech}^2 x = 1$
   h. $\coth^2 x - \operatorname{csch}^2 x = 1$
   i. $\cosh(x \pm jy) = \cosh x \cos y \pm j \sinh x \sin y$
   j. $\sinh(x \pm jy) = \sinh x \cos y \pm j \cosh x \sin y$
3. Series:
   a. $\sinh x = \dfrac{e^x - e^{-x}}{2} = x + \dfrac{x^3}{3!} + \dfrac{x^5}{5!} + \dfrac{x^7}{7!} + \cdots$
   b. $\cosh x = \dfrac{e^x + e^{-x}}{2} = 1 + \dfrac{x^2}{2!} + \dfrac{x^4}{4!} + \dfrac{x^6}{6!} + \cdots$
   c. $e^x = 1 + x + \dfrac{x^2}{2!} + \dfrac{x^3}{3!} + \dfrac{x^4}{4!} + \cdots$

VI.3 LOGARITHMIC

1. $\log_b(MN) = \log_b M + \log_b N$
2. $\log_b(M/N) = \log_b M - \log_b N$
3. $\log_b(1/N) = -\log_b N$
4. $\log_b(M^n) = n \log_b M$
5. $\log_b(M^{1/n}) = \dfrac{1}{n} \log_b M$
6. $\log_a N = \log_b N \cdot \log_a b = \log_b N / \log_b a$
7. $\log_e N = \log_{10} N \cdot \log_e 10 = 2.302585 \log_{10} N$
8. $\log_{10} N = \log_e N \cdot \log_{10} e = 0.434294 \log_e N$

Appendix VII
Vector Analysis

VII.1 VECTOR TRANSFORMATIONS

In this appendix we will indicate the vector transformations from rectangular-to-cylindrical (and vice-versa), from cylindrical-to-spherical (and vice-versa), and from rectangular-to-spherical (and vice-versa). The three coordinate systems are shown in Figure VII.1.

VII.1.1 Rectangular-to-Cylindrical (and Vice-Versa)

The coordinate transformation from rectangular (x, y, z) to cylindrical (ρ, ϕ, z) is given, referring to Figure VII.1(b)

$$\left.\begin{array}{l} x = \rho\cos\phi \\ y = \rho\sin\phi \\ z = z \end{array}\right\} \tag{VII-1}$$

In the rectangular coordinate system we express a vector $\mathbf{A}$ as

$$\mathbf{A} = \hat{a}_x A_x + \hat{a}_y A_y + \hat{a}_z A_z \tag{VII-2}$$

where $\hat{a}_x, \hat{a}_y, \hat{a}_z$ are the unit vectors and A_x, A_y, A_z are the components of the vector $\mathbf{A}$ in the rectangular coordinate system. We wish to write $\mathbf{A}$ as

$$\mathbf{A} = \hat{a}_\rho A_\rho + \hat{a}_\phi A_\phi + \hat{a}_z A_z \tag{VII-3}$$

where $\hat{a}_\rho, \hat{a}_\phi, \hat{a}_z$ are the unit vectors and A_ρ, A_ϕ, A_z are the vector components in the cylindrical coordinate system. The z-axis is common to both of them.

Referring to Figure VII.2, we can write

$$\left.\begin{array}{l} \hat{a}_x = \hat{a}_\rho\cos\phi - \hat{a}_\phi\sin\phi \\ \hat{a}_y = \hat{a}_\rho\sin\phi + \hat{a}_\phi\cos\phi \\ \hat{a}_z = \hat{a}_z \end{array}\right\} \tag{VII-4}$$

Using (VII-4) reduces (VII-2) to

$$\mathbf{A} = \left(\hat{a}_\rho\cos\phi - \hat{a}_\phi\sin\phi\right)A_x + \left(\hat{a}_\rho\sin\phi + \hat{a}_\phi\cos\phi\right)A_y + \hat{a}_z A_z$$

$$\mathbf{A} = \hat{a}_\rho\left(A_x\cos\phi + A_y\sin\phi\right) + \hat{a}_\phi\left(-A_x\sin\phi + A_y\cos\phi\right) + \hat{a}_z A_z \tag{VII-5}$$

which when compared with (VII-3) leads to

$$\left.\begin{array}{l} A_\rho = A_x\cos\phi + A_y\sin\phi \\ A_\phi = -A_x\sin\phi + A_y\cos\phi \\ A_z = A_z \end{array}\right\} \tag{VII-6}$$

In matrix form, (VII-6) can be written as

$$\begin{pmatrix} A_\rho \\ A_\phi \\ A_z \end{pmatrix} = \begin{pmatrix} \cos\phi & \sin\phi & 0 \\ -\sin\phi & \cos\phi & 0 \\ 0 & 0 & 1 \end{pmatrix} \begin{pmatrix} A_x \\ A_y \\ A_z \end{pmatrix} \tag{VII-6a}$$

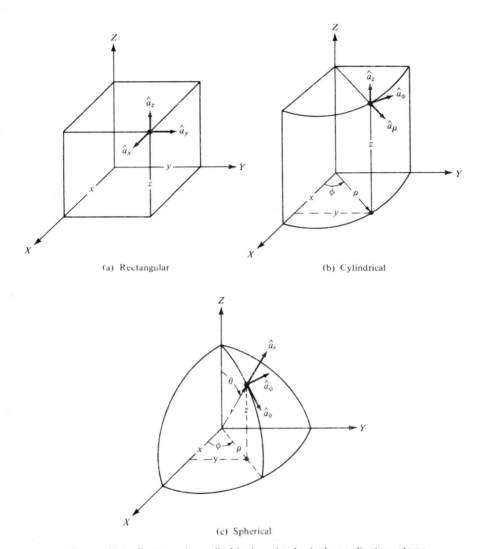

(a) Rectangular

(b) Cylindrical

(c) Spherical

Figure VII-1   Rectangular, cylindrical, and spherical coordinate systems.

where

$$[A]_{rc} = \begin{bmatrix} \cos\phi & \sin\phi & 0 \\ -\sin\phi & \cos\phi & 0 \\ 0 & 0 & 1 \end{bmatrix}$$ (VII-6b)

is the transformation matrix for rectangular-to-cylindrical components.

Since $[A]_{rc}$ is an orthonormal matrix (its inverse is equal to its transpose), we can write the transformation matrix for cylindrical-to-

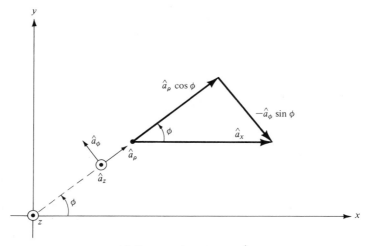

(a) Geometry for unit vector $\hat{a}_x$

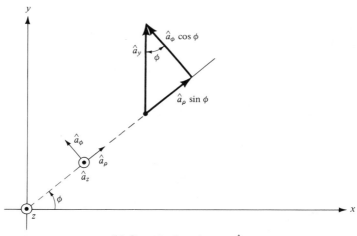

(b) Geometry for unit vector $\hat{a}_y$

Figure VII-2   Geometrical representation of transformation between unit vectors of rectangular and cylindrical coordinate systems.

rectangular components as

$$[A]_{cr}=[A]_{rc}^{-1}=[A]_{rc}^{t}=\begin{bmatrix} \cos\phi & -\sin\phi & 0 \\ \sin\phi & \cos\phi & 0 \\ 0 & 0 & 1 \end{bmatrix} \qquad \text{(VII-7)}$$

or

$$\begin{pmatrix} A_x \\ A_y \\ A_z \end{pmatrix} = \begin{pmatrix} \cos\phi & -\sin\phi & 0 \\ \sin\phi & \cos\phi & 0 \\ 0 & 0 & 1 \end{pmatrix} \begin{pmatrix} A_\rho \\ A_\phi \\ A_z \end{pmatrix} \qquad \text{(VII-7a)}$$

or

$$
\left.\begin{array}{l}
A_x = A_\rho \cos\phi - A_\phi \sin\phi \\
A_y = A_\rho \sin\phi + A_\phi \cos\phi \\
A_z = A_z
\end{array}\right\}
\tag{VII-7b}
$$

VII.1.2 Cylindrical-to-Spherical (and Vice-Versa)

Referring to Figure VII.1(c), we can write that the cylindrical and spherical coordinates are related by

$$
\left.\begin{array}{l}
\rho = r\sin\theta \\
z = r\cos\theta
\end{array}\right\}
\tag{VII-8}
$$

In a geometrical approach similar to the one employed in the previous section, we can show that the cylindrical-to-spherical transformation of vector components is given by

$$
\left.\begin{array}{l}
A_r = A_\rho \sin\theta + A_z \cos\theta \\
A_\theta = A_\rho \cos\theta - A_z \sin\theta \\
A_\phi = A_\phi
\end{array}\right\}
\tag{VII-9}
$$

or in matrix form by

$$
\begin{pmatrix} A_r \\ A_\theta \\ A_\phi \end{pmatrix} =
\begin{pmatrix} \sin\theta & 0 & \cos\theta \\ \cos\theta & 0 & -\sin\theta \\ 0 & 1 & 0 \end{pmatrix}
\begin{pmatrix} A_\rho \\ A_\phi \\ A_z \end{pmatrix}
\tag{VII-9a}
$$

Thus the cylindrical-to-spherical transformation matrix can be written as

$$
[A]_{cs} = \begin{bmatrix} \sin\theta & 0 & \cos\theta \\ \cos\theta & 0 & -\sin\theta \\ 0 & 1 & 0 \end{bmatrix}
\tag{VII-9b}
$$

The $[A]_{cr}$ matrix is also orthonormal so that its inverse is given by

$$
[A]_{sc} = [A]_{cs}^{-1} = [A]_{cs}^{t} = \begin{bmatrix} \sin\theta & \cos\theta & 0 \\ 0 & 0 & 1 \\ \cos\theta & -\sin\theta & 0 \end{bmatrix}
\tag{VII-10}
$$

and the spherical-to-cylindrical transformation is accomplished by

$$
\begin{pmatrix} A_\rho \\ A_\phi \\ A_z \end{pmatrix} =
\begin{pmatrix} \sin\theta & \cos\theta & 0 \\ 0 & 0 & 1 \\ \cos\theta & -\sin\theta & 0 \end{pmatrix}
\begin{pmatrix} A_r \\ A_\theta \\ A_\phi \end{pmatrix}
\tag{VII-10a}
$$

or

$$
\left.\begin{array}{l}
A_\rho = A_r \sin\theta + A_\theta \cos\theta \\
A_\phi = A_\phi \\
A_z = A_r \cos\theta - A_\theta \sin\theta
\end{array}\right\}
\tag{VII-10b}
$$

This time the component A_ϕ and coordinate ϕ are the same in both systems.

VII.1.3 Rectangular-to-Spherical (and Vice-Versa)

Many times it may be required that a transformation be performed directly from rectangular-to-spherical components. By referring to Figure VII.1, we can write that the rectangular and spherical coordinates are related by

$$\left.\begin{array}{l} x = r\sin\theta\cos\phi \\ y = r\sin\theta\sin\phi \\ z = r\cos\theta \end{array}\right\} \tag{VII-11}$$

and the rectangular and spherical components by

$$\left.\begin{array}{l} A_r = A_x\sin\theta\cos\phi + A_y\sin\theta\sin\phi + A_z\cos\theta \\ A_\theta = A_x\cos\theta\cos\phi + A_y\cos\theta\sin\phi - A_z\sin\theta \\ A_\phi = -A_x\sin\phi + A_y\cos\phi \end{array}\right\} \tag{VII-12}$$

which can also be obtained by substituting (VII-6) into (VII-9). In matrix form, (VII-12) can be written as

$$\begin{pmatrix} A_r \\ A_\theta \\ A_\phi \end{pmatrix} = \begin{pmatrix} \sin\theta\cos\phi & \sin\theta\sin\phi & \cos\theta \\ \cos\theta\cos\phi & \cos\theta\sin\phi & -\sin\theta \\ -\sin\phi & \cos\phi & 0 \end{pmatrix} \begin{pmatrix} A_x \\ A_y \\ A_z \end{pmatrix} \tag{VII-12a}$$

with the rectangular-to-spherical transformation matrix being

$$[A]_{rs} = \begin{pmatrix} \sin\theta\cos\phi & \sin\theta\sin\phi & \cos\theta \\ \cos\theta\cos\phi & \cos\theta\sin\phi & -\sin\theta \\ -\sin\phi & \cos\phi & 0 \end{pmatrix} \tag{VII-12b}$$

The transformation matrix of (VII-12b) is also orthonormal so that its inverse can be written as

$$[A]_{sr} = [A]_{rs}^{-1} = [A]_{rs}^{t} = \begin{pmatrix} \sin\theta\cos\phi & \cos\theta\cos\phi & -\sin\phi \\ \sin\theta\sin\phi & \cos\theta\sin\phi & \cos\phi \\ \cos\theta & -\sin\theta & 0 \end{pmatrix} \tag{VII-13}$$

and the spherical-to-rectangular components related by

$$\begin{pmatrix} A_x \\ A_y \\ A_z \end{pmatrix} = \begin{pmatrix} \sin\theta\cos\phi & \cos\theta\cos\phi & -\sin\phi \\ \sin\theta\sin\phi & \cos\theta\sin\phi & \cos\phi \\ \cos\theta & -\sin\theta & 0 \end{pmatrix} \begin{pmatrix} A_r \\ A_\theta \\ A_\phi \end{pmatrix} \tag{VII-13a}$$

or

$$\left.\begin{array}{l} A_x = A_r\sin\theta\cos\phi + A_\theta\cos\theta\cos\phi - A_\phi\sin\phi \\ A_y = A_r\sin\theta\sin\phi + A_\theta\cos\theta\sin\phi + A_\phi\cos\phi \\ A_z = A_r\cos\theta - A_\theta\sin\theta \end{array}\right\} \tag{VII-13b}$$

VII.2 VECTOR DIFFERENTIAL OPERATORS

The differential operators of gradient of a scalar ($\nabla \psi$), divergence of a vector ($\nabla \cdot \mathbf{A}$), curl of a vector ($\nabla \times \mathbf{A}$), Laplacian of a scalar ($\nabla^2 \psi$), and Laplacian of a vector ($\nabla^2 \mathbf{A}$) frequently encountered in electromagnetic field analysis will be listed in the rectangular, cylindrical, and spherical coordinate systems.

VII.2.1 Rectangular Coordinates

$$\nabla \psi = \hat{a}_x \frac{\partial \psi}{\partial x} + \hat{a}_y \frac{\partial \psi}{\partial y} + \hat{a}_z \frac{\partial \psi}{\partial z} \tag{VII-14}$$

$$\nabla \cdot \mathbf{A} = \frac{\partial A_x}{\partial x} + \frac{\partial A_y}{\partial y} + \frac{\partial A_z}{\partial z} \tag{VII-15}$$

$$\nabla \times \mathbf{A} = \hat{a}_x \left(\frac{\partial A_z}{\partial y} - \frac{\partial A_y}{\partial z} \right) + \hat{a}_y \left(\frac{\partial A_x}{\partial z} - \frac{\partial A_z}{\partial x} \right) + \hat{a}_z \left(\frac{\partial A_y}{\partial x} - \frac{\partial A_x}{\partial y} \right) \tag{VII-16}$$

$$\nabla \cdot \nabla \psi = \nabla^2 \psi = \frac{\partial^2 \psi}{\partial x^2} + \frac{\partial^2 \psi}{\partial y^2} + \frac{\partial^2 \psi}{\partial z^2} \tag{VII-17}$$

$$\nabla^2 \mathbf{A} = \hat{a}_x \nabla^2 A_x + \hat{a}_y \nabla^2 A_y + \hat{a}_z \nabla^2 A_z \tag{VII-18}$$

VII.2.2 Cylindrical Coordinates

$$\nabla \psi = \hat{a}_\rho \frac{\partial \psi}{\partial \rho} + \hat{a}_\phi \frac{1}{\rho} \frac{\partial \psi}{\partial \phi} + \hat{a}_z \frac{\partial \psi}{\partial z} \tag{VII-19}$$

$$\nabla \cdot \mathbf{A} = \frac{1}{\rho} \frac{\partial}{\partial \rho} (\rho A_\rho) + \frac{1}{\rho} \frac{\partial A_\phi}{\partial \phi} + \frac{\partial A_z}{\partial z} \tag{VII-20}$$

$$\nabla \times \mathbf{A} = \hat{a}_\rho \left(\frac{1}{\rho} \frac{\partial A_z}{\partial \phi} - \frac{\partial A_\phi}{\partial z} \right) + \hat{a}_\phi \left(\frac{\partial A_\rho}{\partial z} - \frac{\partial A_z}{\partial \rho} \right)$$
$$+ \hat{a}_z \left(\frac{1}{\rho} \frac{\partial (\rho A_\phi)}{\partial \rho} - \frac{1}{\rho} \frac{\partial A_\rho}{\partial \phi} \right) \tag{VII-21}$$

$$\nabla^2 \psi = \frac{1}{\rho} \frac{\partial}{\partial \rho} \left(\rho \frac{\partial \psi}{\partial \rho} \right) + \frac{1}{\rho^2} \frac{\partial^2 \psi}{\partial \phi^2} + \frac{\partial^2 \psi}{\partial z^2} \tag{VII-22}$$

$$\nabla^2 \mathbf{A} = \nabla (\nabla \cdot \mathbf{A}) - \nabla \times \nabla \times \mathbf{A} \tag{VII-23}$$

or in an expanded form

$$\nabla^2\mathbf{A} = \hat{a}_\rho \left(\frac{\partial^2 A_\rho}{\partial \rho^2} + \frac{1}{\rho}\frac{\partial A_\rho}{\partial \rho} - \frac{A_\rho}{\rho^2} + \frac{1}{\rho^2}\frac{\partial^2 A_\rho}{\partial \phi^2} - \frac{2}{\rho^2}\frac{\partial A_\phi}{\partial \phi} + \frac{\partial^2 A_\rho}{\partial z^2} \right)$$

$$+ \hat{a}_\phi \left(\frac{\partial^2 A_\phi}{\partial \rho^2} + \frac{1}{\rho}\frac{\partial A_\phi}{\partial \rho} - \frac{A_\phi}{\rho^2} + \frac{1}{\rho^2}\frac{\partial^2 A_\phi}{\partial \phi^2} + \frac{2}{\rho^2}\frac{\partial A_\rho}{\partial \phi} + \frac{\partial^2 A_\phi}{\partial z^2} \right)$$

$$+ \hat{a}_z \left(\frac{\partial^2 A_z}{\partial \rho^2} + \frac{1}{\rho}\frac{\partial A_z}{\partial \rho} + \frac{1}{\rho^2}\frac{\partial^2 A_z}{\partial \phi^2} + \frac{\partial^2 A_z}{\partial z^2} \right) \qquad \text{(VII-23a)}$$

In the cylindrical coordinate system $\nabla^2\mathbf{A} \neq \hat{a}_\rho \nabla^2 A_\rho + \hat{a}_\phi \nabla^2 A_\phi + \hat{a}_z \nabla^2 A_z$ because the orientation of the unit vectors $\hat{a}_\rho$ and $\hat{a}_\phi$ varies with the ρ and ϕ coordinates.

VII.2.3   Spherical Coordinates

$$\nabla \psi = \hat{a}_r \frac{\partial \psi}{\partial r} + \hat{a}_\theta \frac{1}{r}\frac{\partial \psi}{\partial \theta} + \hat{a}_\phi \frac{1}{r\sin\theta}\frac{\partial \psi}{\partial \phi} \qquad \text{(VII-24)}$$

$$\nabla \cdot \mathbf{A} = \frac{1}{r^2}\frac{\partial}{\partial r}\left(r^2 A_r\right) + \frac{1}{r\sin\theta}\frac{\partial}{\partial \theta}\left(\sin\theta A_\theta\right) + \frac{1}{r\sin\theta}\frac{\partial A_\phi}{\partial \phi} \qquad \text{(VII-25)}$$

$$\nabla \times \mathbf{A} = \frac{\hat{a}_r}{r\sin\theta}\left[\frac{\partial}{\partial \theta}\left(A_\phi \sin\theta\right) - \frac{\partial A_\theta}{\partial \phi} \right] + \frac{\hat{a}_\theta}{r}\left[\frac{1}{\sin\theta}\frac{\partial A_r}{\partial \phi} - \frac{\partial}{\partial r}\left(rA_\phi\right) \right]$$

$$+ \frac{\hat{a}_\phi}{r}\left[\frac{\partial}{\partial r}\left(rA_\theta\right) - \frac{\partial A_r}{\partial \theta} \right] \qquad \text{(VII-26)}$$

$$\nabla^2\psi = \frac{1}{r^2}\frac{\partial}{\partial r}\left(r^2\frac{\partial \psi}{\partial r}\right) + \frac{1}{r^2\sin\theta}\frac{\partial}{\partial \theta}\left(\sin\theta\frac{\partial \psi}{\partial \theta}\right) + \frac{1}{r^2\sin^2\theta}\frac{\partial^2\psi}{\partial \phi^2} \quad \text{(VII-27)}$$

$$\nabla^2\mathbf{A} = \nabla(\nabla \cdot \mathbf{A}) - \nabla \times \nabla \times \mathbf{A} \qquad \text{(VII-28)}$$

or in an expanded form

$$\nabla^2\mathbf{A} = \hat{a}_r \left(\frac{\partial^2 A_r}{\partial r^2} + \frac{2}{r}\frac{\partial A_r}{\partial r} - \frac{2}{r^2}A_r + \frac{1}{r^2}\frac{\partial^2 A_r}{\partial \theta^2} + \frac{\cot\theta}{r^2}\frac{\partial A_r}{\partial \theta} + \frac{1}{r^2\sin^2\theta}\frac{\partial^2 A_r}{\partial \phi^2} \right.$$

$$\left. - \frac{2}{r^2}\frac{\partial A_\theta}{\partial \theta} - \frac{2\cot\theta}{r^2}A_\theta - \frac{2}{r^2\sin\theta}\frac{\partial A_\phi}{\partial \phi} \right)$$

$$+ \hat{a}_\theta \left(\frac{\partial^2 A_\theta}{\partial r^2} + \frac{2}{r}\frac{\partial A_\theta}{\partial r} - \frac{A_\theta}{r^2\sin^2\theta} + \frac{1}{r^2}\frac{\partial^2 A_\theta}{\partial \theta^2} + \frac{\cot\theta}{r^2}\frac{\partial A_\theta}{\partial \theta} \right.$$

$$\left. + \frac{1}{r^2\sin^2\theta}\frac{\partial^2 A_\theta}{\partial \phi^2} + \frac{2}{r^2}\frac{\partial A_r}{\partial \theta} - \frac{2\cot\theta}{r^2\sin\theta}\frac{\partial A_\phi}{\partial \phi} \right)$$

$$+ \hat{a}_\phi \left(\frac{\partial^2 A_\phi}{\partial r^2} + \frac{2}{r} \frac{\partial A_\phi}{\partial r} - \frac{1}{r^2 \sin^2 \theta} A_\phi + \frac{1}{r^2} \frac{\partial^2 A_\phi}{\partial \theta^2} \right.$$

$$+ \frac{\cot \theta}{r^2} \frac{\partial A_\phi}{\partial \theta} + \frac{1}{r^2 \sin^2 \theta} \frac{\partial^2 A_\phi}{\partial \phi^2} + \frac{2}{r^2 \sin \theta} \frac{\partial A_r}{\partial \phi}$$

$$+ \left. \frac{2 \cot \theta}{r^2 \sin \theta} \frac{\partial A_\theta}{\partial \phi} \right) \tag{VII-28a}$$

Again note that $\nabla^2 \mathbf{A} \neq \hat{a}_r \nabla^2 A_r + \hat{a}_\theta \nabla^2 A_\theta + \hat{a}_\phi \nabla^2 A_\phi$ since the orientation of the unit vectors $\hat{a}_r$, $\hat{a}_\theta$, and $\hat{a}_\phi$ varies with the r, θ, and ϕ coordinates.

VII.3   VECTOR IDENTITIES

VII.3.1   Addition and Multiplication

$$\mathbf{A} \cdot \mathbf{A} = |\mathbf{A}|^2 \tag{VII-29}$$

$$\mathbf{A} \cdot \mathbf{A}^* = |\mathbf{A}|^2 \tag{VII-30}$$

$$\mathbf{A} + \mathbf{B} = \mathbf{B} + \mathbf{A} \tag{VII-31}$$

$$\mathbf{A} \cdot \mathbf{B} = \mathbf{B} \cdot \mathbf{A} \tag{VII-32}$$

$$\mathbf{A} \times \mathbf{B} = -\mathbf{B} \times \mathbf{A} \tag{VII-33}$$

$$(\mathbf{A} + \mathbf{B}) \cdot \mathbf{C} = \mathbf{A} \cdot \mathbf{C} + \mathbf{B} \cdot \mathbf{C} \tag{VII-34}$$

$$(\mathbf{A} + \mathbf{B}) \times \mathbf{C} = \mathbf{A} \times \mathbf{C} + \mathbf{B} \times \mathbf{C} \tag{VII-35}$$

$$\mathbf{A} \cdot \mathbf{B} \times \mathbf{C} = \mathbf{B} \cdot \mathbf{C} \times \mathbf{A} = \mathbf{C} \cdot \mathbf{A} \times \mathbf{B} \tag{VII-36}$$

$$\mathbf{A} \times (\mathbf{B} \times \mathbf{C}) = (\mathbf{A} \cdot \mathbf{C}) \mathbf{B} - (\mathbf{A} \cdot \mathbf{B}) \mathbf{C} \tag{VII-37}$$

$$(\mathbf{A} \times \mathbf{B}) \cdot (\mathbf{C} \times \mathbf{D}) = \mathbf{A} \cdot \mathbf{B} \times (\mathbf{C} \times \mathbf{D})$$
$$= \mathbf{A} \cdot (\mathbf{B} \cdot \mathbf{D} \mathbf{C} - \mathbf{B} \cdot \mathbf{C} \mathbf{D})$$
$$= (\mathbf{A} \cdot \mathbf{C})(\mathbf{B} \cdot \mathbf{D}) - (\mathbf{A} \cdot \mathbf{D})(\mathbf{B} \cdot \mathbf{C}) \tag{VII-38}$$

$$(\mathbf{A} \times \mathbf{B}) \times (\mathbf{C} \times \mathbf{D}) = (\mathbf{A} \times \mathbf{B} \cdot \mathbf{D}) \mathbf{C} - (\mathbf{A} \times \mathbf{B} \cdot \mathbf{C}) \mathbf{D} \tag{VII-39}$$

VII.3.2   Differentiation

$$\nabla \cdot (\nabla \times \mathbf{A}) = 0 \tag{VII-40}$$

$$\nabla \times \nabla \psi = 0 \tag{VII-41}$$

$$\nabla (\phi + \psi) = \nabla \phi + \nabla \psi \tag{VII-42}$$

$$\nabla (\phi \psi) = \phi \nabla \psi + \psi \nabla \phi \tag{VII-43}$$

$$\nabla \cdot (\mathbf{A} + \mathbf{B}) = \nabla \cdot \mathbf{A} + \nabla \cdot \mathbf{B} \tag{VII-44}$$

$$\nabla \times (\mathbf{A} + \mathbf{B}) = \nabla \times \mathbf{A} + \nabla \times \mathbf{B} \tag{VII-45}$$

$$\nabla \cdot (\psi \mathbf{A}) = \mathbf{A} \cdot \nabla \psi + \psi \nabla \cdot \mathbf{A} \tag{VII-46}$$

$$\nabla \times (\psi \mathbf{A}) = \nabla \psi \times \mathbf{A} + \psi \nabla \times \mathbf{A} \tag{VII-47}$$

$$\nabla (\mathbf{A} \cdot \mathbf{B}) = (\mathbf{A} \cdot \nabla)\mathbf{B} + (\mathbf{B} \cdot \nabla)\mathbf{A} + \mathbf{A} \times (\nabla \times \mathbf{B}) + \mathbf{B} \times (\nabla \times \mathbf{A}) \tag{VII-48}$$

$$\nabla \cdot (\mathbf{A} \times \mathbf{B}) = \mathbf{B} \cdot \nabla \times \mathbf{A} - \mathbf{A} \cdot \nabla \times \mathbf{B} \tag{VII-49}$$

$$\nabla \times (\mathbf{A} \times \mathbf{B}) = \mathbf{A} \nabla \cdot \mathbf{B} - \mathbf{B} \nabla \cdot \mathbf{A} + (\mathbf{B} \cdot \nabla)\mathbf{A} - (\mathbf{A} \cdot \nabla)\mathbf{B} \tag{VII-50}$$

$$\nabla \times \nabla \times \mathbf{A} = \nabla (\nabla \cdot \mathbf{A}) - \nabla^2 \mathbf{A} \tag{VII-51}$$

VII.3.3 Integration

$$\oint_C \mathbf{A} \cdot d\mathbf{l} = \iint_S (\nabla \times \mathbf{A}) \cdot d\mathbf{s} \qquad \text{Stoke's theorem} \tag{VII-52}$$

$$\oiint_S \mathbf{A} \cdot d\mathbf{s} = \iiint_V (\nabla \cdot \mathbf{A}) \, dv \qquad \text{divergence theorem} \tag{VII-53}$$

$$\oiint_S (\hat{n} \times \mathbf{A}) \, ds = \iiint_V (\nabla \times \mathbf{A}) \, dv \tag{VII-54}$$

$$\oiint_S \psi \, d\mathbf{s} = \iiint_V \nabla \psi \, dv \tag{VII-55}$$

$$\oint_C \psi \, d\mathbf{l} = \iint_S \hat{n} \times \nabla \psi \, ds \tag{VII-56}$$

Appendix VIII
Television and Radio
Frequency Spectrum

VIII.1 TELEVISION

VIII.1.1 *Very High Frequency (VHF) Channels*

CHANNEL NUMBER	2 3 4	5 6	7	8	9	10	11	12	13
FREQUENCY (MHz)	54↑60↑66↑72	76↑82↑88	174↑180↑186↑192 ↑198 ↑204 ↑210 ↑216						

VIII.1.2 *Ultra High Frequency (UHF) Channels**

FREQUENCY (MHz)	470	512	806

VIII.2 RADIO

VIII.2.1 *Amplitude Modulation (AM) Radio*

Number of channels: 107 (each with 10-kHz separation)
Frequency range: 535–1605 kHz

VIII.2.2 *Frequency Modulation (FM) Radio*

Number of channels: 100 (each with 200-kHz separation)
Frequency range: 88–108 MHz

VIII.3 AMATEUR BANDS

BAND	FREQUENCY (MHz)	BAND	FREQUENCY (MHz)
160-m	1.8–2.0	2-m	144.0–148.0
80-m	3.5–4.0	—	220–225
40-m	7.0–7.3	—	420–450
20-m	14.0–14.35	—	1215–1300
15-m	21.0–21.45	—	2300–2450
10-m	28.0–29.7	—	3300–3500
6-m	50.0–54.0	—	5650–5925

*In top ten urban areas in the United States, land mobile is allowed in the first seven UHF TV channels (470–512 MHz).

Index

82 83 84 987654321